Rhododendrons of subgenus Vireya

Rhododendrons of subgenus Vireya

Dr George Argent

Royal Botanic Garden Edinburgh

*with contributions by David Mitchell, Louise
Galloway and Stephan Helfer*

THE ROYAL HORTICULTURAL SOCIETY

Published in association with
the Royal Botanic Garden Edinburgh

First published in 2006 by
The Royal Horticultural Society
80 Vincent Square
London SW1P 2PE
Registered Charity number 222879
www.rhs.org.uk

in association with the Royal Botanic Garden Edinburgh
www.rbge.org.uk

Rhododendrons of subgenus Vireya
Copyright © 2006 Royal Botanic Garden Edinburgh

A CIP catalogue record for this book is available from the British Library

ISBN 1-902896-61-0

Designed and edited by Erica Schwarz
Cover design by Sharon Cluett
Colour reproduction by Capscan, Edinburgh
Printed and bound in the United Kingdom by CPI Bath Press, Bath

For Sue

Contents

Foreword

It is a great pleasure to introduce this magnificent new book on vireya rhododendrons. With over 850 species the genus *Rhododendron* is one of the largest genera of flowering plants and because of its huge diversity and its beautiful flowers it naturally attracts enormous interest. Hardy rhododendrons are particularly popular garden plants and the majority of previous publications are concerned with them. In contrast, although more than a third of all *Rhododendron* species belong to subgenus *Vireya*, much less has been written about them and they have never before been the subject of a fully comprehensive treatment. Perhaps this is not surprising when one considers that although many of the species have quite restricted distributions the subgenus as a whole is widely distributed. Vireyas range from the Himalayas and South China through the thousands of islands of Malesia in South East Asia and into northern Australia. They are difficult to collect: many are mountain-dwelling plants or inaccessible epiphytes and often they are rare. To become familiar with a great many of these species requires outstanding dedication and painstaking research. For more than 25 years Dr George Argent of the Royal Botanic Garden Edinburgh has travelled to study and collect vireya rhododendrons. His field work has enriched both the herbarium collections and the living collections in Edinburgh, making these the most complete and celebrated collections anywhere in the world. From this unique resource for research he has studied many aspects of the taxonomy and wider biology of subgenus *Vireya* including the documentation of such important and difficult to obtain details as their chromosome numbers. Throughout his many expeditions he has had the opportunity of photographing his subjects in their natural surroundings. His skill as a botanical photographer is evident in this richly illustrated book.

George Argent has already written extensively on subgenus *Vireya* but this is undoubtedly the most definitive work ever published on the group. Previously the accounts published in the 1960s by Professor Hermann Sleumer, particularly his treatment for *Flora Malesiana*, included the greatest number of *Vireya* species. Significant though such publications were they are now inevitably rather out of date given the number of new species described in the last 40 years. Sadly, as the number of *Vireya* species known to science has grown so too has the variety of threats they face in the wild. As a result of the destruction of their natural habitats, some are now Red Data Book species, and climate change adds a new danger for the future. Few of us will be fortunate enough to see many, if any, species of vireya rhododendron in the wild. For most of us this inspiring and accessible book will have to suffice. I am sure it will be a delight to all who read it.

Stephen Blackmore FRSE
Regius Keeper
Royal Botanic Garden Edinburgh

Acknowledgements

This book could not have been written without the help and participation of many people. Firstly these are the people who have accompanied me on field work – I especially include the many local villagers who have so willingly given up staying comfortably with their families to endure the privations of camping in cold and uncomfortable conditions and unselfishly shared their local knowledge of plants and places. I am especially indebted to Professor Bob Johns, Clive Jermy, Wandy Swales and Robin Hanbury-Tenison for inviting me to participate in their particularly rewarding expeditions.

Secondly are the expert growers who have been influential in maintaining the Edinburgh *Vireya* collection since before I became interested in the group. These include: Les Bisset, Andrea Fowler, Natacha Frachon, Louise Galloway, Jim Gardner, Mairi Gillies, Tom Grieve, Fiona Inches, Ross Kerby, John Lewis, David Mitchell, David Rae, Alistair Reed, Ronnie Rutherford, John Sandham, Dick Shaw, Ian Sinclair and Paul Smith.

Marjory McFarlane typed all the initial descriptions into the computer and Eve Bennett has most ably drawn and painted to my direction; both have always given their full support to the book and been wonderful friends to work with.

The Royal Botanic Garden Edinburgh has provided financial support latterly from SEERAD for the project and I am grateful for other financial grants from the Iris Darnton Foundation, the Royal Horticultural Society and the Stanley Smith (U.K.) Horticultural Trust. Stephen Blackmore as Regius Keeper and Mary Gibby as Director of Science have supported the work and seen that it has come to fruition. Robert Mill has always been willing to translate the Latin and check the derivation of names. Photographic staff – Ross Eudal, Ken Grant, Sid Clarke, Debbie White and Lynsey Muir – have gone to endless trouble to document the collection and produce the best of the illustrations. Library staff have been most helpful at all times and I am especially grateful to Jane Hutcheon, Graham Hardy and Leonie Paterson. Hamish Adamson as Publications Manager has been both pleasant and efficient to work with and

Erica Schwarz, who copy-edited and typeset the text, has worked with her usual amazing attention to detail and general professionalism.

I also wish to thank the directors of the following herbaria for allowing consultation of their specimens: A, BISH, BM, BO, BRI, FI, GH, K, KEP, KUN, L, MEL, P, PNH, SAN, SAR, SING, SNP, SYD.

The fraternity of rhododendron and vireya enthusiasts and other botanists have helped in very diverse ways and it is a pleasure to acknowledge help from: Keith Adams, Sherla and Richard Bertelman, David Binney, Os Blumhart, Margaret Bodenham, Gillian Brown, Bill Burtt, Chris Callard, Barbara Campbell, David Chamberlain, Frieda Christie, Sheila Collenette, Jim Comber, Mark Coode, Kenneth, Peter and Patricia Cox, Lyn Craven, Norman Cruttwell, Rob Cubey, James Cullen, Michael Cullinane, Richard Currie, John Dransfield, Chris and Aline Fairweather, Lian-Ming Gao, Jonathon Gregson, Ansou Gunsalam, Charlie Heatubun, Stephan Helfer, Steve Hootman, Mark Hughes, Clive Jermy, Paul Kessler, Ruth Kiew, Rogier de Koch, Tony and Anthea Lamb, Chip Lima, Domingo Madulid, John McNeill, John and Mary Mendum, David Middleton, Mitch and Sandy Mitchell, Bill Moyles, Jamili Nais, Simon Owens, Susan Phillipps, John Proctor, Rodella Purves, Sally Rae, Jimmy Ratter, John and Clare Rouse, Lou Searle, Graham and Dora Smith, Graham and Wendy Snell, Peter Stevens, Tim Utteridge, Tim and June Walsh, Kerry Walter, Roy Watling, Peter van Welzen, E. White Smith and Lucy Sorenson, Peter Wilkie, Bob and Hari Withers, and Paddy and Jennifer Woods. Special thanks go to Eric Annal, John Bodenham and Pamela Haywood for most helpful critical comments on the text.

Illustrations

Photographs are by George Argent unless otherwise credited. Those marked 'Kew' are reproduced by kind permission of the Board of Trustees of the Royal Botanic Gardens, Kew. Those marked 'Leiden' are courtesy of the Nationaal Herbarium Nederland (Leiden Branch).

Abbreviations and symbols

°	degrees of longitude, latitude or temperature
†	indicating a herbarium specimen has been destroyed
alt.	altitude
c.	*circa*, about or approximately
cm	centimetre(s)
comb. nov.	a new nomenclatural or name combination
E	east, eastern
et al.	and others
ex	used between two authorities when the name only was supplied by the first author, the description being supplied by the last
f.	form or forma
f.	figure, *filius* (son)
fig.	figure or illustration
fl.	flowering (time)
fr.	fruiting (time)
G.	gunung/gunong – mountain (Indonesian/Malaysian)

in	used when authorship of a name differs from the authorship of the publication in which it was published
loc. cit.	in the location cited
m	metre(s)
mm	millimetre(s)
Mt(s)	mountain(s)
N	north, northern
pl.	plate
S	south, southern
sect.	section
sensu	in the sense of
s.n.	*sine numero* – without number
sp.	species
ssp.	subspecies
sp. nov.	a newly described species
stat. nov.	*status nova*, at a new level
subsect.	subsection
t.	tabula, plate or illustration
var.	variety
W	west, western
x	indicating a hybrid or hybridisation

Herbarium citations

The following herbaria are listed as containing type specimens which are quoted under each species according to their *Index Herbariorum* acronyms (Holmgren & Holmgren 1998 onwards). Those with an asterisk have been consulted and the type specimens studied. The first (or only) acronym is the place where the holotype resides; subsequent acronyms list isotypes. The symbol † indicates that the specimen has been destroyed.

A   Arnold Arboretum, Harvard University, Cambridge, Massachusetts, USA

AA   Ministry of Science, Academy of Sciences, Alma-ata, Kazakhstan

B   Botanischer Garten und Botanishes Museum, Zentraleinrichtung der Freien Universität Berlin, Germany

BISH* Bishop Museum, Honolulu, Hawaii, USA

BM*   Natural History Museum, London, England, UK

BO*   Herbarium Bogoriense, Bogor, Indonesia

BRI*   Brisbane Botanic Gardens, Mt Coot-tha, Brisbane, Queensland, Australia

BRIT   Botanical Research Institute of Texas, Fort Worth, Texas, USA

BRSL Museum of Natural History, Wroclaw University, Wroclaw, Poland

C   University of Copenhagen, Copenhagen, Denmark

CAL   Botanical Survey of India, Kolkata, West Bengal, India

CANB Centre for Plant Biodiversity Research, Canberra, ACT, Australia

CANT South China Agricultural University, Guangzhou, Guangdong, People's Republic of China

CANU University of Canterbury, Christchurch, New Zealand

CGE   University of Cambridge, Cambridge, England, UK

E*   Royal Botanic Garden Edinburgh, Edinburgh, Scotland, UK

FI*   Museo di Storia dell'Universita Botanico, Firenze, Italy

G   Conservatoire et Jardin botaniques de la Ville de Genèva, Genèva, Switzerland

GH   Harvard University, Cambridge, Massachusetts, USA

HN   National Centre for Natural Sciences and Technology, Hanoi, Vietnam

IBK   Guangxi Institute of Botany, Guilin, Guangxi Zhuangsu, People's Republic of China

K*   Royal Botanic Gardens, Kew, England, UK

KEP* Forest Research Institute Malaysia, Kepong, Selangor, Malaysia

KUN* Kunming Institute of Botany, Chinese Academy of Sciences, Kunming, Yunnan, People's Republic of China

L*   Nationaal Herbarium Nederland, Leiden University Branch, Leiden, Netherlands

LAE   Forest Research Institute, Lae, Papua New Guinea

LYJB Jardin Botanique, Lyon, France

MA   Real Jardín Botánico, Madrid, Spain

MAN Universitas Cenderawasih, Manokwari, Indonesia

MEL* Royal Botanic Gardens, Melbourne, Victoria, Australia

MICH University of Michigan, Ann Arbor, Michigan, USA

NY   New York Botanical Garden, Bronx, New York, USA

P*   Muséum National d'Histoire Naturelle, Paris, France

PH   Academy of Natural Sciences, Philadelphia, Pennsylvania, USA

PNH* National Museum, Manila, Philippines

QRS* CSIRO, Atherton, Queensland, Australia

S   Swedish Museum of Natural History, Stockholm, Sweden

SAN* Forest Research Centre, Sandakan, Sabah, Malaysia

SAR* Department of Forestry, Kuching, Sarawak, Malaysia

SING* Singapore Botanic Gardens, Singapore

SNP* Sabah Parks, Kota Kinabalu, Sabah, Malaysia

SYD* University of Sydney, Sydney, New South Wales, Australia

TI   University of Tokyo, Tokyo, Japan

U   Nationaal Herbarium Nederland, Utrecht University Branch, Utrecht, Netherlands

UC   University of California, Berkeley, California, USA

US   Smithsonian Institution, Washington, District of Columbia, USA

1 INTRODUCTION

What is a vireya?

Vireyas are defined as rhododendrons with scales whose seeds have a long tail at each end. Seed morphology is not the most obvious of characters on which to define a group, and it might appear that there would be difficulty in deciding whether plants belong to this group or not when the plants are without fruit. This is especially so as *Vireya* contains the widest range of flower morphology of any of the subgenera in *Rhododendron* and is also very diverse in other respects. In practice there is rarely a problem identifying a rhododendron as a vireya at least when in flower. In biology in general there are rarely absolute differences between large groups of organisms and so here there is a suite of characters that give vireyas a distinctive look. However, no character is absolutely constant; even the tailed seed fails this test, as several of the high altitude species such as *Rhododendron retusum* and *R. abietifolium* lack proper tails to their seeds.

In addition to the tailed seed the majority of vireyas have a tapering ovary–style junction, with distinctive orientation of the seed (Palser *et al.* 1991), and they usually lack any abscission layer between ovary and style which is common elsewhere in the genus. There are scattered exceptions to this character throughout the group, although a distinct ovary–style junction is characteristic of *Pseudovireya* where some species even have a weak abscission layer and the styles may drop off the developing fruit. Vireyas have large idioblasts in the cells of the leaves which appear to be universal and unique to the subgenus for all species so far examined (Nilsen 2003; Nilsen & Scheckler 2003). The twisting of the valves after opening, discussed by Sleumer (1980), and on which the subgeneric status was originally based, has not proved to be a very useful character as it is just too variable. The placentae usually separate (mostly rather irregularly) from the central axis which does not happen in other rhododendrons, but there are exceptions, for example *R. adinophyllum* where they remain firmly attached to the central column with the valves spreading but not twisting. Several species that have short stubby fruits open with stiffly spreading valves which do not reflex at all, for example *R. rushforthii* and *R. mendumiae*.

There are several other negative characteristics common to vireyas. They lack a rhachis, or common stalk, to the inflorescence which is therefore a true umbel, the pedicels arising directly from a dome-like common base. The inflorescence is quite commonly reduced to a solitary flower but even then they lack the joint which indicates the change from peduncle to pedicel which occurs in some other solitary-flowered plants in the Ericaceae. This would indicate that the loss of the peduncle has always preceded the reduction to a single flower which must have taken place many times. Vireyas lack spots of pigment coloration on the flowers, with the exception of *R. emarginatum* and some close relatives (although in section *Malayovireya* they may be prominently spotted with contrastingly coloured scales as in *R. himantodes* and *R. lineare*). They very rarely have obvious zygomorphic patterns of colour although they may have these patterns visible under ultraviolet light (Rouse *et al.* 1986); exceptions that do have visible zygomorphic colour patterns are *R. emarginatum* and *R. wentianum*, both of which can have very distinct bilaterally symmetrical colour patterns on the corolla. Vireyas rarely have a properly developed calyx, this usually being a low disc-like rim of tissue, although *R. ericoides* invariably has a conspicuous calyx with relatively long lobes and other species commonly develop them as occasional irregular structures which may become petaloid. They never have blue flowers and very few have much blue in the purples which are sometimes found; the bluest is perhaps *R. stevensianum*. The indumentum of the leaves never has the irregularly branched hairs found in many other rhododendrons and only very rarely has them on other organs, although they are recorded from the bract margins of *R. rushforthii* and *R. villosulum* and have occasionally been seen on the filaments of some species. Vireyas also lack the multicellular, flat, scurf-like hairs of *Rhododendron* sect. *Tsutsusi* and they have never been reliably recorded with glandular hairs. All vireyas so far examined have 26 chromosomes, that is they are all diploid with $2n = 13$ (Atkinson *et al.* 2000). It was thought that some of the dwarf montane species might be polyploid but this has not been found to be the case so far.

Mark Hughes

Distribution of vireya rhododendrons (Malesia shaded). Numbers refer to the number of species recorded for each island or country.

Rhododendrons of subgenus *Vireya* are referred to here as 'vireyas' but they have also sometimes been called 'Malesian rhododendrons' or, even more vaguely, 'tropical rhododendrons' in common parlance. 'Vireya' is best as a popular name. It derives from the genus *Vireya* created by Carl Ludwig Blume in 1823 for five species from what is now Indonesia. The name was used to honour a French pharmacist friend of that name but it was never widely accepted as a good genus. Malesia (see map), the geographical area of the SE Asian archipelago from the Malay Peninsula and Sumatra in the west, to New Guinea in the east and the Philippine Islands in the north, is the region from which most of the vireyas come, but it is not all-encompassing of the group. A few of the species 'escape' the confines of this zone and a few rhododendrons from other subgenera have inconveniently penetrated this area so 'Malesian' is not without exceptions if used to describe this group. 'Tropical rhododendrons' in the strictest sense is also inappropriate as again, although the majority technically occur within the tropics, a few do occur north of the tropic of Cancer. The term is also badly misleading to growers as the majority are montane plants from high altitudes and like cool conditions far removed from those obtaining in the traditional stove house whose steamy high temperatures suit tropical plants from low elevations.

Name changes and taxonomic concepts

Name changes are rarely welcomed and can be very tiresome but the aim is always to reflect the best understanding of the plants in question with the evidence available according to the latest International Code of Botanical Nomenclature (Greuter *et al*. 2000). Apart from changes due to priority (the oldest name usually taking precedence) most changes reflect changes in taxonomic judgement for which there is never total agreement between different botanists let alone botanists and horticulturists (Cullen 1988). A few words of explanation may help to explain the situation as pertinent to vireyas.

Professor Sleumer's work on vireyas was accomplished with a painstaking study of largely dried herbarium specimens. His concept of a species was for the most part narrow: any specimen which differed significantly from others was described as a distinct species (see below). He did have some field experience with these plants in Borneo, the Philippines and New Guinea, and those specimens which he saw at first hand in the field have more balanced descriptions of variability and especially of naturally occurring hybrids. A few species were treated in a broader sense, from Java and Sumatra in particular, where he had the benefit of advice from Professor van Steenis. Professor Sleumer knew very few vireyas in cultivation although several species were grown in the early 1960s in the Netherlands, notably at Boskoop. He was however responsible for some notable introductions and fully realised their potential as horticultural plants.

Today over 150 species of vireya are cultivated and these have provided a great deal of new morphological information since Professor Sleumer's *Flora Malesiana* account (1966). The descriptions in this book are based wherever possible on living material, both from the large collection of wild collected cultivated plants in the Royal Botanic Garden Edinburgh and from the numerous field visits over more than 25 years to the countries in which these plants grow. There is a natural bias to what has been seen personally but observations of contemporary workers have been incorporated, both of field scientists and of the many growers of these plants. Paul Kores has made a notable contribution with field studies that assessed the variation in populations in his years working in New Guinea (van Royen & Kores 1982), and Lyn Craven and David Hunt have both contributed valuable observations which have allowed some species boundaries to be more clearly defined (Craven 1980, 1996; Hunt 1972). A high proportion of species are still very inadequately known from field studies, and further reductions of names into synonymy are to be expected.

Subgenus, sections and series

The reintroduction of the status of subgenus may be somewhat controversial. This is essentially practical in allowing better subdivisions below this rank. Sleumer's classification has served practical identification well but does not purport to be an evolutionary tree. The classification proposed here is very similar to that of Sleumer (1966) but in that account he did not include the mainland species that occurred outside the Malesian region and the *Discovireya* used here relates back to his earlier classification (Sleumer 1949). There are good morphological grounds for separating

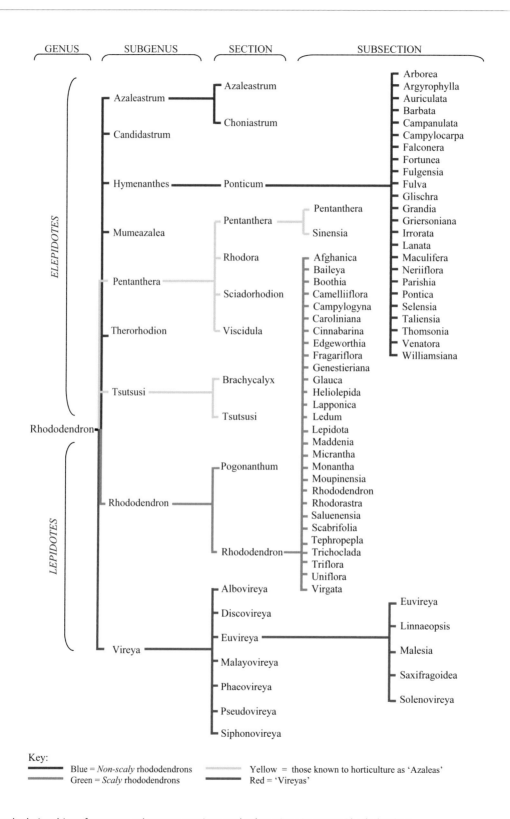

The mutual relationships of genus to subgenera, sections and subsections in genus *Rhododendron*.

the vireyas and not just on the traditional tailed seed. The large idioblasts in the leaves described by Nilsen (2003) are unique, and the ovary, ovule and megagametophyte characters are much more distinct for 'section' *Vireya* than in any other section of the genus (Palser *et al.* 1991). Studies of the flavonoid and carotenoid pigments allowed Professor Spethmann to suggest that subgenus was the appropriate level for this group (Spethmann 1980, 1987). The fact that some of the latest molecular studies do not at present support this are interesting but academic (Hall *et al.* 2006). The present work is not trying to represent evolution or monophyly but to present a practical way of dividing this large group of species into subunits so that species can be identified. There is no doubt that molecular studies are advancing our knowledge of the evolution of the group but it is still in a state of flux. Kurashige *et al.* (2001) and Goetsch *et al.* (2005) found *Vireya* to be monophyletic, as is also suggested by Brown (2006) (albeit weakly so), whereas Hall *et al.* (2006) find them paraphyletic occurring in two groups embedded in the traditional subsection *Rhododendron*.

At sectional level there is a great deal of variation. There appears to be a major distinction between *Pseudovireya* (as defined here) and the remaining vireyas, which was mooted by Rouse and co-workers who found incompatibility barriers both in the breeding systems and in graft experiments (Rouse 1985; Rouse *et al.* 1993; Rouse & Williams 1994a, 1994b). This is indirectly supported by the latest molecular work (Hall *et al.* 2006). The suggestion that *Discovireya* is the odd group (Island *Pseudovireya* of Hall *et al.* 2006) is very thought provoking. It would be interesting to see how well this is supported with additional species such as *R. retusum* which readily hybridise in the wild with the euvireya *R. rarilepidotum*.

The other sections are less well defined. Stevens (1985) thought *Malayovireya*, *Siphonovireya* and *Phaeovireya* were probably monophyletic on morphological grounds. This has not been supported in molecular work (Brown 2006) except for *Siphonovireya* although this must be suspect as only two species were sampled which are possibly extreme ends of a cline of variation. *Phaeovireya* is less well defined than originally thought. There is a gradation in the scale character defining this group, and there is some evidence that species such as *R. leucogigas* and *R. schlechteri* should be included despite the fact that the scales on

mature adults do not sit on typical papillae; seedlings of what is thought to be *R. schlechteri* from Mt Jaya have scales on papillae although the adults collected in the wild do not. *Albovireya* is not very coherent. Sleumer (1966) had doubts about the relationship of the species from the west and eastern ends of the distribution; those from the west he regarded as possibly hybrids with members of *Malayovireya*. They certainly show similarities in the scale morphology but fruit and bract characteristics are different and the group are usually recognisable by the semi-persistent silvery covering of scales on the upper sides of the leaves which is similar to the members from the east. *Malayovireya* is a very coherent section and members of this group are usually instantly recognisable. Certain species within this section, however, have some of the most complex and problematical variation patterns in the whole of *Vireya*: *R. malayanum* is variable in both morphology and ecology; *R. durionifolium* is variable in flower size, colour and shape, with different size classes growing together.

Solenovireya has been included within *Euvireya* and effectively downgraded to subsectional level. Brown (2006) found that it was not monophyletic and it was always a doubtfully coherent group, being based as it was on the trumpet-shaped corolla which must be an extremely labile character. It is treated slightly differently from Sleumer (1966) in that flower colour is used in the definition, which merely reflects the fact that this is a moth-pollinated group. Sleumer in fact used this definition without it being clearly stated, as many of his red-flowered species would happily fit into the definition of trumpet-shaped flowers with lobes less than ¼ the length of the tube but were placed elsewhere. *Euvireya* is still a miscellany of what is left over after the more discrete elements of *Vireya* are removed. The finding of Brown (2006) that the western and eastern elements are different is not surprising in a group which is rapidly evolving and where the most likely relationships will be between species that are growing in close proximity. Vireyas would appear to have travelled from west to east diversifying rapidly wherever mountain building was taking place. Thus the very large number of species found in New Guinea is directly related to the major recent mountain building on this island, and parallels the enormous speciation that has occurred in rhododendrons in the Himalayan region.

Species

Species concepts can simplistically be regarded as changing over time. In a hypothetical example: from an outline description of a single dried herbarium specimen; through description of the variation of several herbarium specimens; description of many herbarium specimens from a range of localities, perhaps swallowing into synonymy some other finds described subsequently under different names; descriptions of living populations of plants in the wild; and then to the beginnings of experimental studies with observations from cultivated plants perhaps growing alongside related species, hybridisation and grafting experiments, chemical and cytological analyses and probably ultimately a DNA profile from a range of samples. Thus our knowledge of a species grows, but this is a very uneven process. For some species we now know very much more than Professor Sleumer did but quite a significant number of species are still known only from the single dried collections that he studied. An interesting and pertinent point was Professor Sleumer's use of 'variety'. This was puzzling and some years ago he was asked what he meant by the use of this term. With disarming honesty he declared 'I use this when I am not sure about the standing of the group'. Thus it is not surprising that a number of his varieties have turned out to be hybrids, good species or quite often what are more acceptable as subspecies – variants insufficiently distinct to be species but with an ecological or geographical basis correlated to their distinctive characteristics. Quite a number of the changes recorded here reflect a more critical analysis of Professor Sleumer's varieties.

The well-known propensity of vireyas to hybridise with each other means that they do not conform to basic zoological dictates about species not interbreeding. A basic 'rule of thumb' used by James Cullen in his 'Revision of *Rhododendron* 1' (Cullen 1980) was that to be different, a species should have at least two distinct and unrelated characters separating it from anything else. This said, species are still very different in kind, and not just in terms of the amount known about them (Argent 2003). A point endemic on a mountain may be a small but distinct population in decline (*R. wilkiei* on Thumb Peak, Palawan in the Philippines) or a young, newly emerged and aggressive species (*R. buxifolium* on Kinabalu in Sabah), or one may have a widespread,

relatively uniform species (*R. bagobonum*) or one that is widespread and very variable (*R. javanicum*). It is the fascination and frustration of taxonomy that biological variation is not easily strait-jacketed into uniform units. It is however units with names which everyone wants and which the taxonomist must provide, and this book is an attempt to describe vireyas as we know them at present and to draw together information from the scattered literature. It aims to facilitate identification of species in the wild or wild collected plants in cultivation. It will not identify hybrids. Vegetative characters (leaf size, etc.) are used as associated with fertile material; young plants will obviously have much smaller leaves than is typical of the mature adult but strongly growing vegetative stems can also produce untypical, often much larger leaves. A good hand lens or a binocular microscope will be needed to see details of indumentum and when observing scales a sample should be looked at. Scale characters mostly refer to those on the undersides of leaves but those characteristic of *Discovireya* and *Siphonovireya* can often most easily be seen on the outside of the corollas if they are present there. If this book stimulates further exploration and research and encourages people to grow these fascinating and often beautiful plants it will have served its purpose.

A note on the descriptions

The description of the species has relied very heavily on Sleumer's *Flora Malesiana* account (Sleumer 1966) but a great deal of new material has been added from observations in the wild and from cultivated collections, especially that at the Royal Botanic Garden Edinburgh. Some modifications have also been made. The mature stems and trunks if any have not been described. The leaf texture is assumed to be leathery and is described only if exceptional. Twigs are defined as the ultimate branches that still have leaves attached. Leaves are described from fertile stems; the leaves on vigorously growing vegetative shoots may differ considerably from those associated with flower buds, flowers or fruits.

The basic geometric shapes, on which the descriptive terms in the glossary are based, follow those published by the Systematics Association in 1962. Leaf measurements are of blade and petiole separately. All measurements without qualification apart from the corolla tube (see below) are of length. Nodes and internodes are not used in the conventional sense (see fig. I, glossary). Node is used here (as it was used by Sleumer 1966) for the region where the leaves are attached where this is a pseudowhorl, and internode is the length of stem between these pseudowhorls of leaves.

The term bract is used for what Sleumer (1966) called perulae. A bract as here defined is a modified leaf associated with a flower or inflorescence. One might divide the floral 'bud scales' into sterile bracts (without flowers in their axils) and fertile bracts with flowers in their axils but this seems superfluous particularly as we still have such poor records of the morphology of the bracts of many species. Perulae as defined in most botanical dictionaries are the scales of leaf buds, not flower buds, and this term is not used by Cullen (1980) who used the term bract, or Chamberlain (1982) who used floral bud scales. Both these authors hardly use the character in their accounts, chiefly on the grounds that there was so little information available in the groups which they studied. I use the term bract in this account mainly to avoid the confusion of having scales on scales which are totally different structures. Scale, for what are technically multicellular epidermal trichomes, is so universally used for these structures that it would not be reasonable to call them anything else. When scales are described they refer to those on the undersurface of the mature leaf usually viewed at about ⅓ of the distance up from the base of the blade and about halfway from margin to mid-vein. However, when examining the scales of specimens it is often necessary to find them wherever they may persist, which is often in corners close to the branches of main veins. It is also necessary to survey scales as they are often very variable even on one leaf and it is important to come to a 'consensus' view of the morphology of these structures. In interpreting the cushion (type E, fig. VI, glossary) scale it is often simpler to see these (when they occur) on the outside of a corolla tube where they are usually very distinct. Pedicel measurements are given from flowering specimens; they often lengthen appreciably and can also thicken as the fruit develops.

Flowers are measured whenever possible from live material and are standard length x width (see fig. VIII, glossary) or sometimes just length only when taken from a reference. In some species (e.g. *R. inconspicuum*) the flowers expand considerably after opening, sometimes as much as doubling in size. Shrinkage also occurs in dried specimens which depends very much on the pressure exerted on the corolla at the time of drying. Good pressure can give very reliable measurements whilst allowing specimens to wither before pressing, and poor pressure on the corollas (often due to bulky twigs or leaves) means extreme shrinkage can occur. This means that some caution and a degree of common sense must be exercised when dealing with differences in flower size. The floral tube is described as a trapezium, length x basal width (often taken 1–2mm above the actual junction with the receptacle) x upper width at the junction with the lobes (see fig. VIII, glossary). In a few cases this does not describe the tube shape adequately and further description or measurements may be given where this expands or contracts in the middle. Where living material has been available an effort has been made to describe the corolla lobes not just in terms of length and width but also the degree to which they overlap, the angle to which they open and whether the margins reflex laterally. Variations in these attributes all give considerable 'character' to the flowers of different species. Descriptions assume 5 corolla lobes; only consistent deviations from this number are recorded.

All the flowers are protandrous, that is the anthers mature and shed pollen before the stigma in the same flower is receptive. The number of stamens is assumed to be 10; only deviations from this number are described. The position of the anthers varies considerably between species and can be a useful character (see fig. X, glossary). This should be recorded by collectors in the field as it can be difficult to see in pressed specimens. Anther lengths can be useful as they do not alter appreciably on drying. Similarly ovary lengths are relatively stable; however, style length must be used with caution as the styles often lengthen appreciably in the period between the first opening of the flowers and the later phase when the stigma is receptive.

The herbaria where type specimens are lodged are listed by their conventional codes (see p.xii). The holotype is listed first; these have been seen where the herbaria are listed with an asterisk but not otherwise. Geographical distributions are not meant to have any political implications. The location of type specimens has followed Sleumer (1960) or that used in the original publication, and there has been no attempt to bring the spelling of names up to date. The distribution at the end of the species description attempts to give the countries which a species is presently known from with up-to-date names for islands and places. Indonesian-administered New Guinea, however, has been designated New Guinea (W), as the modern name, Papua (formerly Irian Jaya), is not well known outside the region and is confusing with the old Papua which was the southern part of what is now the eastern half of the island or the modern state of Papua New Guinea.

2 A HISTORY OF *VIREYA*

Early history

The first vireya described was *Rhododendron malayanum*, in 1822 by **William Jack**, a Scotsman from Aberdeen. He was a surgeon in the East India Company and served as botanist to Sir Stamford Raffles on the west coast of Sumatra. Jack climbed Mt Bunko (Bengkoh), popularly known as the Sugar Loaf, just inland from Bencoolan. He commented that despite the mountain's low elevation 'the character of its vegetation is decidedly alpine'. Here he collected this first vireya, which he correctly attributed to the genus *Rhododendron* despite (for the time) the surprising location. It is tragic that in the same year that Jack published *R. malayanum* he died of pulmonary tuberculosis probably complicated with malaria. Worse still, most of his specimens, drawings and manuscripts were lost two years later when the S.S. *Fame* burnt and sank at sea off Sumatra.

Carl Blume followed, a medical doctor who in 1822 became director of what is now the Bogor Botanic Garden on the island of Java (Indonesia). He travelled widely in Java and published five species under his genus *Vireya* in 1826, three of which he must have seen at first hand. These plants were first brought to the attention of the public in an article in the Journal of the Royal Horticultural Society for 1848. Here John Lindley firmly rejected the concept of the genus *Vireya* and reported on Sir Hugh Low's findings in Borneo where the 'vireyas' were described as 'perhaps the most gorgeous of the native plants'. He also hypothesised about the problems of their cultivation as epiphytes, and the descriptions must have aroused considerable interest. He may well have been partly responsible for the nurserymen Messrs Veitch of Exeter sending **Thomas Lobb** on an expedition to SE Asia from where he is credited with bringing back in 1845 the first five live vireyas for cultivation in Britain. This was a very considerable feat. Anyone who collects today with the advantages of air transport knows to their cost how easy it is to lose vireyas with even a small delay. What care and attention must have been given to these plants over a journey of many weeks by sea in closed glass Wardian cases. There is a remark, however, by James Veitch (1906) to the effect that a man named

Rollison had already introduced *R. javanicum*, a darker form, but his scant mention implies he was not working for Veitch. *Rhododendron javanicum* caused a sensation on its introduction as its bright orange colour was at that time new for the genus. Veitch sent the plant for figuring in the *Botanical Magazine* (t.4336, 1847) with the remark that 'it is certainly one of the finest things ever introduced to our gardens'. *Rhododendron jasminiflorum* quickly followed, in 1848, and was exhibited at the Chiswick Gardens Exhibition in 1850 where it was reported that 'few plants excited greater attention among the visitors most distinguished for taste and judgement' and the strangeness of the flowers caused the *Gardeners' Chronicle* to imply it was 'probably no Rhododendron at all'. **Charles Curtis** followed Lobb as Veitch's collector and sent back *R. multicolor* (the variety *curtisii* was named after him) and *R. teysmannii* (now *R. javanicum* ssp. *brookeanum*) from Sumatra. From seven listed species (six in the modern concept) hundreds of forms were obtained by cross-pollination of what were passingly known as the *javanico–jasminiflorum* hybrids. They included double *balsamaeflorum* types which have never been equalled – these 'gardenia-like' rhododendrons in various colours were said to last 6–7 weeks in good condition (Leach 1978). These Veitch vireyas formed the basis of a remarkable genetic study by Professor **George Henslow** which was published by the Royal Horticultural Society in 1891 (Mendel's classic genetic work on peas was still undiscovered). Several of these hybrids, such as 'Princess Alexandra', 'Ne Plus Ultra', 'Triumphans' and 'Taylori' (commemorating George Taylor, Veitch's main hybridiser), are still in cultivation today.

From 1865 the great Italian explorer **Odoardo Beccari** was making his massive collections of plants in SE Asia, amongst which he collected several notable rhododendrons. In *Malesia* (1878, I) he described nine new species and put together a synopsis of the known species of this group up to this time. He listed 27 species in total from four islands; 23 of the species still stand today. Five were from Java, 7 from Sumatra, 14 from Borneo and four from New Guinea, the first to be listed from this island, including the superb *R. konori* now so well known and admired in cultivation for its enormous and beautifully scented, pale pink to white flowers.

In 1886 **Sebastian Vidal**, a Spanish botanist, listed six species of *Rhododendron* in his *Revision de Plantas Vasculares Filipinas*. Two species, *R. apoanum* and *R. kochii*, were described in 1883 by Stein with comment about their great potential for cultivation – a potential which it took over 100 years to realise (*R. apoanum* was introduced in 1992 and *R. kochii* only a few years before this). The first collection of a vireya from the Philippines was actually made as early as 1839 by Hugh Cuming, a British naturalist, on Mt Banahao. Cuming was noted for collecting living orchids for Loddige's nursery but there is no evidence of his having collected any vireyas as living material – it is most likely that they failed to survive the difficult journey.

The twentieth century

As the Victorian period came to a close, vireyas were in decline; the limited genetic base of rather lowland species and somewhat unrealistic ideas about growing even these in very hot stove conditions meant fewer people troubled with them. They were also being overtaken by an enormous influx of new and exciting hardy species from China and the eastern Himalayas. Partly vireyas went out of fashion, partly they were squeezed out of the hothouses by tougher and even more gaudy orchids. They certainly could not compete in Britain with the new hardy Chinese rhododendrons, both species and hybrids, which were being grown more and more widely. The First World War almost gave the *coup de grâce* when ornamental horticulture went into decline with the shortage of manpower and conservatories everywhere being left abandoned and unheated. What was rather surprising, however, was that although the cultivation of these plants was in decline the number of species being described increased. In the 1890s, eight species were newly described; in the 1900s, 15 more species were described; but from 1910 to 1919, fifty additional species were described, despite the ravages of the Great War. The next four decades saw only 45 more species names appear in the literature. **Johannes Jacobus Smith** was amongst the most productive in describing vireyas at this time; although more famous for his work on orchids he also took special interest in the family Ericaceae. He described 66 species of *Vireya*, 49 of which are still valid, publishing from 1910 to 1937. **Friedrich (Rudolf) Schlechter**, another who was

better known for his orchid collections, also made a significant contribution, collecting in the field between 1901 and 1910 under the very arduous conditions in New Guinea before air transport was common. He described seven species and is remembered by the magnificent *Rhododendron schlechteri* which he collected in the Kani and Bismarck mountains and which is described with flowers up to 17cm long.

Herbert Copeland, an American, produced a landmark account of the Philippine vireyas in the *Philippine Journal of Science* (Copeland 1929). He described five new species in a paper which enumerated 21 species of *Rhododendron* (20 of them vireyas) and provided a very workable account of the group with a serious attempt at a natural sectional classification. Another significant piece of work was that of Professor **Holttum**, who was experimenting in the Singapore Botanic Gardens to produce good, free-flowering vireyas that would be successful in the tropical lowlands. These were described in the *Malayan Agricultural/Horticultural Magazine* in 1939 (parts 9 and 11). Using the local species, especially *R. longiflorum*, *R. jasminiflorum* and *R. javanicum* (*R. brookeanum*), all of which can occur at sea level in the tropics, he was raising plants of great promise when the work was curtailed by the invasion of the Japanese in the Second World War. This work has never really been developed since within the tropics, and it is very sad that the most commonly encountered cultivated rhododendrons in most tropical gardens are poorly growing azaleas. An effort was made by John Swisher to grow low altitude vireyas in Florida, and Graham and Wendy Snell have produced some fine heat tolerant hybrids using *R. baenitzianum*, *R. macgregoriae* and *R. zoelleri*, but no formal breeding programme to produce vireyas which would flourish in the lowlands as Professor Holttum envisaged has been established.

When Australia took possession of German New Guinea at the beginning of the First World War the interior of the island was a great blank on maps. Very little penetration of this area by the outside world occurred until a prospector, Ned Rowlands, found gold in 1929. Subsequent to the announcement of this, New Guinea gold fever became rife and exploration started in earnest. Missionaries and the administration followed the prospectors and plant collecting started to be conducted with considerable vigour as the wonderful new mountainous area was opened up. An article by **C.R. Stonor** in the *Rhododendron Yearbook* (1951) gave a glimpse of what was to be found in terms of the rhododendrons. He managed to bring back seed which was germinated at Edinburgh in the late 1940s, and a few of his plants still survive today – a '*beyerinckianum*' hybrid is the longest surviving vireya in the Edinburgh collection, having been accessed in 1949. Felix Dury also visited New Guinea in the 1950s and spent time in Mt Hagen collecting *R. macgregoriae* and *R. zoelleri*, later developing a major nursery for vireyas in New Zealand.

A significant publication, also in 1949, was that of Professor **Hermann Sleumer**, who, in a 'Systema Generis *Rhododendron* L.', gave the first properly organised classification of the genus into subgenera and sections including the vireyas. It was a portent of his future contribution to the group. **Leonard Brass**, who was responsible for the plant collections on the three large-scale and highly successful Archbold Expeditions to New Guinea culminating in the 1938–39 expedition to Mt Wilhelmina (G. Trichora) and the Lake Habbema area, provided Professor Sleumer with abundant materials of exciting new species. It was in 1953 that Professor Sleumer started work on a revision of *Rhododendron* for *Flora Malesiana* on appointment to the Flora Malesiana Foundation in Leiden. A

great wealth of material had accumulated from recent botanical exploration and this was rapidly being added to by the New Guinea Department of Forests. **John Womersley**, for many years Chief of the Division of Botany in New Guinea, took a particular interest in the genus and made many collections of herbarium specimens as well as distributing seed and live plants. The **Rev. Norman Cruttwell**, an Anglican missionary with the benefit of a first class honours degree in botany, spent a lifetime in New Guinea and was very active in the pioneer days (and up to the late 1980s). He collected many new plants and had the elegant *Rhododendron cruttwellii* named after him; he also caused *R. christianae* to be named after his mother. He distributed seed of this last species and it became the first New Guinea rhododendron to be grown in Australia (Clancy 1973a). It caused such interest there that the Australian Rhododendron Society wrote to Professor Sleumer requesting more seed. It just happened that he was in the concluding phase of a seven-month expedition in New Guinea and the letter being forwarded to him Professor Sleumer obliged with viable seed of nine species of some of the most decorative vireyas yet in cultivation.

In the early years of the 1960s Professor Sleumer published 122 new species of *Vireya*, the last great explosion in the size of the genus *Rhododendron*. In 1966 his account of the genus for *Flora Malesiana* appeared, the classic reference work, even today. This work has enabled the vast majority of subsequent collections to be named as, unlike any other work on the group before, it was broad in its scope, provided keys for identification and gave full descriptions of all the species known from the Malesian region. This, together with progeny from his seed, stimulated a great revival in vireya growing, particularly in Australia, New Zealand and America, all countries where the species could, in selected places, be grown outdoors. It is worth pointing out that Hermann Sleumer has sometimes been accused of being associated with the Nazi party on account of his having spent some years in Argentina. Nothing could be further from the truth since he had to flee there from Berlin when the Nazi persecution of critical academics was rife. Certainly he would never have been tolerated, let alone celebrated as he was, by the Rijksherbarium in Leiden if he had had the slightest leanings in such a right wing direction.

Leiden

Hermann Sleumer.

The experimental station at Boskoop in the Netherlands started importing vireyas in 1955 and by 1966 had a collection of 30 species of which six had flowered. Dr **Michael Black** went collecting in New Guinea in 1967. The Royal Botanic Garden Edinburgh sent **Paddy Woods** and **Bill Burtt**, who brought new species back into cultivation from the Malay Peninsula, Borneo and New Guinea, but much of the activity and interest in the group was moving out of Britain. There were Australians like **Lou Searle**, an agricultural extension officer for the Australian Administration working in the highlands, who took a fancy to the group and spent much of his leisure searching for vireyas. He will be remembered for the exquisite *Rhododendron searleanum* named in his honour but deserves mention as someone who strove to beautify the New Guinea highland roads and towns with plantings of the native species; both then and since his efforts were often unappreciated. More than once he had to rescue his plantings from the bulldozers as they were being swallowed up by unannounced road widening schemes, but he doggedly grew, propagated and generously distributed plants from his highland base. Lou had been a coastwatcher during the Second World War in New Guinea and had several 'close shaves' with the enemy. Soon after the war he sent his son to his old school in Australia where the latter was surprised to find his father listed among the honourable dead. Fortunately for vireya enthusiasts Lou's career in New Guinea had barely begun. **Lyn Craven** from Canberra collected for the Australian Rhododendron Society

in 1964 and 1966, and introduced at least seven species including the magnificent *R. leucogigas* 'Hunstein's Secret'. These expeditions sparked a lifetime interest in *Vireya*, with many critical papers describing new species and a useful 'History of their introduction and cultivation' (Craven 1973). Royal Pullen collected extensively in New Guinea and introduced *R. pachycarpon* to Australia from the Finisterre Mountains. Leslie Keith Wade introduced several species from Papua New Guinea, including probably the first introductions of *R. atropurpureum*, *R. culminicola*, *R. saxifragoides* and *R. womersleyi* in 1966 and 1967. J.H. Willis collected *R. commonae* in 1970.

Peter Sullivan showed considerable expertise in growing and flowering vireyas at the Strybing Arboretum, San Francisco, under the direction of and with enthusiastic support from P.H. (Jock) Brydon. Strybing were active in importing plants and seed and creating new hybrids, and were one of the earliest gardens to feature vireyas flowering. They claimed to be the first to flower the spectacular *Rhododendron leucogigas* in the western hemisphere in 1968. Peter Sullivan also planted up what became known in vireya circles as 'The Church Garden', a narrow strip of land alongside St John's Church in San Francisco where he planted and tended a wonderful bed of vireyas in his retirement. This is still worth a visit as it has been well maintained first by Chip Lima and then by Danny Pritchard following in the master's footsteps. This early work all stimulated great interest in the group in California, and Pete introduced **William Moynier** to these plants.

Paddy Woods (second from left) and Michael Black (in shorts), with unknown guides.

William, or 'Bill' to his friends, very largely pioneered the growing of vireyas in southern California, running a nursery, producing and naming many hybrids and giving lectures to promote these plants. Experiments growing and hybridising were simultaneously being undertaken at Boskoop in the Netherlands from the new materials which were being sent out from SE Asia, but the greatest interest was growing in Australia and New Zealand, where people who had often seen the plants at first hand were returning from tours of duty in New Guinea. John Womersley in retirement from his post in Papua New Guinea led rhododendron tours which bred a band of enthusiasts in Australia and New Zealand. **Graham Smith**, the remarkable and energetic director of the Pukeiti Rhododendron Garden, collected many species and developed the group as a feature which stimulated much of the interest which is current in New Zealand today. These New Zealand plants have been augmented by the collections made by **Keith Adams** and **David Binney**, both of whom have visited remote mountains in the quest for new species. **Graham and Wendy Snell** abandoned a solid livelihood growing camellias to invest everything in a vireya nursery and became outstanding breeders of modern vireya hybrids, developing especially small-leafed plants with large flowers as well as the heat tolerant forms already mentioned. **Michael Cullinane**, who similarly invested his heart as well as his money into a vireya nursery in New Zealand, went collecting twice in New Guinea, firstly with a group and on the second occasion on his own when he notably introduced *R. truncicola* into cultivation for the first time, making what was only the second collection of this species. **Clyde Smith** wrote the beautiful introductory book *Vireya Rhododendrons* for the Australian Rhododendron Society (1989). **Os Blumhart**, another nurseryman who went on to collect on his own account, has bred some amazing new hybrids, compacting the growth with the use of the tufted cushion-like and aptly named *R. saxifragoides*. This difficult plant from the alpine bogs high in New Guinea once in hybrid combination has the ability to compact many of the flamboyant but straggly forms; the resulting plants grow with true hybrid vigour and show none of the temperamental nature of the *R. saxifragoides* parentage. The progeny of this species also tend to inherit the long pedicels which throw the flowers well clear of the foliage to make them even more attractive display plants. **Brian Clancy** also championed vireyas, writing articles to popularise them and to explain how they should be grown from his nursery near Melbourne where he grew and sold many species and hybrids.

Another major contribution was made by **Paul Kores**, an American funded by the Stanley Smith Foundation to collect and study vireyas in Papua New Guinea over a four-year period with a special remit to introduce plants into cultivation. Many plants were distributed via the American Rhododendron Species Foundation, and an account of high altitude vireyas was published in *The Alpine Flora of New Guinea* (van Royen & Kores 1982). This was a consolidation of Sleumer's mainly herbarium-based taxonomy, with more species being reduced to synonymy than were newly described, but it added considerably to our understanding of the wild populations of these plants. Others contributed in very different ways. **Peter Valder**, whose lively broadcasting and sharp mind have both entertained and stimulated many people in Australia, collected on isolated forays into SE Asia. He gave a remarkable account of the collection of *R. aequabile* from Mt Singgalang following the travel instructions from a Dutch East Indies railway guide for about 1919 (this must rank as one of the most offbeat ways to use a railway guide!). The guide stated: 'Singgalang (2,877m) can be climbed from Koto Toeo, which can be reached by trap from Fort de Kock [Bukkit Tinggi] in ¾ hr. Leaving Fort de Kock early in the morning, one will be able to reach the summit before noon. There is a small lake surrounded by old trees, whose trunks are thickly covered with moss. It is a calm and restful sight, and, when the weather is fine, its beauty is enhanced by the open scenery of the surrounding country, over which the eye can roam for several hundred miles'. 'The only significant difference to the journey as described', Valder dryly remarked, was 'that there were buses instead of horse drawn carriages'. 'The views of the surrounding volcanoes, lakes, countryside and the Indian Ocean were marvellous', he declared.

John Rouse deserves special mention for a major contribution to the vireya scene. A professional physicist, he applied a sharp scientific mind, an eye for beauty and a very generous spirit to the group. He built up what at the time was probably the finest collection of species and hybrids in cultivation in his garden at Toorak in Melbourne where he could grow most of the plants outside. He developed the best seed raising apparatus yet devised for these plants and made numerous hybrids but used this work to develop our understanding of the breeding systems, often leaving others to register his best forms. He had grafted specimens both within and without *Vireya* and used this information to provide remarkable insights into the relationships of *Rhododendron*. He has published many papers and superb photographs, shown plants and helped both scientists and laymen all over the world. He is remembered by the elegant *R. rousei* (Argent & Madulid 1998) named in his honour.

The present and beyond

There are at least five 'vireya buffs' newsletters: *Vireya Venture*, *Vireya News*, *Viva Vireyas*, *European Vireya World* and *Vireya Vine*. The last (and oldest) is a tribute to the Education Committee of the Rhododendron Species Foundation and owes a great deal to the efforts and vigour of **E. White Smith**, its sometime editor. He persistently asked, persuaded and cajoled people to write down all manner of news, thoughts, recipes, observations and anecdotes, and his energy in getting these mailed all over the world has made this a truly international medium of communication. It has brought together very diverse people in very different places – growers, nurserymen and scientists – and is a must for all who take a serious interest in the group. White also produced with his wife Lucy Sorenson a very useful anthology of articles that had been printed over the years by the American Rhododendron Society. Another of the Americans who should not be forgotten is **Bill Moyles**, who worked on behalf of the American Rhododendron Society patiently cleaning, packeting and testing seed and sending out many thousands of packets, which has certainly been important in spreading these plants to diverse collections all over the world. He has also developed a really wonderful vireya garden at Lakeside Park in Oakland, California, where the plants are grown in raised beds which produces wonderful growth and shows them off to great effect.

Richard Currie has developed an amazing collection of species and varieties in his suburban garden in New Zealand and is active in distributing the many plants that he raises.

The vulnerability of all plant collections if they are maintained only in one place cannot be over stressed. It is a tribute to the fraternity of vireya growers that so many species are quickly spread around but it does require dedicated work to do this on a large scale and the tragedy is that so often the original provenance of the acquisition is lost. Germany is playing its part in stimulating interest in vireyas: the group plays a prominent role in the '*botanika*' project in Bremen opened in 2003, which owes much to the energies and inspiration of **Hartwig Schepker** and **Michael Werbeck**. The irrepressible **Martin Monthoffer** also evangelises vireyas to a world audience. **Hansjörg and Margot Brentel** have made exciting discoveries in their explorations for rhododendrons in some very remote parts of SE Asia, especially in West Papua (the Indonesian part of the island of New Guinea), and brought many species into cultivation for the first time.

Vireyas are having another vogue period but largely outside the UK. An explosion of interest in Hawaii was started by **Mitch Mitchell** from his retirement home above the village of Volcano on Hawaii, 'The Big Island'. His garden is in an ideal climate zone with a beautiful framework of native *Cibotium* tree-ferns which have been underplanted since 1982 with a great range of both species and hybrid vireyas. In the humid climate around the town of Hilo Mitch discovered that stems with trusses of flowers would root as cuttings surprisingly easily. He developed a spectacular auction of floral trusses at the meetings of what became the Hawaiian branch of the American Rhododendron Society where people could see exactly what they were going to get if they grew the stems after the flowers had died. The ease with which vireyas grow without protection and the general enthusiasm which has been generated now make Hawaii the undoubted centre of the vireya world. **Sherla Bertelman** and

Mitch Mitchell's auction of floral trusses.

partner **Richard Marques** have taken on the baton, converting an orchid nursery almost entirely to vireyas and carrying the main load of organising international meetings of vireya enthusiasts.

There is very little hybridising going on in Britain at present and very few of the newer hybrids are commercially available here. **Christopher Fairweather** holds the national collection of hybrids in the UK and evangelises on behalf of these plants, listing 91 as potentially available from his nursery out of the more than 400 registered by the Royal Horticultural Society. In contrast, Australia, New Zealand and the USA are producing exciting new forms which are more vigorous, more compact and very free flowering with a range of habit, colour and perfume to suit most plant lovers' tastes. They also have several specialist nurseries to cater for enthusiasts. There is potential for these plants to be grown, with protection, in north temperate regions – vireyas require relatively little heat in winter and flower throughout the year but they do not take kindly to the dry air of modern living rooms.

Chris Callard, working from his home in London, has been largely responsible for putting vireyas on 'the Web'. www.vireya.net was started in 1998 initially to display a few photos of vireyas but it has expanded steadily with the input of an increasing number of people who supply pictures and information. It is now a vital reference point for both beginners and those who seek detailed information on the group. This website now attracts over 25,000 visits a year from more than 30 different countries. It has illustrations of over half the species and many hybrid cultivars, an extensive bibliography and the most comprehensive list currently available of named hybrid cultivars, both registered and unregistered.

The big challenge for the future is to develop a vireya garden within the SE Asian area from which they come. This must be done with care as where species are moved they could so easily hybridise with wild populations and play havoc with indigenous species. However, if an accessible, well-maintained garden can be found in an isolated mountain area without its own endemic species this could prove a great attraction for rhododendron lovers and a site for further study. There is still enormous potential for the development of these plants: many areas which do not grow them could do so in the future, and the potential for hybrids given the species we already have in cultivation is unbounded. There are still also many regions in SE Asia which are under- or unexplored. Many new species await discovery and description.

People who have had vireya rhododendrons named after them

Domingo Madulid (*R. madulidii*).   Peter Wilkie (*R. wilkiei*) with his collection of *R. alborugosum*.

Peter Stevens (in shorts) (*R. stevensianum*) with Bob Johns (left), the author (second left) and Mark Coode (right).

Tony Lamb (*R. lambianum*) on Kinabalu.

Domingo Madulid

Eston Reynoso (*R. reynosoi*) with Maribel Agoo
(Philippine botanist).

Andrew Bacon
(*R. baconii*), a
gourmet cook
on expeditions!

3 CONSPECTUS OF CLASSIFICATION

The large size of the genus *Rhododendron*, the sometimes unhappy relationship between 'species' cultivated from the wild and wild collected plants and the widespread ability of rhododendrons to hybridise have resulted in disparate interpretations on how to divide the genus. This classification of *Vireya* is an attempt at a practical way of dividing the group so that species can be identified and named. It is based on what can be recognised morphologically. Recent molecular work has not yet given a clear, unequivocal way of marrying morphology to monophyletic groups. This classification is based largely on that developed by Professor Sleumer (1949, 1960, 1966) but it incorporates the observations and treatment of Copeland (1929, 1943) and observations made particularly on the living collections in Edinburgh.

Genus *Rhododendron*. Type: *R. ferrugineum* L.

Subgenus *Vireya* (Blume) Clarke in Hook.*f.*, Fl. Brit. India. 1882. 3: 462. Type: *R. javanicum* (Blume) Benn.
Vireya Blume, Bijdr. 1826. 854; G.Don, Gen. Syst. 1834. 3: 846.
R. sect. *Vireya* (Blume) H.F.Copel., Phil. J. Sc. 1929. 40(2): 136, 151; Sleumer, Bot. Jahr. 1949. 74: 536; Sleumer, Reinwardtia 1960. 5(2): 50; Sleumer, Flora Malesiana 1966. I, 6(4): 480.

Scaly rhododendrons whose seeds have tails at both ends; usually with a tapering style–ovary junction; possessing an umbellate (or solitary-flowered) inflorescence, without any rhachis; the leaves not deciduous and with large idioblasts; flowers without spots of pigment, calyx mostly represented by a low disc of tissue and the plants lacking floccose, branched, glandular or lamellar hairs.

The status of subgenus was first proposed by Clarke in the *Flora of British India* but it was followed by Copeland (1943) and more recently by Professor Spethmann (1980, 1987). It is followed here for two reasons. Firstly it recognises the distinctness of the group (there are no intermediates or species that are doubtfully placed). Secondly it allows for more practical subdivisions given that the classification is very artificial. The latest molecular work (Hall *et al.* 2006) casts doubt on the monophyly of *Vireya* and indicates that *Discovireya* as defined here is isolated. This is at variance with the traditional view that it is *Pseudovireya* which is the most isolated group.

Section I: *Pseudovireya* (Clarke) Sleumer, Bot. Jahr. 1949. 74: 537. Type: *R. vaccinioides* Hook.*f.*
Subgenus *Pseudovireya* Clarke in Hook.*f.*, Fl. Brit. India 1882. 3: 464.
Subsection *Discovireya* Sleumer, Bot. Jahr. 1949. 74: 539; Sleumer, Reinwardtia 1960. 5(2): 50, *pro parte* (based on *R. retusum* (Blume) Benn.).

Fruit not peeling an outer layer before splitting. Flower bud scales (sterile bracts or perulae) fringed with simple white hairs. Filaments with hairs in the middle part, glabrous both distally and proximally. Anthers extrorse or apical. Flowers small, less than 15mm long, campanulate, usually broader than long and with the lobes about the same length as or longer than the tube. Style–ovary junction abrupt. Scales mostly disc-shaped with a large swollen centre and narrow flange. Scales well spaced with the lower epidermis of the leaf clearly visible between them.

In addition to the type this section includes *R. santapaui* from India, *R. kawakamii* from Taiwan, *R. rushforthii* from Vietnam and all the Chinese species described in section *Vireya*.

Clarke in *Flora of British India* (*loc. cit.*) created a new subgenus for *R. vaccinioides* on the grounds that the valves of the capsule are recurved but not twisted after dehiscence. This does not appear to be a very significant character and is very variable, differing greatly from species to species. This section is very distinct on morphological grounds and was found to be remote from other vireyas on breeding compatibility (Rouse & Williams 1994a). Recent DNA work has resulted in ambiguous results.

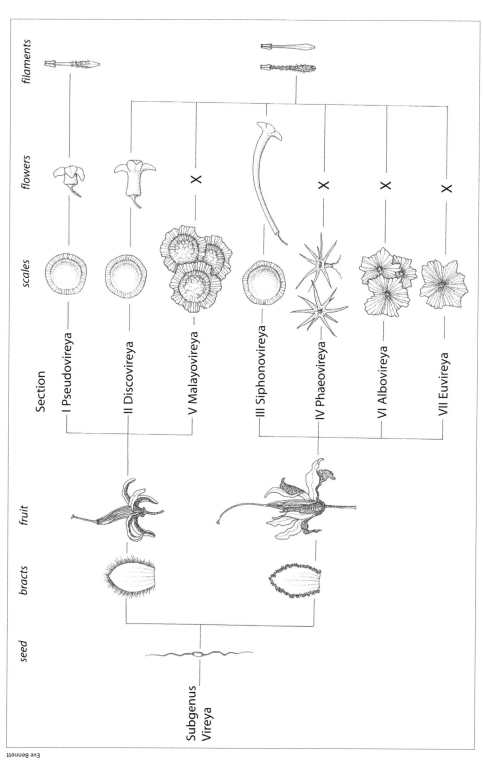

Diagrammatic representation of some of the morphological features.

Eve Bennett

Section II: ***Discovireya*** (Sleumer) Argent *stat. nov.* Type: *R. retusum* Benn.
Subsection *Discovireya* Sleumer, Bot. Jahr. 1949. 74: 539.
Subsection *Zygomorphanthe* Schltr., Bot. Jahr. 1918. 55: 145, *pro parte*.
Subsection *Pseudovireya* (Clarke) Sleumer, *pro parte*.
Section *Lepipherum* G.Don, *sensu* H.F.Copel., Phil. J. Sc. 1929. 40(2): 136, *pro parte*.

Fruit not peeling an outer layer before splitting. Flower bud scales (sterile bracts or perulae) fringed with simple white hairs. Filaments hairy from the base or glabrous. Anthers introrse. Flowers mostly tubular-cylindric, the lobes distinctly shorter than the tube. Style–ovary junction sub-abrupt to tapering. Scales mostly disc-shaped with a large swollen centre and narrow flange, well spaced with the lower epidermis of the leaf clearly visible between them.

This comprises Sleumer's (1966) species 1–25 excepting *R. vanderbiltianum* Merr. which should be included in section *Maddenia* (Argent *et al.* in manuscript) and *R. vinkii* which is transferred to subsection *Malesia*. It also includes Sleumer's subsequently described *R. detznerianum* and *R. buxoides*.

Section III: ***Siphonovireya*** (Sleumer) Argent *stat. nov.* Type: *R. habbemae* Koord.
Subsection *Siphonovireya* Sleumer, Reinwardtia 1960. 5(2): 68.
Section *Hadranthe* Schltr., Bot. Jahr. 1918. 55: 157, *pro parte typo excluso*.

Fruit irregularly peeling an outer layer before splitting. Flower bud scales (sterile bracts or perulae) fringed with scales (multicellular trichomes). Filaments hairy from the base or glabrous. Anthers introrse. Flowers trumpet-shaped, the lobes less than ¼ the length of the corolla. Style–ovary junction tapering. Scales mostly disc-shaped with a large swollen centre and narrow flange, well spaced with the lower epidermis of the leaf clearly visible between them.

Sleumer's species 26–32 with the addition of *R. gideonii* and *R. searleanum*.

Section IV: ***Phaeovireya*** (Sleumer) Argent *stat. nov.* Type: *R. beyerinckianum* Koord.
Subsection *Phaeovireya* Sleumer, Bot. Jahr. 1949. 74: 539.
Section *Schistanthe* Schltr., Bot. Jahr. 1918. 55: 140, *pro parte typo excluso*.
Section *Zygomorphanthe* Schltr., Bot. Jahr. 1918. 55: 145, *pro parte typo excluso*.
Section *Hadranthe* Schltr., Bot. Jahr. 1918. 55: 157, *pro parte typo excluso*.

Fruit irregularly peeling an outer layer before splitting. Flower bud scales (sterile bracts or perulae) fringed with scales (multicellular trichomes). Filaments hairy from the base or glabrous. Anthers introrse. Flower shape various. Style–ovary junction usually tapering. Scales dendroid, each from the top of an epidermal tubercle on the lower epidermis of the leaf.

Sleumer's species 33–74 with the addition of *R. caliginis*, *R. evelyneae*, *R. kawir* and *R. tintinnabellum*.

Section V: ***Malayovireya*** (Sleumer) Argent *stat. nov.* Type: *R. malayanum* Jack.
Subsection *Malayovireya* Sleumer, Blumea 1958. Suppl. IV: 48.
Section *Lepipherum* G.Don, *sensu* H.F.Copel., Phil. J. Sc. 1929. 40(2): 136, *pro parte typo excluso*.

Fruit not peeling an outer layer before splitting. Flower bud scales (sterile bracts or perulae) fringed with simple white hairs. Filaments hairy from the base or glabrous. Anthers introrse. Flowers various. Style–ovary junction tapering. Scales very variable in size, lobed, with a swollen centre which in the largest scales is dark coloured. Scales usually at least touching, mostly forming a coherent layer over the epidermis of the leaf.

Sleumer's species 75–88 with the addition of *R. lamrialianum*.

Section VI: *Albovireya* Sleumer, Reinwardtia 1960. 5: 107. Type: *R. album* Blume.
Section *Zygomorphanthe* Schltr., Bot. Jahr. 1918. 55: 145, *pro parte typo excluso*.

Fruit irregularly peeling an outer layer before splitting. Flower bud scales (sterile bracts or perulae) fringed with scales (multicellular trichomes). Filaments hairy from the base or glabrous. Anthers introrse. Flowers various. Style–ovary junction abrupt to tapering. Scales deeply lobed, mostly pale coloured. Scales usually at least touching, mostly forming a coherent layer over the lower epidermis of the leaf.

Sleumer's species 89–102.

Section VII: *Euvireya* (H.F.Copel.) Argent *stat. nov.* Type: *R. javanicum* (Blume) Benn.
Subsection *Euvireya* H.F.Copel., Phil. J. Sc. 1929. 40(2): 137. Including subsection *Solenovireya* H.F.Copel., Phil. J. Sc. 1929. 40(2): 136.

Fruit peeling an irregular outer layer at maturity. Flower bud scales (sterile bracts or perulae) fringed with multicellular trichomes (scales). Filaments hairy from the base or glabrous. Anthers introrse. Flowers various, often large (mostly more than 15mm long) and showy, mostly funnel-shaped or trumpet-shaped. Scales (multicellular epidermal trichomes) thin with small centres, moderately to deeply stellately lobed occasionally sub-dendroid or dendroid. Scales well spaced with the lower epidermis of the leaf clearly visible between them.

Subsection i: *Linnaeopsis* (Schltr.) Sleumer, Bot. Jahr. 1949. 74: 541. Type: *R. linnaeoides* Schltr. (= *R. anagalliflorum* Wernham).
Series i *Linnaeoidea* Sleumer, Reinwardtia 1960. 5: 134.
Section *Linnaeopsis* Schltr., Bot. Jahr. 1917. 55: 144, *f*.2.

Leaves small, the majority of well-developed leaves less than 1cm long. Stomata on the abaxial (lower) leaf surface only. Small creeping or erect shrubs.

Subsection ii: *Saxifragoidea* (Sleumer) Argent *stat. nov.* Type: *R. saxifragoides* J.J.Sm.
Series ii *Saxifragoidea* Sleumer, Reinwardtia 1960. 5: 141.

Cushion forming plant with stomata on both sides of the leaf.

Subsection iii: *Solenovireya* H.F.Copel., Phil. J. Sc. 1929. 40(2): 136. Type: *R. jasminiflorum* Hook.
Subsection *Solenovireya* H.F.Copel.; Sleumer, Bot. Jahr. 1949. 74: 537, *pro parte*.
Series I subseries 7 *apud* Hook.*f.* in Benth. & Hook.*f.*, Gen. Pl. 1876. 2: 600.
Section *Hadranthe* Schltr., Bot. Jahr. 1918. 55: 157, *pro parte typo excluso*.

Flowers trumpet-shaped (hypocrateriform), white or pale pink, the lobes less than ¼ the length of the tube. Medium to large shrubs with stomata on the abaxial (lower) leaf surface only.

This has not been raised to sectional level as it is defined only on flower shape which is not considered to be a strong taxonomic character.

Subsection iv: *Malesia* H.F.Copel., Phil. J. Sc. 1929. 40(2): 136, 151. Type: *R. bagobonum* H.F.Copel.
Series iii *Buxifolia* Sleumer, Reinwardtia 1960. 5: 145. Type: *R. buxifolium* Low *ex* Hook.*f.*
Subsection *Linearanthera* H.F.Copel., Phil. J. Sc. 1929. 40(2): 136, 152 (based on *R. vidalii* Rolfe).
Subsection *Astrovireya* Sleumer, Bot. Jahr. 1949. 74: 539 (based on *R. commonae* Foerster).
Section *Zygomorphanthe* Schltr., Bot. Jahr. 1918. 55: 145, *pro parte typo excluso*.

Leaves medium sized, the majority of well-developed leaves mostly 1–4cm long. Stomata on the abaxial (lower) leaf surface only.

Frieda Christie

Scanning electron micrographs of bract margins (A, B) and scale types (C–G).

Bract margins: A, *R. rarum* (*Phaeovireya*); B, *R. durionifolium* (*Malayovireya*).

Scale types: C, circular, *R. searleanum* (*Siphonovireya*); D, overlapping, *R. malayanum* (*Malayovireya*); E, stellate, *R. aurigeranum* (*Euvireya*); F, dendroid, *R. phaeochitum* (*Phaeovireya*); G, lobed, *R. pubigermen* (*Euvireya*).

Subsection v: *Euvireya* H.F.Copel., Phil. J. Sc. 1929. 40(2): 137, 159 *s.str.* Type: *R. javanicum* (Blume) Benn.
Section *Schistanthe* Schltr., Bot. Jahr. 1917. 55: 140, *pro parte* (lectotype *R. hansemanni* Warb.).
Section *Hapalanthe* Schltr., Bot. Jahr. 1918. 55: 155 (lectotype *R. zoelleri* Warb.). Section *Zygomorphanthe* Schltr.,
Bot. Jahr. 1918. 55: 145, *pro parte* (based on *R. keysseri* Foerster).
Subsection *Leiovireya* H.F.Copel., Phil. J. Sc. 1929. 40(2): 137, 167 (based on *R. crassifolium* Stapf).
Subsection *Schizovireya* Sleumer, Bot. Jahr. 1949. 74: 538 (based on *R. macgregoriae* F.Muell.).

Leaves large, the majority of well-developed leaves more than 4cm long. Stomata on the abaxial (lower) leaf surface only. Medium to large shrubs or small trees.

4 ARTIFICIAL KEY TO THE SECTIONS AND SUBSECTIONS

1   Scales on the undersides of the leaves with a broad lamina, overlapping or at least touching with little epidermis clear to be viewed unless the scales are broken or damaged ⎯⎯⎯⎯⎯⎯⎯ 2
+   Scales on the undersides of the leaves rarely touching or overlapping (unless dendroid and then lacking a broad lamina), generally more than two diameters distant from each other so that areas of the epidermis are clearly visible ⎯⎯⎯⎯⎯⎯⎯⎯⎯⎯⎯⎯⎯⎯⎯⎯⎯⎯⎯ 3

2   Scales on the undersides of the leaves variable in size, the largest with very dark brown almost black centres. Flower buds with the bracts fringed with simple white hairs ⎯⎯⎯⎯⎯⎯ **V. Malayovireya**
+   Scales on the undersides of the leaves mostly pale in colour and with relatively small centres, the largest scales sometimes with mid-brown centres. Flower buds with the bracts fringed with scales ⎯ **VI. Albovireya**

3   Scales on the undersides of the leaves (and those on the corollas if they have them) with large swollen dome-shaped centres and relatively narrow marginal flange ⎯⎯⎯⎯⎯⎯⎯⎯⎯ 4
+   Scales on the undersides of the leaves (and those on the corollas if they have them) with small centres and a broad marginal flange or narrow dendroid arms ⎯⎯⎯⎯⎯⎯⎯⎯⎯⎯⎯ 6

4   Flowers short-campanulate the tube rarely longer than the lobes, flowers less than 15mm long, stamens with the filaments hairy in the middle (glabrous at both base and apex) ⎯⎯⎯⎯⎯ **I. Pseudovireya**
+   Flowers various but the tube longer than the lobes, flowers often longer than 15mm, stamens with the filaments hairy from the base upwards or glabrous ⎯⎯⎯⎯⎯⎯⎯⎯⎯⎯⎯ 5

5   Bracts of the flower buds fringed with simple white hairs. Flowers usually coloured red, orange or yellow, the corolla lobes usually more than ¼ the length of the tube ⎯⎯⎯⎯⎯⎯⎯ **II. Discovireya**
+   Bracts of the flower buds fringed with scales. Flowers usually white or flushed lightly with pink, rarely solid pink, the corolla lobes usually less (mostly much less) than ¼ the length of the tube ⎯⎯ **III. Siphonovireya**

6   Scales on the undersides of the leaves dendroid, each from a persistent epidermal tubercle which persists after the scales have gone ⎯⎯⎯⎯⎯⎯⎯⎯⎯⎯⎯⎯⎯⎯⎯⎯ **IV. Phaeovireya**
+   Scales on the undersides of the leaves an irregular disc, star-shaped to dendroid, each from a relatively smooth epidermis or often somewhat impressed ⎯⎯⎯⎯⎯⎯⎯⎯⎯⎯ **VII. Euvireya** 7

7   Flowers trumpet-shaped, the tube more than 4x as long as the lobes, usually white or pale pink ⎯⎯⎯⎯⎯⎯⎯⎯⎯⎯⎯⎯⎯⎯⎯⎯⎯⎯⎯⎯⎯⎯⎯⎯ **Subsection iii. Solenovireya**
+   Flowers campanulate, tubular, or funnel-shaped, the tube less than 4x as long as the lobes, mostly strongly coloured, sometimes white or pale pink ⎯⎯⎯⎯⎯⎯⎯⎯⎯⎯⎯⎯⎯ 8

8   Pedicels much longer than the solitary flowers, densely leaved, low cushion plant ⎯⎯⎯⎯⎯⎯⎯⎯⎯⎯⎯⎯⎯⎯⎯⎯⎯⎯⎯⎯⎯ **Subsection ii. Saxifragoidea**
+   Pedicels shorter than the flowers or if longer then in many-flowered umbels ⎯⎯⎯⎯⎯⎯⎯ 9

9   Most leaves less than 15mm long ⎯⎯⎯⎯⎯⎯⎯⎯⎯⎯⎯⎯⎯ **Subsection i. Linnaeopsis**
+   Most leaves more than 15mm long ⎯⎯⎯⎯⎯⎯⎯⎯⎯⎯⎯⎯⎯⎯⎯⎯⎯ 10

10 Most leaves less than 4cm long ⎯⎯⎯⎯⎯⎯⎯⎯⎯⎯⎯⎯⎯ **Subsection iv. Malesia**
+   Most leaves more than 4cm long ⎯⎯⎯⎯⎯⎯⎯⎯⎯⎯⎯⎯ **Subsection v. Euvireya**

5 DESCRIPTIVE ACCOUNT WITH KEYS TO THE SPECIES

SECTION I: *Pseudovireya* (Clarke) Sleumer

Bot. Jahr. 1949. 74: 537

Type: *R. vaccinioides* Hook.*f.*
Subgenus *Pseudovireya* Clarke in Hook.*f.*, Fl. Brit. India 1882. 3: 464.
Subsection *Discovireya* Sleumer, Bot. Jahr. 1949. 74: 539; Sleumer, Reinwardtia 1960. 5(2): 50, *pro parte* (based on *R. retusum* (Blume) Benn.).

Fruit not peeling an outer layer before splitting. Flower bud scales (sterile bracts or perulae) fringed with simple white hairs. Filaments with hairs in the middle part, glabrous both distally and proximally. Anthers extrorse or apical. Flowers small, less than 15mm long, campanulate, usually broader than long and with the lobes about the same length as or longer than the tube. Style–ovary junction abrupt. Scales mostly disc-shaped with a large swollen centre and narrow flange. Scales well spaced with the lower epidermis of the leaf clearly visible between them.

This is a poorly known group of species. *Rhododendron vaccinioides* is the best known, from numerous collections over a wide geographical range. *Rhododendron datiandingense* is still known from only a single collection. The flower shape and structure is remarkably uniform, and further collections are badly needed to establish the distinctness or otherwise of the entities recognised here. Recent collections of the essentially solitary, yellow-flowered plants from North Vietnam have come in under various names but most that have been examined as living plants are referable to *R. emarginatum*.

Key to the species

1	Flowers white or pink	2
+	Flowers yellow or orange	4
2	Leaves spirally arranged over extended lengths of stem	**1. vaccinioides**
+	Leaves in distinct pseudowhorls	3
3	Leaves in tight pseudowhorls, with 3–4 lateral veins per side visible from above	**2. santapaui**
+	Leaves in loose pseudowhorls, the lateral veins obscure	**3. asperulum**
4	Flowers mostly solitary or paired	5
+	Flowers in umbels of 3 or more	9
5	Ovary with simple hairs overtopping scales	7
+	Ovary with scales only	6
6	Twigs distinctly and persistently rough with the stalks of scales	**6. emarginatum**
+	Twigs smooth, without persistent scale stalks, the scales on the stems essentially sessile	**7. sororium**
7	Leaf blades to 5mm wide	**8. densifolium**
+	Leaf blades more than 8mm wide	8
8	Leaf blades to 20mm long, pedicels hairy and scaly, flowers with red spots	**5. rupivalleculatum**
+	Leaf blades to 30mm long, pedicels with scales only, flowers without red spots	**4. insculptum**
9	Leaf apex rounded to broadly obtuse (Taiwan)	**11. kawakamii**
+	Leaf apex broadly acute (mainland Asia)	10
10	Petiole to 5mm (ovary indumentum unknown)	**10. datiandingense**
+	Petiole more than 8mm (ovary without simple hairs)	**9. rushforthii**

1. Rhododendron vaccinioides Hook.*f.*

Rhod. Sikkim. Himal. 1851. ii: 3.

Type: Hooker *s.n.*, 3 Aug. 1848. Lachen, Sikkim Himalaya, 2400m (K). Flowering material Herb. Sikk. Treutlerianum, 2 July 1874.

Derivation: Named from the resemblance of the plants to species of *Vaccinium*.

Synonym: *R. sino-vaccinioides* Balf.*f.* & Forrest, Notes RBG Edinb. 1922. 13: 295.

Shrub to 1m. Twigs green, with moderately dense brown scales set on persistent stalks, rough with stalks after the scales have fallen. **Leaves** spirally arranged along the twigs, although rapid extension growth may look bare with only small cataphylls which quickly fall. **Blade** 7–30 x 3–13mm, obovate-spathulate or elliptic, glossy dark green above, dull and paler below; apex obtuse or retuse but with a conspicuous mucronate gland; margin narrowly cartilaginous, entire, flat or slightly revolute; base narrowly tapering; moderately to sparsely scaly, the scales set in shallow depressions, glabrescent above, persistently scaly beneath. **Scales** circular, with narrow marginal zones and variably developed centres. Mid-vein impressed above, broadly and shallowly raised below; lateral veins obscure. **Petiole** *c.*1–3 x 1mm, not clearly demarcated from the blade, grooved above, scaly, especially beneath.

Flower buds to 5 x 4mm, ovoid, green passing to pale brown, smooth except for the slightly spreading tips of the lowest bracts. Bracts ovate, acutely pointed, scaly outside near the midline and apex and densely fringed with long white hairs, glabrous inside, often persisting around the base of the pedicels until fruiting. Bracteoles 6–7 x 0.75–1.25mm, with a few scales outside distally, long marginal hairs at the apex, much shorter ones on the sides. **Flowers** solitary, occasionally 2 or 3 together held horizontally or semi-erect. Pedicels 12–20 x *c.*1mm, scaly. Calyx lobes 2–3 x *c.*1.5mm, elongate-ovate to sub-rounded, scaly outside and fringed with scales on the margins. **Corolla** *c.*8 x 6mm, white or flushed pink; tube *c.*4 x 3 x 4mm, broadly cylindrical, scaly outside, glabrous inside; lobes *c.*4 x 3mm, round or obovate, wide-spreading, not overlapping when fully open, glabrous or with a few scales outside. **Stamens** exserted to *c.*5mm; filaments densely long-hairy in the upper ⅔ to a level with the base of the anthers, but then glabrous; anthers *c.*2.5 x 1.5mm, pink. Disc glabrous. **Ovary** *c.*2 x 1mm, densely scaly but without simple hairs; style *c.*2.5mm, glabrous, expanded upwards, club-shaped. **Fruit** 20–25 x *c.*5mm, sometimes reported as bright red, spindle-shaped, the valves recurving. Seeds 10–15mm, without tails *c.*1mm, the longest tail 7mm.

Ross Eudal

Rhododendron vaccinioides.

Nepal (E). **Bhutan**. **Myanmar** (N). **Tibet** (SE). **India**, Sikkim, Assam Himalaya, Lachen and Darjeeling. **China**, Yunnan. Epiphytic in forest, sometimes pendulous from the trunks of trees and on exposed rocks and cliffs, 1800–4200m. *Fl.* April–May.

It was cultivated by Lord Headfort of Kells, Co. Meath from seed collected by George Forrest's 1924 expedition and flowered on 19 June 1933 from which material it was figured in the *Botanical Magazine* (*t.*9407b). A comment with the cultivated specimen at Kew reads: 'Find it tender and several plants died outside. Hates the sun. Only remaining plant now about four inches high and ten inches across growing in a cold frame and full shade, very healthy'. It does appear to be weakly growing in cultivation in Britain and intolerant of high temperatures, the plants mostly failing in summer in the UK although apparently growing vigorously in New Zealand.

One form in cultivation has distinctive pink undersides to the leaves. The flowers are small and not at all showy but sometimes the plants produce as many as four in the inflorescence when cultivated well. Recorded as flowering in cultivation by Loder Plants as April–July in the UK, but in bloom in August in New Zealand and probably somewhat erratic. In the wild it flowers in July, the fruit ripening in October–November.

---

2. Rhododendron santapaui Sastry, Kataki, P.A.Cox, P.B.Cox & Hutchison
J. Bombay Nat. Hist. Soc. 1969. 65: 744.
Type: Sastry 45720, 23 May 1966. Begi, Subansiri District, N.E.F.A. India (CAL).
Derivation: Named after the Rev. H. Santapau for his devoted service in the cause of taxonomic research and the promotion of the floristic exploration of India.

Shrub to 1.5m. Twigs slender, spreading, rounded, rough, densely white-scaly, quickly glabrescent; internodes 3–8.5cm with 1–2 deciduous scale leaves. **Leaves** in tight pseudowhorls of 5–9. **Blade** 15–30 x 5–12mm, elliptic to obovate, sub-sessile; apex acute to sub-obtuse, shortly apiculate; margin entire, cartilaginous, recurved when dry; base tapering; densely scaly above at first but quickly glabrescent, dark green; below sparsely brown-scaly, pale green. **Scales** circular or sub-circular, moderately dense, with a broad marginal zone and small centre. Mid-vein prominent, impressed above, raised beneath; lateral veins 3–4 per side, impressed above, obscure beneath. **Petiole** 2–3 x *c.*1.5mm, grooved above, sparsely scaly.

Bud to 10 x 8mm, green, smooth, sub-spherical. Bracts to 5–8 x 3–6mm, outer ovate mucronate, inner larger, sub-

hemispherical, deeply concave, cuspidate, shortly and irregularly ciliate along the margins and sometimes with a few scales. Bracteoles *c.*10.5 x 0.6mm, subulate with long stalked brown scales around the margins. Inflorescence a 2–6-flowered umbel. Pedicels 10–20mm, slender, slightly curved, densely silvery scaly. Calyx of low triangular lobes to 1 x 1.5mm, densely pale brown scaly outside and with a fringe of scales. **Corolla** *c.*10 x 15–25mm, campanulate, white, fleshy; tube 3.5–8 x *c.*4 x *c.*8mm, sparsely scaly outside, hairy inside in a broad band just above the base; lobes 6–8 x 5–8mm, sparsely scaly outside, rounded or broadly oblong, sub-acute, or obtuse, erect gradually becoming reflexed. **Stamens** *c.*12mm, slightly dimorphic, exserted to 7mm; filaments white, hairy in the middle; anthers *c.*2.5mm, oblong, cream with brown margins to the pores. Disc circular, 10-lobed, glabrous. **Ovary** *c.*5 x 2.5mm, ovoid, 5-ridged, densely scaly; style *c.*5mm, thick, bent to the lower side of the flower, glabrous, slightly enlarged upwards, often becoming deciduous later; stigma truncate. **Fruit** 20–27 x 4–5mm, straight, spindle-shaped with persistent brown scales; splitting without peeling an irregular layer but the outer layer sometimes separating after the capsule has split; valves opening to a wide angle and the placentae opening lantern-like. Seeds to 11mm, without tails 1.2mm, the longest tail 5.5mm, the tails extremely slender, filiform and flexuous.

First collected from the Api Tani valley, Arunachal Pradesh, **India** where it was growing hanging from large tree trunks with little moss at 1600m (Cox 1985). A second locality was discovered in 2005 by Kenneth Cox, Steve Hootman and Hartwig Schepker along a tributary of the Upper Siang River, close to the Indian/Tibetan border, at *c.*900m.

First introduced into cultivation in 1966 by the authors of the species and first flowered in cultivation at Shillong in India in July 1967. This was followed by a flowering in September 1967 at the garden of Peter and Patricia Cox, at Glendoick, Perthshire, Scotland, from where it has been widely distributed. It is now growing in many collections around the world. In cultivation it is a compact plant which flowers freely. The neat white flowers are more of an oddity than an object of great beauty, although the plant has a certain charm. Peter Cox states: 'This has proved rather tricky in cultivation and [is] inclined to die suddenly'. The plants in Edinburgh grow slowly but steadily. The authors suggested that this species is allied to *R. kawakamii* but it is very distinct and crosses with that species only with great difficulty (John Rouse *pers. comm.*). In greenhouse cultivation in Edinburgh it regularly produces more than the two flowers in the inflorescence which it was described as exhibiting in the wild.

It also usually flowers earlier in July or August than the first flowering and rarely throws out of season flowers. The scales on the leaves are interesting in that they have small centres and broad flanges, which are irregular for this section, but those on the corolla are more typical. The seed morphology appears to be highly distinctive, with extraordinarily long tails which are filiform but which unusually broaden abruptly at the junction with the seed. In New Zealand a hybrid in David Binney's collection was said to be *R. santapaui* x *R. lochiae*. This certainly looks like *R. santapaui* but with red flowers. The origin of this collection was unknown.

3. Rhododendron asperulum Hutch. & Kingdon-Ward
Notes RBG Edinb. 1931. 16: 182.
Type: Ward 6801, 30 May 1926. Upper Burma, Seinghku Wang (K, E).
Derivation: Latin – *asper* – rough – the diminutive form – slightly or minutely rough, referring to the stems.

Small shrub. Twigs reddish, densely covered with rounded scales on stalks later rough with the persistent scale stalks and when dry, the surface rugulose. **Leaves** in loose to moderately compact pseudowhorls of 4–8 together. **Blade** 16–22 x 7–10mm, broadly spathulate to elliptic; apex rounded to slightly emarginate with a shortly protruding, mucronate gland; margin recurved especially proximally; base tapering or narrowly tapering, somewhat decurrent; upper surface sparsely scaly, the scales not impressed and the surface becoming glabrescent; below moderately to sparsely and persistently scaly. **Scales** round and impressed with broad swollen centres and narrow flanges. Mid-vein impressed above and raised below throughout its length; lateral veins 1–2 per side, narrowly impressed above, and weakly raised below, in smaller leaves totally obscure. **Petiole** 1.5–2 x *c.*1mm, scaly.

Outer bracts subulate, scaly outside, fringed with hairs and with a few hairs inside near the apex, inner bracts ovate scaly outside, fringed with short hairs, glabrous inside. Bracteoles sub-linear, becoming broader distally, fringed with hairs, the truncate apices especially fringed with long white hairs. Inflorescence 3-flowered. Pedicels 10–20 x *c.*1mm, densely to sparsely scaly. Calyx 2.5–3 x 1.5–2mm, lobes broadly elliptic, scaly outside and with scales on the margin whose stalks give the lobes an irregular edge. **Corolla** *c.*7 x 5mm, pale pink; tube *c.*5 x 4 x 5mm, densely scaly outside, glabrous inside; lobes *c.*3 x 2.5mm, with a few scales outside in the basal ½.

Stamens exserted, with long hairs in the middle part of the filaments; anthers 1.5mm, orange in colour. **Ovary** *c.*3 x 1.75mm, densely scaly but without simple hairs; style *c.*3mm, glabrous. **Fruit** *c.*25mm. Seeds small with tails.

Myanmar, (upper), Base Camp, Seinghku Wang, 28°5′N 97°30′E. Epiphytic on alders and other trees in open pastures. On boulders in the valley of the Di Chu (Kingdon-Ward 7163), 1900–2100m.

A very imperfectly known species very similar to *R. vaccinioides*, differing chiefly in the pseudowhorled arrangement of the leaves. The isotype in Edinburgh is mixed with *R. insculptum*, and the paratype 7163 (also in Edinburgh) shows some variation in that it has faint pinnate venation which is not evident in the type, but this specimen is without flowers. This species apparently grows with *R. insculptum* but besides having differently coloured flowers is said to flower about one month later. It also differs in the smaller leaves without the very distinct lateral veins of *R. insculptum* and lacks simple hairs on the ovary.

A collection distributed under this name has yellow flowers and is not this species.

4. Rhododendron insculptum Hutch. & Kingdon-Ward
Notes RBG Edinb. 1931. 16: 182.
Type: Ward 6735, 20 May 1926. Upper Burma, Seinghku Wang (K, E, L).
Derivation: Latin – *insculptus* – engraved or with sunken markings due to the deeply impressed veins on the leaf.

Shrub to 2m. Twigs 1–2mm in diameter, with stalked scales, conspicuously rough with persistent protruding scale bases after the scales have fallen; internodes 2–10cm. **Leaves** 4–7 together in tight pseudowhorls. **Blade** 20–30 x 8–16mm, obovate to spathulate; apex emarginate or rounded, with a small protruding mucronate gland; margin entire, revolute especially in the basal ½; base narrowly tapering; upper surface green, glabrescent, lower surface sparsely covered with scales, paler green. **Scales** sub-circular, brown or translucent, mostly pale, variable in size and slightly impressed. Mid-vein impressed above and raised beneath; lateral veins 1–4 per side, impressed above and strongly and conspicuously raised beneath. **Petiole** 2–4 x 1–1.5mm, grooved above, rounded below, brown scaly and very shortly hairy above.

Flower buds to 8 x 3mm, green becoming pale brown, the bracts with a few scales mainly outside and fringed with white hairs, glabrous inside. Bracteoles to 5mm, slender, glabrous except for a few hairs near the apex. Pedicels 15–25 x *c*.1mm, green, moderately to densely scaly. Inflorescence of solitary, or paired, flowers, these held semi-erect, horizontal to half-hanging. Calyx green, densely scaly; lobes *c*.1 x 1.5mm, rounded or triangular. **Corolla** *c*.12 x 12mm (dry!), orange, or yellow, moderately densely scaly outside, and with long patent white hairs just below the mouth inside; lobes probably reflexed but semi-erect in dry specimens, overlapping up to ⅔. **Stamens** arranged all round the mouth, dimorphic, the long filaments hairy towards the base only, the short ones along their entire length and protruding up to 5mm. Disc green, mainly glabrous, but with just a few hairs on the upper side. **Ovary** green, densely covered in scales and moderately densely hairy; style *c*.5 x 1mm, deflexed, glabrous. **Fruit** *c*.20 x 5mm, green passing to brown, cylindrical with longitudinal grooves and a persistent deflexed style; valves splitting to the base and curving backwards, straight, not twisting, placentae becoming detached from the base of the central column. Seeds reported to be tailed (not seen).

Myanmar, (upper), Seinghku Wang and Adung Valley. **China**, Yunnan, Gongshan Qiqi. An epiphyte in temperate rain forest at 1800–2100m. Said to grow with *R. vaccinioides* but to flower earlier than that species, the flowers being reported for April and as almost over in May.

Rarely collected and not yet known to be cultivated. This species is very similar to *R. emarginatum* but differs in that the flowers were originally described as orange in colour and it lacks hairs on the outside of the bracts; it has more distinct venation on the leaves than most of the specimens attributed to *R. emarginatum* although the type specimen of that species at Kew has equally distinct venation to *R. insculptum*.

5. **Rhododendron rupivalleculatum** P.C.Tam

Guihaia 1982. 2(2): 69.
Type: Qin & Lee 70860, 27 July 1957. Guangxi, Longsheng Xian, Shaling (IBK).
Derivation: Latin – *rupis* – a rock; *valleculum* – little valley. Alluding to the habitat of the species.

Shrub to 60cm. Twigs rounded, rough, scaly and densely papillose with scale bases. **Leaves** 3–4 together in pseudowhorls. **Blade** 14–20 x 8–10mm, spathulate-obovate; apex emarginate, apiculate with a small protruding gland; margin conspicuously recurved; base tapering; upper surface yellowish-green, lower paler, sparsely scaly. Mid-vein conspicuous; laterals veins 3–4 per side, just visible above, inconspicuous below. **Petiole** to 3mm.

Inflorescence terminal, 1-flowered. Pedicels 10–15mm, slender, shortly hairy and scaly. Calyx shortly hairy and sparsely scaly, 5-lobed, the lobes rounded, to 1.2 x 1mm, sparsely bristly-ciliate. **Corolla** 10–12 x *c*.14mm, broadly campanulate, yellow; tube sparsely scaly outside; lobes 6–7.5mm, ovate-spathulate, spotted with red. **Stamens** 8–10mm, the filaments hairy about the middle. **Ovary** to 2.2mm, shortly cylindrical, densely hairy and scaly; style *c*.5mm, bent downwards; stigma depressed-rounded to broadly 5-lobed. **Fruit** 9–12mm, oblong, scaly and hairy.

China, Guangxi Province, Longsheng Xian, Shaling Da Miao Shan. Guangdong Province, Lechang Xian, Yenbay Shan. Growing terrestrially amongst rocks.

A very imperfectly understood species. The red spots on the flowers may be distinctive or could be an imperfect rendering of the orange spots which are common on *R. emarginatum*.

6. **Rhododendron emarginatum** Hemsl. & E.H.Wilson

Kew Bull. 1910: 118.
Type: Henry 9166. China, Yunnan, Mountains SW of Mengtsze (K).
Derivation: Latin – *emarginatus* – shallowly notched, alluding to the often emarginate tips to the leaves.
Synonyms:
R. euonymifolium H.Lév., Fedde Rep. 1913. 12: 228.
R. poilanei Dop, Fl. Gén. I.-C. 1930. 3: 739.
R. maguanense K.M.Feng, Acta Bot. Yunnan. 1983. 5(3): 268.
R. leiboense Z.J.Zhao, Bull. Bot. Research 1987. 7(3): 57, *f*.1, 63.

Var. **emarginatum**

Shrub to 2m. Twigs 1–2mm in diameter, green, with stalked scales, conspicuously rough with the persistent protruding scale bases; internodes 1–4cm. **Leaves** 4–7 together in tight pseudowhorls. **Blade** 12–40 x 5–25mm, broadly elliptic to obovate; apex emarginate or rounded, with a small protruding mucronate gland; margin entire, slightly revolute; base narrowly tapering; upper surface green, glabrescent, lower surface sparsely covered with scales, pale green. **Scales** sub-circular, brown or translucent, mostly pale, variable in size and slightly impressed. Mid-vein impressed above and raised beneath, lateral veins 2–4 per side, weakly impressed above and raised beneath or obscure in smaller leaves. **Petiole** 2–4mm, grooved above, rounded below, brown scaly and very shortly hairy above.

Flower buds 6–8 x 3–4mm, green becoming pale brown, ovate, smooth with broadly acute points. Bracts minutely shortly hairy outside and fringed with longer white hairs, glabrous inside. Bracteoles 1.5mm, filiform with a few white hairs, withering quickly. Pedicels 15–25 x *c.*1mm, green, moderately to densely scaly from an uneven surface. Inflorescence of solitary, or paired, flowers, semi-erect, horizontal to half-hanging. **Flowers** 6–8 x 16–22mm, campanulate. Calyx green, densely scaly, wavy to distinctly lobed with rounded or weakly triangular lobes to 3mm. **Corolla** yellow; tube 4–5 x 4–5 x 4–5mm, moderately densely scaly outside with inconspicuous translucent scales, and with long patent white hairs just below the mouth inside; lobes 6–8 x 5–7mm, the three upper patterned with rows of faint orange-brown spots on the inner side and with a few translucent scales outside, reflexed to the horizontal or a little beyond, overlapping up to ⅓. **Stamens** arranged all round the mouth but with a gap on the lower side where the style is placed, irregularly dimorphic and exserted to 5mm; filaments yellow, tapering to the base in the lower ⅓ and also upwards for about ⅔, with long patent white hairs in the middle part; anthers 2–2.5 x *c.*1mm, brown. Disc green, glabrous. **Ovary** 2.8 x 2.2mm, green, densely covered in silvery scales. **Fruit** 12–16 x 4–5mm, the pedicel turning to place them erect, green passing to brown, cylindrical with longitudinal grooves and a persistent deflexed style; valves splitting to the base and curving backwards, straight, not twisting, the placentae remaining firmly adherent to the central column. Seeds 4–4.7mm, bright orange-brown, without tails 1.2–1.9mm, the longest tail 1.2–1.5mm, tails mostly straight, sometimes a little crimped usually at just one end.

China, SE Yunnan, Pingbian, Xichou, Malipo and Mengzi. Guangxi, Daimiaoshan Xian, Pingshixiang, Jiuwandai shan. **Vietnam**, Province Lao Cai. In tropical monsoon forests, often epiphytic on branches of trees, 1200–2900m.

Professor Sleumer compared the types of *R. euonymifolium* and *R. poilanei* (Sleumer 1958) and reduced these species to synonymy. These types have also been examined for the present study and their reduction appears logical. *Rhododendron leiboense* was differentiated in having more slender branches, triangular calyx lobes and flowers in twos. It does not appear to warrant even varietal recognition on these characters. I have reduced *R. maguanense* after examining the type material. Feng (1983) said this species was close to *R. emarginatum* but differentiated it on its smaller leaves and longer calyx lobes. Neither of these characters are sufficiently significant. The calyx lobe development is considered variable in *R. emarginatum* and the smaller leaves with less conspicuous venation appear to be reduction due to exposure.

This is one of the hardiest vireyas, withstanding up to −4°C, but then tending to defoliate and slower to grow away after being severely chilled. Grown more for interest than beauty, the flowers being small and not especially conspicuous but yet having a dainty charm. In a mild climate or under glass it will flower throughout the year but its most profuse flowering in Britain is in late summer; outside in Britain it flowers as late as November. The fruit ripens in about three months.

Var. **eriocarpum** K.M.Feng
Acta Bot. Yunnan. 1983. 5(3): 268.
Type: K.M. Feng 4852, 10 Oct. 1954. China, Yunnan, Pingbian Xian, Daiweishan (KUN).
Derivation: Greek – *erio* – woolly; *carpon* – fruit. Alluding to the hairy ovary.

Differing chiefly in that the ovary is both hairy and scaly. The calyx lobes are also well developed, 1.8 x 2mm, with scales along the margins of the lobes. Seeds 2.5–3mm, without tails *c.*1mm, the longest tail 1.2mm.

Known from the type locality in **China** and Guangxi Province, Daimiaoshan Xian, Pingshixiang, Jiuwandai shan, 1200–2180m. Recorded flowering in Aug. and Oct.

Not yet known to be in cultivation. The hairy ovary is one of the significant characters separating *R. emarginatum* from *R. insculptum*. This variety confuses this distinction.

The leaves of var. *eriocarpum* are quite distinct in being less revolute and more distinctly tapering towards the base than those of *R. emarginatum*. It might yet warrant specific status.

7. Rhododendron sororium Sleumer
Blumea 1958. Suppl. IV(2): 47.
Type: Pételot *s.n.*, July 1931. N Vietnam, Prov. Lao-Kay, environs de Chaa-pa, massif de Fan-Si-Pan (P).
Derivation: Latin – *soror* – of the sisters, presumably referring to the closely related species in this group.

Shrub. Twigs rounded, *c.*2mm in diameter, smooth, laxly covered with rounded, sessile scales, older parts glabrescent. **Leaves** arranged up to 5 together in pseudowhorls, very variable. **Blade** 25–45 x 10–20mm, obovate; apex rounded to minutely emarginate and with a small apical gland; margin very slightly revolute; base narrowly tapering and partly decurrent; above dark green becoming glabrescent, below paler and laxly scaly. Mid-vein distinct, impressed above and raised below; lateral veins 2–3 per side, curved, impressed above, slightly raised beneath. **Petiole** 3–5 x 1.5–2mm, flattened.

Bracts to 10 x 5mm, the outer shortly ovate and obtuse, long-hairy outside, with the margin densely white ciliate; the inner narrowly ovate with longer sub-acuminate apices. Inflorescence of solitary flowers or rarely in pairs. Pedicels densely scaly, without simple hairs, at flowering 15–20mm. Calyx *c.*3mm in diameter, oblique, with obtuse lobes to 1mm, frequently indistinct. **Corolla** *c.*14mm long, colour not recorded but presumably yellow, tubular-campanulate; tube *c.*8 x 4mm, shortly cylindrical, outside densely scaly, inside white-hairy; lobes 6–7 x *c.*4mm, spreading, obovate, outside laxly scaly, inside glabrous. **Stamens** dimorphic, 8 and 10mm long; filaments linear, flattened, at the base glabrous, in the middle part white-hairy, the upper part glabrous; anthers *c.*3 x 0.7mm. Disc glabrous. **Ovary** *c.*5 x 2.5mm, conical, strongly contracted distally, densely scaly; style columnar, club-shaped above, glabrous; stigma truncate, rounded. **Fruit** (immature) *c.*17 x 3mm, with a thick persistent glabrous 5–6mm style.

Vietnam, Province Lao-Kay, on the summit ridge of the Chaa-pa, massif de Fan-Si-Pan, 1400–1700m. *Fl.* July.

Differing from *R. emarginatum* in the smooth not rough twigs, a slightly longer corolla (14mm vs. to 12mm in *R. emarginatum*) and having thicker pedicels. This appears to be doubtfully distinct from *R. emarginatum*. The type material in Paris has minute protruding scale bases on the very youngest twigs and the other differences between these species do not seem particularly significant. There is however one herbarium specimen in Edinburgh (Y. Tsiang 4698) from Na-kan, Chengfeng, Kewichow with smooth twigs, fruits with long-tailed seeds and distinctive leaves that unfortunately has no flowers but could represent this species, or an undescribed one. However, Keith Rushforth is growing material from Vietnam which is said to be more erect and vigorous than *R. emarginatum* and has almost completely smooth vegetative stems. These plants have short flowering stems that are distinctly rough with scale bases and they would appear to conform to *R. sororium*.

---

8. Rhododendron densifolium K.M.Feng
Acta Bot. Yunnan. 1983. 5(3): 266.
Type: K.M. Feng 12815, 3 Nov. 1947. Yunnan, Mar-li-po: Chung-dzai, 1600–1800m (KUN).
Derivation: Latin – *densus* – dense; *folium* – leaf. Alluding to the densely leafy stems.

Shrub to 1.3m. Twigs *c.*1.5mm in diameter, red or green, densely covered with warty scale bases and brown scales; internodes 3–10mm. **Leaves** in loose pseudo-whorls, 7–15 together, 5–15mm apart, when in exposed places, clustered at the ends of the twigs. **Blade** 6–12 x 3.5–5mm, obovate, spathulate; apex emarginate and mucronate with a small gland at the apex; margin entire and revolute; base tapering; upper surface green shiny and glabrescent; lower surface paler green, sparsely but persistently scaly. **Scales** small, brown, circular or slightly lobed with large centres. Mid-vein slightly impressed above, raised below; lateral veins obscure. **Petiole** 2–3 x 0.7–1mm, faintly grooved above, sparsely scaly.

Flower buds to 6 x 2.5mm, ovate, green, turning brown before opening, smooth, glabrous except along the margins of the bracts. Outer bracts ovate, glabrous with shortly ciliate margins. Inflorescence of solitary flowers held horizontally to half-hanging. **Flowers** 6–7 x 15–18mm. Pedicels 9–14 x 1mm, sparsely scaly, without hairs. Calyx shallowly 5-lobed, lobes *c.*1.5–2 x 1.5mm, scaly outside. **Corolla** 8–10mm, campanulate, yellow, without spots or visible markings; tube *c.*5 x 4 x 4mm, sparsely scaly outside, hairy inside, lobes 6–7 x 3.5–4.5mm, elliptic, spreading to the horizontal or slightly reflexed, not or only slightly overlapping. **Stamens** exserted to *c.*5mm, arranged all round the mouth, filaments hairy; anthers brown. **Ovary** ovoid, densely scaly and hairy; style 2–4mm, curved downwards; stigma globose. **Fruit** 7–11 x 3–4mm, with a persistent style. Seeds 4mm, without tails *c.*1mm, the longest tail 1.5mm.

China, SE Yunnan, Malipo and Xichou. In mixed forests on the ground in light shade or exposed on ridges on rocky sometimes limestone mountains, 1000–1800m. *Fl.* Sept.–Oct., although one plant was flowering in June. The fruit said to be ripe Sept.–Oct. of the following year.

Very similar to *R. emarginatum* but with consistently smaller, narrower leaves which gradually broaden upwards to near the apex. It also has hairs on the ovary as well as scales. It might be thought to be a high altitude form of *R. emarginatum* except that this species is reported at even higher altitudes than *R. densifolium*. These two species do grow together in the wild and are clearly distinct on leaf size. The marginal hairs on the bracts are exceptionally short, barely reaching 0.1mm. Recently introduced into cultivation but not yet known to have flowered.

9. Rhododendron rushforthii Argent & D.F.Chamb.

The New Plantsman 1996. 3(4): 195.

Type: Rushforth, KR 2357 clone A, 12 May 1992. Side road to Ban Khoang, from Dèo Hoàng Liên Són from the main road Dèo Hoàng Liên Són to Ban Khoang, Sapa District, Laokai Province, Vietnam (HN, E).

Derivation: This species is named after Keith Rushforth, the collector.

Erect shrub to 1.5m. Twigs smooth and rounded with a few low disc-shaped scales, somewhat striate after drying. **Leaves** in loose pseudowhorls, with a few bladeless cataphylls at the base of each flush of growth but quickly changing upwards to fully formed foliage leaves. **Blade** 18–110 x 17–42mm, elliptic; apex broadly acute and mucronate with the mid-vein protruding as a terminal gland; margin entire, cartilaginous, flat when fresh, narrowly recurved after drying; base tapering with the margin narrowly decurrent; upper surface bluish or silvery-green, at first silvery-scaly, the scales later turning brown and falling off; lower surface pale green, persistently, moderately and finely brown-scaly. **Scales** circular, variable in size and irregularly distributed, slightly impressed. Mid-vein narrowly impressed to the apex above; strongly and broadly raised below, less so distally but often remaining slightly raised to the apex; lateral veins 5–6 per side, broadly arching upwards and narrowly impressed above, slightly raised below, reticulation distinct when dry less so when fresh. **Petiole** 8–15 x 2–3mm, grooved above and with narrow marginal wings, scaly.

Flower buds 8–10 x 5.5–6.5mm, ovoid. Bracts long acuminate with the apices slightly spreading, the margins somewhat irregular; central bracts broadly ovate, deeply hooded, obtuse and mucronate to almost rounded at the apex, softly white-hairy near the base and apex and also sparsely covered in brown scales outside; inner bracts spathulate with longer white hairs near the apex, margin sometimes slightly irregular in the proximal parts, with both simple white hairs and brown scales distally. Bracteoles small, linear, quickly withering. Inflorescence of 3–8 flowers in an open umbel. **Flowers** half-erect to half-hanging, stiffly held. Pedicels 10–14 x 1–1.5mm, green, with silvery or pale-brown scales and very short white erect hairs. Calyx with 5 lobes; 3 longer, elliptic with rounded tips, c.4 x 2mm, and 2 shorter, which are triangular with broadly pointed apices, c.3 x 2mm, all scaly and sparsely hairy outside. **Corolla** 10–15 x 15–20mm, shortly campanulate, yellow; tube 4–7 x 5–6 x 5–6mm, shortly cylindrical, finely scaly outside, white-hairy inside; lobes 6–7 x 6–7mm, scaly and with a greenish vein in the centre of the lobes outside, reflexed to the perpendicular

Rhododendron rushforthii.

or a little beyond. **Stamens** protruding regularly from the mouth of the flower; filaments 8 and 9mm, white or pale-yellowish, broadest towards the middle where they also have the longest white hairs, these becoming shorter both proximally and distally and are glabrous at the very base and apex; anthers c.2.5 x 1mm, brown with darker brown tips, very finely granular, the pores circular, apical. Disc swollen, circular, with 10 lobes, shortly but densely hairy on the upper side (the inner side when fresh, the hairs mostly in the depression facing the style). **Ovary** c.4 x 2.5mm, densely covered in white discoid scales (brown after drying) and patent simple white hairs, abruptly contracted distally and impressed at the style junction; style c.5 x 0.75mm, greenish-yellow, depressed to the lower side of the flower on opening, rising towards the centre as the flower ages, sparsely hairy near the base, broadening upwards to the green, 5-lobed stigma which is 1.5–2mm in diameter. **Fruit** 9–12 x 4–6mm, brown, ellipsoid, but with distinct longitudinal grooves, held erect and surmounted by the curved persistent stigmas; valves opening to c.45°, straight, not twisting. Seeds bright orange-brown, c.2.5mm, without tails 1.3mm, the longest tail broad and flat, often as wide as the seed *c*.0.8mm, the shorter tail slender and often branched near the base.

The original collections were made in **Vietnam**, Laokai Province, Sapa District, on a roadside bank facing east in secondary, broad-leaved forest with a few conifers at 1800m altitude. The species is presumably normally epiphytic but it was not seen in this state by the collectors. Apart from the type it is also known from a second collection (KR 3097) that was found nearby, 2–3km from Ban Khoang at *c*.1500m. It is known at present from a very limited area in N Vietnam and from across the border in **China**. This species was first mentioned in Rushforth (1993) as 'species 26 *aff. sororium*'.

This species is distinctive in the field even at a distance by its bluish-green leaves which are much larger (particularly longer) than those of all closely related species. It is apparently most closely related to *R. kawakamii* from Taiwan, sharing the multi-flowered umbel and many other characteristics with this species, but apart from leaf shape and colour it also differs in the hairy and scaly ovary, the hairy style and very unusually the flower bud scales, which are fringed with both simple hairs, branched hairs, and scales. Branched hairs of this type are very rare in subgenus *Vireya* and the combination of simple hairs and typical scales together is a characteristic which is very rare in the subgenus. Vireyas usually have one or other of these hair types on the scale margins. Of other closely related species: *R. sororium* is distinguished by its solitary or occasionally paired flowers, shorter obovate leaves and pedicels without simple hairs; *R. emarginatum* is quite distinct in its rough twigs and solitary flowers; and *R. densifolium* has very much smaller leaves (to 10mm long) and again solitary flowers.

Rhododendron rushforthii was first flowered in cultivation by Keith Rushforth in his garden at Fareham, Hampshire on 26 June 1995, having been planted out for the summer after being wintered in an unheated east-facing conservatory. A sister clone was left outside over winter and survived a recorded low of −8°C. This species has attractive bright yellow flowers and has very beautiful bluish-cast foliage which makes it a most attractive horticultural plant. This should be a good plant for vireya enthusiasts to try outside in parts of the world where there is the occasional frost or even in the milder parts of Britain. Since its first flowering in June it has normally flowered in July or August. The flower buds are initiated in winter and develop very slowly, and appear to be inhibited on branches with developing fruit. *Rhododendron rushforthii* flowers only once a year and the plants suffer in high temperatures, one plant reportedly having nearly died from staying too long in the heat of the conservatory in the summer.

10. Rhododendron datiandingense Z.J.Feng

J. South China Agr. Univ. 1996. 17(1): 59.

Type: Z.J. Feng 54123, 10 June 1990. Datianding, Xinyi, Guangdong, China (CANT).

Derivation: Named after Datianding, the place of the original collection.

Shrub to 50cm. Body of the plant sparsely scaly. Lower branches creeping, curved, the upper spreading, grey-brown. **Leaves** in pseudowhorls of 3–5 near the apices of the branches. **Blade** 20–40 x 10–20mm, elliptic to narrowly obovate or elliptic-obovate; apex bluntly acute; margin entire but distinctly revolute; base narrowed, often decurrent; shiny dark-green above, paler below. Mid-vein and lateral veins impressed above when dry, the laterals quickly becoming obscure beneath. **Petiole** 3–5mm, flattened.

Flower buds rounded-ovate, bracts ovate or ovate-spathulate, ciliate on the margins. Inflorescence a terminal umbel with 4–7 flowers. Pedicels 7–12mm. **Flowers** yellow, the calyx small; lobes reflexed, obtuse-crenulate. **Corolla** 8–10 x *c*.12mm, shortly campanulate; tube 4–5 x 3–4mm, with white hairs within the upper part; lobes 5 x 4mm, rounded-ovate; apex broadly rounded. **Stamens** 6mm; filaments cylindrical above, flattened below the middle, glabrous at the base, white hairy below the middle. **Ovary** 3mm, ovate-rounded; style shorter than the stamens, *c*.3mm, club-shaped, downwardly curved; stigma flattened rounded, to 5-lobed. **Fruit** 10–13 x 6mm, elongate-ellipsoid.

China, Guangdong, Xinyi, Datianding. Epiphytic. *Fl*. June, *fr*. Oct.

Said to be similar to *R. rupivalleculatum* but differing in the oblong-elliptic leaves, 2–4 x 1–2cm; the leaf apex obtuse, not recurved; the inflorescence of a 4–7-flowered umbel; the stamens and pistil much shorter, and the ellipsoidal capsule. Very reminiscent of *R. rushforthii* in the umbellate inflorescence. The much smaller vegetative measurements may be accounted for by differences between growing in cultivation and in a harsh wild environment but the lack of description of the indumentum on the ovary and style leaves doubt about the identity of this species. Only an examination of the type specimen will settle the matter of whether these two species are truly different. *Rhododendron datiandingense* is the older name by a few months and would take precedence if they are found to be conspecific.

11. Rhododendron kawakamii Hayata

J. Coll. Sci. Univ. Tokyo 1911. 30(1): 171.

Type: Kawakami & Mori 2005, 12 Oct. 1906. Mt Morrison, Taiwan (TI, L, fragment).

Derivation: Named after Takiya Kawakami, 1871–1915, a Japanese collector in Taiwan.

Synonyms:

R. kawakamii Hayata var. *flaviflorum* Liu & Chuang, Quart. J. Taiwan Mus. 1960. 13: 64.

R. taiwanianum Ying, Quart. J. Chinese Forest. 1976. 9(4): 116.

Rhododendron kawakamii.

Shrub to 1.5m. Twigs green, *c.*2mm in diameter, laxly covered with brown scales each slightly raised on a short stalk; internodes 1–4cm. **Leaves** arranged in loose pseudo-whorls. **Blade** 30–45 x 12–22mm, obovate, or elliptic; apex broadly obtuse often mucronate with a small protruding pale gland; margin entire, slightly to strongly revolute; base broadly to narrowly tapering, often a little decurrent; upper surface green, glabrescent; lower surface covered with blackish-brown scales each about 3–5 times their own diameter apart. **Scales** circular with narrow marginal flanges and large centres. Mid-vein narrowly impressed above throughout its length, more broadly raised below, strongly so in the proximal ½, becoming smooth distally; lateral veins 3–5 per side, spreading at 45° to almost 90°, minutely impressed above, very slightly raised below or obscure. **Petiole** 4–8 x *c.*1.5mm, grooved above, sparsely scaly.

Flower buds to 16 x 8mm, pale green, ellipsoid, smooth with an acute apex. Bracts fully appressed, ovate, broadly acute but often splitting to appear emarginate, brown scaly outside especially in a broad strip along the midline, also minutely sub-papillose hairy or long appressed hairy, glabrous inside, fringed with short white hairs along the margins. Bracteoles to 10 x 1mm, narrowly spathulate, glabrous except for marginal hairs at the apex. Inflorescence of 3–7 flowers in an open umbel. **Flowers** semi-erect to half-hanging. Pedicels 15–25mm, sparsely scaly and minutely shortly hairy, sometimes becoming vertically striate. Calyx small, distinctly 5-lobed; lobes broadly rounded, scaly outside and fringed with scales. **Corolla** 8–10mm, light yellow, campanulate; tube *c.*5 x 4 x 3.5mm, densely scaly outside and hairy in the distal part inside; lobes *c.*7–9 x 4–7mm, elliptic, scaly outside, without markings. **Stamens** exserted to *c.*6mm in an irregular cluster, later spreading back against the corolla lobes, dimorphic; filaments glabrous for *c.*1mm proximally, then densely long hairy, the hairs gradually decreasing in length and density distally, becoming glabrous for *c.*2mm apically; anthers *c.*2 x 0.8mm, brown. **Ovary** scaly and shortly hairy; style very short, patently hairy at the base or completely glabrous. **Fruit** *c.*6 x 3mm, hairy, turning to

become erect; valves spreading to a wide angle; placentae remaining fixed to the central column. Seeds to 2.6mm, without tails 1.1mm, the longest tail 1.1mm.

Taiwan, Ilan Co., Ta-yuen-shan, Yuan-yang Lake. Chiayi Co., Yu-shan (Mt Morrison). Co.: Kuei-hu: Taipei Co., below summit of Mt Chilanshan. Growing in sub-montane, humid forest, epiphytic on the trunks of *Chamaecyparis formosensis* Matsum. or terrestrial in open areas at 1400–2400m. *Fl.* June–July.

Rhododendron kawakamii has been in cultivation for many years. It was first introduced into cultivation through Mr J. Patrick's expeditions, collected by Sir John Holford who collected the original material from Rrwanping, below Alishan on 11 Nov. 1969 (Nos S 69202 and S 69200), and was widely distributed as seed from America. It was introduced to Edinburgh in 1971. It grows easily and flowers well with its bright but small yellow flowers once a year, usually in June or July. It is relatively hardy and has been growing outside in Edinburgh without protection for several winters, although it is likely to succumb in extreme conditions. The original description does not include flower colour nor is it recorded on the type specimen but it was reported as 'red or white' by Liu & Chuang (1960) when they described *R. kawakamii* var. *flaviflorum*. This was subsequently reported by Withers & Womersley (1986) and has led to considerable confusion as to the status of the yellow-flowered plant in cultivation. Shen-you Lu & Yuen-po Yang (1989) firmly reduced *R. kawakamii* var. *flaviflorum* to *R. kawakamii* and there appears to be no evidence that pink- or white-flowered forms of this species ever existed.

Ross Eudal

SECTION II: *Discovireya* Sleumer *stat. nov.*

Type: *R. retusum* Benn.
Subsection *Discovireya* Sleumer, Bot. Jahr. 1949. 74: 539.
Subsection *Zygomorphanthe* Schltr., Bot. Jahr. 1918. 55: 145, *pro parte.*
Subsection *Pseudovireya* (Clarke) Sleumer, *pro parte.*
Section *Lepipherum* G.Don, *sensu* H.F.Copel., Phil. J. Sc. 1929. 40(2): 136, *pro parte.*

Fruit not peeling an outer layer before splitting. Flower bud scales (sterile bracts or perulae) fringed with simple white hairs. Filaments hairy from the base or glabrous. Anthers introrse. Flowers mostly tubular-cylindric, the lobes distinctly shorter than the tube. Style–ovary junction sub-abrupt to tapering. Scales mostly disc-shaped with a large swollen centre and narrow flange, well spaced with the lower epidermis of the leaf clearly visible between them.

This comprises Sleumer's (1966) species 1–25 excepting *R. vanderbiltianum* Merr. which should be included in section *Maddenia* (Argent *et al.* in manuscript) and *R. vinkii* which is transferred to subsection *Malesia.* It also includes Sleumer's subsequently described *R. detznerianum* and *R. buxoides. Rhododendron quadrasianum* is not keyed as it is the only discovireya from the Philippines.

Key to species from the Malay Peninsula

1   Leaves more than 15mm wide _____ **13. scortechinii**
+   Leaves less than 12mm wide _____ 2

2   Twigs minutely hairy, smooth and with sessile scales _____ **14. seimundii**
+   Twigs without hairs but rough with stalked scales _____ 3

3   Leaves strongly revolute, flowers yellow _____ **12. perakense**
+   Leaves flat or only very weakly revolute, flowers orange _____ **15. spathulatum**

Key to species from Sumatra and Java

1   Leaves spirally arranged, up to 5mm wide, flower buds spherical ____ **16. adinophyllum**
+   Leaves in pseudowhorls, more than 10mm wide, flower buds elliptic __ **17. retusum**

Key to species from Borneo

1   Twigs rough with persistent scale bases, largest leaves up to 14mm wide ____ **19. buxoides**
+   Twigs rough with leaf bases, largest leaves less than 10mm wide _____ 2

2   Calyx with 5, 2mm lobes, above 2700m (Kinabalu only) _____ **21. ericoides**
+   Calyx without distinct lobes or sometimes with just 2 long lobes, below 2800m ____ 3

3   Ovary densely hairy, the pedicels covered with hairs and scales (below 2000m) _____ **18. borneense**
+   Ovary scaly only, pedicels with scales only (above 2000m) _____ **20. cuneifolium**

Key to species from Sulawesi

1   Twigs with stalked scales, rough with persistent bases when the scales have gone _____
    _____ **34. lindaueanum** var. **bantaengense**
+   Twigs smooth, the scales flat without persistent stalks _____ 2

2   Leaves in pseudowhorls, style more than 15mm _____ **24. meliphagidum**
+   Leaves regularly spirally arranged, style less than 8mm _____ 3

3   Largest leaves more than 5mm wide _____ **23. monodii**
+   Largest leaves less than 3mm wide _____ **22. nanophyton**

Key to species excluding the Philippines and New Guinea

1	Leaves more than 10mm wide	2
+	Leaves less than 10mm wide	5
2	Twigs minutely hairy	**13. scortechinii**
+	Twigs scaly only	3
3	Twigs smooth, style more than 4x as long as the ovary	**24. meliphagidum**
+	Twigs minutely rough with scale bases, style less than 3x as long as the ovary	4
4	Corolla hairy and laxly scaly outside	**17. retusum**
+	Corolla densely scaly only outside	**19. buxoides**
5	Twigs minutely hairy	6
+	Twigs with scales only	14
6	Largest leaves up to 5mm wide	7
+	Largest leaves more than 5mm wide	11
7	Pedicels scaly only, without hairs, calyx equally 5-lobed to 2mm	**21. ericoides**
+	Pedicels hairy and scaly, calyx lobed to 1mm or with only 2 longer lobes	8
8	Corolla scaly only outside	9
+	Corolla scaly and hairy outside	10
9	Scales on the upper surface of the leaves not impressed, the surface smooth when the scales have gone	**22. nanophyton**
+	Scales on the upper surface of the leaves deeply impressed leaving pits in the surface when the scales have gone	**20. cuneifolium** var. **microcarpum**
10	Ovary hairy and scaly	11
+	Ovary scaly only	**16. adinophyllum**
11	Leaves less than 2mm wide	**18. borneense** ssp. **angustissimum**
+	Leaves more than 2mm wide	**18. borneense** ssp. **villosum**
12	Ovary hairy and scaly	**18. borneense** ssp. **borneense**
+	Ovary scaly only	13
13	Leaves obtusely pointed, bracts hairy outside	**14. seimundii**
+	Leaves rounded or retuse, ? bracts scaly only outside	**20. cuneifolium**
14	Calyx with 5, 2mm calyx lobes (Kinabalu only)	**21. ericoides**
+	Calyx saucer-shaped, lobed to less than 1mm	15
15	Twigs smooth, without persistent scale stalks, style more than 4x as long as the ovary	**24. meliphagidum**
+	Twigs rough with persistent scale stalks	16
16	Flowers yellow	**12. perakense**
+	Flowers orange, pink or red	17
17	Corolla very densely scaly outside with many of the scales touching	**19. buxoides**
+	Corolla laxly scaly outside, the scales well spaced	18
18	Corolla tube 16–20mm (Sulawesi)	**34. lindaueanum** var. **bantaengense**
+	Corolla tube 20–26mm (Peninsular Malaysia)	**15. spathulatum**

Key to species from New Guinea

(*R. capellae* transferred to *Linnaeoidea*, *R. vinkii* transferred to *Malesia*)

1	Leaves narrowly elliptic, 4x as long as wide	**26. taxoides**
+	Leaves of other shape, less than 3x as long as wide	2
2	Scales on outside of corolla stellate, laxly leaved prostrate plant	**122. muscicola**
+	Scales on outside of corolla rounded, densely leaved mostly erect plants	3
3	Leaves more than 2cm long	4
+	Leaves less than 1.5cm long, bases various	6
4	Leaves narrowly tapering at the base	5
+	Leaves truncate or rounded at the base	**35. cyrtophyllum**
5	Young stems with protruding scale stalks	**34. lindaueanum**
+	Young stems smooth without protruding scale stalks	**36. ciliilobum**
6	Leaves ovate, broadest in the lower ½	**29. gaultheriifolium**
+	Leaves not ovate, broadest in the middle or distal ½	7
7	Scales on undersides of the leaves lax, some with 1mm between them	**27. pulleanum**
+	Scales on undersides of the leaves denser, with up to 0.5mm between them	8
8	Leaves up to 1.5x as long as broad	9
+	Leaves 2x or more as long as broad	13
9	Ovary abruptly contracted to the style	**115. yelliotii (saruwagedicum)**
+	Ovary tapering to the style	10
10	Corolla up to 1.2cm long	**28. nummatum**
+	Corolla more than 1.5cm long	11
11	Erect shrubs	12
+	Creeping shrubs	**33. hameliiflorum**
12	Margin of leaf strongly and distinctly recurved even in the upper part of the leaf, bracts scaly only abaxially, simple hairs restricted to the marginal fringe	**30. oreites**
+	Margin of leaf hardly recurved in the distal part, bracts densely lanate-hairy abaxially	**31. erosipetalum**
13	Leaf apex rounded	14
+	Leaf apex broadly pointed	16
14	Twigs minutely verruculose by scale stalks	15
+	Twigs smooth	**36. ciliilobum**
15	Leaves up to 5mm wide	**31. erosipetalum**
+	Leaves more than 5mm wide	**34. lindaueanum**
16	Leaves up to 4mm wide	17
+	Leaves more than 4mm wide	18
17	Some leaves spathulate, broadest in the distal ½, pedicels without hairs	**32. detznerianum**
+	Leaves elliptic, to sub-circular, broadest in the middle, pedicels with minute hairs	**29. gaultheriifolium** var. **expositum**
18	Stems smooth, bracts hairy and scaly on the upper, outer part	**36. ciliilobum**
+	Stems rough with scale bases, bracts scaly outside but without hairs abaxially (i.e. excluding the marginal fringe)	**30. oreites**

12. Rhododendron perakense King & Gamble

J. As. Soc. Beng. 1905. 74(2): 76.

Type: Wray 1574. Malay Peninsula, Pahang, Cameron Highlands, G. B(e)rumbun (CAL).

Derivation: Named after the state of Perak in Malaysia.

Small shrub, occasionally up to 1.8m. Twigs slender, rounded, warty with the dense covering of stalked scales in the youngest parts, later rough with these persistent scale stalks. **Leaves** 3–7 together in pseudowhorls. **Blade** 13–20 x 5–10mm, obovate to spathulate; apex rounded-obtuse, sometimes minutely retuse; margin entire, strongly recurved; base narrowly tapering; silvery scaly at first above later glabrescent, laxly to sub-densely and more persistently brown scaly beneath. **Scales** sparsely distributed, sessile, circular, entire or undulate with a narrow to quite broad marginal zone, and thick somewhat impressed centre, sometimes with two concentric rings and a small brown centre. Mid-vein strongly impressed above, sometimes with a few white hairs proximally in the groove, thick and prominent beneath; lateral veins 2–3 per side, spreading, slightly impressed above, and slightly raised beneath, reticulation obscure. **Petiole** 2–3 x 1–1.5mm, grooved above, yellow, scaly and very shortly hairy.

John Rouse

Rhododendron perakense.

Flower buds to 9 x 5mm, obovate with obtuse to rounded apices, smooth, the bract tips appressed. Outer bracts shortly subulate, scaly outside, glabrous inside, the inner ones to 6 x 3mm, ovate, obtuse often mucronate, scaly at the top outside, densely white-ciliate on the margins. Bracteoles to 6.5mm, filiform, glabrous except for one or two scales near the apex. Inflorescence an open umbel with 3–5 flowers per umbel (up to 7 in cultivation), the flowers held more or less horizontally. Pedicels 5–7 x 0.75mm, green, densely covered with stalked scales, without hairs. Calyx minute, shortly obtusely 5-lobed, sometimes with one or two longer, acute lobes, to 3mm, densely scaly. **Corolla** 8–10 x 4–7mm, white? or bright yellow; tube 5.5–6.5 x 3–3.5 x 4.5–5.5mm, straight, cylindrical, or widening slightly distally, moderately silvery or translucent-scaly outside, glabrous inside; lobes 2.2–2.5 x *c*.3mm, held stiffly erect, or only very slightly spreading, overlapping up to ¾, retuse, with some silvery, translucent scales outside except near the margins. **Stamens** irregularly clustered centrally in the mouth of the flower; filaments linear, yellow, slightly broadened towards the base, glabrous; anthers *c*.0.6 x 0.5mm, brown, strongly inwardly curved. Disc glabrous. **Ovary** conical, *c*.2mm, densely scaly; style 3–4mm, green, glabrous; stigma rounded. **Fruit** 8–11 x 3–4mm, sub-cylindrical, yellow, deeply 5-furrowed longitudinally, scaly; valves curving outwards, straight or a little twisted, placentae remaining coherent with the central column. Seeds 1.8–2.3mm, without tails 0.7–1mm, the longest tail 1mm, the tails distinctly broad and often with more than one point.

Malaysia (W), Pahang, Cameron Highlands, Mt Brinchang. In mossy summit forest, usually epiphytic, locally common, at *c*.1830m. *Fl. fr.* April, Aug.

Considered a difficult plant in cultivation. John Rouse (Melbourne, Australia) always grew it grafted on a hybrid rootstock. In Edinburgh it has been successfully grown on its own roots since 1997 but it remains a small, neat plant. It may well be one of the species that are prone to *Phytophthora* attack at high temperatures. It flowers well with its very distinctive tiny yellow flowers (reports of white flowers are probably erroneous) and the foliage is quite attractive, but it is grown more out of interest than for its beauty. It sets fruit in cultivation readily and may be habitually self-pollinated due to the arrangement of the stamens which presents the pollen downwards towards the stigma; the style elongates slightly as it becomes receptive so that it would touch any pollen that had not already been removed from the flowers. First introduced into cultivation by an unknown Japanese collector who supplied material to John Rouse. It was later collected by Keith Adams and grown at Pukeiti in New Zealand. Both these introductions have been widely distributed.

13. Rhododendron scortechinii King & Gamble
J. As. Soc. Beng. 1905. 74(2): 76.
Type: Scortechini 401b, 1884. Malay Peninsula, Perak: without locality (CAL, K, L, fragment).
Derivation: Named after the collector, Rev. Father Benedetto Scortechini, Roman Catholic Priest and Government botanist, Perak (Malaysia), 1884–1886.

Synonym: *R. orion* Ridl., J. Fed. Mal. St. Mus. 1914. 5: 39.

Shrub or small tree. Twigs rounded, the youngest parts red-brown with dense scales and minutely patently hairy; internodes 1.5–5cm. **Leaves** 3–7 together in well-marked pseudowhorls. **Blade** 25–35 x 15–30mm, elliptic, broadly elliptic, obovate to sub-circular; apex obtuse to rounded and with a small terminal gland, sometimes a little emarginate; margin strongly recurved; base tapering; upper surface light green, glabrescent, shining, undersurface yellowish when fresh, paler brown when dry, densely scaly. **Scales** sessile, round; marginal zone narrow, entire or nearly so; centre thick, dark, large and impressed. Mid-vein impressed above, thick and obtusely prominent beneath; lateral veins 4–6 per side, spreading at a wide angle (45–90°), sometimes obscure, anastomosing, slightly to deeply depressed above, distinct and raised beneath, reticulation obscure. **Petiole** 2–5 x 1.5–2mm, grooved above, brown-scaly except in the groove which is minutely but densely patently hairy.

Bracts to 7 x 4mm, ovate to spathulate, obtuse, scaly and hairy distally outside, ciliate on the margins. Bracteoles to 5mm, linear, slightly hairy. Inflorescence a 4–7-flowered open umbel. Pedicels 15–20mm, densely scaly, without hairs. Calyx short-cupular, scaly, with 5 ovate, obtuse, lobes sometimes ciliate on the margins. **Corolla** *c.*18 x 15–20mm, yellow, sometimes paler, white, or yellow at the lobes, orange at the tube, funnel-shaped; tube 9–14 x 3–4 x 8–10mm, densely covered with dark scales, glabrous inside; lobes 6–8 x 5–7mm, broadly obovate to sub-circular, overlapping up to ¼. **Stamens** unequal, the longest exserted to 8mm; filaments linear, dilated to 0.5mm at the base, filiform upwards, glabrous; anthers *c.*1.8mm, oblong. Disc glabrous. **Ovary** *c.*2.8 x 1.8mm, conical, densely covered with scales, gradually tapering distally; style glabrous, becoming exserted; stigma conical-globose, slightly 5-lobed. **Fruit** 10–13 x 3.5mm, cylindrical, shortly apiculate, densely scaly.

Rhododendron scortechinii.

Malaysia (W), Main Range from Perak to Selangor. A record for Borneo was from a misidentification of *R. buxoides*. Epiphytic or terrestrial shrub in summit vegetation, sometimes regenerating along roadside cuttings, 1465–2135m. *Fl. fr.* Jan.–April.

Apparently only recently introduced into cultivation and not yet reported to have flowered.

14. Rhododendron seimundii J.J.Sm.
Gard. Bull. S.S. 1935. 8(3): 262.
Type: Seimund 343, March 1921. Malay Peninsula, Pahang, G. Tahan, 1675m (SING, lectotype, L, fragment).
Derivation: Named after the collector, E. Seimund, who for some time worked in the Museums Department of what was then the Federated Malay States.

Shrub. Twigs slender, patent, minutely patently hairy and laxly covered with sessile scales; internodes 0.7–6cm. **Leaves** in 4–10 together in pseudowhorls at the upper nodes. **Blade** 13–28 x 5–11mm, elliptic-obovate to narrowly elliptic; apex broadly tapering, obtuse and ending in a small protruding gland; margin entire or minutely crenulate with impressed scales, slightly revolute; base tapering, rugulose when dry, shining above, laxly scaly initially, becoming glabrescent above, dull and laxly scaly beneath. **Scales** sessile, circular; margin entire or nearly so; centre thick, darker and distinctly impressed. Mid-vein impressed above, strongly raised beneath; lateral veins obscure or sometimes faintly visible underneath. **Petiole** 2–4mm, slender, scaly and minutely hairy.

Bracts to 7 x 4mm, ovate, obtuse, densely shortly hairy outside, laxly scaly and with a ciliate margin.

Bracteoles to 6mm, filiform, hairy. Inflorescence 2–4-flowered. Pedicels 9–12mm, slender, densely covered with sessile scales, sometimes also minutely hairy. Calyx oblique, unequally obtusely 5-lobed, scaly but not ciliate. **Corolla** 16–19 x 15–25mm, funnel-shaped; tube 8–9 x *c*.2.5 x 4–6mm, laxly scaly outside, glabrous inside; lobes 9–10 x 6–7mm, obovate, with scales outside except near the margins. **Stamens** very slightly or not exserted; filaments linear, glabrous; anthers *c*.1.5mm, oblong. Disc glabrous. **Ovary** *c*.2.5 x 2mm, ovoid-conical, obtuse, 5-grooved longitudinally, densely scaly, gradually tapering distally; style *c*.16mm, glabrous; stigma 5-lobed. **Fruit** 8 x 2.5mm.

> **Malaysia** (W), Pahang, Mt Tahan, 1675m. *Fl.* Feb.–March.

> Not known in cultivation.

15. **Rhododendron spathulatum** Ridl.

J. Str. Br. R. As. Soc. 1912. 61: 25.
Type: Haniff SF 3973, May 1909. Malay Peninsula: Perak, G. Kerbau, 1525–2135m (SING, K, L, fragment).
Derivation: Latin – *spathulatus* – spatula-shaped, alluding to the shape of the leaves.

Shrub to 1.5m. Twigs dark brown, slender, the upper internodes densely covered with stalked scales, rough with persistent stalks when the scales have gone, finally smooth; internodes 0.5–2cm. **Leaves** 3–7 together in well-marked pseudowhorls at the upper nodes. **Blade** 10–20 x 5–10mm, obovate-spathulate; apex rounded, mostly slightly retuse; margin flat or slightly revolute; base tapering, laxly impressed-scaly, becoming glabrescent and shining above, more densely and minutely scaly and dull beneath. **Scales** circular, marginal zone narrow, entire or nearly so; centre dark and thick, distinctly impressed, entire or minutely crenulate. Mid-vein mostly impressed above proximally, prominent beneath; lateral veins 3–4 per side, faintly impressed above and raised beneath, or almost invisible. **Petiole** *c*.2mm, scaly, slender.

Bracts to 5 x 3mm, ovate, sub-acute, scaly outside distally, ciliate on the margins. **Flowers** solitary, or rarely in twos. Pedicels 6–8mm, slender, densely scaly, sometimes also minutely laxly hairy. Calyx oblique, very small, scaly, obscurely obtusely 5-lobed. **Corolla** 20–26mm, tubular, slightly dilated towards the mouth, zygomorphic and laterally compressed, straight, dark or orange-red; tube 18–22 x *c*.3 x 5–6mm, laxly scaly outside, glabrous inside; lobes 4–5 x 2.5–3mm, obovate, spreading, distinctly ciliate. **Stamens** unequal, exserted; filaments glabrous, linear; anthers 2 x 0.8mm, oblong. Disc glabrous. **Ovary**

2.5 x 1.5mm, broadly ellipsoid, densely scaly, without hairs, gradually tapering distally; style glabrous becoming long exserted; stigma rounded to indistinctly lobed. **Fruit** 7–8 x 2.5–3mm, shortly cylindrical or conical, densely scaly.

> **Malaysia** (W), Perak, Mt Kerbau; Pahang, Mt Siku, Ulu Telom. Epiphytic in mossy forest or on moss-covered ground, said to be locally plentiful on Mt Kerbau, 1525–2135m.

> Not recorded as ever cultivated.

16. **Rhododendron adinophyllum** Merr.

Notes Natl. Acad. Nat. Sci. Philad. 1940. 47: 3.
Type: Ripley & Ulmer 58. Indonesia, Sumatra, Atjeh, Mt Losir (PH, A).
Derivation: Greek – *adinos* – close; *phullon* – leaf. Alluding to the densely leafy stems.

Shrub to 1m. Twigs erect, rounded, 2–3mm in diameter, densely covered with low sub-circular scales, and sparsely very shortly hairy. Stems with prominent leaf scars and low rounded axillary protrusions. **Leaves** densely, spirally arranged. **Blade** 7–12 x 2–5mm, elliptic to narrowly elliptic, gradually acuminate; apex acute to obtuse; margin flat or slightly recurved sometimes slightly

Rhododendron adinophyllum.

crenulate; base tapering, shiny dark green above, and gradually glabrescent, paler and sub-densely scaly beneath. **Scales** sessile, impressed, rounded, with the margin narrow, entire to undulate; centre large and dark brown. Mid-vein impressed above and obtusely raised beneath especially in the proximal ½, lateral veins obscure. **Petiole** 1–2.5 x *c.*1mm, grooved, laxly scaly and hairy above, densely scaly below, curved to a right angle with the blade.

Flower buds 10–12 x 7–10mm, ovate, smooth with the bracts fully appressed, brown near the base and the tips of the bracts, otherwise green. Bracts to 7 x 4mm, gradual changing from the upper foliage leaves, ovate to obovate, apiculate, scaly in the distal ½ and with short appressed hairs outside throughout; fringed with long white hairs at the margins. Bracteoles to 6mm, filiform, hairy. Inflorescence 6–12-flowered, the flowers half-hanging to hanging. Pedicels 10–14 x *c.*1mm, pink, densely covered with patent hairs of various lengths and sparsely scaly. Calyx oblique, small, undulate, with white hairs and scales outside and at the margin, glabrous inside. **Corolla** 18–21 x 8–9mm, tubular, bright orange-red, without scent; tube 13–15 x 5–6 x 7–8mm, with long white patent hairs and small laxly spaced scales outside, glabrous inside; lobes 3–5 x *c.*4mm, straight not reflexed, overlapping up to *c.*¾, obovate, apex rounded, hairy and scaly along the midline to the apex. **Stamens** exserted to *c.*2mm, loosely clustered on the lower side of the mouth, unequal; filaments linear, glabrous; anthers oblong-ellipsoid, *c.*1.5mm. Disc glabrous. **Ovary** *c.*3 x 2mm, ovoid-conical, densely covered with overlapping scales, without hairs; style glabrous, green; stigma elongate-obconical. **Fruit** *c.*11 x 4–6mm, elongate-ovoid, densely scaly, 5-ribbed, with a *c.*10mm persistent style; valves half-spreading, slightly curved, not twisted, the placentae remaining firmly attached to the central column. Seeds 1.3–1.8mm, without tails *c.*1mm, the longest tail to 0.5mm. The very short tails are often highly branched.

Indonesia, N Sumatra, Atjeh, Gajolands: Mt Losir, Mt Lembuh, Mt Putjuk Angasan and Mt Kemiri. In open summit heathland, 2600–3460m. A wild hybrid of this species with *R. sumatranum* was collected by David Binney on Mt Kemiri, Sumatra (19982482) in 1998. *Fl.* Jan.–April.

First introduced into cultivation in 1998 by David Binney, this distinctive species grows slowly but flowers regularly. Although in the wild it grew to about 1m in height, in cultivation it remains much shorter, up to about 25cm, with the branches terminating in a flower head and then often dying back to be replaced by basal shoots. The softly hairy flowers have a certain appeal but the habit leaves a lot to be desired from a horticultural point of view.

17. Rhododendron retusum (Blume) Benn.

In Benn. & Br., Pl. Jav. Rar. 1838. 86 in text, 88 *t.*20.
Type: Blume Java *s.n.*, *sine loc.* (L, U).
Derivation: Named from the distinctively retuse leaves.

Synonyms:
Vireya retusa Blume, Bijdr. 1826. 856.
Azalea retusa (Blume) Kuntze, Rev. Gen. Pl. 1891. 2: 386.

Var. **retusum**

Shrub or small tree to 7m, erect or more rarely prostrate. Twigs rounded, younger parts red, at first densely covered with stalked round scales, which fall early, the persistent stalks making the twigs rough; internodes 2–6cm. **Leaves** 4–7 together in pseudowhorls at the upper nodes. **Blade** 20–60 x 10–20mm, obovate to broadly elliptic; apex distinctly retuse more rarely rounded; margin flat or distinctly recurved, entire; base tapering, dark green and shining above, paler to almost whitish green and dull beneath, laxly to sub-densely scaly on both sides initially, quickly glabrescent above but persistently scaly beneath. **Scales** disc-like, variable in size, marginal zone narrow and entire, the centre large and thick, distinctly impressed. Mid-vein impressed above, strongly raised beneath; lateral veins 4–7 per side, the lower ones ascending, distal ones irregularly spreading, all slightly impressed above in fully mature leaves, often only faintly visible when fresh, obscure beneath. **Petiole** 1–5 x 1.5–2mm, thick, grooved above, scaly and becoming rugose, often minutely hairy above.

Flower buds to 14 x 9mm, ellipsoid or narrowly ellipsoid, pink, both terminal and lateral, smooth, the bracts fully appressed. Bracts to 13 x 8mm, outer subulate to ovate-acuminate, inner gradually increasing in size and broadly ovate to spathulate, shortly acute, scaly and densely appressed hairy outside, glabrous inside, all densely and long white-ciliate on the margins. Bracteoles to 8mm, linear to filiform, slightly expanded at the apex and hairy in the upper part. Inflorescence a 4–10-flowered open umbel; flowers often semi-erect on opening, becoming half-hanging to hanging. Pedicels 12–20 x *c.*1mm, densely patently hairy, scaly only near the apex. Calyx *c.*4mm in diameter, oblique, shortly 5-lobed, densely scaly outside, the lobes *c.*1mm, long ciliate. **Corolla** 22–35 x 13–15mm, narrowly funnel-shaped to tubular, red to orange-red; tube 12–28 x 4–6 x 7–8mm, straight, the base slightly dilated in the form of a ring, laxly to densely yellow-scaly and shortly white patent hairy outside, glabrous inside; lobes 4–6 x 3–6mm, erect to half-spreading, broadly elliptic to sub-circular, hairy and scaly outside

Rhododendron retusum var. *retusum*.

One of the earliest vireyas to be introduced into cultivation. It was figured in *Curtis's Botanical Magazine* in 1855 (*t.*4859) from seed collected by Mr Henshall in Java for Rollisons of Tooting Nursery in London, probably about 1850. It is unlikely that any of the original collection survived, and it was not one of the species used by Henslow (1891) in his classic study of hybridisation. The oldest accession still living in Edinburgh dates from 1967 and was received via Australia from Tom Lelliot, but there are no further details as to who collected the plant or when. It grows and flowers well, so that although the flowers are quite small it can produce a profusion of bloom. It can also flower over a long period if the plant is dead-headed as lateral flower buds are often produced at the sides of the terminal one.

Var. **trichostylum** Sleumer
Reinwardtia 1960. 5: 55.
Type: van Steenis 9169, 23 Feb. 1937. Indonesia, Sumatra, Atjeh, Gajo Lands, top of G. Lembuh (L, A, BO, K, SING).
Derivation: Greek – *tricho* – hairy; *stylum* – the style. Alluding to the hairy style in this variety.

Leaves 15–25 x 7–14mm. The style laxly patently hairy at the base or in the proximal ½.

Indonesia, N Sumatra, Atjeh: Goh Lembuh, Putjuk Angasan, Bur ni Tèlong, on forested slopes, 1350–2700m.

Rhododendron x **epilosum** (J.J.Sm.) Argent *comb. nov.*
Basionym: *R. retusum* var. *epilosum* J.J.Sm., Bull. Jard. Bot. Buit. III, 1935. 13: 446.
Type: Bünnemeijer 5732, 16 Nov. 1918. Indonesia, Sumatra, West coast, Padang Highlands, G. Gombak (BO, A, K, L, SING).

Corolla tubular-campanulate, *c.*4mm long, scaly but not hairy outside.

Indonesia, C Sumatra, Padang Highlands, Mt Gombak, in low forest at 2330m.

Considered to be a hybrid with *R. sumatranum*.

except near the margins. **Stamens** alternately slightly dimorphic, exserted to 6–8mm, loosely spreading around the mouth or more tightly clustered on the lower side; filaments linear, widened below, glabrous; anthers *c.*1.5 x 1mm, broadly oblong, truncate at the top. Disc glabrous. **Ovary** 3–4 x *c.*2mm, conical, 5-angular or grooved, densely scaly, not hairy at all; style filiform, scaly at the base only, otherwise glabrous; stigma globose, shortly 5-lobed at the mouth of the flower when it opens, becoming exserted on the lower side of the flower to 8mm. **Fruit** 10–18 x 5–6mm, erect, oblong-fusiform; valves recurving to about horizontal, the placentae remaining coherent to the central column at first, eventually breaking away at the base and slightly spreading.

Indonesia, Sumatra, Java especially W Java; in C Java known only from Mt Prahu (Dieng) and Mt Merapi; in E Java from Mt Ardjuno. Mostly terrestrial in sub-alpine mossy forests or shrubberies, in soil rich in humus and the moss-cushions of old fallen trees, but also on sandy, stony or rocky ground, often near craters and solfataras, where it occurs as very low, creeping, small-leafed, exposed forms. The root system extends near the surface of the ground and the stems root adventitiously; locally common, 1350–3400m. Flowering throughout the year; the flowers are recorded as visited by small honey birds (*Aethopyga*) and bumble bees.

18. Rhododendron borneense (J.J.Sm.) Argent, A.Lamb & Phillipps
Rhododendrons of Sabah, Sabah Parks Publ. 1988. 8: 74.
Type: Endert 4256, 17 Oct. 1925. Borneo, Central East, W Kutei, Mt Kemul (BO, A, L).
Derivation: Latin – *borneense* – from Borneo, indicating the island of origin.

Synonym: *R. quadrasianum* S.Vidal var. *borneense* J.J.Sm., Bull. Jard. Bot. Buit. III, 1935. 13: 444.

Ssp. **borneense**

Shrub to 2m. Twigs rounded, shortly hairy and scaly, quickly glabrescent, older stems rough with raised leaf scars. **Leaves** arranged spirally but mostly only persisting at the very ends of the twigs. **Blade** 14–18 x 5–8mm, obovate or spathulate; apex rounded or slightly retuse; margin entire, slightly revolute; base tapering, sparsely scaly and quickly glabrescent above, sparsely but persistently scaly below and sometimes with a few short hairs near the base. **Scales** round, slightly impressed. Mid-vein slightly impressed above and raised below, the lateral veins weak, up to 3 per side, not raised or impressed, sometimes not visible. **Petiole** 2–3 x *c.*1mm, weakly grooved above, scaly and often shortly hairy.

Flower buds to 6 x 2mm, slender, ellipsoid, with scattered scales outside and a distinct fringe of hairs around the bract margins. Bracts ovate to spathulate. Bracteoles 3.5 x *c.*0.5mm, narrowly spathulate, with a few hairs near the apex. Inflorescence of mostly solitary flowers, occasionally 2 or 3 together, horizontal to half-hanging. Pedicels 6–8 x *c.*1mm, hairy and scaly, pink. Calyx a low hairy and scaly disc. **Corolla** 20 x 10mm, red or yellow, without scent; tube 15 x 6 x 8mm, straight, lobed near the base, densely scaly and with white erect hairs at least in the proximal ½ outside, glabrous inside; lobes 4 x 5mm, erect, or slightly spreading, overlapping for about ½ their length, scaly outside, rarely with a few simple hairs. **Stamens** loosely arranged on the lower side of the mouth, exserted to *c.*4mm; filaments *c.*18mm, glabrous; anthers 7mm, brown. **Ovary** *c.*2 x 1mm, densely subpatently hairy and with a few scales; style 13–16mm, entirely glabrous or hairy in the proximal ½, slightly swollen distally, lying on the lower side of the tube; stigma exserted to *c.*5mm, club-shaped, purple, 0.75mm in diameter. **Fruit** *c.*8 x 3mm. Seeds 1.6mm, without tails 0.7mm, the longest tail 0.6mm.

Indonesia, Kalimantan. **Malaysia** (Borneo), Sarawak and Sabah. **Brunei**. Widespread on the mountains of Borneo, said to be common on Mt Kemul, but only recorded in Sabah from Mt Lotung in the south. Mostly epiphytic in montane forest.

Not known to be in cultivation.

Ssp. **villosum** (J.J.Sm.) Argent, A.Lamb & Phillipps Rhododendrons of Sabah, Sabah Parks Publ. 1988. 8: 75. Type: Hallier 575, 1893–94. Borneo (W), Mt Damus, Upper Sambas River (BO, CAL, K, L, P, U).
Derivation: Latin – *villosum* – with long soft hairs, presumably alluding to the hairs on the twigs, pedicels and flowers.

Synonym: *R. quadrasianum* S.Vidal var. *villosum* J.J.Sm., Bull. Jard. Bot. Buit. III, 1935. 13: 444.

Shrub to 3m. Leaves 8–13 x 2–4mm, narrowly obovate. Corolla hairy (sometimes only sparsely so), and scaly, red or yellow, *c.*15mm. Pedicels scaly and hairy. Ovary scaly and densely white-hairy.

Malaysia (Borneo), Sabah, northern in distribution, from Mt Kinabalu, along the Crocker Range, to Mt Lotung. Sarawak, Mt Murud, Mt Dulit and Mt Tanggoi. **Brunei**, Mt Pagon. Mostly epiphytic in sub-montane mossy forest, low shrubby kerangas and amongst bare sandstone rocks, 1200–1900m. *Fl.* Jan.–Dec. Leaves consistently smaller than in ssp. *borneense* but larger than in ssp. *angustissimum*.

Cultivated in Edinburgh since 1982, it has attractive small dark green leaves but the flowers are not produced in sufficient quantity to make it an attractive horticultural plant.

Rhododendron borneense ssp. *villosum*.

Rhododendron borneense ssp. *angustissimum.*

Ssp. **angustissimum** (J.J.Sm.) Argent, A.Lamb & Phillipps Edinb. J. Bot. 1995. 52(3): 363.
Type: Anderson 4215, 28 June 1961. Borneo, Sarawak, Mt Mulu, path from Melinau Paku (SAR, K, L, fragment).
Derivation: Latin – *angusti* – narrow; *issimum* – the superlative. The most narrow leaved.

Synonym: *R. quadrasianum* S.Vidal var. *angustissimum* Sleumer, Blumea 1963. 12: 92.

Shrub to 2m. Twigs shortly hairy. **Leaves** spiral. **Blade** *c.*10 x 1–1.5mm, narrowly obovate to almost linear, densely spirally arranged especially towards the tips of the young shoots. Pedicels slender, *c.*5mm, hairy. Calyx both hairy and ciliate on the margins, lobes very short. **Corolla** *c.*10 x 3–4mm, tubular, slightly dilated distally, red, densely covered with round scales and sparse long white hairs. **Stamens** exserted; anthers 0.5mm. Ovary hairy.

Malaysia (Borneo), Sarawak, Mt Mulu. Epiphytic in submontane forest, or terrestrial in open peaty locations, locally abundant. *c.*1300m. *Fl.* June.

This is an extreme form of *R. borneense* which approaches *R. ericoides* in the size of its leaves. Not known to have been cultivated.

19. Rhododendron buxoides Sleumer
Blumea 1973. 21: 359.
Type: Nooteboom & Chai 1973, 6 April 1970. Borneo, Sarawak, 5th Div., Mt Murud, towards the top (L, K, SAR).
Derivation: Like the 'European box' *Buxus sempervirens*, the leaves being superficially similar.

Shrub to 2m. Twigs 2–3mm in diameter, scaly at first with stalked scales, warty with persistent scale bases after the scales have gone; internodes 0.5–1.5cm. **Leaves** in tight to loose pseudowhorls, 2–5 together or spirally arranged. **Blade** 10–30 x 4–14mm, broadly obovate to elliptic; apex obtuse, to rounded, often emarginate; margin strongly and broadly revolute, sometimes crenulate with impressed scales; base tapering, decurrent; densely and persistently scaly on both sides. **Scales** large, thick, rounded, entire, strongly impressed; the narrow margin tending to disintegrate, the centre persistent. Mid-vein impressed above, raised below; lateral veins 3–4 per side, obscure to strongly raised below at least when dry, reticulation obscure. **Petiole** 1.5–2mm.

Bracts *c.*5mm, obovate, densely scaly and white-hairy distally outside and with a ciliate margin. Inflorescence 2–4 flowers in an open umbel, hanging vertically. Pedicels 6–14 x 0.5–0.6mm, slender, densely scaly, without hairs. Calyx obliquely disc-shaped, obscurely lobed or undulate, densely scaly. **Corolla** tubular, red; tube 13–15 x 3–4 x 4–7mm, completely very densely covered in thick rounded scales, glabrous inside; lobes 3–4 x 3–4mm, erect, obovate, spathulate, or sub-circular, scaly in the central part outside. **Stamens** exserted to *c.*3mm; filaments linear, glabrous; anthers 1.5 x 1mm, obovoid. Disc glabrous. **Ovary** *c.*2.5 x 1.5mm, conical, densely scaly, gradually tapering distally; style scaly at the base only, glabrous distally, about as long as the corolla; stigma slightly broadened, obliquely truncate. **Fruit** 7–9 x 3–4mm, shortly cylindrical, deeply grooved. Seed 1.2–1.5mm, without tails *c.*1mm, the longest tail to 0.4mm, mostly broadly triangular at one end with a short narrow tail at the other.

Malaysia (Borneo), Sarawak, Mt Murud, Mt Mulu and Batu Lawi, 1800–2300m. *Fl.* Apr, Oct.; probably continuously.

Sleumer (1973) commented that this species was 'close to' *R. perakense* but differed in the slightly crenulate leaves, red corolla and the bracts being both hairy and scaly outside. It is usually a much larger plant with bigger leaves and flowers. This species is not known to have been cultivated. In its small, dull red, densely scaly flowers it very much parallels *R. inconspicuum* and *R. yelliotii* from New Guinea. The almost tail-less seeds are like those of other species from the highest points on high mountains.

20. **Rhododendron cuneifolium** Stapf

Trans. Linn. Soc. London, II, Bot. 1894. 4: 198, *t.*15, *f.*B,3.
Type: Haviland 1180. North Borneo, Mt Kinabalu, 1650–2745m (K, SAR).
Derivation: Latin – *cuneus* – a wedge; *folium* – leaf. Alluding to the wedge-shaped leaf base.

Var. **cuneifolium**

Shrub to 2m. Twigs smooth apart from some raised leaf scars, red or green passing to brown, minutely shortly hairy and sparsely scaly. **Leaves** spirally arranged, or only weakly grouped into loose pseudowhorls. **Blade** 10–30 x 3–7mm, narrowly obovate to spathulate; apex retuse to rounded; margin entire or sometimes crenulate in the distal ½; base tapering, laxly silvery scaly becoming glabrescent above, laxly and more persistently impressed scaly beneath. **Scales** circular with a moderately broad flange which is often marked with radial furrows and a broad centre. Mid-vein deeply impressed above and raised below but obscure in high altitude forms; lateral veins obscure, rarely 1 or 2 per side. **Petiole** 2 x 1mm, without a conspicuous groove, sparsely scaly and often very finely hairy.

Flower buds *c.*6 x 3mm, ellipsoid, brown, with a few scales outside distally and a broad fringe of white hairs. Bracts ovoid. Inflorescence of mostly solitary flowers, occasionally up to 3-flowered, flowers half-hanging, occasionally horizontal or vertically hanging. Pedicels *c.*5 x 1mm, green with white scales but no hairs. Calyx of 5 equal ovate-triangular lobes to 1.5mm or sometimes with 2 longer lobes to 2mm. **Corolla** 15–20 x *c.*8mm, pale red to orange-red, without scent, sub-cylindrical or narrowly funnel-shaped; tube *c.*15 x 6 x 7mm, densely scaly outside, glabrous inside; lobes *c.*5 x 4mm, semi-erect to spreading, overlapping ½–⅔, scaly outside except near the margin. **Stamens** in a loose cluster on the lower side of the mouth, exserted to 8mm; filaments *c.*18mm, pale pink, glabrous, tapering from just above the base; anthers *c.*1 x 0.75mm, dark brown. **Ovary** *c.*2.5 x 2mm, green, densely covered with silvery scales but no hairs; style 16–20 x *c.*1mm, glabrous apart from a few scales at the base, pale yellow, lying on the lower side of the corolla but curving upwards; stigma circular. **Fruit** 7–11 x 4–5mm, the valves curving back on opening. Seeds *c.*1.9mm, without tails 0.7mm, the longest tail 0.6mm.

Malaysia (Borneo), Sabah, Mt Kinabalu and Mt Alab. Reported from Sulawesi but this has not been properly substantiated (Monod de Froideville 187 from Makale, Makale-Bi(n)tuang, Rante Karua, (Rantepao), SW Central Sulawesi, 1200m). Mostly terrestrial, sometimes epiphytic. Common on Mt Kinabalu from 1500 to 2800m, where it occupies a zone between that of *R. borneense* and *R. ericoides*. Fl. Jan.–Dec. but apparently not continuously, having rest periods between flushes of flowers.

Hybridising in the wild with *R. ericoides* to give *R.* x *silvicolum*. Cultivated in the past but not particularly attractive and not presently known to be in cultivation.

Rhododendron cuneifolium
var. *cuneifolium*.

Sheila Collenette

Rhododendron cuneifolium var. *microcarpum*.

Var. **microcarpum** Argent, A.Lamb & Phillipps
Notes RBG Edinb. 1984. 42(1): 118.
Type: Collenette 646b, 7 Jan. 1961. Sabah, Mt Trus Madi, Crest of main ridge, 2300m (K).
Derivation: Greek – *micro* – little or small; *carpus* – fruit. Alluding to the very small fruit of this variety.

Differing from the type mainly in the following. Twigs prominently grooved with leaf supports and covered in scales but without hairs. **Blade** 5–8 x 1.5–2.5mm, narrowly obovate; lateral veins always obscure. **Ovary** 1.5–2 x 1.5–2mm. **Fruit** 4–4.5 x 3mm. Seeds 0.8–0.9mm, without tails 0.4mm, the longest tail 0.3mm.

An extreme form of *R. cuneifolium* known only from Mt Trus Madi, Sabah, E Malaysia. Brought into cultivation in 1984, it has retained its small leaf form and very small fruits. Not really a horticultural plant but it has occasionally produced an abundance of flowers which makes it colourful, and the small leaves and slow growth give the plant a neat bonsai appearance. A similar small-leafed form has been collected on Mt Nunkok but this has larger fruits, up to 9mm.

21. Rhododendron ericoides Low *ex* Hook.*f.*
Hook. Icon. Pl. 1852. *t*.887.
Type: Low *s.n.*, March 1851. Borneo, North Borneo, Mt Kinabalu (CGE, K).
Derivation: Greek – *Erica* – a genus of mainly South African shrubs; *oides* – indicating resemblance, the small leaves of this species being very like those of an *Erica*.

Erect wiry shrub, to 1.5m, dwarfed at its highest localities. Twigs densely leafy, scaly and sometimes minutely

hairy on the youngest growth. Stems with protruding leaf-cushions in the younger parts. **Leaves** spirally and evenly arranged, very dense and imbricate in the upper part of the twigs and held sub-erect. **Blade** 4–8 x 0.8–1.6mm, 'ericoid', linear or very narrowly elliptic; apex acute (with the extreme point rounded), with an obtuse glandular point; margin entire or somewhat indented with irregular crenulations, somewhat thickened and slightly or not revolute; base tapering, glabrescent above, laxly scaly beneath. **Scales** disc-shaped, entire with the darker centre thick and slightly impressed. Mid-vein very slightly impressed above, swollen underneath; lateral veins obscure. **Petiole** 0.6–1 x 0.4–0.6mm, scaly and with a few simple hairs, minutely grooved above and with a swollen, bulbous base.

Flower buds to 3.5 x 2.5mm, pink, scaly outside. Bracts all appressed, the outermost subulate, inner ovate, scaly in the upper ½ outside, all with a ciliate margin of white hairs. Inflorescence of solitary flowers or paired, rarely up to 4 in an umbel, hanging vertically. Bracteoles *c*.3 x 0.5mm, linear-spathulate, long-ciliate upwards, falling early. Pedicels 5–8mm, slender, densely scaly, without hairs. Calyx slightly oblique, scaly outside, glabrous inside, with 5 distinct erect lobes, *c*.2 x 1–1.3mm, initially appressed to the corolla, later spreading, narrowly sub-ovate-triangular,

Rhododendron ericoides.

obtuse. **Corolla** bright red, tubular, not or slightly oblique and curved, *c*.15 x 11mm; tube *c*.11 x 6 x 7mm, densely scaly outside, glabrous inside; lobes *c*.4 x 5mm, scaly outside except near the margins, broadly ovate to rounded, half-spreading and overlapping to *c*.halfway, the margins irregularly denticulate. **Stamens** grouped on the lower side of the flower, slightly exserted to *c*.1mm; filaments glabrous, *c*.11mm; anthers brown, *c*.0.9mm. Disc glabrous. **Ovary** *c*.1.8mm, conical, green, densely scaly, gradually tapering distally; style red, to 14mm, glabrous, finally exserted, to *c*.3mm; stigma club-shaped. **Fruit** oblong-ovoid, often a little oblique and curved, 7–10 x 3–4mm. Seeds 1.5–2mm, without tails 0.75mm, the longest tail to 0.5mm, the tails often with multiple points.

    Malaysia (Borneo), Sabah, Mt Kinabalu, endemic (records from other mountains are all referable to *R. borneense*). In primary mossy forest, abundant terrestrially on the open granite dome in exposed sunny places, 2700–4000m. *Fl. fr.* Jan.–Dec.

    Cultivated with difficulty. Introduced into cultivation in the late 1960s. It tends to be slow growing and most introductions into cultivation fail. Possibly those from the lower end of its altitudinal range are more successful. Its bizarre 'ericoid' appearance makes it one of the most unusual rhododendrons.

Rhododendron x silvicolum Sleumer (*R. cuneifolium* x *R. ericoides*)

Rhododendrons of Sabah, Sabah Parks Publ. 1988. 8: 102.

Type: J. & M.S. Clemens 30081, April–June 1932. Borneo, North Borneo, Mt Kinabalu, Tenompok, 5000ft (E, K).

Derivation: Latin – *silva* – wood or forest; *cola* – inhabitant. An inhabitant of the forest since it was first thought to be a shade form of *R. ericoides*.

Synonym: *R. ericoides* var. *silvicolum* Sleumer, Reinwardtia 1960. 5: 62.

    Shrub to 3m. Similar to *R. ericoides* but with larger leaves, 9–11 x 1.8–2mm, flowers red, usually with elongate calyx lobes.

    Malaysia (Borneo), Sabah. Fairly common on Mt Kinabalu around the zone of overlap between the two parent species. Recent records are all between 2800 and 3200m although the type collection was recorded at 1525m – this is possibly an error. A large shrub of this hybrid has persisted over more than 20 years beside the main trail up Kinabalu where it is very conspicuous.

    Widely cultivated since it grows more vigorously than *R. ericoides* although having a very similar habit.

22. Rhododendron nanophyton Sleumer

Reinwardtia 1960. 5: 62.

Type: Eyma 682, 17 June 1937. Indonesia, Celebes (C), Enrekang, Rantemario (L, A, BO, K).

Derivation: Greek – *nanos* – dwarf; *phyton* – a plant. Originally thought to be a very small plant.

Var. **nanophyton**

    Shrub to 2m. Twigs erect, slender, tips shortly patent hairy and moderately scaly, stems covered with the scars and the thick cushions of fallen leaves. **Leaves** densely and regularly spirally arranged. **Blade** 4–7 x 1.5–2.5mm, elliptic to narrowly elliptic; apex shortly tapering, obtuse to rounded; margin flat or slightly recurved, entire or crenulate by impressed scales; base tapering, laxly, silvery and sub-persistently scaly on the upper surface, finally glabrescent; persistently laxly brown-scaly beneath. **Scales** circular, marginal zone narrow, entire or a little wavy; centre dark brown, thick, distinctly impressed. Mid-vein narrowly impressed above, distinct, but not raised beneath; lateral veins not visible. **Petiole** 1.5–2 x *c*.0.5mm, semi-rounded, grooved above, hairy and scaly.

    Flower buds to 6 x 2.5mm, narrowly ovoid, dark purplish-red. Outer bracts triangular, subulate; inner ovate to elliptic with a short obtuse point, sparsely scaly outside, glabrous within and with a conspicuous fringe of white hairs on the margins. Bracteoles 4–5mm, filiform, sub-spathulate distally and densely ciliate. Inflorescence of solitary flowers, or in twos, red, cylindrical, hanging vertically. Pedicels 5–7 x 0.75mm, slender, shortly hairy and moderately scaly. Calyx minute, disc-shaped, wavy and obscurely 5-lobed, scaly outside, glabrous inside. **Corolla** 17–20 x *c*.9mm, slightly oblique, straight or slightly curved; tube 12–14 x 4–6 x 7–8mm, straight, or slightly curved, moderately covered with scales outside; lobes 3–5 x 2–4mm, half-spreading, overlapping for ½ their length, scaly outside except near the margins, also with a few hairs near the tips, glabrous inside, entire or irregularly crenulate, but not irregularly denticulate at the apex. **Stamens** slightly dimorphic, exserted to *c*.2mm, irregularly and variously arranged; filaments linear, slightly broader towards the base, glabrous; anthers 1.3–1.8mm, broadly oblong, dark purple. Disc glabrous. **Ovary** 2–2.8 x 1.2–1.8mm, conical-ovoid, 5-furrowed, densely scaly, gradually tapering distally; style 7–8mm, pink, glabrous or with scales for *c*.1mm proximally, deflexed to the lower side of the corolla; stigma *c*.0.9mm in diameter, shortly club-shaped hardly thicker than the style, dark purple. **Fruit** to 7 x 3.5mm, shortly cylindrical, deeply grooved, not becoming erect, the valves curving back, the placentae not separating. Seeds 1–1.4mm, without tails 0.7–0.9mm, the longest tail 0.2mm.

Rhododendron nanophyton var. *nanophyton.*

Indonesia, Sulawesi, Latimodjong Range, Mt Rantemario, scattered plants in the open country near the summit at 3100–3300m. *Fl.* March, June, probably continuously.

Cultivated since 2000, flowering for the first time in March 2004 in Edinburgh but later also flowering in August and October. Described originally as a dwarf shrub, it was in fact seen growing to nearly 2m on the open summit area of Mt Rantemario.

Var. **petrophilum** Sleumer
Reinwardtia 1960. 5: 63.
Type: Eyma 1046, 28 June 1937. Indonesia, Celebes (C), Enrekang, Latimojong Range (L, A, BO, K).
Derivation: Greek – *petra* – a rock or stone; *philus* – loving. Alluding to the rocky habitat.

Differs from the type variety by less distinctly hairy twigs, leaf blade 2.5–6 x 1.5–2.5mm, obovate-elliptic, obtuse and mostly a little retuse at the apex and shortly hairy in the lower ½. With shortly but distinctly ciliate calyx lobes, minutely hairy pedicels and sub-globose-obovoid anthers *c.*1mm.

Indonesia, SW Central Sulawesi, Latimodjong Range, frequent on rocks just below the western edge of the plateau of bivouac Heinrich, at 3200–3250m; known only from the type collection. *Fl.* June.

23. Rhododendron monodii (H.J.Lam) Argent *comb. nov.*
Basionym: *R. quadrasianum* f. *monodii* Lam, Blumea 1945. 5: 576.
Type: Monod de Froideville 120, 1937–39. Mt Mambuliling, N of Mamasa, 2700m (BO, L).
Derivation: Named after the collector of the type specimen.

Synonym: *R. quadrasianum* var. *selebicum* J.J.Sm., Bull. Jard. Bot. Buit. III, 1935. 13: 443.

Shrub or tree to 4m. Twigs 2–4mm in diameter, rounded, at first densely patently short-hairy and laxly brown scaly, bright red; internodes 0.5–10cm, branches arising in pseudowhorls. **Leaves** regularly spirally arranged. **Blade** 6–14 x 4–8mm, broadly obovate; apex rounded, sometimes slightly retuse, without a distinct terminal gland; margin flat or very slightly revolute, sub-entire but with widely spaced scales which are sometimes faintly indented; base tapering, glossy bright green above, paler and dull beneath; glabrous or sparsely scaly above, laxly scaly beneath. **Scales** circular or nearly so; marginal zone relatively broad, mostly about the same diameter as the central region. Mid-vein impressed above, often with a few simple hairs in the proximal area, prominent beneath especially in the proximal ½; lateral veins not visible. **Petiole** to 2 x 1mm, shallowly grooved, sub-densely hairy especially above and laxly brown-scaly.

Flower buds to 4 x 2mm, ovoid or ellipsoid, brown. Outer bracts subulate, erect, densely scaly outside, inner ones broadly ovate, with a few scales distally outside but with numerous semi-erect hairs and densely fringed with white hairs, obtuse or slightly apiculate, with dark brown thickened apices. **Flowers** solitary, half-hanging or hanging. Pedicels 3–5mm, green, densely hairy with spreading hairs, or hairy and scaly or exclusively scaly. Calyx disc-shaped, densely covered with long patent hairs. **Corolla** scaly, but without hairs outside, 10–15mm, red or orange, sometimes with a yellow tube. Ovary exclusively scaly.

Indonesia, Sulawesi (C and SE). Open forest or sub-montane shrubberies, 2000–3000m. *Fl.* June–Nov.

Differing from *R. quadrasianum* in that the leaves are regularly spirally arranged, with the margins indented with scale attachments. The scales have a broad flange and relatively small centre and the pedicels are very short, only 3–5mm. A curious feature is the fact that sometimes the upper surface of the leaves is completely glabrous even when young and developing. Superficially similar to the New Guinean *R. pulleanum* in the leaf shape and very lax scales with up to 1mm between them. It differs from *R. pulleanum* in having hairy stems and the broad flanges on the scales.

24. Rhododendron meliphagidum J.J.Sm.

Fedde Rep. 1932. 30: 162.

Type: Stresemann 374, Feb. 1912. Moluccas, Buru, summit of Mt Togha, 1800–2050m (L).

Derivation: Named after the bird *Meliphaga stigmatops* Deningeri (a honey eater); said to be one of this bird's favourite flowers.

Shrub to 5m. Twigs rounded, laxly covered with rounded or lobed, slightly elevated scales, becoming glabrescent, leaving the surface smooth; internodes 1.5–7cm. **Leaves** in loose pseudowhorls, 5–11 together at the 2 or 3 upper nodes. **Blade** 18–40 x 8–19mm, obovate; apex rounded and mostly shortly retuse; margin entire, distinctly but narrowly revolute; base narrowly tapering, laxly to sub-densely scaly on both sides initially; above the scales in depressions, the centres sub-persistent, often bleaching to white; below, slightly impressed, brown, more persistent. **Scales** very variable in size, sessile, circular, sub-entire, marginal flange narrow, centre thick. Midvein impressed above, strongly raised beneath especially in the proximal ⅔; lateral veins 2–5 per side, or obscure. **Petiole** 2–4 x 0.75–1mm, grooved above, brown-scaly.

Flower buds to 7 x 3mm, green, narrowly ovate, apiculate, smooth. Outer bracts subulate, densely scaly, inner ones ovate, acuminate, apiculate, appressed white-hairy and brown scaly outside, mostly distally. Bracteoles *c.*3.3 x 0.5mm, filiform, slightly broadened upwards. **Flowers** solitary (rarely in pairs), half-hanging to vertically hanging. Pedicels 8–12 x 0.75mm, laxly hairy and scaly, or scaly only. Calyx oblique, small, obtusely 5-lobed, scaly outside, margin white ciliate. **Corolla** 25–30 x 12–15mm, orange or yellow; tube 20–25 x 4–6 x 6–8mm, cylindrical, straight or very slightly curved, laxly scaly outside, glabrous inside; lobes 6–7 x 4–5mm, ovate, half-spreading, only slightly overlapping at the base, minutely crenulate and/or ciliolate around the margins. **Stamens** clustered on the lower side of the flower, exserted to *c.*4mm; filaments 25–29mm, linear, flat, nearly 1mm wide at the base, filiform upwards, glabrous; anthers *c.*1mm, sub-orbicular, dark brown. Disc glabrous. **Ovary** 3–4 x *c.*1.8mm, oblong-conical, densely scaly, gradually tapering distally; style 16–24mm, lying on the lower side of the flower, glabrous or with a few scales at the base; stigma club-shaped, green, *c.*1mm in diameter. **Fruit** 11–16 x 4–5mm, fusiform, longitudinally grooved, scaly, the valves curving back, the placentae only weakly breaking away from the base.

Indonesia, Maluku, Buru, summit of Mt Togha, C Seram, Mt Murkele, Mt Binaia; Sulawesi, (C) Mt Roroka Timbu, (NW) Mt Sojol. Locally common to abundant, mostly epiphytic, often in limestone areas. *Fl.* Feb., July.

Rhododendron meliphagidum.

Introduced into cultivation from Seram in 1988 to the Royal Botanic Garden Edinburgh and later by David Binney from Sulawesi to New Zealand. It flowers freely but irregularly several times a year, the extremely long flowers making it more an object of curiosity than one of great beauty but it has a certain charm. Despite being reported as growing up to 5m in the wild it will flower when only 15–20cm in cultivation.

25. Rhododendron quadrasianum S.Vidal

Rev. Pl. Vasc. Filip. 1886. 170.

Type: Vidal 819. Philippines, Luzon, Albay, Mt Mayon, 1330–2000m (K).

Derivation: Named after J.F. Quadras, a Spanish friend and associate of Vidal who collected in the Philippines.

Synonym: *R. retusum* (*non* Benn.) Fern.-Vill., Nov. App. 1883. 353.

For further synonyms see under varieties.

51

Key to the varieties

1   Corolla scaly or glabrous, occasionally with a few simple hairs at the base (Luzon, Mindoro) _____ var. **quadrasianum**

+   Corolla scaly and laxly hairy outside, often only minutely so _____ 2

2   Corolla 20mm or more long, tubular (Mindanao, Camiguin) _____ var. **malindangense**

+   Corolla up to 16mm long, slightly campanulate, expanded distally _____ 3

3   Pedicels densely scaly, with or without simple hairs. Bracts scaly and/or hairy outside _____ 4

+   Pedicels hairy and sparsely or not scaly. Bracts glabrous, or almost so outside _____ 5

4   Leaves shortly and broadly obovate, 5–10mm wide (Mindoro, Leyte, Negros, S Luzon) __ var. **davaoense**

+   Leaves elongate-obovate, 3–6mm wide (Mindoro, Biliran, Luzon) _____ var. **rosmarinifolium**

5   Leaves obovate, more than 4mm wide (Luzon, Mindoro) _____ var. **marivelesense**

+   Leaves narrowly obovate, less than 4mm wide (Luzon) _____ var. **intermedium**

Note: Plants previously referred to *R. quadrasianum* from outside the Philippines are all referable to other species; see *R. borneense*, *R. cuneifolium* and *R. monodii*.

Var. **quadrasianum**

Shrub or small tree to 3m. Twigs rounded, slender, younger parts densely patently short hairy and laxly to sub-densely brown scaly; internodes 0.5–10cm. **Leaves** 4–8 in lax pseudowhorls. **Blade** 15–30 x 7–13mm, obovate, more rarely elliptic, sub-sessile; apex broadly obtuse or rounded, sometimes slightly retuse, terminal gland small and on the undersurface within the margin; margin revolute; base tapering, dark green and shiny above, paler and dull beneath; laxly silvery scaly initially above, gradually glabrescent, the pits of the scales remaining, sub-densely scaly beneath often with short hairs proximally especially when young. **Scales** small, circular or nearly so; marginal zone narrow, entire to crenulate; centre thick, brown, distinctly impressed. Mid-vein impressed above, prominent beneath especially in the proximal ½; lateral veins 2–4 per side, curved-ascending and anastomosing, minutely depressed above, slightly raised beneath, often inconspicuous. **Petiole** very short, to 1.5mm (the blade

being decurrent nearly to the base), shallowly grooved, sub-densely brown-scaly and shortly white hairy.

Flower buds *c*.10 x 6mm, ovoid or ellipsoid. Outer bracts ovate to sub-circular, inner ones broadly obovate-spathulate, obtuse or minutely apiculate, with a few scales distally outside and densely appressed hairy outside in the exposed areas, glabrous inside, shortly ciliate on the margins. Bracteoles to 6mm, filiform, glabrous, or with a few scales and hairs. Inflorescence of solitary flowers or in twos, rarely 3 or 4 in an umbel, half-hanging to hanging. Pedicels 10–15mm, slender, densely, shortly, patently hairy, laxly to sub-densely scaly. Calyx small, disc-shaped, 5-lobed, scaly and hairy; lobes *c*.0.5mm, broad-ovate and obtuse. **Corolla** 12–18 x 13–15mm, red, tubular, slightly oblique and dilated distally; tube 10–13 x 5–6 x 7–8mm, sub-densely scaly and with some scattered hairs at the very base outside (but not hairy all over the tube), glabrous inside; lobes 5–6 x 5–6mm, somewhat irregular, broadly elliptic-obovate or sub-circular, finely irregularly denticulate or entire at the apex, semi-erect to spreading, overlapping to *c*.½. **Stamens** loosely clustered on the lower side of the mouth, exserted to *c*.4mm; filaments linear, glabrous; anthers *c*.1mm, sub-globose. Disc glabrous. **Ovary** *c*.2 x 1.5mm, obliquely cylindrical, gradually tapering distally, grooved, densely scaly; style *c*.8mm, glabrous; stigma rounded, irregularly lobed. **Fruit** 10–15 x 2.5–3.5mm, obliquely cylindrical, densely brown-scaly. Seeds *c*.2mm including the narrow tail at both ends.

Philippines, Luzon, Albay Province, Mayon Volcano, Mindoro, Mt Isarog. Terrestrial, or rarely epiphytic. On rocky open slopes, 1330–2100m, abundant. *Fl. fr.* May–June, Sept.

Sleumer (1966) notes that 'This is the "typical" form, *i.e.* the first one described of this variable species, collected again and again on Mayon Volcano, but not found elsewhere [see above]. Within the general aspect of *R. quadrasianum s.lat.*, this is a homogeneous, glabrescent, big leaved form'. Sleumer reduced the number of infraspecific taxa that Copeland (1929) recognised. It is still not a very satisfactory treatment and needs much more field work to really understand the patterns of variation on the different mountains and islands in the Philippines. Certainly the variants seem less well differentiated than the discovireyas in New Guinea, and it was impossible to include *R. quadrasianum* in the key to *Discovireya* for West Malesia because of the complex morphological variation. This account largely follows Sleumer but the non-Philippine elements are excluded (see *R. cuneifolium*, *R. borneense* and *R. monodii*).

Var. **davaoense** (H.F.Copel.) Sleumer
Reinwardtia 1960. 5: 65.
Type: Williams 2543. Philippines, Mindanao, Davao, Mt Apo, 2440m (PNH†, GH, K, NY, US).
Derivation: Named after Davao, the province from which this was first collected.

Synonyms:
R. quadrasianum f. *davaoense* H.F.Copel., Phil. J. Sc. 1929. 40: 143, *t*.1, *f*.9, 10.
R. quadrasianum f. *negrosense* H.F.Copel., Phil. J. Sc. 1929. 40: 142, *t*.1, *f*.6.

Small tree or shrub. **Leaves** 15–28 x 5–10mm, broadly and shortly obovate. **Corolla** 10–16mm, sub-campanulate broadening distally, scaly and at least laxly hairy outside. Pedicels hairy and scaly. **Ovary** with scales only.

Philippines, Mindanao, Leyte, Negros, S Luzon. Dense moss forest on summits, sometimes epiphytic, 1600–2440m. *Fl. fr.* Jan.–Dec.

Var. **rosmarinifolium** (S.Vidal) H.F.Copel.
Phil. J. Sc. 1929. 40: 144, *t*.1, *f*.13–18.
Type: Vidal 1530, Bontoc (K, A, FI).
Derivation: Latin – *Rosmarinus officinalis* L. – the herb 'rosemary' (Lamiales); *folium* – leaf. Alluding to the resemblance of the leaves to those of rosemary.

Synonyms:
R. rosmarinifolium S.Vidal, Rev. Pl. Vasc. Phil. 1886. 172.
R. cuneifolium (*non* Stapf) Rendle, J. Bot. 1896. 34: 355.
R. quadrasianum f. *halconense* H.F.Copel., Phil. J. Sc. 1929. 40: 141, *t*.1, *f*.5.

R. quadrasianum f. *banahaoense* H.F.Copel., Phil. J. Sc. 1929. 40: 145, *t*.1, *f*.24.
R. quadrasianum f. *pulogense* H.F.Copel., Phil. J. Sc. 1929. 40: 144, *t*.1, *f*.19–23.

Shrub to 2m, or rarely a tree to 6m. **Leaves** 10–22 x 3–6mm, narrowly elongate-obovate. Flower buds hairy and scaly outside. **Corolla** 10–16 x 9–11mm, elongate-campanulate, red to orange; tube straight, narrowly funnel-shaped, scaly and at least laxly hairy outside. Pedicels hairy and densely scaly. **Ovary** scaly, without hairs.

Philippines, Mindoro, Biliran, Luzon, Negros. Mossy oak (*Castanopsis*) forest, also in open secondary areas; locally common, 1300–2400m. *Fl. fr*. Jan.–Dec.

This variety has been in cultivation since at least 1980 from an unknown source. It has neat foliage and small, freely produced pink flowers; sometimes a pink tube with orange lobes.

Var. **malindangense** (Merr.) H.F.Copel.
Phil. J. Sc. 1929. 40: 142, *t*.1, *f*.7, 8.
Type: Hutchinson 4705, May 1906. Mt Malindang, Misamis province, Mindanao (PNH†, BO, K, NY, US).
Derivation: Named after the mountain on which the type was collected.

Synonym: *R. malindangense* Merr., Phil. J. Sc. (Bot.) 1908. 3: 256, 381.

Shrub or small tree to 7m. **Leaves** obovate to spathulate. **Blade** 13–25 x 5–10mm. **Petiole** 2–4mm. **Corolla**

Rhododendron quadrasianum var. malindangense.

strictly cylindrical, red, 20–25 x 12–13mm; tube 16–20 x *c*.4 x *c*.5mm, laxly hairy and scaly outside; lobes *c*.5 x 4mm. **Anthers** 0.7mm. Pedicels *c*.8 x 0.75mm, hairy and scaly. **Ovary** 4 x 2mm, scaly only.

Philippines, Mindanao, Camiguin. Mossy forest, sometimes epiphytic, 1000–1600m. *Fl. fr.* March–Sept.

In cultivation from Mt Apo since 1993. Not particularly attractive.

Var. **marivelesense** (H.F.Copel.) Sleumer
Reinwardtia 1960. 5: 66.
Type: Merrill 3215. Luzon, Bataan, Mt Mariveles (PNH†, BO, K, NY, US).
Derivation: Named after the mountain from which it was described.

Mostly a small tree. **Leaves** obovate, 11–20 x 4–8mm. **Corolla** to 17 x 15mm, tubular, shortly hairy and scaly outside, the lobes half-spreading. Pedicels hairy without, or with just a few, scales. **Ovary** scaly, without hairs.

Philippines, Luzon, Mindoro. Mossy forest, 1200–2500m. *Fl. fr.* March–Nov.

Var. **intermedium** Merr.
Phil. J. Sc. (Bot.) 1908. 3: 382.
Type: Curran & Merritt F.B. 8063. Luzon, Zambales, Mt Tapulao (PNH†, US).
Derivation: Latin – *intermedius* – between or intermediate, alluding to its intermediate characters.

Small tree or shrub. **Leaves** narrowly obovate, 8–11 x 2–4mm. **Corolla** tubular below, sub-campanulate distally, *c*.10mm, hairy and scaly outside. Pedicels hairy, almost without scales. **Ovary** with scales only.

Philippines, Luzon, Mt Tapulao, Mt Pinatubo, Mt Sisipatan and Mt Paraga. Open exposed ridges, 1800–2400m.

26. Rhododendron taxoides J.J.Sm.
Nova Guinea 1936. 18: 92, *t*.18, 2.
Type: Lam 1598, 17 Oct. 1920. New Guinea (W), Doorman-top, 3250m (BO, L).
Derivation: Named after *Taxus baccata*, the 'yew', from the resemblance of the leaves to those of this tree.

Shrub to 1.5m. Twigs densely covered with fragile scales on short stalks, which remain in form of small, dense warts. **Leaves** densely spirally arranged. **Blade** 6–12 x 2–3mm, narrowly elliptic, apex obtusely acuminate,

margin recurved in dry specimens, the edge somewhat thickened and crenulate with impressions where the scales are attached; base tapering gradually but finally broadly tapering to rounded, shining green above and light green with brown scales beneath, glabrescent above; beneath laxly scaly, more densely so on the mid-vein, convex. **Scales** sessile, circular or nearly so, entire to irregularly undulate; marginal zone narrow; centre large, thick, dark and impressed. Mid-vein very slightly grooved proximally above, thick and obtusely raised beneath; lateral veins indistinct. **Petiole** 1.5–2mm, thick, scaly.

Bracts to 6 x 3mm, narrowly ovate, apiculate; outer ones laxly scaly outside, inner ones densely hairy, ciliate along the margins. Bracteoles to 5mm, linear, hairy outside. **Flowers** mostly in twos, sometimes solitary, hanging vertically down. Pedicels 8–9mm, slender, sub-densely covered with shortly stalked scales and short hairs. Calyx *c*.3mm in diameter, oblique, small disc-shaped, wavy, shortly obtusely 5-lobed, scaly, margin laxly set with white hairs. **Corolla** 14–18mm, dark red; tube 10–14 x 2.5 x 5mm, cylindrical, oblique and curved, densely scaly outside, glabrous inside; lobes 2.5–3.5 x 2–3mm, sub-circular to ovate, minutely irregularly crenulate and ciliolate, scaly outside except the upper part of the lobes, which bears some sparse hairs. **Stamens** unequal, the longest nearly equalling the corolla; filaments filiform, glabrous; anthers *c*.1mm, sub-elliptic. Disc glabrous. **Ovary** *c*.2.5 x 1.5mm, obliquely conical, 5-ribbed, densely scaly, gradually tapering distally; style glabrous, *c*.10mm; stigma thick-obconical, distinctly lobed. **Fruit** 8.5–12 x 2–3mm, obliquely fusiform, sparsely scaly.

Indonesia, New Guinea (W), Mt Doorman, on open slopes or summits on serpentine rocks, 3250–3520m. *Fl.* Oct.

Known only from the two original collections from the same locality; never cultivated.

27. Rhododendron pulleanum Koord.
Nova Guinea 1912. 8: 879, *t*.154, 4.
Type: Römer 1198, Nov. 1909. New Guinea (W), Hellwig Mts, Mt Agathodaemon, 2000–2500m (BO, lectotype, L, fragment).
Derivation: Named after A.A. Pulle, eminent Dutch botanist who collected in New Guinea.

Synonym: *R. minimifolium* Wernham, Trans. Linn. Soc. London, II, Bot. 9: 98, 1916, *pro parte.*

Var. **pulleanum**

Shrub to 2m. Twigs rounded, covered with stalked scales when young, older parts glabrescent though still rough with scale stalks. **Leaves** densely spirally arranged. **Blade** 4–9 x 2.5–5mm, elliptic or elliptic-obovate; apex obtuse or sub-acute; margin revolute, the whole blade convex when dry; base tapering, deep green above, paler beneath, glabrescent above, very laxly scaly beneath. **Scales** large, reddish-brown, sessile, circular; marginal zone narrow, entire or nearly so; centre thick, slightly or not impressed. Mid-vein obscure above, slightly prominent beneath, lateral veins not visible above, faintly so beneath. **Petiole** 1–1.5mm, slender.

Bracts to 7 x 4mm, ovate to sub-acute, glabrous except for the ciliate margins. Bracteoles 5–7mm, linear to narrowly spathulate, very shortly hairy. Inflorescence of solitary flowers, rarely pairs. Pedicels 5–15mm, very slender, densely scaly and finely patently hairy. Calyx oblique, scaly, irregularly lobed, 3 lobes shortly triangular to 1mm, 2 others larger to 3mm, spreading. **Corolla** 13–20mm, red; tube 10–12 x 3–4 x 5–6mm, cylindrical, straight, densely scaly outside, glabrous inside; lobes 2–4 x 2–2.5mm, erect, obovate-elliptic. **Stamens** not or slightly exserted; filaments linear, filiform, glabrous; anthers *c*.1mm, oblong-obovate, truncate. Disc glabrous. **Ovary** *c*.3 x 1mm, ovoid-conical, tapering distally, entirely covered with scales; style to 10mm, scaly at the base, otherwise glabrous; stigma club-shaped, moderately thickened, indistinctly 10-lobed.

Indonesia, New Guinea (W), Nassau Mts, Mt Jaya, Mt Doorman, Hellwig Mts and Mt Goliath. Terrestrial or epiphytic, in mossy forest, or in dense low scrub on exposed summits or in open moss-covered *Vaccinium* forest, 1420–3450m. *Fl.* Jan.–Dec.

Not known to have been cultivated. Distinctive in the relatively large, well-spaced scales on the small leaves.

Var. **maiusculum** Sleumer
Reinwardtia 1960. 5: 56.
Type: Brass 10834, Oct. 1938. New Guinea (W), 20km N of Lake Habbema, 2300m (A, L, fragment).
Derivation: Latin – *maiusculus* – somewhat greater, alluding to the larger leaves and flower.

Leaves 6–10 x 4–6mm. Corolla 17–20mm. Pedicels densely scaly and entirely without hairs, otherwise as var. *pulleanum*.

Indonesia, New Guinea (W), near Lake Habbema; Mt Antares. Common on open sandy ridges and in alpine shrub vegetation, 2300–3400m. *Fl.* July, Oct.

Differing from the type variety in the larger leaves and corolla. This variety was said by Sleumer (1966) to approach *R. hameliiflorum* in many respects. It differs, however, in its non-scaly bracts.

28. Rhododendron nummatum J.J.Sm.
Nova Guinea 1936. 18: 91, *t*.17, 2.
Type: H.J. Lam 1807, 29 Oct. 1920. New Guinea (W), Doormantop, 3200m (BO, L).
Derivation: Latin – *nummatum* – rich or wealthy, alluding to the leaves being rounded like coins.

Stiffly erect shrub to 1.5m. Twigs slender, rounded, tips densely covered with stalked scales, lower parts rough after the scales have gone. **Leaves** spirally arranged, more densely towards the tips. **Blade** 10–15 x 4–9mm, broadly obovate to nearly rounded; apex rounded, broadly obtuse or slightly retuse; margin slightly or not revolute; base broadly tapering or rounded, convex above; initially densely scaly on both sides, glabrescent above at maturity. **Scales** round, large, sessile, marginal zone entire or nearly so; centre thick, slightly or not impressed. Mid-vein smooth above, prominent beneath, often obscure; lateral veins 2 or 3 or obscure. **Petiole** 1–1.5mm, slender.

Bracts to 3mm, narrowly ovate, sub-acute to obtuse, glabrous, but ciliate on the margins. Bracteoles to 4mm, linear-spathulate, shortly hairy distally. Inflorescence of solitary flowers, rarely in twos, hanging vertically. Pedicels 5–6.5mm, thick, densely scaly (the scales on very short stalks), very sparsely or not hairy. Calyx oblique, small, irregularly 5-lobed, scaly outside with triangular, obtuse, lobes, to 0.5mm. **Corolla** pink or dark-red, sometimes yellow at the base, tubular, slightly zygomorphic; tube *c*.10 x 3.5 x 3.5mm, cylindrical, straight, sparsely to sub-densely scaly outside, glabrous inside; lobes 1.2–1.8 x 1.5–2mm, erect, ovate-circular, irregularly denticulate, laxly scaly outside, in the proximal ½. **Stamens** included within the mouth; filaments linear, slightly dilated towards the base, glabrous; anthers 0.8–1mm. Disc glabrous. **Ovary** *c*.3mm, cylindrical, 5-ribbed, covered with brown scales, tapering distally; style 4–5mm, thick, laxly scaly in the proximal ½; stigma club-shaped, indistinctly 10-lobed. **Fruit** 8–13 x 2.5–3mm, fusiform, distinctly 5-ribbed.

Indonesia, New Guinea (W). **Papua New Guinea** (E). Along the Main Range from Mt Doorman and the Hellwig Mts to Mt Victoria, also throughout the Huon Peninsula. Terrestrial or epiphytic in sub-alpine shrubberies as part of the understory, forest margins, open mossy or grassy areas, clearings in ridge forest, or open clayey ground of old gold workings, 2000–3500m. *Fl. fr.* Jan.–Dec.

This species usually has almost circular leaves with distinct scales on their undersides, although not as distinct or as far apart as in *R. pulleanum*. Not known in cultivation.

29. Rhododendron gaultheriifolium J.J.Sm.

Nova Guinea 1936. 18: 90, *t*.17, 1.

Type: Lam 1661. New Guinea (W), Doormantop, 3520m (BO, lectotype, L).

Derivation: Latin – *Gaultheria* – a genus in the Ericaceae; *folium* – leaved. With leaves like a *Gaultheria*.

Var. **gaultheriifolium**

Slender erect shrub to 5m. Twigs slender, tips covered with stalked scales, lower parts densely rough with the persistent scale stalks. **Leaves** spirally arranged, crowded towards the ends of the twigs. **Blade** 5–10 x 4–7mm, ovate, rarely elliptic-ovate; apex shortly obtusely acuminate; margin thickened and revolute, irregularly crenulate with impressed scales; base rounded to sub-truncate, dark to yellowish green, paler below, sparsely scaly and early glabrescent above, sub-densely and persistently brown scaly below. **Scales** round, sessile, entire, with a broad dark centre, thick and impressed. Mid-vein slightly impressed above, slightly raised beneath, lateral veins indistinct. **Petiole** 1.5–2mm, grooved above, scaly and minutely hairy.

Flower buds to 8 x 4mm, ovate, acutely pointed, brown, with both scales and short appressed hairs outside. Outer bracts subulate, densely scaly, inner ones to 7 x 4mm, ovate-acuminate, apiculate, shortly hairy and scaly outside in the upper part, shortly hairy or glabrous inside, all bracts densely white ciliate on the margins. Bracteoles to 7mm, linear, glabrous, or hairy and scaly distally. Inflorescence of solitary or paired flowers, rarely 3–4 together, hanging vertically. Pedicels 6–9 x *c*.1mm, densely scaly and laxly minutely hairy. Calyx oblique, disc-shaped, densely scaly outside, obtusely 5-lobed, occasionally one or a few lobes elongate-triangular, acute, to 1mm. **Corolla** 12–17 x *c*.9mm, deep red to brownish red, sometimes greenish yellow or orange, tubular, somewhat zygomorphic; tube 8–12 x 3–8 x 5–7mm, straight, densely scaly outside, glabrous inside; lobes 3–5 x 3–5mm, sub-circular, erect or a little spreading, scaly outside except along the margins and laxly hairy outside in the distal ½, and distinctly ciliate crenulate-denticulate on the distal margin. **Stamens** clustered on the lower side at the corolla mouth, or exserted to 2mm, slightly unequal; filaments 9–10mm, red, linear at the base, filiform upwards, glabrous; anthers *c*.1mm. Disc glabrous. **Ovary** *c*.3 x 2.5mm, conical, densely scaly, gradually tapering distally; style *c*.7mm, lying on the lower side of the tube, thick, scaly at the base, otherwise glabrous; stigma shortly club-shaped, irregularly lobed. **Fruit** 8–9 x 3.5–4mm, erect, narrowly conical, longitudinally 5-ribbed, densely scaly.

Indonesia, New Guinea (W), Oranje Mts, Mt Doorman. **Papua New Guinea**, Star Mts, Eastern and Western Highlands. In shrubberies bordering the sub-alpine forest, occupying patches of wet sandy or peaty soil, or on the more sterile peaty ridges; also in grassland above the timber line, between summit rocks. Locally common, occasionally dominant, 2900–4150m. *Fl.* June–Feb.

Rhododendron gaultheriifolium var. *gaultheriifolium*.

Var. **expositum** Sleumer
Reinwardtia 1960. 5: 56.
Type: Brass & Meijer Drees 10122. New Guinea (W), 2km east of the top of Mt Wilhelmina, 3000–3800m (L, A).
Derivation: Latin – *expositus* – exposed, alluding to the extreme habitat of this variety.

Shrub of erect ascending or prostrate habit, 0.05–1m. Leaves 2–5 x 3–4mm, elliptic, very leathery and shining. Flowers dark-red or orange-red. Fruit 6–7 x 2.5–3mm.

Indonesia, New Guinea (W), Mt Jaya (Carstensz), Mt Antares and the Burgers Mts. Growing in open alpine grassland, on exposed limestone or sandstone slopes. Locally abundant, 3000–3800m. *Fl. fr.* June–Feb.

An alpine form with smaller leaves and capsules.

30. Rhododendron oreites Sleumer
Reinwardtia 1960. 5: 57.
Type: Brass & Meijer Drees 9992, Sept. 1938. New Guinea (W), 7km north of Mt Wilhelminatop, 3560m (A, L).
Derivation: Greek – *oreites* – a mountaineer; *oreo* – pertaining to mountains.

Var. **oreites**

Erect shrub to 2.5m. Twigs 1.5–2mm in diameter, rounded, densely covered with stalked scales, glabrescent and rough when the scales have gone. **Leaves** spiral, crowded at the ends of the new shoots. **Blade** 8–12 x 4–7mm, elliptic; apex gradually sub-acuminate to obtuse; margin revolute in the proximal ½, crenulate where impressed scales are attached; base broadly tapering or rounded to truncate, sub-densely persistently scaly on both sides. **Scales** circular, marginal zone narrow, entire or nearly so; centre large, thick, somewhat impressed. Midvein slightly impressed above, prominent beneath, lateral veins slightly or not visible. **Petiole** *c.*2mm, slender, scaly.
Bracts to 5 x 2.5mm. Outer bracts triangular, inner ones ovate to elliptic, apiculate, scaly outside at the apex, sometimes with a few hairs, otherwise glabrous, densely long-ciliate, often persisting around the base of the pedicel. Bracteoles *c.*6mm, filiform, laxly hairy. Inflorescence of solitary flowers, half-hanging. Pedicels *c.*10mm, slender, with dense scales on very short stalks, not hairy. Calyx *c.*2.5mm in diameter, oblique, cup-like, shortly 5-lobed, lobes to 1mm, sub-acute or obtuse, appressed to the corolla. **Corolla** tubular, slightly zygomorphic, red; tube 16–17 x 3 x 6mm, densely scaly outside, glabrous inside; lobes 3–4 x 3–4mm, sub-circular, scaly outside except near

the margins which may be shortly hairy outside, glabrous inside, margin crenulate or irregularly denticulate, not ciliate. **Stamens** as long as the corolla, slightly unequal; filaments glabrous, linear below, filiform distally; anthers *c.*1mm, brown, obovate-oblong. Disc glabrous. **Ovary** *c.*4 x 1.5mm, shortly ovoid-cylindrical, densely covered with very slightly stalked or sessile scales, gradually tapering distally; style slender and glabrous; stigma at first at the mouth, later distinctly exserted. **Fruit** 8–12 x 3.5mm, cylindrical, deeply 5-grooved, densely scaly, valves not or slightly twisted.

Indonesia, New Guinea (W), Mt Trichora (Wilhelmina). Terrestrial in sub-alpine forest or forest borders, or in shrubberies, occupying patches of wet sandy or peaty soil. Common, 2900–3650m. *Fl. fr.* Sept.–Oct.

Not known to have been cultivated.

Var. **chlorops** Sleumer
Reinwardtia 1960. 5: 58.
Type: Brass 10668, Oct. 1938. New Guinea (W), 6km NE of Lake Habbema (A, L).
Derivation: Greek – *chloro* – green, alluding to the green colour of the flowers.

Leaves 11–15 x 5–8mm, elliptic or ovate-elliptic. Corolla greenish-yellow.

Indonesia, New Guinea (W), Lake Habbema; Mt Jaya, locally common in shrubberies at *c.*3000m. *Fl. fr.* Oct.

Differing from the type variety only really in the colour of the flowers.

31. Rhododendron erosipetalum J.J.Sm.
Nova Guinea 1936. 18: 91, *t.*18, 1.
Type: Mayr 18, 27 May 1928. New Guinea (W), Arfak Mts, 1800m (BO, lectotype, L, fragment).
Derivation: Latin – *erosus* – having an irregular apparently gnawed margin; *petalum* – of the petals. The corolla lobes having an erose, or raggedly irregular, margin.

Erect or spreading shrub to 2m. Twigs densely covered with stalked scales, the lower parts rough where the scales have gone and the stalks remain. **Leaves** spiral, often somewhat crowded in the upper part of the twigs. **Blade** 6–13 x 2–4mm, narrowly obovate; apex obtuse or mostly rounded, often slightly retuse; margin revolute; base gradually tapering, dark green above, paler beneath, glabrescent above, laxly scaly beneath. **Scales** circular, their marginal zone narrow, entire; centre darker, thick, slightly impressed. Mid-vein slightly or not impressed above, raised beneath; lateral veins not visible. **Petiole** 1–1.5mm.

Bracts to 4 x 3mm, ovate, apiculate, hairy and laxly scaly outside, shortly white-ciliate on the margins. Bracteoles to 5mm, filiform. Inflorescence of solitary flowers, hanging vertically. Pedicels 8–10mm, laxly to sub-densely covered with scales and minute white, patent hairs. Calyx small, disc-like, 5-angular or shortly obtusely 5-lobed, scaly. **Corolla** *c.*20 x 10mm, tubular, somewhat curved and a little compressed laterally, deep pink to dark red; tube 15–18 x 3–4 x 5–6mm, laxly scaly outside, glabrous inside; lobes *c.*3–4 x *c.*3mm, unequal, minutely hairy distally outside, ovate or ovate-elliptic, the apex rounded and minutely irregularly denticulate. **Stamens** unequal, some slightly exserted from the corolla; filaments narrowly linear, glabrous; anthers *c.*1.2mm. Disc glabrous. **Ovary** *c.*3mm, obliquely conical, longitudinally 5-grooved, densely scaly, tapering distally; style *c.*13mm, glabrous, somewhat thickened distally to the club-shaped irregularly lobed stigma. **Fruit** 8–15 x *c.*3mm, sub-cylindrical, deeply 5-grooved. Seeds 0.15–2mm, shortly tailed at both ends.

Indonesia, New Guinea (W), Vogelkop Peninsula, Arfak Mts, Tohkiri, Tamrau and Nettoti Range. Epiphytic or terrestrial, rare on a burnt open summit, mostly on the edge of moss forest, or summit scrub on peaty soil, 1400–2650m. *Fl. fr.* Jan.–Dec.

Not known to have been cultivated.

32. Rhododendron detznerianum Sleumer

Blumea 1973. 21(2): 359.
Type: Hartley 12959, 10 Feb. 1964. New Guinea (E), Central District, Goilala subdistrict, Mt Dickson, 3500m (L, CANB, K, LAE).
Derivation: Dedicated to the memory of H. Detzner, an admirer of New Guinea rhododendrons who was in the Mt Dickson area with the Kaiser Wilhelm Land Boundary Commission in 1914.

Rigidly erect shrub to 1.5m. Twigs with shortly stalked scales, later rough and minutely warty after the scales have fallen. **Leaves** densely spirally arranged. **Blade** 10–15 x 2–4mm, elliptic to spathulate; apex broadly acute to obtuse, margin narrowly revolute, sub-crenulate with scale attachments; base narrowly tapering, decurrent, laxly scaly above but quickly glabrescent, below sub-densely and persistently scaly. **Scales** with a narrow marginal flange and thick rounded and partly impressed centre. Mid-vein

impressed above, slightly raised below; lateral veins and reticulation not visible. **Petiole** *c.*1mm, scaly.

Bracts to 4mm, ovate sub-acuminate to apiculate, outside scaly along the middle line, without hairs except for the ciliate margins. Inflorescence of 1–3 vertically hanging flowers. Pedicels 6–8mm, slender, densely scaly but without hairs. Calyx *c.*2.5mm in diameter, shortly 5-lobed, densely scaly. **Corolla** *c.*12mm, red, cylindrical; tube *c.*10 x 3 x 4mm, densely scaly outside, glabrous inside; lobes *c.*3 x 3mm, sub-circular, semi-erect, scaly outside, without hairs but with a denticulate margin. **Stamens** as long as the corolla tube; filaments *c.*10mm, glabrous; anthers 1.5mm, broadly oblong. Disc glabrous but with scales on the upper side. **Ovary** *c.*2 x 1mm, cylindrical, vertically striate, densely round-scaly; style *c.*8mm, slender, densely scaly for the proximal 1mm, glabrous distally; stigma club-shaped. **Fruit** 6–7 x *c.*3mm, sub-cylindrical.

Papua New Guinea, Central District, Goilala subdistrict, Mt Dickson; Morobe District, above Bakaia, *c.*15 miles SE of Garaina. In the grassland border with *Podocarpus/Papuacedrus* forest, and tree fern grassland, *c.*2745–3500m.

Said to be closely related to *R. erosipetalum* from the Vogelkop Peninsula but that species has bracts and pedicels which are both hairy and scaly outside and also has hairs on the corolla lobes. Never cultivated.

33. Rhododendron hameliiflorum Wernham

Trans. Linn. Soc. London, II, Bot. 1916. 9: 98.
Type: Kloss *s.n.* New Guinea (W), Mt Carstensz (BM, L, fragment).
Derivation: Named after *Hamelia* (Rubiaceae), tropical American ornamental shrubs, alluding to a similarity of the flowers.

Very low, probably creeping shrublet. Twigs slender, tips densely covered with stalked scales or rough in the lower parts where the scales have gone. **Leaves** spiral or sub-opposite. **Blade** 7–10 x 5–8mm, broadly obovate to sub-circular; apex rounded or minutely retuse; margin entire, not or very slightly recurved; base broadly tapering or mostly rounded, laxly scaly initially, early glabrescent above, persistently scaly beneath. **Scales** circular, entire, flat, the large, dark, centre slightly impressed. Midvein impressed above, prominent beneath; lateral veins obscure. **Petiole** 1.5–2mm.

Bracts elliptic-obovate, sparsely hairy outside, densely white-ciliate on the margins. Inflorescence of solitary or rarely paired flowers. Pedicels 5–6mm, slender, densely scaly. Calyx small, obscurely 5-lobed. **Corolla** 17–20 x 3–4mm, tubular, sub-densely scaly all over outside, glabrous inside; lobes *c*.4 x 3mm, obovate to sub-circular, with an entire margin. **Stamens** nearly equalling the corolla in length; filaments linear, glabrous; anthers 1mm. Disc glabrous. **Ovary** *c*.3mm, sub-conical, densely scaly, tapering distally; style laxly scaly in the proximal ¼, glabrous distally, equalling or slightly exceeding the corolla in length; stigma club-shaped.

Indonesia, New Guinea (W), Mt Jaya (Carstensz), 2350–3350m, once collected.

Very imperfectly known species which has not been recollected from the type locality despite considerable recent botanical activity there.

34. Rhododendron lindaueanum Koord.
Nova Guinea 1912. 8(4): 878.
Type: Römer 1043, 30 Nov. 1911. New Guinea (W), Hellwig Mts, Erica Top, *c*.2500m (BO, lectotype, L, fragment).
Derivation: Named after G. Lindau, German botanist.

Var. **lindaueanum**

Synonyms:
R. lindaueanum var. *latifolium* J.J.Sm., Nova Guinea 1914. 12(2): 130, *t*.29A.
R. retusum [*non* (Blume) Benn.] Wernham, Trans. Linn. Soc. London, II, Bot. 1916. 9: 94.
R. fuchsioides Schltr., Bot. Jahr. 1918. 55: 147.

R. lindaueanum var. *psilacrum* Sleumer, Reinwardtia 1960. 5: 58.
R. lindaueanum var. *cyclopicum* Sleumer, Reinwardtia 1960. 5: 59.

Shrub to 3m. Twigs rounded, slender, tips densely covered with stalked scales, lower parts rough with the remaining scale stalks. **Leaves** densely spirally arranged, or in loose to tight pseudowhorls. **Blade** 8–25 x 5–15mm, obovate to spathulate or elliptic-obovate; apex rounded, often slightly retuse; margin strongly revolute, the lamina often convex; base tapering, dark green above, greyish green below, shiny and laxly scaly becoming glabrescent above, persistently laxly scaly beneath. **Scales** red-brown, disc-shaped; marginal zone narrow, entire; centre thick, not or slightly impressed. Mid-vein distinctly impressed above, prominent beneath; lateral veins 3–5 per side, the lower 1–2 ascending, upper ones spreading, anastomosing, faintly impressed above, somewhat raised beneath, sometimes hardly visible. **Petiole** 1.5–2.5mm, scaly and rough.

Bracts to 7 x 4mm; outer ones narrowly ovate, sub-acute, scaly outside, inner ones larger, broadly ovate to sub-circular, scaly and/or with grey hairs outside in the distal part and ciliate margins. Bracteoles 6–7 x 1–1.5mm, linear to spathulate, hairy towards the apex. Inflorescence of solitary flowers, or up to 3 together, half-hanging to hanging. Pedicels 7–12mm, slender, densely scaly and often laxly short hairy. Calyx oblique, scaly, obtusely 5-lobed to *c*.5mm, the lobes spreading, reflexed or adpressed to the corolla, sometimes shortly ciliate. **Corolla** 16–24mm, deep

Rhododendron lindaueanum
var. *lindaueanum*.

Nova Guinea

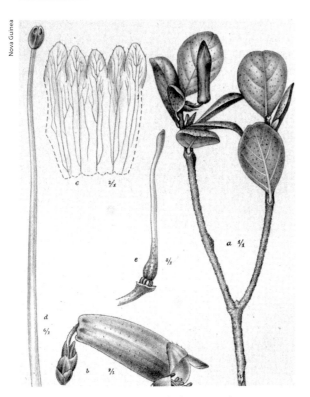

Rhododendron lindaueanum var. *lindaueanum* (as var. *latifolium*).

red to pink, tubular, slightly zygomorphic; tube 16–20 x *c*.2.5 x 4–5mm, laterally compressed, straight, somewhat pouched at the base, laxly scaly all over outside, glabrous inside; lobes 3–5 x *c*.2.5mm, ovate-elliptic, obtuse, erect or half-spreading, overlapping ¼–½, often with minute hairs near the apex outside and ciliate. **Stamens** clustered on the lower side of the mouth, slightly, or not, exserted, unequal; filaments filiform, glabrous; anthers 1–1.5mm, blackish purple or brown, oblong-ovate. Disc glabrous or rarely slightly hairy. **Ovary** *c*.2.5 x 1.5mm, narrowly ovoid-conical, densely scaly, gradually tapering distally; style 10–13mm, becoming exserted as the flower ages, glabrous, swollen distally to a club-shaped, shortly and irregularly 10-lobed stigma. **Fruit** 10–18 x 3–4mm, sub-cylindrical, longitudinally grooved.

Indonesia and **Papua New Guinea**. New Guinea from the Arfak Mts in the west to Mt Saruwaged in the east. In forests, generally epiphytic, but also terrestrial in swampy or alpine shrubberies, on exposed summits, on poor clay or sandy soil, 1250–3200m. *Fl.* Jan.–Dec.

This is a widespread and variable species. The differences between *R. lindaueanum* and *R. erosipetalum* do not appear to be significant but there are considerable

differences between the west New Guinea and east New Guinea specimens of this species. West New Guinea specimens of *R. lindaueanum* have larger leaves (more than 15mm), usually in loose to tight pseudowhorls. East New Guinea specimens have much smaller leaves (less than 10mm) which are spirally arranged. More detailed work is required to better understand this problem.

Not known to have been cultivated.

Var. **bantaengense** J.J.Sm.
Fedde Rep. 1932. 30: 163.
Type: Bünnemeijer 12250, 17 June 1921. Celebes, SW, G. Bantaeng (Peak of Ponthain), 2890m (BO, L).
Derivation: Named after the mountain on which it was first collected.

Differs from the typical variety by longer calyx lobes (*c*.1mm) which are appressed to the corolla. Corolla lobes not ciliate.

Indonesia, Sulawesi, (SW) Mt Bantaeng (Peak of Bonthian), Mt Bawakraeng, summit, in brushwood at 2800–2890m.

35. Rhododendron cyrtophyllum Wernham
Trans. Linn. Soc. London, II, Bot. 1916. 9: 97.
Type: Kloss *s.n.* New Guinea (S), Mt Carstensz (BM).
Derivation: Greek – *kryptos* – hidden; *phyllon* – leaf. A somewhat obscure allusion!

Shrub. Twigs thick, *c*.2mm in diameter, rounded, the tips densely covered with sessile or very shortly stalked roundish scales, lower parts glabrescent, becoming smooth; internodes 2–4cm. **Leaves** 3–5 together in loose pseudowhorls at the upper nodes, sometimes spiral. **Blade** 25–32 x 12–19mm, elliptic or ovate-elliptic; apex gradually tapering, obtuse, apiculate; margin strongly revolute in the distal ⅔, hardly at all proximally; base rounded or sub-truncate, sub-densely to laxly scaly on both sides initially, slowly glabrescent above, persistently scaly beneath. **Scales** round, entire, marginal zone narrow; centre thick, little or not impressed. Mid-vein slightly impressed above, very prominent beneath; lateral veins 5–6 per side, irregular, spreading, a little raised above, more distinctly so beneath, reticulation obscure. **Petiole** 2–3 x *c*.0.8mm, thick, scaly.

Bracts to 10 x 6mm, ovate, obtuse, glabrous except for some scales near the top outside, shortly patently hairy inside. Inflorescence a 5–8-flowered umbel. Pedicels 7–12mm, slender, scaly. Calyx oblique, obscurely 5-lobed, *c*.2.5mm in diameter. **Corolla** *c*.35mm, pinkish-red, tubular below, dilated upwards; tube 25–30 x 4 x 7–10mm, very densely scaly outside, glabrous inside, curved; lobes *c.*8mm, spreading, rounded. **Stamens** *c.*25mm; filaments linear, sparsely hairy proximally, glabrous upwards; anthers 2.5mm, broadly oblong. Disc glabrous. **Ovary** *c.*5 x 2mm, densely scaly and laxly patently short-hairy; abruptly contracted distally; style 20mm, glabrous.

Indonesia, New Guinea (W), Mt Jaya (Carstensz), along the Utakwa R., 2520–3050m. *Fl.* Jan.

Not yet recollected and remaining poorly known. Very distinctive in the unusual feature of the leaves being more revolute distally than proximally which is the reverse of the usual situation. Never cultivated.

36. Rhododendron ciliilobum Sleumer

Reinwardtia 1960. 5: 64.
Type: Eyma 4787, 29 March 1939. New Guinea (W), Wissel Lake Region, Enarotali-Kugapa, Egogitoagapa (L, BO).
Derivation: Latin – *cilium* – a hair-like outgrowth; *lobus* – a rounded flattened organ. Referring to the characteristic cilia on the margin of the corolla lobes.

Erect shrub. Twigs rounded, sub-densely covered with reddish sessile or sub-sessile scales, without simple hairs. **Leaves** in a loose pseudowhorl, or spirally arranged several together at the tips of the stems. **Blade** 12–20 x 5–10mm, obovate; apex very shortly retuse, rarely rounded; margin very shortly revolute proximally, otherwise flat; base tapering, laxly scaly above, glabrescent with age and becoming a little rough, sub-densely scaly beneath. **Scales** sub-circular, sessile, marginal zone narrow and thin, sub-entire, centre large, thick and distinctly impressed. Midvein slightly impressed above, obtusely raised beneath, disappearing distally; lateral veins obscure above, weakly or not visible beneath. **Petiole** 2–3mm, rounded, scaly.

Bracts to 6 x 3mm, ovate to obovate-spathulate, apiculate, with silky hairs and scaly in the upper outer part, densely white-fringed along the margins. Bracteoles to 5mm, filiform, hairy at the apex. Inflorescence of solitary or paired flowers, hanging vertically. Pedicels 6–10mm, slender, densely to laxly scaly with shortly stalked scales, and sometimes laxly short-hairy. Calyx *c.*2mm in diameter, minute, wavy and spreading, or with the narrow margin reflexed, scaly and very shortly hairy outside, with very short and obtuse lobes. **Corolla** 20mm, tubular; tube *c.*18 x 3 x 5mm, laxly scaly outside, glabrous inside; lobes *c.*4 x 3–4mm, ovate to sub-circular, erect at first, later spreading, distinctly irregularly-denticulate and ciliate at the apex. **Stamens** as long as the corolla on opening, finally slightly exserted; filaments filiform, glabrous; anthers 1.3mm. Disc glabrous. **Ovary** *c.*2.5 x 1.5mm, sub-ovoid-cylindrical, very densely scaly, gradually tapering distally; style *c.*17mm, thick-filiform, glabrous; stigma club-shaped, irregularly lobed. **Fruit** *c.*13 x 3.5mm, obliquely sub-cylindrical, deeply 5-grooved.

Indonesia, New Guinea (W), Wissel Lakes region; Mt Kobre near Manokwari. In heath vegetation or *Leptospermum* forest from 1755 to 2000m. *Fl.* March, April.

A form without hairs at the calyx and corolla lobes is known from the Balim Valley at 1600m. Not known in cultivation.

SECTION III: *Siphonovireya* (Sleumer) Argent *stat. nov.*

Type: *R. habbemae* Koord.
Subsection *Siphonovireya* Sleumer, Reinwardtia 1960. 5(2): 68.
Section *Hadranthe* Schltr., Bot. Jahr. 1918. 55: 157, *pro parte typo excluso*.

Fruit irregularly peeling an outer layer before splitting. Flower bud scales (sterile bracts or perulae) fringed with scales (multicellular trichomes). Filaments hairy from the base or glabrous. Anthers introrse. Flowers trumpet-shaped, the lobes less than ¼ the length of the corolla. Style–ovary junction tapering. Scales mostly disc-shaped with a large swollen centre and narrow flange, well spaced with the lower epidermis of the leaf clearly visible between them.

The smallest section, with just nine species, and doubtfully homogeneous. Some but not all have resinously smelling foliage, a character not recorded for any species outside the section. Known only from mainland New Guinea with the exception of *R. gideonii* recorded from the island of New Ireland (Papua New Guinea). Species of this section are easily identified if in flower, with the disc-shaped scales very evident on the outside of the elongated trumpet-shaped corolla. Without flowers the scales on the leaves are a little more difficult to see but will separate this group in New Guinea from all but section *Discovireya* which usually have much smaller leaves and flowers, and bracts with a fringe of simple hairs on the flower buds.

Key to the species

1 Flowers red; corolla tube up to 4x as long as the broadest part of it _____ **38. incommodum**
+ Flowers white or flushed pale pink; corolla tube more than 6x as long as the broadest part of it _____ 2

2 Ovary with simple white hairs in addition to the scales _____ 3
+ Ovary scaly only, without simple white hairs _____ 6

3 Corolla more than 30mm, the lobes spreading; the stigma not protruding or protruding up to c.5mm beyond the mouth of the tube _____ 4
+ Corolla less than 25mm, the lobes strongly reflexed; the stigma clearly protruding *c.*10mm or more from the mouth of the tube _____ **40. protandrum**

4 Petiole 2–5mm. Corolla with a few hairs and scales inside; filaments hairy in the lower ⅓ only _____ **44. gideonii**
+ Petiole 6–9mm. Corolla densely hairy inside; filaments hairy for ¾ of their length _____ 5

5 Leaves without a distinct network of veins. Corolla up to 4cm, style with simple hairs only to halfway _____ **39. inundatum**
+ Leaves with a distinct network of veins. Corolla more than 6cm, style with simple hairs or scales to more than halfway _____ **45. searleanum**

6 Corolla tube glabrous inside _____ 7
+ Corolla tube with simple hairs inside _____ 8

7 Corolla more than 35mm; leaves distinctly prominently reticulate underneath when dry _____ **41. habbemae**
+ Corolla less than 35mm; leaves not reticulate underneath when dry _____ **42. cinchoniflorum**

8 Corolla tube with a distinct 'belly', i.e. broadest at about ⅔ from the base and distinctly constricted just below the mouth; lobes (dry) 8–12mm wide _____ **37. agathodaemonis**
+ Corolla tube gradually expanding from the base to the apex or more or less parallel; lobes (dry) 5–6mm wide _____ **43. herzogii**

37. Rhododendron agathodaemonis J.J.Sm.

Fedde Rep. 1913. 12: 209.

Type: von Römer 1245. Mt Agathodaemontop, Hellwig Mts, Papua New Guinea, 2577m (BO).

Derivation: Named after the mountain from which it was first collected which in turn was named after the Greek god Agathodaimon, the good genius, to whom a cup of pure wine was drunk at the end of dinner.

Shrub or small compact tree to 6m. Twigs rounded, tips laxly to densely reddish-brown, scaly. **Leaves** 4–5 together in pseudowhorls, spaced 7–20cm apart. **Blade** 40–75 x 25–48mm, elliptic to obovate-elliptic; apex broadly acuminate to obtuse, sometimes apiculate by a small gland or a little retuse; margin entire, somewhat revolute proximally; base broadly tapering to the petiole or rounded-obtuse, sparsely to sub-densely minutely scaly on both sides especially beneath. **Scales** circular, entire or shallowly undulate at the marginal zone; centre large, impressed. Mid-vein slightly impressed above, distinctly raised though somewhat flattened beneath; lateral veins 6–10 per side, straight, anastomosing with each other and the primary veins near the edge, very slightly impressed above, a little raised or inconspicuous beneath, reticulation obscure, rarely distinct. **Petiole** 9–22 x 1.5–2mm, grooved above, somewhat flattened and sparsely scaly.

Bracts *c.*15 x 10mm, ovate to obovate, scaly outside. Bracteoles *c.*12 x 1mm, filiform below, linear-spathulate distally, sparsely scaly. Inflorescence an open umbel of 6–12 flowers. Pedicels 6–18mm, thick, densely scaly. Calyx very small, circular, irregularly denticulate. **Flowers** trumpet-shaped but broadest just above the middle, white or with the tube tinged with pink, with the scent of carnations. **Corolla** 80–100 x 15–20mm; tube 70–85 x 3 x 4–6.5mm, cylindrical at least below, curved, sparsely to sub-densely scaly outside, laxly hairy and often sparingly scaly, in the lower ½ inside; lobes 10–15 x 8–12mm, rounded to obovate, spreading at a right angle, sparsely scaly or mostly glabrous outside, glabrous inside. **Stamens** slightly or not exserted from the throat; filaments very slender, sub-densely to sparsely covered with spreading hairs in the lower ½, glabrous above; anthers 3–4 x 0.8mm, orange, oblong, the cells apiculate at the base. Disc glabrous. **Ovary** 7–10 x *c.*2mm, elongate-conical, densely scaly; style slender, slightly exserted, densely to laxly scaly almost to the top, without hairs; stigma shortly conical, crenulate. **Fruit** *c.*100 x 5–6mm, red-brown, cylindrical, tapering at both ends, obtusely 5-angled.

Indonesia, New Guinea (W), Mt Agathodaemontop in Hellwig Mts; Mts Hubrecht and Wichmann on the southern and near Lake Habbema on the northern side of the Orange Mts; Mt Amdutakin in the Hindenberg Range. **Papua New Guinea**, Telefomin, West Sepik District and W of Oksapmin. Moss forest, in damp ground or swampy open places, 2500–3450m. *Fl.* Feb., Aug., Nov.

Not known in cultivation. An odd form was collected by Katik & Taho (NGF 37952) from Tukwabit village, Lae, Morobe District. This is much further east than all the other collections and from considerably lower altitude (1800m). It had remarkably short broad flowers *c.*60mm long and with a broad tube up to 10mm wide. The bracts were shortly hairy outside and this specimen would appear to be intermediate between this species and *R. herzogii* or possibly a hybrid. The differences between *R. agathodaemonis* and *R. herzogii* are not clearly established. Sleumer (1973) modified his view of the difference from his (1966) *Flora Malesiana* account in the light of observations on flower length made by Peter Stevens and then made the chief difference fruit size. On the basis of limited herbarium specimens especially of *R. agathodaemonis* there does seem to be a difference in the corolla tube shape which is used in this account, and bract shape may produce further good morphological differences. Further observations are needed to clarify the situation.

38. Rhododendron incommodum Sleumer

Reinwardtia 1960. 5: 70.

Type: Clemens 4733, 23 Dec. 1936. Papua New Guinea, Morobe District, Sattelberg region, Ogerammang, 1830m (A, B, L).

Derivation: Latin – *incommod* – unsuitable or troublesome, probably due to the ambiguous position of this species in the section (see below).

Shrub to 1m. Twigs slender, rounded, scaly when young; internodes 0.5–6cm. **Leaves** 3–4 together in pseudowhorls at the upper nodes. **Blade** 50–75 x 25–40mm, elliptic; apex broadly and obtusely acuminate; margin slightly revolute proximally; base tapering, sub-densely and persistently scaly beneath; laxly scaly initially, finally glabrescent above. **Scales** small, round, entire or nearly so, yellowish, somewhat impressed. Mid-vein a little impressed above; beneath strong and very prominent in the proximal part, gradually less so distally; lateral veins 4–6 per side at an acute angle with the mid-vein, obscurely anastomosing, slightly impressed above, raised beneath, reticulation obscure. **Petiole** 4–20 x *c.*1.5mm, semi-circular, rugose.

Bracteoles filiform, very sparsely scaly. Inflorescence a *c.*8-flowered open umbel. Pedicels *c.*10 x 0.5mm, slender, sub-densely covered with pale yellow scales. Calyx *c.*2.5mm in diameter, sub-obliquely disc-shaped, wavy, very shortly 5-lobed. **Corolla** tubular, 50–55mm, red; tube 35–40 x 3 x 10mm, straight or slightly curved, laxly to sub-densely covered with small yellowish scales outside, very laxly hairy and sparingly scaly inside; lobes 10–15 x 5–7mm, obovate or elliptic-obovate, spreading, very sparsely scaly outside, glabrous inside. **Stamens** well exserted from the mouth; filaments filiform, sparsely hairy especially proximally, glabrous distally or completely glabrous; anthers 2–3 x 1mm, obovate-oblong, base obtuse. Disc glabrous. **Ovary** *c.*5 x 1.7mm, elongate-conical, very densely scaly, gradually tapering distally; style to 50mm, sparsely scaly to the top; stigma shortly obconical, small.

Papua New Guinea, Ogeramnang in the Sattelberg–Saruwaged area, and Purosa in the Okapa area, Eastern Highlands. Locally common, a high epiphyte in mixed rain forest, 1830–2070m. *Fl.* Sept., Dec.

Not known in cultivation. A puzzling species which has not been recollected recently. It is the only really red-flowered species in *Siphonovireya* and has a much broader flower tube in relation to its length than any of the other species (the lobe to tube length is rather more than the ¼ allowed for this section). It would be tempting to regard it as a hybrid between a *Siphonovireya* and a red-flowered species from another section if it was not reported as locally common.

39. Rhododendron inundatum Sleumer
Blumea 1963. 12: 92–93.
Type: Versteegh BW 10454, 24 June 1961. Wiligimaan, 1650m, Balim River Valley, New Guinea (L).
Derivation: Named after the seasonally flooded area in which the original plants collected were growing.

Shrub to 1m. Twigs striate, slightly whitish when dry, variously obtusely compressed, *c.*3–4mm in diameter, sparsely scaly, but the scales quickly falling; internodes 6–12cm. **Leaves** spreading, 4–5 in tight pseudowhorls, pleasantly resinously aromatic when crushed. **Blade** 40–70 x 20–50mm, broadly elliptic to elliptic-obovate; apex obtuse to rounded, sometimes apiculate; margin slightly revolute in dry specimens; base broadly tapering, quickly glabrescent above, persistently sub-densely scaly beneath. **Scales** small, rounded, distant from each other by about their own diameter; marginal zone thin, narrow;

Rhododendron inundatum.

centre small and impressed. Mid-vein narrowly impressed above, as thick as the petiole at the base; moderately raised beneath; lateral veins 6–7 per side, with some additional less conspicuous ones in between, straight, obscurely anastomosing before the margin, slightly impressed above, a little prominent or indistinct below, with no obvious reticulation. **Petiole** 6–9 x 1–1.5mm, densely scaly, grooved above.

Flower buds to 11 x 9mm, pink, ovoid, quite smooth with all the bracts appressed. Bracts to 10 x 6mm; outer bracts ovate-acuminate, often mucronate by a small protracted apex, densely covered with thick scales and very short hairs at the base and the middle outside; inner ones spathulate, thinner, the margin minutely divided with scale stalks. Bracteoles *c.*12mm, linear, sparsely scaly, not hairy. Inflorescence of 4–8 flowers, the flowers with an upward curving tube so that the lobes are displayed vertically. Pedicels 10–12 x *c.*0.5mm, green or pink, densely scaly but without hairs. Calyx *c.*2.5mm in diameter, a little oblique, obscurely lobed. **Corolla** 40 x 25mm, white, trumpet-shaped; tube 32 x 4 x 7mm, densely white-scaly outside and distinctly fluted longitudinally to the base of the lobes, expanded mostly in the distal ½, inside densely patently white-hairy; lobes to 12 x 9mm, spreading perpendicularly, overlapping to *c.*⅓, the lateral margins often at least partially reflexed, inconspicuously scaly outside except for the margins. **Stamens** exserted to *c.*6mm, irregularly clustered in the mouth; filaments white, narrowly linear and densely, patently, white-hairy in the proximal ¾, filiform and glabrous distally; anthers *c.*2mm, cream, oblong, the base obtuse. Disc hardly prominent, glabrous. **Ovary** 4–5 x *c.*1.5mm, sub-cylindrical, densely scaly and sparsely patently white-hairy, tapering gradually distally; style slender, as long as the corolla tube or very slightly protruding when receptive, densely scaly and sometimes laxly patently hairy in the proximal ½, exclusively densely scaly in the distal ½; stigma sub-globose. **Fruit** to 20 x 6mm, pale green when immature. Seeds 3–4.2mm, without tails *c.*2mm, the longest tail 2mm.

Indonesia, New Guinea (W), mountain valleys above Wamena. First recorded from a temporarily flooded grass-plain on peaty soil, at 1650m, where it was reported to be locally common. It was also a common terrestrial constituent of the poor open heath-forest vegetation on white sand in the area around Wamena where it has been reported in flower in June and Oct.–Nov.

This species was first brought into cultivation in 1992 and is now widely available. It has a good erect habit, flowers regularly at least twice a year and has beautifully and powerfully scented, but rather small, pure white flowers. Winter flowers in Britain have been observed to be pollen sterile. A natural hybrid between this species and a red-flowered *Rhododendron* is in cultivation with handsome deep pink flowers and considerably more vigour than the parent but it has only feebly scented flowers. Another wild collected hybrid (probably with *R. konori*) is in cultivation. It has intermediate-sized flowers between the putative parents and is very strongly scented.

40. Rhododendron protandrum Sleumer

Blumea 1961. 11 : 114.
Type: Kalkman 4284, 15 June 1959. Orion Mts, Sibil River Valley, 1260m (L).
Derivation: Greek – *pro* – in front of; *andro* – male. An allusion to the distinctively exserted anthers.

Spreading shrub to 2.5m. Twigs *c.*2mm in diameter, slender, the youngest parts densely scaly; internodes 2–8cm. **Leaves** 4–5 together in pseudowhorls. **Blade** 30–50 x 16–30mm, elliptic; apex broadly sub-acuminate, or sometimes obtusely apiculate; margin entire, narrowly revolute; base broadly tapering, sub-densely scaly initially, glabrescent above with age, persistently scaly beneath. **Scales** small, round, marginal zone narrow; centre thick, yellowish, slightly impressed. Mid-vein narrowly impressed above, as thick as the petiole and very prominent in the proximal part beneath; lateral veins 4–6 per side, spreading, straight, faintly impressed above, very slightly raised beneath, or commonly obscure on both sides, without visible reticulation. **Petiole** 4–6 x *c.*1mm, grooved above.

Bracts to 10 x 8mm, membranous, glabrous outside, fringed with scales towards the apices; outer ones ovate, apiculate or obtuse; inner ones obovate-elliptic to elliptic. Bracteoles to 8 x 1mm, linear sub-spathulate, glabrous. Inflorescence of 5–10 flowers. Pedicels 5–10mm, slender, sub-densely scaly. Calyx *c.*2.5mm in diameter, obliquely disc-shaped, shortly and irregularly 5-lobed. **Corolla** trumpet-shaped, pure white or greenish white, or pale pink at the tube and white at the lobes; tube *c.*25 x 2.5–3 x 2–2.5mm, straight or slightly curved, parallel sided except slightly expanded at the extreme base, densely scaly outside; inside with short retrorse hairs in the proximal ⅓, glabrous distally; lobes 5–6 x *c.*3mm, subspathulate, becoming reflexed in older flowers. **Stamens** exserted to *c.*15mm from the corolla tube when the flowers are young and the style is still included in the corolla tube, erect, and recurved with the upper part of the filaments as the flowers age, when the style becomes greatly exserted; filaments almost filiform, white, laxly or more densely hairy in the proximal ¼; anthers 1.8 x 0.5mm, oblong, the base obtuse. Disc slightly prominent, sparsely erect-hairy on the upper margin only. **Ovary** *c.*5 x 1.5mm, cylindrical, sub-densely sub-appressed, short-hairy and scaly, tapering distally; style slender, scaly almost to the top and sparsely hairy in the proximal 10mm; stigma sub-globose, very shortly 5-lobed. **Fruit** (immature) 25–30 x 2.5–3mm, narrowly fusiform, reddish, sparsely scaly and hairy, deeply 5-furrowed lengthwise.

Indonesia, New Guinea (W), Sibil River Valley. In shrubberies on poor, impervious white clay, 1260m, common. *Fl.* June, *fr.* Aug.

Not known in cultivation.

41. Rhododendron habbemae Koord.
Nova Guinea 1912. 8(4): 877.
Type: von Römer 1208. Hellwig Mts, 2000–2600m (BO, L, lectotype).
Derivation: Named either after the locality from which it was originally collected, Lake Habbema, or after D. Habbema, after whom the lake was named. D. Habbema commanded the military detachment covering the 2nd Lorentz expedition to Dutch Southern New Guinea and helped collect plants on the ascent of Mt Wilhelmina (G. Trichora).

Synonym: *R. bodenii* Wernham, Trans. Linn. Soc. London, II, Bot. 1916. 9: 94.

Shrub. Twigs smooth, the tips laxly scaly; internodes 4–9cm. **Leaves** 3–5 together in tight pseudowhorls. **Blade** 35–60 x 15–30mm, obovate or obovate-elliptic; apex obtuse to rounded, often apiculate by a small protruding gland; margin entire, recurved when dry; base broadly tapering to truncate-rounded or sub-cordate, shining and brownish-green above, dull and paler beneath. **Scales** lax to sub-dense, small, rounded, and slightly immersed on both sides in fully mature leaves. Mid-vein strongly impressed above, distinctly raised beneath; lateral veins 6–10 per side, straight, inarching near the margin, very slightly impressed above, prominent beneath, reticulation inconspicuous or very slightly impressed above, dense and clearly raised beneath. **Petiole** 4–7 x *c.*1.5mm, grooved above, densely scaly.

Bracts to 15mm, ovate to obovate, outer ones acuminate, inner ones obtuse, scaly outside, glabrous inside. Bracteoles 10–15mm, filiform to linear-spathulate, glabrous. Inflorescence a 5–8-flowered umbel. Pedicels 6–15mm, slender, densely scaly. Calyx small, shortly and irregularly 5-toothed. **Corolla** trumpet-shaped, white; tube 33–55 x 5–6 x 6–7mm, narrowly-cylindrical, straight

or slightly curved, pouched at the base, densely covered with small rounded scales outside, glabrous inside; lobes 10–14 x 6–10mm, obovate, obtuse, scaly outside. **Stamens** unequal; filaments 35–40mm, linear, laxly to very laxly hairy; anthers 3 x 1mm, oblong. Disc glabrous or almost so. **Ovary** 6–7 x 1.5mm, sub-cylindrical, 5-ribbed, very densely scaly; style 27–35mm, slender, becoming exserted from the mouth, with spreading hairs and scales proximally, then exclusively hairy, the distal part glabrous; stigma obconical.

Indonesia, New Guinea (W), Main Range from Mt Carstensz to the Hellwig Mts and Mt Goliath. Both in forest on wet mossy ground and on humus- and moss-covered exposed rocks, 2000–3450m. *Fl.* Jan.–Dec.

Not known in cultivation.

42. Rhododendron cinchoniflorum Sleumer
Reinwardtia 1960. 5: 68.
Type: Eyma 5264, 11–17 Oct. 1939. Papua, Wissel Lake Region, Look-out Perai, 2400m (BO, L).
Derivation: Latin – *Cinchona* – a South American plant in the Rubiaceae from which was derived the antimalarial 'quinine'; *florum* – pertaining to the flower. The flowers are reminiscent of those of the quinine plant.

Erect shrub. Twigs slender, rounded, tips scaly; internodes 2–11cm. **Leaves** 4–6 together in tight pseudowhorls, not aromatic. **Blade** 30–60 x 30–40mm, ovate-elliptic or mostly elliptic; apex shortly obtusely acuminate, sometimes apiculate with a small gland; margin entire, slightly revolute; base sub-truncate, rounded or cordate, sub-densely scaly above but quickly glabrescent, densely and persistently scaly beneath. **Scales** nearly round, wavy at the margin, very distinctly impressed, the scale pits becoming blackish with age. Mid-vein impressed above, strongly prominent beneath; lateral veins 3–4 per side, very slightly impressed above in fully mature leaves, somewhat prominent in younger ones, mostly not easily visible, especially beneath, reticulation obscure. **Petiole** 1.5–3 x 1–1.5mm, scaly, grooved above.

Bracts to 10 x 7mm; outer bracts ovate, acute; inner ones obovate, scaly dorsally along the middle line. Bracteoles *c.*6 x 1mm, linear. Pedicels 5–8mm, slender, densely reddish-brown scaly. Calyx *c.*2.5mm in diameter, disc-like, scaly outside, glabrous inside, the margin undulate and shortly 5-lobed, spreading or reflexed at flowering. **Corolla** 32 x 14mm, (dry), white, trumpet-shaped; tube 25–30 x 2.5–3 x 2.5–3mm, nearly straight, 5-pouched at the base, very densely scaly outside, glabrous inside; lobes 10–12 x

Rhododendron herzogii.

8–9mm, spreading horizontally, obovate-elliptic, sparsely scaly outside, glabrous inside. **Stamens** unequal, not or slightly exserted from the throat; filaments filiform, laxly hairy; anthers 2–2.5mm, broadly oblong. Disc low, densely white-hairy. **Ovary** *c.*4 x 2mm, cylindrical-conical, densely and exclusively scaly, abruptly narrowed to the style, slightly 5-ribbed; style *c.*23mm, scaly and shortly patently hairy in the proximal ⅓, gradually becoming glabrous distally; stigma shortly obconical, minutely crenulate.

Indonesia, New Guinea (W), Wissel Lakes, 2400m, and on the southern side of Mt Jaya (Carstensz). In open montane shrubberies especially in disturbed areas at roadsides. *Fl.* Oct.–Nov.

Introduced into cultivation in 2001 but not yet established. The leaves of this species are not aromatic as they are in *R. herzogii*. A single hybrid has been recorded, probably with *R. schlechteri* that was growing with this species in the Mt Jaya region. Distinguished from the parent species by the intermediate flower size.

43. Rhododendron herzogii Warb.

Bot. Jahr. 1892. 16: 25.
Type: Hellwig 306, 14 Oct. 1888. Finnisterre Mts, New Guinea (B†, BO, K, L, fragment).

Derivation: Named after Th. Herzog, a missionary in the Finisterre Mountains in New Guinea.

Erect shrub to 2m. Twigs rounded, sub-densely scaly when young, glabrescent and whitish later; internodes 3–13cm. **Leaves** 4–6 together in tight pseudowhorls; aromatic with a pleasantly resinous smell when crushed. **Blade** 40–60 x 20–40mm, elliptic or obovate-elliptic; apex broadly obtusely acuminate, sometimes rounded; margin slightly revolute towards the base; base broadly tapering to almost rounded, sub-densely scaly when young, though early glabrescent above persistently impressed-scaly beneath. **Scales** rounded, pale yellow, their marginal zones narrow and shallowly irregularly crenate. Mid-vein slightly grooved above, robust and prominent beneath; lateral veins 6–10 (rarely up to 12) per side, slightly curved, parallel to each other, obscurely anastomosing, faintly impressed above, raised beneath, reticulation obscure. **Petiole** 4–10 x 1.5–2mm, semi-circular, grooved above, scaly, pink or green.

Flower buds *c.*20 x 10mm, obovoid, pale green when fresh. Bracts to 15 x 10mm, ovate, thin, densely scaly outside except for a glabrous marginal area, with scales along the edges and some sparse short hairs on the outer side, the scales transparent-silvery in fresh specimens. Bracteoles to 30mm, narrowly linear. Inflorescence a 5–10-flowered umbel of stiffly semi-erect flowers. Pedicels 4–8 x *c*.1.5mm, thick, densely scaly. Calyx very small, oblique, disc-shaped, sub-entire. **Corolla** 40–90mm, pure white, or slightly pinkish at the tube externally, fragrant, semi-erect, trumpet-shaped; tube 35–85 x 3–4 x 5–6mm, straight or slightly curved, densely scaly outside, densely hairy and sparingly or not scaly in the proximal part inside; lobes 8–9 x 5–6mm, spreading to somewhat reflexed, circular to elliptic-obovate, scaly outside, glabrous inside. **Stamens** exserted in a tight cluster beyond the recurved corolla lobes at first, later deflexed to lie against the lower lobes; filaments white, very slender, densely and patently hairy in the proximal ⅔ only; anthers orange, oblong. Disc very sparsely hairy or glabrous. **Ovary** 6–7 x 1.5mm, narrowly cylindrical, very densely scaly, abruptly tapering distally; style exserted from the mouth, densely scaly below, less so or glabrous distally; stigma green, shortly obconical. **Fruit** 30–50 x 4–5mm, reddish, cylindrical, straight, scaly.

Indonesia and **Papua New Guinea**. New Guinea, the Main Range from the Wissel Lakes to the Owen Stanley Range, Mt Garatun in the Milne Bay District, the Cromwell Mts and on Mt Saruwaged. Terrestrial or epiphytic, on cliff faces, landslides, steep eroded banks or slopes, also in montane forest or heath-like scrub on infertile sandy or clayey soil, occasionally found in fern re-growth, as a coloniser in sluiced areas or in gullies of old garden land, 1530–2500m. Recorded flowering and fruiting throughout the year.

Introduced repeatedly into cultivation from Papua New Guinea in the early 1960s and also subsequently. A popular relatively free-flowering species with resinously aromatic foliage and beautifully scented white, or pink-flushed, flowers freely produced. For comments on the difference between this species and *R. agathodaemonis* see under that species. Several hybrids have been produced. 'Starburst' is a hybrid with *R. culminicola* which grows and flowers spectacularly in the Pukeiti garden in New Zealand.

44. Rhododendron gideonii Argent
Folia Malaysiana 2003. 4(2): 104.
Type: Gideon & Obedi LAE 77179, 1 Nov. 1984. Papua New Guinea, New Ireland, Northern Hans Meyer Range, 70km SE of Namatanai (LAE, L).
Derivation: Named in honour of Osia Gideon, botanist with the Lae herbarium and collector of this species.

Shrub to 1.5m. Twigs rounded, sub-densely scaly when young, glabrescent and whitish later; internodes

5–9cm. **Leaves** 2–4 together in tight pseudowhorls. **Blade** 35–60 x 14–25mm, elliptic or very slightly obovate-elliptic; apex broadly acute to obtuse; margin narrowly revolute; base broadly to narrowly tapering; sub-densely scaly when young, though quickly glabrescent above, persistently impressed-scaly beneath. **Scales** rounded, brown, dome-shaped with a narrow marginal zone, impressed and surrounded by transparent depressions. Mid-vein slightly grooved above, strong and prominent beneath; lateral veins 1–4 per side, obscure, slightly curved, parallel to each other, smooth, reticulation obscure. **Petiole** 2–5 x 1–3mm, semi-circular in section, grooved above, scaly.

Bracts broadly ovate, fringed with scales and with a few scales on the outer surface near the tip, especially along the median line, otherwise glabrous. Bracteoles to 10mm, narrowly linear. Inflorescence a 5–8-flowered umbel. Pedicels to 7 x 0.5mm, slender, sparsely scaly. Calyx very small, disc-shaped, sub-entire, moderately scaly. **Corolla** 30–35 x 11mm, trumpet-shaped, white; tube 28 x 3.5 x 4mm, straight or very slightly curved, almost parallel sided, densely scaly outside, hairy and with a few scales inside near the base; lobes 5 x 4mm, spreading, circular to elliptic, with a few scales outside, glabrous inside. **Stamens** exserted to *c*.5mm; filaments slender, sparsely and patently hairy in the proximal ⅓ only, glabrous distally; anthers *c*.1.5 x 0.7mm, oblong. Disc hairy on the upper side, otherwise glabrous. **Ovary** 2.8 x 1.2mm, narrowly cylindrical, moderately hairy with semi-appressed white hairs and very densely scaly, abruptly tapering distally; style exserted from the mouth, laxly hairy and with scattered scales to within 2mm of the stigma, this distal part glabrous; stigma shortly-obconical.

Papua New Guinea, Province of New Ireland, subprovince Namatanai, Northern Hans Meyer Range, 70km SE of Namatanai (the type) and also from subprovince Konos, E of Letet Farm. Epiphytic shrub growing in montane rain forest on ridge tops dominated by *Dacrycarpus*, *Decussocarpus* (*Retrophyllum*) and *Serianthes* and in steep limestone country dominated by *Weinmannia*. Recorded between 850 and 1020m altitude.

Not yet introduced into cultivation and at present known only from two herbarium collections.

This species is in some respects like *R. protandrum* Sleumer and would be a surprising distributional pattern if it were this species as *R. protandrum* at present is known only from the Sibil River Valley in West New Guinea a great distance away. It does in fact differ from *R. protandrum* in several respects. The stamens and stigma are not as dramatically exserted from the mouth of the flower (up to *c*.5mm whereas in *R. protandrum* they are exserted to 10mm or more). The style is both scaly and hairy almost to the stigma, whereas in *R. protandrum* the style is hairy only in the basal 10mm, although scaly almost to the summit. Other small differences are that there are scales on the bracts and bracteoles and there are no backwardly pointing hairs on the inside of the corolla tube in this species.

It would make a more likely distribution pattern if it were a form of *R. herzogii* which is widespread on the mainland of New Guinea, but the ovary and style of that species totally lack simple hairs, the flowers are much larger and the anthers longer. Shrinkage of the corollas has undoubtedly taken place in the herbarium specimens studied so that the real dimensions of the flower might be larger, but the anthers usually remain constant and the indumentum certainly does not change with poor pressing. Overall the impression of this species is of a smaller and more delicate plant than *R. herzogii*.

45. Rhododendron searleanum Sleumer

Blumea 1973. 21(2): 367.

Type: Searle 39, 10 June 1972. New Guinea, Eastern Highlands District, Gumine subdistrict, Yani area, Dirima–Gomgali road, 2135m (LAE, L).

Derivation: Named after the collector, L.K. Searle, who worked in New Guinea for many years and who had a passionate interest in vireyas, collecting and growing many specimens.

Synonym: *R. reevei* Argent, Folia Malaysiana 2003. 4(2): 106.

Shrub to 4m. Twigs 6–8mm in diameter, densely scaly; internodes 5–12cm. **Leaves** 4–6 together in tight pseudowhorls. **Blade** 60–110 x 40–75mm, broadly elliptic or elliptic; apex obtuse to rounded; margin very narrowly cartilaginous, flat or minutely revolute; base broadly tapering to rounded occasionally sub-cordate; at first densely scaly above with fragile scales standing up on stalks, slightly less densely scaly below. **Scales** sub-circular, very variable in size, deeply impressed with large centres and narrow lobed margins. Mid-vein weakly raised above in the proximal ¼–⅓ but deeply grooved here also; broadly raised in the proximal ½–⅔ below; lateral veins 4–7 per side, spreading at *c*.45°, looping and joining before the margin, reticulation somewhat obscure above, distinct below. **Petiole** 7–20 x 3–4mm, weakly grooved in the distal part only, densely brown-scaly.

Rhododendron searleanum.

Bracts to 50 x 30mm, sub-spathulate, obovate, densely scaly and shortly appressed hairy outside, inside shortly appressed hairy. Bracteoles to 40 x 5mm, linear proximally, spathulate distally, hairy. Inflorescence of 11–16 flowers in an open, flat, umbel; the flowers held horizontally. Pedicels 8–10 x 2–2.5mm, densely scaly and sparsely hairy distally. **Corolla** 80–125 × 40–55mm, trumpet-shaped, pink, scented; tube 65–75 × 4–5 x 10–14mm, straight, very sparsely scaly outside, densely retrorse-hairy inside; lobes *c*.25 × 25mm, sub-circular, sometimes slightly retuse, spreading and overlapping to *c*.½. **Stamens** exserted to 10mm, clustered in a group in the mouth; filaments densely hairy at the base, becoming less so and glabrous for the distal ⅓; anthers 3.5–4.5 × *c*.1.5mm. Disc prominent, densely hairy. **Ovary** 10–13 × 3–4mm, densely covered in appressed hairs which cover scales, tapering gradually distally; style densely hairy and scaly proximally, becoming less hairy distally, the central part entirely scaly, glabrous for the ultimate 15mm; stigma 4–5mm in diameter, disc-shaped. **Fruit** 55–80 x 7–9mm.

Papua New Guinea, Simbu (Chimbu) District, Gumine subdistrict, towards the lower slopes of Mt Digine, 2134m. Enga Province, on the Laiagam–Porgera road, Mt Maip (Tipinini side), 2100–2600m. *Fl.* June, Sept.

Cultivated since 1974 from type material collected by Lou Searle. It grows well and has magnificent powerfully scented flowers. It is tempting to think of it as a hybrid but seeds appear to come true with little variation. Sleumer (1973) placed this species in 'Solenovireya', commenting that 'the scales are almost entire in the dry specimens'. In fact the scales are entire with large centres in the living state, especially so on the pedicels and corollas, as is quite typical of 'Siphonovireya' and hence this is where it is placed in the present treatment.

SECTION IV: *Phaeovireya* (Sleumer) Argent *stat. nov.*

Type: *R. beyerinckianum* Koord.
Subsection *Phaeovireya* Sleumer, Bot. Jahr. 1949. 74: 539.
Section *Schistanthe* Schltr., Bot. Jahr. 1918. 55: 140, *pro parte typo excluso.*
Section *Zygomorphanthe* Schltr., Bot. Jahr. 1918. 55: 145, *pro parte typo excluso.*
Section *Hadranthe* Schltr., Bot. Jahr. 1918. 55: 157, *pro parte typo excluso.*

Fruit irregularly peeling an outer layer before splitting. Flower bud scales (sterile bracts or perulae) fringed with scales (multicellular trichomes). Filaments hairy from the base or glabrous. Anthers introrse. Flower shape various. Style–ovary junction usually tapering. Scales dendroid, each from the top of an epidermal tubercle on the lower epidermis of the leaf.

This section is most diverse in New Guinea where all but two species are endemic. The dendroid scales on epidermal tubercles are not completely unknown outside this section (cf. *R. edanoi* from Borneo and the Philippines and some forms of *R. jasminiflorum*), but they are never so well developed as in true phaeovireyas and the section is reasonably coherent. The large-flowered species form a distinctive, presumably pollinator, group that shows similarities to *R. leucogigas* and *R. schlechteri* outside the section.

Key to species from Sulawesi

1	Flowers yellow, leaves less than 10mm wide; petiole up to 2mm, hardly longer than wide _____ **46. eymae**
+	Flowers red, leaves more than 12mm wide; petiole *c.*5mm, distinctly longer than wide _____ **47. psilanthum**

Key to species from New Guinea

1	Ovary densely stellate-scaly, without any simple hairs except possibly near the apex at the junction with the style _____	2
+	Ovary densely covered all over with simple hairs, with or without scales _____	21
2	Style up to 2mm long _____	3
+	Style more than 5mm long _____	5
3	Largest leaves more than 20mm _____	**89. tintinnabellum**
+	Largest leaves less than 16mm _____	4
4	Style hardly longer than wide, anthers extrorse _____	**57. extrorsum**
+	Style distinctly longer than wide, anthers introrse _____	**76. revolutum**
5	Style thick, more than 2mm in diameter, ovary more than 4mm in diameter _____	6
+	Style slender, up to 2mm in diameter, ovary less than 2.5mm in diameter _____	7
6	Corolla deep red, up to 8cm long, the style up to 4cm _____	**60. hellwigii**
+	Corolla white, cream or pale pink, more than 10cm long, the style more than 5cm _____	**83. superbum**
7	Leaves linear or narrowly elliptic, up to 15mm wide _____	8
+	Leaves various, the largest leaves more than 25mm wide _____	14
8	Corolla glabrous outside, flowers lilac in colour _____	**73. prainianum**
+	Corolla hairy and/or scaly outside, flowers red, pink or white _____	9
9	Corolla scaly and hairy outside _____	**81. stelligerum**
+	Corolla scaly or hairy outside _____	10
10	Corolla with white hairs outside but no scales _____	**54. delicatulum**
+	Corolla scaly but with no simple white hairs outside _____	11
11	Pedicels up to 5mm _____	**68. neriifolium**
+	Pedicels more than 5mm _____	12

12 Bracts ovate, the apices blunt and appressed without subulate points. Leaves strictly linear, the margins very strongly revolute – to the mid-vein when dry _____ **61. hooglandii**

+ Bracts ovate-subulate, the points spreading. Some leaves narrowly elliptic or if linear the margins only weakly revolute _____ 13

13 Leaves up to 6mm wide, densely brown scaly above, flowers up to 12mm wide _____ **53. caliginis**

+ Leaves more than 6mm wide, green above even when young, flowers more than 20mm wide _____ **75. rarum**

14 Style with simple hairs at least at the base, totally without scales _____ 15

+ Style without hairs, with or without scales _____ 18

15 Leaves up to 5mm wide _____ **63. kerowagiense**

+ Leaves more than 5mm wide _____ 16

16 Filaments glabrous, corolla completely glabrous _____ **67. neobritannicum**

+ Filaments hairy at least in the basal ⅓, corolla with scales outside or hairs inside _____ 17

17 Petiole up to 3mm, corolla glabrous outside, pedicels to 12mm _____ **51. bryophyllum**

+ Petiole more than 4mm, corolla scaly outside, pedicels more than 14mm _____ **70. phaeochitum**

18 Leaves spirally arranged, filaments densely hairy to more than halfway _____ **69. opulentum**

+ Leaves in well-marked pseudowhorls, filaments glabrous or with some scattered hairs at the base _____ 19

19 Style scaly at the base only _____ **56. dielsianum**

+ Style scaly almost to the top _____ 20

20 Petiole more than 5mm, leaves strongly concave _____ **50. beyerinckianum**

+ Petiole less than 5mm, leaves flat or only weakly concave _____ **65. leptanthum**

21 Petiole less than 5mm _____ 22

+ Petiole more than 6mm _____ 33

22 Filaments completely glabrous _____ 23

+ Filaments hairy at least in the basal ⅓ _____ 24

23 Leaves up to 5mm wide _____ **63. kerowagiense**

+ Leaves more than 12mm wide _____ **82. stolleanum**

24 Ovary scaly with only scattered hairs _____ 25

+ Ovary densely hairy, the hairs covering the scales _____ 26

25 Pedicels up to 15mm, anthers 2mm, ovary 4mm _____ **48. asperrimum**

+ Pedicels more than 15mm, anthers 3mm, ovary 7mm _____ **86. tuberculiferum**

26 Petiole as broad as long _____ 27

+ Petiole distinctly longer than broad _____ 29

27 Disc glabrous, anthers 2–3mm _____ **80. spondyllophyllum**

+ Disc hairy on the upper margin, anthers 3–4mm _____ 28

28 Filaments hairy at the base only (1–2mm) _____ **87. evelyneae**

+ Filaments sparsely hairy to ½–⅔ (10–12mm) _____ **49. asperum**

29 Style completely glabrous, corolla glabrous outside _____ **82. stolleanum**

+ Style with hairs and/or scales at the base, corolla hairy or scaly outside _____ 30

30 Corolla hairy outside _____ **66. melantherum**

+ Corolla scaly outside _____ 31

31 Leaves broadly elliptic, largest more than 30mm wide _____ **77. rhodochroum**

+ Leaves narrowly elliptic to elliptic, largest up to 25mm wide _____ 32

32   Erect shrub, twigs to 4mm diameter, style hairy near the base only ————— **56. dielsianum** var. **stylotrichum**

+   Prostrate to hanging shrub, twigs *c.*2mm diameter, style hairy almost to the stigma ————— **75. rarum**

33   Petiole at least some more than 25mm ————————————————— 34

+   Petiole less than 25mm, or corolla hairy inside ————————————— 35

34   Leaves puckered, inflorescence of 10–12 flowers ————————— **52. bullifolium**

+   Leaves smooth, inflorescence of up to 5 flowers ————————— **58. gardenia**

35   Corolla glabrous outside ———————————————————— 36

+   Corolla scaly outside ————————————————————— 41

36   Style scaly only in the proximal ½ (without hairs) ——————— **69. opulentum**

+   Style hairy and/or scaly in the proximal ½ ——————————— 37

37   Style hairy and scaly in the proximal ½ ————————————— 38

+   Style hairy only in the proximal ½ ——————————————— 40

38   Corolla tube more than 80mm, lobes 6 or 7 ————————————— **64. konori**

+   Corolla tube less than 45mm, lobes 5 —————————————— 39

39   Corolla tube up to 8mm wide at the mouth, flowers white or pink ————— **74. rappardii**

+   Corolla tube more than 10mm wide at the mouth, flowers red ————— **78. rubellum**

40   Corolla tube up to 40mm, lateral veins more than 8 per side, petiole 10–15mm ————— **55. dianthosmum**

+   Corolla tube more than 60mm, lateral veins 6–7 per side, petiole 7–12mm ————— **62. hyacinthosmum**

41   Corolla lobes 6 or 7, anthers more than 6mm ————————————— 42

+   Corolla lobes 5, anthers less than 6mm ————————————— 43

42   Style hairy and scaly for at least ½ the length ————————————— **64. konori**

+   Style with scales at the base only, glabrous for *c.*¾ of the length ————— **84. thaumasianthum**

43   Style scaly at the base, without hairs ————————————————— 44

+   Style hairy and scaly, at least at the base ————————————— 45

44   Pedicels hairy and scaly, corolla glabrous outside ————————— **69. opulentum**

+   Pedicels scaly only, corolla sparsely scaly outside ————————— **88. kawir**

45   Pedicels hairy and scaly, at least just below the calyx ————————— 46

+   Pedicels scaly only ————————————————————— 47

46   Corolla tube up to 8mm wide at the mouth, flowers white or pink ————— **74. rappardii**

+   Corolla tube more than 10mm wide at the mouth, flowers red ————— **78. rubellum**

47   Corolla tube less than 25mm ————————————————— 48

+   Corolla tube more than 30mm ————————————————— 49

48   Leaf base tapering, corolla tube 15–20mm, bracts with scales outside ————— **71. phaeochristum**

+   Leaf base broadly tapering or rounded, corolla tube 20–25mm, bracts glabrous except for the fringe of scales on the margins ——————————————————— **85. truncicola**

49   Leaves puckered with lateral veins strongly impressed above and raised beneath, disc hairy on the upper margin ——————————————————— **79. solitarium**

+   Leaves smooth, lateral veins only slightly impressed above and raised beneath, disc glabrous ————— 50

50   Corolla 30–55mm, anthers 3.5–4mm ————————————— **59. haematophthalmum**

+   Corolla 55–60mm, anthers 5–5.5mm ————————————— **72. phaeops**

46. Rhododendron eymae Sleumer
Reinwardtia 1960. 5: 74.
Type: Eyma 684, 17 June 1937. Indonesia, Celebes, Central, Enrekang, Rante Mario (L, A, BO, K, PNH, SING, U).
Derivation: Named after Pierre Joseph Eyma, 1903–1945, who first collected this species. Eyma was a Dutch botanist who made considerable collections in Indonesia, some of which were lost due to the unrest as a result of war.

Dwarf shrub to 25cm. Twigs stiffly erect, rounded, *c*.2mm in diameter, the tips densely covered with pale brown scurfy scales, otherwise rough and dark coloured. **Leaves** spirally arranged, not in proper pseudowhorls, although some areas of stem are almost bare of normal-sized leaves. **Blade** 8–13 x 4–7mm, ovate, elliptic or broadly elliptic; apex shortly acuminate, with acute, often mucronate points; margin entire, strongly revolute; base sub-truncate, rounded; young leaves stellate scaly on both sides, mature ones glabrescent above, persistently scaly beneath. **Scales** scurfy, the margin deeply stellately divided, sub-sessile, the minute centre deepened, each scale on top of a persistent epidermal tubercle. Mid-vein obscure or faintly impressed above, slightly prominent beneath, lateral veins not visible, rigid and very thick and leathery, silvery grey above, brown beneath. **Petiole** 1–2 x 1–2mm, very shallowly grooved, often broader than long, densely scaly.

Flower buds broadly ovoid, 8–10 x *c*.7mm, the points appressed or slightly spreading. Bracts ovate-acuminate, densely scaly outside and on the margins, glabrous inside, to 10 x 6mm. Bracteoles filiform, glabrous, to 8mm. Inflorescence of paired or solitary flowers, rarely up to 4 together, horizontal to hanging. Pedicels 7–12mm x *c*.1mm, densely brown scurfy-scaly. Calyx small, densely scaly, irregularly 5-toothed, the teeth broadly triangular, sub-acute, 1mm or one or the other of them elongate to 3mm. **Corolla** 12–16 x 12–15mm, pale yellow, sometimes with a violet flush and with conspicuous brown scales outside; tube 8–10 x 4–5 x 7–8mm, sub-cylindrical or slightly expanded upwards, very densely brown stellate-scaly outside, glabrous inside; lobes 4–5mm in diameter, sub-erect or a little spreading, sub-spathulate to circular, densely scaly outside except for the margin, glabrous inside. **Stamens** slightly unequal, clustered round the mouth of the flower; filaments filiform, slightly dilated above the base, glabrous; anthers *c*.1.5 x 1mm, broadly oblong. Disc low, glabrous. **Ovary** 3–4 x *c*.2.5mm, ovoid-conical, very densely stellate-scaly, abruptly contracted distally; style 1.6–2mm, thick-columnar, densely scaly at the base but abruptly becoming completely glabrous; stigma shortly 5-lobed. **Fruit** 8–10 x 5–6mm, ovoid, shortly contracted distally,

Rhododendron eymae.

densely brown or greyish-brown scaly, with a persistent style; valves not twisted, placentae remaining coherent with the central column. Seeds 1–1.3mm, without tails *c*.1mm, the longest tail *c*.0.2mm.

Indonesia, SW Central Sulawesi, Latimodjong Range, Mt Rantemario, 3100–3300m. Common in the open summit area. *Fl. fr.* March–June.

A very pretty species which was introduced into cultivation in Edinburgh in 2000 and into Australia in 2001. It does not thrive and will doubtfully persist, it being very difficult to reproduce the high light levels but cool temperatures of its exposed habitat in the wild.

47. Rhododendron psilanthum Sleumer
Reinwardtia 1960. 5: 81.
Type: Eyma 516, 15 June 1937. Indonesia, Sulawesi, Enrekang, Pintealón, spur of Mt Pokapindjang, ridge (BO).
Derivation: Greek – *psilos* – bare; *anthos* – flower. Presumably alluding to the completely glabrous corolla.

Shrub. Twigs slender, rounded, *c*.2mm in diameter, the tips densely brown-stellate-scaly when young, quickly becoming glabrescent and smooth; internodes *c*.6.5cm.

Leaves sub-opposite or 3 together in a pseudowhorl. **Blade** 35–45 x 13–22mm, elliptic; apex shortly sub-acutely acuminate and apiculate; margin slightly revolute; base tapering into the petiole; stellately scaly on both sides initially. **Scales** minute, dendroid, each on top of minute epidermal tubercle, quickly glabrescent above, less so beneath, but finally glabrescent and rough on both sides. Mid-vein a little impressed above and raised beneath, the lateral veins inconspicuous. **Petiole** 5–6 x c.1mm, densely scaly.

Inflorescence a 3-flowered umbel. Pedicels 12–15 x c.0.5mm, slender, very densely stellately scaly. Calyx c.2mm in diameter, minute, oblique, in the form of a short cup, sub-entire. **Corolla** 35–38mm, tubular below, dilated upwards, slightly zygomorphic, red; tube c.25 x 4–5 x c.8mm, pouched at the base, completely glabrous on both sides; lobes 10–12 x 8–10mm, spreading, broadly obovate-spathulate. **Stamens** c.30mm, slightly unequal; filaments narrowly linear, glabrous; anthers c.2.2 x 1mm, obovate-oblong, very shortly appendaged at the base. Disc prominent, glabrous. **Ovary** c.4 x 2mm, sub-ovoid-cylindrical, very densely stellately scaly, and abruptly tapering distally; style 25mm, stellately scaly at the base, otherwise entirely glabrous; stigma sub-globose.

Indonesia, SW Central Sulawesi, Latimodjong Range, Pintealón, spur of Mt Pokapindjang, on the ridge at 2400–2600m. *Fl.* June.

Not yet recollected since the original find. Never cultivated.

48. Rhododendron asperrimum Sleumer
Blumea 1963. 12: 97.
Type: Koster 13744, March 1962. New Guinea, Wandamen Peninsula, Wondiwoi Mts, 1800m (A, CANB, K, L).
Derivation: Latin – *asper* – rough or uneven; *erimum* – the superlative ending, very rough. Alluding to the large persistent epidermal tubercles on the leaves.

Epiphytic, spreading shrub. Twigs c.2mm in diameter, slender, initially covered with reddish, dendroid scales; internodes 3–7cm. **Leaves** 3–4 together in pseudowhorls at the upper 2–3 nodes, sub-sessile. **Blade** 25–45 x 15–30mm, ovate; apex very broadly tapering to rounded; margin revolute distally; base a little cordate; sub-densely scaly above, quickly glabrescent but rough with the persistent epidermal scale bases, densely scaly and more persistently scaly beneath, eventually glabrescent here also but remaining rough with epidermal tubercles. **Scales** reddish-brown, stellate-dendroid, the tubercles

often very pale in colour after the scales have fallen. Mid-vein impressed above, prominent beneath; lateral veins inconspicuous on both sides, without reticulation. **Petiole** 2 x 1.5mm, scaly.

Bracts to 15 x 7mm, thin, ovate to spathulate, sparsely scaly at first becoming glabrous. Bracteoles c.10mm, linear to filiform, glabrous. Inflorescence 3–6-flowered. Pedicels 11–15mm, slender, very densely stellate-scaly, not hairy. Calyx 2–3mm in diameter, obliquely rimmed, shortly or hardly 5-lobed, densely scaly outside. **Corolla** 26–30mm, tubular, zygomorphic, pink to purplish; tube c.20 x 4–5 x 6–7mm, curved, initially, densely, later more sparsely scaly, often finally glabrescent outside, laxly papillose-hairy inside; lobes c.10 x 6mm, unequal, spreading, obovate-spathulate. **Stamens** almost equalling the corolla in length; filaments linear, laxly papillose-hairy in the proximal ½, glabrous distally; anthers 2 x 1.3mm, obovate-elliptic, the base obtuse. Disc glabrous below, hairy on the upper margin. **Ovary** c.4 x 1.5mm, sub-cylindrical, densely covered with reddish-brown, stellate scales and more sparsely with paler hairs, abruptly contracted distally; style scaly at the base, and sometimes sparsely patently hairy in the proximal ¼, otherwise glabrous; stigma sub-globose.

Indonesia, New Guinea (W), Wandamen Peninsula, Wondiwoi Mts. Primary forest, 800–1800m. *Fl.* March.

Not known in cultivation.

49. Rhododendron asperum J.J.Sm.
Nova Guinea 1914. 12: 137, *t.*34.
Type: Gjellerup 1203, 30 April 1912. New Guinea, Arfak Mts, Angi Lakes (lectotype, BO, L).
Derivation: Latin – *asper* – rough, alluding to the leaves which are rough due to the persistent epidermal tubercles.

Shrub to 2m. Twigs 2–4mm in diameter, thick, densely stellate-scaly, rounded, densely warty and rough to the touch; internodes 3–10cm. **Leaves** 5–10 together in pseudowhorls. **Blade** 25–60 x 15–50mm, ovate, elliptic or sub-circular, sometimes obovate-elliptic, sub-sessile; apex obtuse to rounded; margin distinctly recurved in dry specimens; base broadly rounded or mostly shortly cordate; densely stellate-scaly on both sides at first, quickly glabrescent above, the scales more persistent beneath, rough with the numerous minute tubercles on both sides especially beneath. **Scales** small, deeply divided, sub-sessile each on top of a small persistent elevated pale tubercle. Mid-vein a little impressed above, strongly

Nova Guinea

Rhododendron asperum.

obtusely prominent in its basal ½ beneath, gradually less so distally; lateral veins 5–9 per side, inconspicuous, spreading irregularly, faintly anastomosing before the margin, very slightly impressed in fully mature leaves above, somewhat prominent beneath, rigid, greyish green to dark green above, brown below. **Petioles** 1–2.5 x 1–2mm, somewhat flattened.

Bracts to 20 x 10mm, membranous, outer ones smaller, ovate to sub-circular, shortly subulate-acuminate, scaly and shortly hairy outside at the apex; inner ones larger, obovate to spathulate, glabrous. Bracteoles to 20 x 1mm, linear, laxly hairy or nearly glabrous. Inflorescence a 5–9-flowered umbel. Pedicels 15–30 x *c.*1mm, red, densely stellate-scaly. Calyx *c.*4mm in diameter, oblique, in the form of a shallow cup, densely scaly outside, very shortly and obtusely 5-lobed. **Corolla** 35–45 x 35–45mm, regular, white or to deep pink, sometimes with the tube of a more intense colour than the lobes, scented; tube 20–28 x 4 x 10mm, funnel-shaped, laxly scaly outside and sparsely hairy inside; lobes 15–19 x 15–19mm, spreading perpendicularly, sub-circular with some scales at the base outside, glabrous otherwise. **Stamens** somewhat exserted from the throat; filaments linear, sparsely hairy in the proximal ½–⅔, glabrous distally; anthers 3–4 x 1mm,

oblong. Disc low, hairy at the upper margin only. **Ovary** conical-cylindrical, densely covered with white spreading hairs and stellate scales which are often hidden between and below the hairs, gradually tapering distally; style 20–23mm, slender and covered with spreading hairs and some scales in the lower ½–⅔, glabrous distally; stigma globose. **Fruit** 15–18 x 6–8mm, sub-cylindrical, densely brown-stellate-scaly and hairy.

Indonesia, New Guinea (W), Arfak Mts. Terrestrial in heath-forest on ridges at the edge of degraded *Nothofagus* forest, or on the burnt open summit areas, on poor clayey soil, granite and quartzite, 2150–2750m. *Fl.* Jan., April, July.

Sleumer (1966) described wild hybrids of this species with *R. laetum*. These hybrids were characterised by glossy, shortly acuminate leaves, less distinct epidermal tubercles, the bracts densely hairy outside and *c.*2.5cm long. The pedicels were also scaly and hairy, the anthers *c.*4mm long, the ovary densely hairy and the corolla varying from pale greenish-yellow to pink and then often with yellow or greenish colour in the lower part of the tube.

50. Rhododendron beyerinckianum Koord.
Nova Guinea 1912. 8(4): 876, *t.*150.
Type: von Römer 1199, Aug. 1876. W New Guinea, Hellwig Mts, Mt Agathodaemon (BO, L).
Derivation: Named after M.W. Beyerinck, 1851–1931, a Dutch microbiologist.

Synonyms:
R. schultzei Schltr., Bot. Jahr. 1918. 55: 154.
R. dasylepis Schltr., Bot. Jahr. 1918. 55: 153, *f.*4.
R. saavedranum Diels, Bot. Jahr. 1929. 62: 486.
R. beyerinckianum var. *longipetiolatum* J.J.Sm., Nova Guinea 1936. 18: 94.
R. chrysopeplon Sleumer, Bot. Jahr. 1949. 74: 540.

Slender, loosely branched, erect shrub or small tree to 5m. Twigs 1.5–4mm in diameter, thick to slender, densely to very densely covered with deep brown stellate scales which easily fall off and are absent from the older parts which are brown and rough with the numerous fine persistent tubercles; internodes 1.5–10cm. **Leaves** 3–7 together in pseudowhorls, often variable in shape and size in the same whorl. **Blade** 30–60 x 10–35mm, narrowly ovate, to broadly elliptic, obovate or sub-circular; apex obtuse, broadly acute, sometimes apiculate; margin strongly revolute to almost flat and more densely and often more persistently scaly than the rest of the leaf beneath; base broadly tapering or rounded; very densely

Rhododendron beyerinckianum.

reddish-brown scaly on both sides at first, quickly glabrescent especially above where it can become shiny but rough, more persistently scaly below. **Scales** irregularly stellately divided to the centre, dendroid, very fragile, each from the top of a minute, persistent, epidermal tubercle. Mid-vein slightly impressed above, strong and prominent beneath; lateral veins 4–7 per side, straight below, curved and anastomosing before the margin, very slightly impressed above and raised beneath, often inconspicuous or completely covered by the scales beneath, reticulation dense, visibly prominent on both sides in fully mature leaves, occasionally slightly impressed above. **Petiole** 4–15 x *c.*2mm, weakly grooved in the distal ½, or the groove inconspicuous, densely covered with brown stellate scales.

Flower buds *c.*12 x 8mm, densely brown scaly with erect to slightly spreading bract points. Bracts to 10 x 7mm; the outer ones ovate subulate, densely scaly outside and fringed with marginal scales; the inner ones ovate acuminate and apiculate. Bracteoles to 10mm, linear and glabrous or scaly at first proximally, subspathulate and laxly hairy distally. Inflorescence a 1–5-flowered open umbel. **Flowers** horizontal to half-hanging. Pedicels 10–15 x 7–10mm, densely brown-stellate scaly, becoming glabrescent. Calyx 3–4mm in diameter, disc-shaped or cup-shaped, densely stellate scaly or shallowly and obtusely 5-lobed. **Corolla** 20–45 x 10–18mm, most commonly dark red, at least at higher altitudes, sometimes pink or cream, rarely greenish or white; tube 15–25 x 4–7 x 6–10mm, curved or straight, at first densely covered with golden-brown stellate scales outside, completely glabrous inside; lobes 7–12 x 6–11mm, spreading perpendicularly, sub-circular, overlapping ½–⅔, scaly on the proximal part outside. **Stamens** unequal, clustered on the upper side of the mouth, slightly exserted to *c.*5mm; filaments linear, red, glabrous or rarely with a few hairs; anthers 2–2.5 x *c.*1.2mm, obovate-oblong, brown to dark

red. Disc low, without simple hairs but sometimes with a few scales. **Ovary** 6–8 x 2.5–3mm, elongate-conical or sub-ovoid, densely stellate-scaly, usually abruptly tapering distally; style thick, as long as the stamens and exclusively stellate-scaly to the top at flowering, but becoming glabrescent distally as the fruit develops; stigma broadly obconical, slightly 5-lobed. **Fruit** 20–40 x 5–6mm, thick-fusiform, often a little wider in the distal ½, longitudinally grooved, densely brown scaly, usually with the persistent remains of the style. Seeds 2–4mm, without tails to 1.2mm, the longest tail *c.*1.5mm.

Indonesia, New Guinea (W), along the Main Range from the Wissel Lakes. **Papua New Guinea**, main range east to Mt Victoria and Mt Dayman; also on Mt Saruwaged and Bismarck Mts. Predominantly terrestrial but also epiphytic in mossy forest and on tree-ferns in grassland. 1400–4000m. *Fl.* Jan.–Dec. but peak flowering is reported from April to Dec.

Cultivated with difficulty, the high alpine forms especially. A collection made by Stonor (CR7) is the oldest surviving vireya in the Royal Botanic Garden Edinburgh, having been introduced in 1949. Several collections were made in Papua New Guinea in the 1960s and 1970s but most have not survived. This species has been repeatedly brought into cultivation but most introductions have failed and the species does not generally perform well. A high altitude form originating from an unknown source in Papua New Guinea has been in cultivation since at least 1980 in Australia and this has been distributed. It grows slowly but has attractive scaly foliage and deep red flowers. A plant corresponding to one of Kores (1982) lower altitude forms is in cultivation at Pukeiti in New Zealand, and has larger flatter leaves and pink flowers.

A widely distributed species, both altitudinally and geographically. Sleumer (1966) conceived this species in a broad sense and acknowledged that it might ultimately be united with *R. phaeochitum*. For differences between this species and *R. phaeochitum* see under that species.

Kores (1982) reported that it had been found on all major mountain ranges from the Nassau Mts to Mt Dayman and that 'it is an extremely polymorphic species. Plants from different geographic locations vary considerably in stature, flower color, leaf size, leaf shape and texture. In addition the species also appears to vary throughout its altitudinal range'. Specimens of *Rhododendron beyerinckianum* obtained from lower altitudes tend to be larger, more robust than high altitude collections, their leaves are larger, less leathery and the indumentum is poorly to moderately well developed. Material from higher altitude tends to be more compacted than low altitude material, the leaves are smaller, more leathery, frequently somewhat revolute and the indumentum is generally very well developed'.

51. Rhododendron bryophyllum Sleumer

Reinwardtia 1960. 5: 79.
Type: Cheesman 51, March 1936. New Guinea (NW), Mt Cyclops (BM).
Derivation: Greek – *bryo* – relating to moss; *philos* – loving. Alluding to the mossy branches on which this species was originally found growing.

Shrub to 2m. Twigs 1–2mm in diameter, slender, rounded, laxly leaved, the tips brown, at first densely covered with stellate scales, older parts glabrescent and rough with scale bases; internodes 2–8cm. **Leaves** 3–5 together in tight pseudowhorls. **Blade** 40–55 x 10–22mm, narrowly elliptic, widest in the middle; apex acute to obtuse; margin slightly revolute; base broadly tapering or sub-truncate-rounded, sub-densely scaly on both sides initially. **Scales** minute, deeply stellately divided and sub-dendroid, falling early, and becoming glabrescent, each on top of a persistent epidermal tubercle, which gives a rough texture. Mid-vein scaly for a long time, very slightly impressed above, prominent beneath; lateral veins 4–6 per side, curved and anastomosing, faintly visible on both sides. **Petiole** 2–3 x *c*.1mm, scaly, flattened.

Bracts to 8 x 6mm, ovate to obovate-spathulate, apiculate or obtuse, membranous, glabrous, minutely fringed with scales. Bracteoles to 10mm, filiform, sub-glabrous. Inflorescence a *c*.3-flowered open umbel. Pedicels 10–12 x 0.4mm, very slender, densely minutely stellate-scaly, without hairs. Calyx *c*.2mm in diameter, sub-oblique, small, obscurely 5-lobed, stellately scaly outside. **Corolla** 30–40mm, tubular, distinctly zygomorphic, pale pink, thin; tube 20–28 x 4–5 x 7–10mm, cylindrical, curved, glabrous outside, laxly hairy inside; lobes 10–12 x *c*.7mm, elliptic to spathulate, spreading and somewhat reflexed, not or only very slightly overlapping. **Stamens** exserted, 6–7mm, clustered on the upper side of the flower; filaments narrowly linear, glabrous at the base, then laxly hairy, but again glabrous distally; anthers 1.8–2 x 1mm, oblong. Disc very shortly hairy at the upper margin, glabrous elsewhere. **Ovary** *c*.4 x 1.5mm, elongate-ovoid, densely and exclusively stellate-scaly, gradually tapering distally; style *c*.18mm, relatively thick, laxly covered with short, sub-patent hairs almost to the top; stigma shortly club-shaped.

Indonesia, New Guinea (W), Cycloop Mts. Epiphytic in tall forest, 1065–1830m. *Fl.* March–June.

Introduced into cultivation from seed sent by Professor Sleumer in 1966 and now widely distributed. An attractive but not very flamboyant species. The distinction between this species and *R. dielsianum* is not clearly established; the best difference appears to be that *R. dielsianum* has a glabrous style except for a few hairs at the base whereas in *R. bryophyllum* the style is covered with simple hairs for most of its length.

52. Rhododendron bullifolium Sleumer

Blumea 1963. 12: 93.
Type: Sleumer & Vink 4444, 26 Jan. 1961. Indonesia, W New Guinea, Arfak Mts, Mt Saru-mot near Iray, Anggi Gigi Lake (A, CANB, G, K, L, LAE, P, PNH, UC).
Derivation: Latin – *bullatus* – puckered; *folium* – leaf. Alluding to the leaves being deeply puckered.

Erect, few-stemmed shrub or small tree to 6m, the trunk 2–3m to 5cm in diameter. Twigs 3–10mm in diameter, rounded, covered with a persistent though fragile covering of reddish-brown stellate scales; internodes 6–25cm. **Leaves** 4–6 together in tight pseudowhorls. **Blade** 8–20 x 4.5–13cm, elliptic or ovate-elliptic, rarely broadly elliptic or ovate, slightly unequal sided; apex very shortly sub-acuminate, obtuse or rounded; margin flat; base rounded; young leaves thickly covered with stellate reddish-brown scales, mature ones glabrescent above, more persistently scaly beneath especially along the main veins. **Scales** dendroid, with the marginal zone deeply divided and the small centre deepened or prolonged downwards into a kind of foot. Mid-vein as wide as the petiole at the base, and hardly prominent there, becoming impressed distally above and raised below; lateral veins irregular, 10–14 per side, curved and anastomosing before the edge, impressed above, prominent beneath as are the smaller veins which are distinct and reticulate towards the leaf margin; dark green and glossy above, paler and dull beneath, deeply puckered in both the fresh and dry state. **Petiole** 25–50 x 2.5–3.5mm, densely stellate-scaly initially.

Immature buds *c*.20 x 20mm, bracts ovate, the outer ones sub-acuminate, the inner ones obtuse, with long appressed hairs on both sides and scaly outside. **Corolla** (immature) densely scaly on the tube outside, glabrous at the lobes. **Fruit** pedicel densely scaly, *c*.25 x 1.5mm. Young fruit 25mm, fusiform, densely covered with scales and pale coarse hairs, as is the style, of which only the lower part (for *c*.3cm) is known. Twisted valves of the mature fruit 30–55mm.

Indonesia, New Guinea (W), Arfak Mts, Mt Sarumot, Anggi Gigi Lake, once collected. Undershrub or tree in transitional zone of *Castanopsis* to *Nothofagus* forest, at 2050–2100m. *Fr.* Jan.

Still apparently known only from the very imperfect type specimen and the collectors' field notes.

53. Rhododendron caliginis Kores

Blumea 1984. 30(1): 45.
Type: Kores WEI 1600, 7 Aug. 1976. Papua New Guinea, West Sepik Province, Victor Emanuel Range, Mt Womtakin, 2850m (LAE, BISH, E, L).
Derivation: Latin – *caligo* – of mist or fog, the type collection being made from plants that seemed perpetually enshrouded in mist.

Small, straggling, much-branched shrub to 50cm. Twigs 1–2mm in diameter, slender, rounded, tips densely scaly with brown, stellate scales, the older parts glabrescent, smooth; internodes 1–8cm. **Leaves** 4–7 together in tight pseudowhorls, often noticeably different in size in the same pseudowhorl. **Blade** 10–70 x 1–6mm, linear or occasionally very narrowly ovate or narrowly elliptic; apex sub-obtuse; margin entire or slightly revolute; base very broadly tapering or rounded, very densely red-brown scaly on both sides initially. **Scales** deeply stellately divided, sub-sessile or shortly dendroid, each on top of a minute epidermal tubercle, becoming glabrous and smooth above, persistently red-brown scaly beneath. Mid-vein faintly impressed above, as thick as the petiole and prominently raised beneath; lateral veins obscure. **Petioles** 2–5 x 1–1.5mm, weakly grooved distally, densely brown-scaly.

Rhododendron caliginis (pink form).

Flower buds to 12 x 7mm, densely brown-scaly when young, becoming green just before opening, narrowly elliptic, sharply acute at the apex. Outer bracts subulate, inner ones ovate-subulate to ovate-acuminate, densely stellate-scaly in a patch on the outer upper part, glabrous otherwise, margin fringed with scales. Bracteoles to 8mm, linear to very narrowly obovate, margin laxly fringed with scales. Inflorescence of solitary flowers or up to 3 together. **Flowers** hanging vertically downwards. Pedicels 6–12mm, slender, densely stellately scaly. Calyx *c.*2.5mm in diameter, small, disc-like, densely stellate-scaly externally. **Corolla** 30–35mm, white to cream, sometimes very pale pink, without scent, tubular below, slightly expanded at the mouth, a little curved, zygomorphic; tube 20–25 x 4–6 x 6–10mm, densely stellately scaly and without hairs outside, glabrous inside; lobes 7–9 x 6–9mm, broadly obovate to sub-circular, spreading horizontally and overlapping to *c.*¼, scaly at the base outside. **Stamens** clustered on the upper side of the flower, unequal, exserted to *c.*10mm; filaments white, linear, glabrous or sparsely hairy in the proximal ½; anthers *c.*2 x 1mm, brown. Disc glabrous below, densely stellate-scaly on the upper margin. **Ovary** sub-ovoid, gradually tapering to the style, very densely stellate-scaly and conspicuously 5-ribbed, *c.*7 x 3.5mm; style greenish-white, on the upper side of the tube, slender, scaly throughout the proximal ⅓, glabrous distally or with sparse white hairs almost to the top, equalling the corolla in length when receptive; stigma white or green, club-shaped to globose, obscurely 5-lobed. **Fruit** fusiform, the valves ultimately curling right back, the placentae breaking away at the base and irregularly splaying apart.

Indonesia, New Guinea (W), Koruppun Valley (139°38′E 4°28′S). **Papua New Guinea**, West Sepik Province, Hindenburg Range, Mt Amdutakin; Victor Emanuel Range, Mt Womtakin. Enga Province, Laiagam–Porgera Divide, Mt Maip. Western Highlands District, Mt Sigal Mugal; Waghi–Sepik Divide, Mt Manduil. Growing from 2400 to 2900m altitude in open sub-montane shrubberies, cliffs and on fallen logs.

A striking species owing to its linear leaves which are densely covered with dark brown, dendroid scales when immature and its apparent association with limestone outcrops. Similar to *R. hooglandii* from which it is best distinguished by its subulate bracts which are densely scaly outside. For a discussion of other differences see under *R. hooglandii*.

A dainty plant now widely cultivated. A pink form in cultivation under the name has broader narrowly elliptic leaves and is probably a hybrid.

54. Rhododendron delicatulum Sleumer

Reinwardtia 1960. 5: 78.

Type: Brass 11876, Jan. 1939. New Guinea (W), Northern part, 15km SW of Bernhard Camp, Idenburg River, mossy forest (A).

Derivation: Latin – *delicatulus* – delicate, alluding to the delicate or dainty nature of the specimen.

Var. **delicatulum**

Shrub to 50cm. Twigs 1–2mm in diameter, very slender, rounded, laxly leafy, the tips densely stellate-scaly, glabrescent below; internodes 3–6cm. **Leaves** 3–4 together in pseudowhorls at the upper nodes. **Blade** 30–65 x 4–7mm, very narrowly ovate-elliptic to almost linear, mostly widest below the middle; apex gradually acuminate and somewhat curved, sub-acute; margin slightly revolute; base broadly tapering to nearly rounded; very young leaves densely covered on both sides with deeply stellately divided or shortly dendroid scales, which are on top of persistent epidermal tubercles, early glabrescent and rough to the touch above, slowly so beneath. Midvein impressed above, prominent beneath; lateral veins obscure. **Petiole** *c.*2 x 0.5–0.7mm, scaly.

Bracts to 20 x 6mm; outer bracts subulate; inner ones ovate, with a subulate acumen for the ultimate 3–10mm, densely stellately scaly outside, glabrous internally, fringed with scales. Bracteoles to 15 x 1mm, linear-subspathulate, very laxly hairy. Inflorescence *c.*3-flowered. Pedicels *c.*12mm, slender, densely reddish-brown stellately scaly. **Flowers** hanging or half-hanging. Calyx *c.*2mm in diameter, small, oblique, circular or obscurely lobed, thin, stellately scaly, shortly fringed. **Corolla** *c.*27mm, tubular below, widened at the mouth, zygomorphic, pink; tube 15–18 x 3 x 6mm, sub-densely, shortly, whitish hairy (but not scaly) outside, laxly hairy inside; lobes 5–7 x 5–6mm, spreading, broadly obovate-spathulate or sub-circular. **Stamens** almost equalling the corolla in length; filaments filiform, very laxly hairy proximally, glabrous distally; anthers 1.3 x 0.8mm, broadly oblong. Disc very shortly yellowish hairy at the upper margin, glabrous below. **Ovary** *c.*5 x 1.8mm, conical-cylindric, densely dark-brown stellately scaly, gradually tapering distally; style slender, as long as the corolla and covered with spreading yellowish hairs to the top; stigma sub-globose.

Indonesia, New Guinea (W), Bernard Camp, Idenburg R., in mossy forest at 1800m. *Fl.* Jan.

Known only from the type collection.

Var. **lanceolatoides** Sleumer

Blumea 1961. 11: 116.

Type: Kalkman 4400 (A, L).

Derivation: Latin – *lanceolatus* – spear-shaped, the leaves being lanceolate in shape.

Differing from the type in that the leaves are wider, 25–50 x 7–12mm, and the pedicels shorter, 5–7mm.

Indonesia, New Guinea (W), Star Mts, 1km E of the mouth of the Minam R. in the Bon R. On peaty soil at 1500m. Once collected. *Fl.* July.

55. Rhododendron dianthosmum Sleumer

Blumea 1963. 12: 100.

Type: van Royen & Sleumer 5736, 8 June 1961. New Guinea (N), Cycloop Mts, Faita R. camp (L, A, CANB).

Derivation: Named after the genus *Dianthus* because the flowers have a similar perfume.

Shrub to 2m. Twigs slender, densely scaly, early glabrescent and often whitish; internodes 6–16cm. **Leaves** 3–4 together in pseudowhorls at the upper 2 or 3 nodes. **Blade** 70–140 x 30–55mm, broadly elliptic or elliptic or slightly obovate; apex broadly acute to obtuse; margin entire, flat, a little recurved when dry; base broadly tapering to rounded, young leaves densely reddish-brown stellate-scaly, mature ones glabrescent, on both sides covered with numerous epidermal tubercles which make them feel rough to the touch. **Scales** dendroid; marginal zone divided to, or almost to, the centre; centre small, deepened or prolonged into a short stalk. Mid-vein slightly prominent proximally above, gradually becoming flat in the distal part above; below as thick as the petiole in the proximal part, gradually decreasing distally; lateral veins 8–12 per side, irregular, inarched before the margin, slightly prominent on both sides, veins laxly reticulate, not very conspicuous. **Petiole** 10–15 x 2–2.5mm, densely scaly initially.

Bracts 10–35 x 10–15mm, dull red; outer ones ovate, inner ones elliptic-ovate and apiculate, innermost ones broadly spathulate, scaly and/or appressed-hairy. Bracteoles *c.*20 x 1–2mm, linear, glabrous. Inflorescence a 3–6-flowered open umbel, the flowers held stiffly horizontally or half-hanging. Pedicels 10–15 x 1.5mm, very densely brown stellate-scaly, without hairs. Calyx *c.*3mm in diameter, obliquely disc-shaped. **Corolla** 50–70 x *c.*70mm, pure white, or pink with darker pink edges, with a scent of carnations; tube 25–40 x 6–10 x 12–15mm, tubular, straight, glabrous outside, shortly hairy inside; lobes 6–7 in number, 20–35 x 20–30mm, spathulate, 3 or 4 of them generally smaller than the others, horizontally spreading. **Stamens** exserted to *c.*10mm; filaments linear, densely or more laxly hairy in the proximal ¾, glabrous distally; anthers

3.5–4 x *c*.1mm, elongate-oblong, the base obtuse. Disc glabrous below, hairy at the upper margin. **Ovary** 8–10 x 2–3mm, sub-cylindrical, covered with whitish to yellow-ish, distally directed hairs, which cover the scales, tapering gradually; style *c*.30mm, slender, densely hairy proximally, the hairs becoming laxer distally and completely glabrous in the uppermost ¼, without scales; stigma 2.5–3mm.

Indonesia, New Guinea (W), above Jayapura on the W slope of Mt Dafonsero; Cycloop Mts, Faita R. camp and along path from Ifar to Ormu. Epiphytic in primary forest, 800–1400m, descending along ravines to *c*.500m. *Fl*. May–July.

In cultivation since 1961 when Professor Sleumer sent seed from New Guinea to the USA from where it has been distributed. Probably all genuine materials of this species are from this introduction. Slow growing and fairly com-pact. The beautiful and strongly scented flowers are usu-ally produced in Edinburgh just once a year in August or September.

56. Rhododendron dielsianum Schltr.

Bot. Jahr. 1918. 55: 150.
Type: Schlechter 17770. New Guinea (NE), Kani Mts, Above Bolobo, *c*.1400m (B†, P).
Derivation: Named after Friedrich L.E. Diels, 1874–1945, a German botanist.

Synonym: *R. laureola* Schltr., Bot. Jahr. 1918. 55: 151.

Var. **dielsianum**

Shrub to 1.5m. Twigs rounded, 1.5–3mm in diameter, the tips densely brown with stellate scales which give an almost hairy appearance; older parts glabrescent, smooth, brown; internodes 1.5–8cm. **Leaves** mostly 3–4 together in tight pseudowhorls at the upper 2–3 nodes. **Blade** 30–55 x 8–25mm, elliptic; apex shortly acuminate, apiculate, sub-acute; margin flat or slightly revolute; base broadly tapering, or rarely almost rounded; densely scaly on both sides initially, quickly glabrescent above, more persistently scaly beneath especially near the mid-vein, finally glabrescent and a little rough to the touch on both sides. **Scales** small, deeply stellately divided, sessile or shortly dendroid and on top of low, persistent, epidermal tubercles. Mid-vein somewhat impressed above, raised beneath; lateral veins *c*.6 per side, very faintly impressed above and raised beneath, inconspicuous on both sides. **Petiole** 2–5mm, grooved above, slender, densely scaly.

Flower buds to 18 x 6mm, slenderly ellipsoid or ovate, the apex acute, the bract tips appressed or only slightly

spreading. Bracts to 15 x 6mm; the outer subulate, often with the point as long as the broad part; inner ones ovate-subulate to ovate-apiculate, stellate-scaly in the upper ½ and shortly fringed with stalked scales. Bracteoles to *c*.10mm, filiform, laxly scaly. Inflorescence of mostly soli-tary or paired flowers, hanging or half-hanging, rarely in up to 5-flowered open umbels. Pedicels 10–13mm, slen-der, densely brown-stellate-scaly. Calyx *c*.2.5mm in diam-eter, often slightly oblique, disc-shaped, densely stellately scaly, very shortly obtusely 5-lobed. **Corolla** 25–35 x 11–14mm, tubular to *c*.⅘ of its total length, slightly curved and zygomorphic, pale pink; tube 12–20 x 8–10 x 6–8mm, slightly laterally compressed, narrowest about the mid-dle, weakly pouched at the base, sparsely scaly outside, glabrous or sparsely hairy inside; lobes *c*.6–8 x 5–7mm, broadly spathulate to sub-circular, spreading. **Stamens** clustered on the upper side of the flower, unequal, the longest exserted from the mouth to *c*.6mm, shorter ones at the mouth; filaments red, linear to filiform, glabrous or very slightly hairy; anthers *c*.2 x 1mm, brown. Disc prom-inent, glabrous. **Ovary** 5–6 x *c*.1.5mm, sub-cylindrical, densely stellate-scaly, gradually tapering distally; style slender, glabrous or scaly at the very base only, becoming slightly exserted from the mouth when receptive; stigma sub-globose, slightly 5-lobed. **Fruit** 17–30 x 3–5mm, cylin-drical, grooved longitudinally and often curved. Seeds 40–52mm, without tails 10–11mm, the longest tail *c*.25mm, irregularly crimped.

Rhododendron dielsianum var. *dielsianum*.

Papua New Guinea, Upper Sepik R. region; Kani, Finisterre and Saruwaged Mts. Common in the Eastern Highlands, also in the Simbu and Western Highlands. Possibly in W New Guinea; see notes under *R. bryophyllum*. Epiphytic on tall trees in ravines and wooded slopes, in dense shade, terrestrial in secondary grassland and along roadsides, 1200–1940m. *Fl.* May–Sept.

Common and easy in cultivation. The flowers are a pretty pink but rather small. For a discussion on the status of *R. laureola* see Sleumer (1960).

Var. **stylotrichum** Sleumer
Reinwardtia 1960. 5: 80.
Type: Hoogland & Pullen 5307. Papua New Guinea, Eastern Highlands, Goroka subdistrict, Upper Dunantina valley, near Sosomepari village (LAE, B, BRI, CANB, K, L).
Derivation: Latin – *stylus* – the style; *trichoma* – hair. Alluding to the hairs at the base of the style which distinguishes this variety from the type one.

Slender erect shrub to 3m. Corolla pink. Differs from var. *dielsianum* by the style which is laxly shortly hairy with spreading hairs in its lower ½.

Papua New Guinea, Eastern Highlands: Upper Dunantina Valley, the road between Kami and Lufa and Mt Kesegete, Namaro, Benabena District. Hillside secondary grasslands, at 1700–2000m, locally common. *Fl.* Aug.

Not known to be in cultivation.

57. **Rhododendron extrorsum** J.J.Sm.
Nova Guinea 1936. 18: 95, *t*.19, 2.
Type: Lam 1668, 18 Oct. 1920. New Guinea (W), Northern part, Doormantop (BO, L, P).
Derivation: Latin – *extrorsus* – towards the outside, alluding to the distinctive anther dehiscence.

Shrub to 1.2m, with long tortuous branches and leaves only at the extreme ends. Twigs rounded, densely brown scurfy-scaly at the tips, glabrescent and rough below, blackish when dry; internodes 0.8–4cm. **Leaves** 4–5 together in pseudowhorls, with some much reduced ones scattered along the internodes, stiff, dull light green above, light greenish yellow beneath. **Blade** 10–16 x 3–7mm, ovate; apex shortly acuminate, sub-acute; margin strongly revolute, often to the mid-vein; base rounded-obtuse; very densely scaly with stellate scales on both sides initially, early glabrescent above, more slowly so beneath, leaving the surface rough. **Scales** deeply and irregularly narrowly divided, commonly to the minute centre; each scale shortly dendroid and mounted on top of a distinct epidermal tubercle. Mid-vein slightly

grooved above, somewhat prominent beneath; lateral veins obscure. **Petiole** 2–3mm, thick, scaly.

Bracts to 15 x 5mm, ovate, acuminate, ciliate and scaly along the outside middle line, otherwise glabrous. Bracteoles to 10mm, linear to linear-sub-spathulate, glabrous. Pedicels *c*.5 x 1mm, densely reddish-brown scaly. Calyx *c*.2.5mm in diameter, oblique, disc-shaped, very shortly obtusely 5-lobed, densely scaly. **Corolla** *c*.19mm, very pale-yellow, nearly white, broadly funnel-shaped, 5-lobed halfway or slightly more; tube 8–9 x 3–4 x 8–9mm, sub-densely covered with brown scales outside, glabrous inside; lobes *c*.12 x 12mm, half-spreading, wavy, sub-circular, glabrous except for some scales at the very base outside. **Stamens** 7–8mm, slightly unequal; filaments linear, slightly dilated above the base, pale green, glabrous; anthers *c*.1.5mm, red-brown, oblong, dehiscing by distinctly outwardly facing pores. Disc very small. **Ovary** *c*.4 x 3mm, ovoid-conical, obtuse, densely stellately scaly, abruptly contracted distally; style to 1mm, very shortly obconical, glabrous; stigma convex, slightly lobed. **Fruit** *c*.12 x 6mm, ovoid, densely brown-stellate-scaly.

Indonesia, New Guinea (W), Mt Doorman. Open slope, also in the saddle between the summits, scattered though common, 3500m. *Fl.* Oct.

Not recently recollected and never cultivated.

58. **Rhododendron gardenia** Schltr.
Bot. Jahr. 1918. 55: 158.
Type: Ledermann 12024. New Guinea (E), Northeastern part, Sepik R. region, Schrader Mts (B†). Lectotype: Brass 10832, Oct. 1938. New Guinea (W), Bele R. Valley, 25km NE of Lake Habbema (A, L).
Derivation: Named after the genus *Gardenia* in the Rubiaceae as the white, strongly scented flowers are reminiscent of this genus.

Shrub to 2.5m. Twigs 6–8mm in diameter, thick, rounded, brown scaly when young quickly becoming glabrescent and often glaucous white in the older parts; internodes 15–20cm. **Leaves** 3–5 together in well-marked pseudowhorls at the upper nodes, very stiff and leathery. **Blade** 80–150 x 55–90mm, patent, elliptic or broadly elliptic, rarely sub-obovate-elliptic; apex obtuse, or rounded to a little retuse; margin cartilaginous, flat or narrowly but distinctly revolute; base broadly tapering to rounded; densely brown scaly initially on both sides, soon becoming glabrescent and rough to the touch due to the persistent tubercles on both sides but especially beneath. **Scales** minute, deeply stellately divided and distinctly dendroid,

Rhododendron gardenia.

each on top of a paler minute epidermal tubercle. Mid-vein robust in the lower ½ of the blade, impressed above, very prominent beneath, flat and wrinkled in dry specimens; lateral veins 8–10 per side, straight below, curved and indistinctly anastomosing before the margin, very slightly prominent on both sides or somewhat impressed above, often becoming inconspicuous towards the edge, no distinct reticulation visible. **Petiole** 20–40 x 2.5–4mm, brown scaly initially, often glaucous.

Flower buds to 50 x 30mm, green or purple, ovoid with a broadly acute apex, the bracts all appressed. Bracts broadly elliptic, to obovate to spathulate, often splitting at the apex to become emarginate, scabrid with short erect hairs outside and short appressed hairs inside. Bracteoles to 60 x 4mm, linear, slightly broadened upwards, laxly hairy. Inflorescence an open 3–4-flowered umbel, the flowers semi-erect to half-hanging. Pedicels 10–35 x 3–5mm, thick, densely covered with brown sessile scales and laxly hairy, more densely near the calyx. Calyx 8–10mm in diameter, oblique, scaly and hairy outside, glabrous inside and irregularly obtusely 5–8-lobed; the lobes triangular, 2–3mm, white-ciliate along the margins. **Corolla** 90–110 x 110–140mm, tubular-funnel-shaped, white or suffused with pink, cream, or even (when very young) green on the tube, sometimes with pink 'dimpled' spots at the base of each lobe, fleshy, (the tube up to 3mm thick just below the lobes), strongly fragrant; tube 50–70 x 10–12 x 15–25mm, straight, glabrous outside, densely covered with retrorse white hairs in its lower ½–¾ inside; lobes 50–60 x 30–50mm, 5–8, spreading perpendicularly, overlapping to ¾, or with reflexed lateral margins in which case they hardly overlap, broadly obovate, glabrous. **Stamens** 10–16, slightly unequal, clustered on the lower side of the mouth, drooping downwards with age, exserted to *c.*20mm; filaments linear and densely patently hairy below, glabrous and filiform distally; anthers 10–12 x 1.5mm, curved upwards, pale brown, linear-oblong, base obtuse. Disc prominent, very densely hairy. **Ovary** oblong-cylindrical, densely covered with sub-appressed, yellowish, stiff hairs which completely cover the numerous scales, *c.*13 x 5mm, abruptly tapering distally; style 60–110 x 3–5mm, strong, glabrous except for some hairs at the very base; stigma 4–6mm in diameter, sub-globose, obtusely 5–8-lobed, becoming exserted to 50mm. **Fruit** 75–85 x 14–15mm, ellipsoid. Seeds 6.5–8mm, without tails *c.*1mm, the longest tail 3.8mm, crimped.

Indonesia, New Guinea (W), Bele R. Valley, 25km NE of Lake Habbema; E of Baliem R. Valley, Angguruk. **Papua New Guinea**, Sepik R. region, Schrader Mts, W Sepik region: above airfield at Telefomin; Along Eliptamin track, Telefomin; Oksapmin near Telefomin; Star Mts between Busilmin airstrip and Bielga R. High epiphyte in forest, but also a terrestrial shrub in sandy openings in mossy forest on the crest of mountain ridges, said to be locally abundant and conspicuous around Telefomin. 1400–2300m. *Fl.* June–July, Oct.–Nov.

Cultivated locally in New Guinea around Telefomin. Introduced into cultivation in the UK in 1964 by Herklots but plants were not recorded as flowering until 1990. Two forms now in cultivation, both with creamy flowers, one with flat overlapping lobes, the other with the lobes having strongly revolute lateral margins. Supposedly grown in Australia but most if not all early plants were identified as a hybrid: *Rhododendron* 'Gardenia Odyssey' (see Craven 1993; Clancy 2005). Slow growing and rather shy to flower but with distinctive very 'fleshy' flowers and very strongly perfumed. Recent visits to the Bele R. Valley have failed to re-find this species in the type locality although a very similar plant which keys out to *R. superbum* is common there.

59. Rhododendron haematophthalmum Sleumer

Reinwardtia 1960. 5: 89.

Type: Brass 9571, Aug.–Oct. 1938. New Guinea (W), Northern Part: Lake Habbema, 3225m (A, L).

Derivation: Greek – *haemat* – blood red; *opthalmum* – eye. Referring to the colour of the flowers.

Erect rigid shrub to 2.5m. Twigs 2–3mm in diameter, rounded, stellate-scaly but very early glabrescent, and rough due to the numerous minute tubercles; internodes 2–8cm. **Leaves** often spirally arranged, more rarely 3–5 together in loose pseudowhorls, stiffly spreading. **Blade** 50–90 x 20–35mm, broadly elliptic; apex shortly acuminate, apiculate or obtuse; margin entire, revolute; base truncate to rounded, sometimes slightly cordate; when young densely scaly, early glabrescent and very rough with the persistent tubercles on both sides. **Scales** minute, stellate and shortly dendroid, each of which is on top of a pale epidermal tubercle. Mid-vein as thick as the petiole proximally, raised (and grooved when dry) in the proximal ⅓ above otherwise level or slightly impressed, distinctly

raised throughout its length below; lateral veins 7–10 per side, irregular, spreading, straight, indistinctly anastomosing, inconspicuous above, slightly raised beneath; very rigid, yellowish or bluish green above, often brown from the colour of the scales below. **Petiole** 6–17 x 2–3mm, semi-rounded, rugose.

Bracts to 20 x 10mm, ovate to obovate or spathulate, obtuse, membranous, glabrous. Bracteoles to *c*.20 x 1mm, linear, apex sub-spathulate, glabrous. Inflorescence a 4–10-flowered open umbel. Pedicels 15–40 x *c*.2mm, very densely brown stellate-scaly, without hairs. Calyx *c*.4mm in diameter, oblique, disc-shaped, irregularly 5-lobed, or sometimes with 1 or 2 elongate, acute lobes up to 3mm, densely scaly outside, without hairs. **Corolla** distinctly zygomorphic, tubular below, dilated towards the mouth, red; tube 30–55 x 5–7 x 10–15mm, densely brown stellate-scaly outside, very shortly hairy inside, distinctly curved; lobes 15–20 x 9–15mm, irregularly broadly obovate or sub-circular, densely scaly outside except near the margins. **Stamens** unequal, exserted to *c*.10mm, arranged in a distinct group on the upper side of the flower; filaments linear, laxly patently hairy below, glabrous distally; anthers 3.5–4 x 1.3–1.5mm, purple, broadly oblong to obovate-oblong. Disc glabrous. **Ovary** 5–6 x *c*.3mm, cylindrical, abruptly tapering distally; style thick, as long as the stamens, densely shortly patent-hairy and scaly in the proximal ½ with the scales clearly visible amongst the hairs, glabrous distally; stigma thick-globose, distinctly 5-lobed.

Rhododendron haematophthalmum.

Indonesia, New Guinea (W), near Wamena, Lake Habbema. Common at the edges of mossy thickets, frequent in shrubberies on peaty ridges or peaty treeless areas in forest or in mossy thickets, observed to have regenerated strongly on one burnt over slope, 3000–3225m. *Fl.* Aug., Oct.

A spectacular plant in the wild with its stiffly rigid habit and beautiful flowers. It was introduced into cultivation in 1992 but failed to establish.

60. Rhododendron hellwigii Warb.

Bot. Jahr. 1892. 16: 26.

Type: Hellwig 315. New Guinea (E), Finisterre Mts; Clemens 7184a, (7139a), Mt Saruwaged, Sambanga, Lectotype (L, A, B†).

Derivation: Named after Franz Carl Hellwig, collector of this species.

Shrub or small tree. Twigs 4–6mm in diameter, at first densely brown, stellate-scaly, quickly glabrescent, rounded, or slightly angular; internodes 2–12cm. **Leaves** 3–5 together in pseudowhorls, or sometimes with 2 or 3 more loosely arranged. **Blade** 80–160 x 50–100mm, ovate to ovate-elliptic, sometimes sub-circular; apex obtuse to rounded; margin entire and flat; base rounded to cordate; brown with stellate scales on both sides initially quickly glabrescent both above and below. **Scales** small, irregularly lobed, sessile or very shortly stalked, each on top of a minute epidermal tubercle which remains visible for a long time beneath. Mid-vein grooved above in the proximal ½ and somewhat impressed distally, below strongly raised throughout its length; lateral veins 8–10 per side, irregular, the lowest 2 from near the base of the blade, all straight below, curved-anastomosing to the margin, smooth to slightly prominent on both sides, veins coarse, much less visible, reticulation obscure. **Petiole** 10–20 x 3–4mm, robust, a little flattened, not or only faintly grooved above, densely brown-scaly.

Flower buds to 60 x 35mm, ovoid, dark purple, the bracts all tightly appressed, rough with short white hairs outside. Outer bracts ovate to sub-circular, inner ones broadly spathulate, obtuse or very shortly apiculate, densely covered with short, thick hairs on both sides, glabrescent but remaining rough, fringed with scales. Bracteoles *c.*20–35 x 1–4mm, linear to sub-spathulate, hairy below, glabrous distally. Inflorescence an open umbel of

Rhododendron hellwigii.

2–6 flowers, held horizontally or slightly hanging. Pedicels 6–15 x 3–5mm, densely dark-brown scaly. Calyx *c.*6mm in diameter, rim-like, very shortly obtusely 5–6-lobed. **Corolla** 65–90 x 50–60mm, broadly funnel-shaped, dark blood-red, fleshy; tube 40–55 x 10–15 x 17–23mm, slightly dilated upwards, curved upwards and longitudinally channelled, glabrous outside, densely covered with short retrorse hairs inside in the proximal ½, lobes *c.*31 x 30–35mm, 6–7, spreading to the perpendicular, broadly spathulate or obovate, overlapping to ¾. **Stamens** 12–14, clustered on the lower side of the mouth of the flower, exserted to 12mm; filaments pink, linear, (1mm wide), with retrorse or patent hairs in their proximal ⅔, glabrous and filiform distally; anthers 7–8 x *c.*1.5mm, dark purple, linear-oblong, the base of each cell shortly obtusely bilobed. Disc glabrous, purple. **Ovary** *c.*10 x 4–5mm, sub-ovoid-cylindrical, densely covered with small flattened scales, abruptly tapering distally; style 30–40 x *c.*2mm, upwardly curved, presenting the stigma on the upper side of the mouth, thick, glabrous, sometimes shining; stigma shortly thick-globose, obscurely 5–6-lobed.

Papua New Guinea, restricted to the Huon Peninsula on the Finisterre and Saruwaged Mts, locally common. Mostly epiphytic, high in large trees in montane *Nothofagus* forest, occasionally terrestrial on steep slopes among grasses, 1065–3050m. *Fl.* Jan.–May, Sept., Oct.

Commonly forming hybrids at the western end of its range with *R. superbum* which has white to pink, strongly scented flowers. The hybrids are intermediate in colour and scent, with deep pink flowers.

Cuttings of this species were almost certainly sent back to the UK for cultivation by Jermy and Sayers, who reported this species dramatically in their account of the 1964 expedition to New Guinea (Jermy & Sayers 1967): 'This is a most glorious species with the petals a very dark blood red and so thick and fleshy that one can easily squeeze them so that the red sap runs out through the fingers. It was a devil to collect for although very common it prefers to live in the crown of only the tallest trees'. These collections unfortunately did not persist to flowering. Paul Kores collected the first living plants that flowered in cultivation from the Finisterre Mts in 1976. These were distributed as seed of *R. superbum* but they were confirmed as *R. hellwigii* by Withers & Rouse (1988) when they flowered for the first time in March 1988 in Melbourne, Australia and simultaneously at Pukeiti in New Zealand. The first flowering of this material in Edinburgh was in September 1989. There is no record of earlier flowering in the USA but it is possible that collections there did in fact flower earlier. Subsequent collections of

this species were made by Sandham in 1986 from above Iloko village (near Konge) on the slopes of Mt Bangeta; these have also flowered and been distributed.

This species is undoubtedly one of the most dramatic, with its very large, dark red flowers, but it is slow growing. The first flowering was 12 years from seed; cuttings may flower quite quickly if taken from mature plants but it requires a large plant to produce good flowers. The Edinburgh accession from cuttings took 13 years to the first flowering although the plants now flower regularly every year provided they are not allowed to set seed. The poor pollen reported by Withers & Rouse (1988) was probably due not to hybridity but to the fact that the plants were insufficiently vigorous to produce fully fertile anthers.

61. Rhododendron hooglandii Sleumer

Reinwardtia 1960. 5: 75.

Type: Hoogland & Pullen 5576, 9 July 1956. Papua New Guinea, E Highlands district, Goroka subdistrict, near Kerigomna Camp, *c.*3000m (L, CANB).

Derivation: Named after Ruurd Dirk Hoogland of CSIRO Land Research, and later of Research School of Biological Sciences, Canberra, Australia. One of the collectors of the type and very active in research and plant collecting in New Guinea.

Straggling, much-branched shrub to 2.5m. Twigs densely covered with stalked scales, warty and rough to the touch in the youngest parts; internodes 2–8cm. **Leaves** 4–6 together in pseudowhorls. **Blade** 20–55 x 2–6mm, linear; apex sub-obtuse; margin entire, strongly revolute to near the midrib; base tapering; densely covered on both sides with yellowish stalked, deeply stellately divided scales which fall early, leaving the stalks, thus making the surface of the lamina rough. Mid-vein faintly impressed above, as thick as the petiole and somewhat prominent beneath; lateral veins not visible. **Petiole** 3–8mm, thick, densely scaly with stalked scales.

Flower buds *c.*10–12 x 5–6mm. Bracts to 3–7 x 1–4mm; outer bracts ovate, appressed, inner ones ovate-sub-acuminate, almost blunt, glabrous or with just a few scales along the outer middle line and on the margins. Bracteoles filiform, minute. Inflorescence 1–2-flowered, the flower half-hanging to hanging. Pedicels 10–12 x *c.*1.5mm, densely covered with yellowish, stalked scales. Calyx *c.*3mm in diameter, obliquely circular, very obtusely and shortly 5-lobed, densely set with nearly sessile scales. **Corolla** 30–35 x 17–22mm, pinkish-red or cream, without scent; tube 20–25 x 5–6 x 7–8mm, slightly broadened upwards and somewhat curved, densely scaly outside, glabrous inside; lobes *c.*10 x 8mm, scaly outside except for the margins. **Stamens** exserted to 10mm, clustered on the upper side of the flower; filaments linear, glabrous; anthers 1.5 x 1mm. Disc glabrous. **Ovary** *c.*5 x 2mm, conical, gradually tapering to the style, very densely scaly, without simple hairs; style *c.*20mm, red or cream, slender, with some scales at the base, glabrous distally; stigma sub-globose, greenish yellow, 5-lobed. **Fruit** 15–20 x 3–5mm, fusiform.

Papua New Guinea, Eastern Highlands, Goroka subdistrict, Kerigomna; Western Highlands, Upper Minj Valley on the Minj–Nona Divide; Mt Ormogadzin. Growing near the margins of forest grassland or alpine shrubberies, 3000–3400m. Recorded in the wild flowering in March, May and July; probably to be found flowering throughout the year.

There is still some confusion between this species and *R. caliginis*. Kores (1984) distinguished *R. caliginis* from *R. hooglandii* 'on the basis of its patent, slightly or non-revolute leaves; golden-brown more or less stellate scales; conspicuously verrucose [warty] older branchlets; ovate perulae [bracts] which are either entirely glabrous or with a few scattered scales and tubular pink or red flowers'. There is also a distributional and altitude difference cited: *R. hooglandii* is said to be from 'the north central portion of Papua New Guinea', 3050–3400m, while *R. caliginis* is restricted to the extreme north western portion of Papua New Guinea from 2400 to 2850m. A collection by T.M. Reeve (444) from Mt Miap combines the narrow revolute leaves with very scaly, subulate bracts coming from the classic area of *R. caliginis*. The collection of J.M. Mangen (2021) from West New Guinea also has extremely narrow revolute leaves, is from the lowest elevation recorded (1650m) and should therefore be referred to *R. caliginis*; unfortunately this specimen lacks flower buds. Both species are likely to have both white- and pink-flowered forms, and the colour of the scales is difficult as a character. The most reliable difference would appear to be the difference in flower bud morphology which at present correlates with altitude and is used here to discriminate between these two species.

Collected as living material by Michael Black in 1965 it was cultivated in his greenhouse at Grasmere in the Lake District (UK) but has not survived. Subsequent collections also seem to have perished so that this species does not appear to be in cultivation at the present time.

62. Rhododendron hyacinthosmum Sleumer
Blumea 1973. 21(2): 363.
Type: Cruttwell 1529, 6 June 1969. New Guinea (E), Milne Bay District, Mt Wayaat on the Gamatawa side, 1900m (K, L).
Derivation: The collector making a comparison between the scent of this species and that of hyacinth plants (Liliaceae), noted for their powerfully scented flowers.

Shrub to 3m. Twigs *c.*4mm in diameter, rounded, stellate scaly; internodes 3–6cm. **Leaves** 3 together in pseudo-whorls and spirally along the internodes. **Blade** 60–90 x 35–50mm, elliptic, broadly elliptic or ovate elliptic; apex rounded or obtuse; margin revolute; base rounded to weakly cordate; when young golden stellate-scaly on both sides, becoming glabrescent above but rough with epidermal tubercles; below more persistently scaly. **Scales** stellately divided, tapering to a short foot with distinct, whitish epidermal tubercles when mature and dry, rough to the touch. Mid-vein only slightly impressed above, grooved for 5–8mm proximally; strongly raised beneath; lateral veins 6–7 per side, irregular, visibly raised on both sides, reticulation obscure below. **Petiole** 7–12 x 2–3.5mm, only faintly grooved, densely scaly, the scales leaving a papillose surface when they have gone.

Flower buds to 35 x 17mm, ovoid, smooth, green. Bracts to 45 x 20mm, ovate to sub-spathulate, appressed hairy on both sides and with a few small brown scales outside and prominent brown marginal scales. Bracteoles 18–30mm, linear, channelled, somewhat broadened upwards to 2mm wide, densely hairy and with scales along the margins. Inflorescence 2–5-flowered in an open umbel, the flowers horizontal to half-hanging. Pedicels 8–10 x 2mm, densely scaly and with hairs protruding above the scales. Calyx *c.*7mm in diameter, 5-lobed, densely scaly and white hairy outside, glabrous inside, the lobes *c.*2mm long. **Corolla** 70–100 x 70–75mm, 5-lobed, tubular below, expanded above, white with a waxy appearance but spotted with pink at the base of the lobes, strongly scented; tube 60–70 x 7–8 x 15–20mm, glabrous outside, hairy for 40–50mm proximally inside; lobes 30–40 x 26–30mm, rounded to spathulate, glabrous. **Stamens** *c.*60mm long, exserted to *c.*15mm, at first in a tight cluster in the centre of the flower, later spreading irregularly around the mouth; filaments densely to laxly hairy, white; anthers 7–8 x *c.*1.5mm, creamy to pale yellow, obtuse at the base, the pollen pale yellow. Disc, white hairy. **Ovary** cylindrical, *c.*10 x 4mm, white hairy, gradually contracted distally; style *c.*50mm, the proximal 40mm densely covered in distally pointing white hairs, the ultimate 10mm glabrous,

Ken Grant

Rhododendron hyacinthosmum.

lying on the lower side of the flower, curving upwards later; stigma green, *c.*2mm in diameter. **Fruit** (sub-mature) 30–40 x *c.*10mm, oblong, grooved, hairy.

Papua New Guinea, Milne Bay District, Daga country, Mt Wayat, on the very top of the pass; Mt Mon, Maneau Range; Mt Suckling area, Mt Gauru. Epiphytic or terrestrial shrub at 1800–2070m, in mossy forest.

Seedlings were reported growing in Melbourne in 1971 from material sent by Canon Cruttwell at an unconfirmed date (Cruttwell 1971). It was material from these plants from which the species was later described. It has been widely distributed but also confused, so that not all plants grown under this name are correctly attributable to this species. It grows well in Edinburgh, but slowly, flowering sparingly with deliciously scented flowers mostly in the autumn.

63. Rhododendron kerowagiense Argent
Folia Malaysiana 2003. 4(2): 108.
Type: Umba for Katik, LAE 74842, 20 Aug. 1980. Papua New Guinea, Simbu Province, Kerowagi Subprovince, Mt Wilhelm, *c.*3600m (LAE, E, K).
Derivation: Named after the subprovince from which this plant was collected.

Shrub to 2m. Twigs 1–2mm in diameter, at first minutely rough with stellate scales which leave hair-like stalks but quickly the stems become smooth; internodes 1.5–4cm. **Leaves** clustered into loose pseudowhorls of 7–12 variably sized leaves. **Blade** 7–15 x 3–5mm, ovate or sometimes broadly elliptic, mostly widest in the lower ⅓, occasionally about the middle; apex acute, occasionally obtuse to rounded and sometimes apiculate; margin strongly revolute; base narrowly to broadly tapering; glabrescent above, densely brown scaly below. **Scales** dendroid, deeply stellately divided, each on top of a minute epidermal tubercle. Mid-vein weakly impressed above, very prominent beneath; lateral veins obscure. **Petiole** 1–2 x 1mm, densely scaly.

Flower buds ovoid, acute, often lateral. Bracts to 8 x 5mm; outer appressed, with short subulate points, inner, ovate, abruptly subulate-acuminate, fringed along the margins with large scales and densely but fragilely scaly outside, revealing short, white semi-appressed simple hairs in the upper ½ outside when the scales have fallen, glabrous inside. **Flowers** solitary or up to 4 in an open umbel. Pedicels *c.*10 x 1mm, slender, densely stellate-scaly. Calyx *c.*2mm in diameter, disc-like, not or very shortly obtusely lobed, scaly outside. **Corolla** 15–20mm, dark red, tubular, slightly expanded distally; tube *c.*12 x 4 x 5mm, slightly curved, densely stellate-scaly but without hairs outside, very laxly patent hairy inside; lobes *c.*7 x 5mm, broadly obovate to sub-circular. **Stamens** unequal, well exserted from the mouth, about as long as the corolla; filaments narrowly linear, glabrous; anthers *c.*2 x 1mm, oblong. Disc glabrous or very minutely hairy on the upper margin. **Ovary** *c*.6 x 2–2.5mm, sub-cylindrical, densely stellate-scaly, and with a few simple white hairs, which are completely obscured by the scales, gradually tapering distally; style thick, scaly and with simple hairs in the proximal ⅓, then laxly patently hairy for another ⅓, glabrous distally; stigma broadly rounded, obscurely 5-lobed. **Fruit** (immature) 20 x 4mm, fusiform.

Papua New Guinea, Simbu Province, Kerowagi Subprovince, Mt Wilhelm. Terrestrial in open montane shrubbery at *c*.3600m. *Fl*. Aug.

Distinctive with its very small ovate leaves. It is undoubtedly closely related to *R. rarum*, with which it shares many characters. *Rhododendron rarum* does not have hairs on the ovary although they are hidden and difficult to see in this species. Where hairs occur on the style of *R. rarum*, they are much longer, and clearly overtop the scales. In *R. kerowagiense* the hairs and scales are about the same length on the style. The material examined is slightly mouldy which makes it difficult to be absolutely certain that the filaments are glabrous.

---

64. Rhododendron konori Becc.

Malesia 1878. I: 200.
Type: Beccari 5809. New Guinea (W), Mt Arfak (Fl, A, B, L, fragment).
Derivation: Named after a god or semi-mythical leader of the Hattam people in New Guinea.

Var. **konori**

Shrub or small tree to 6m. Twigs 3–9mm in diameter, robust, rounded, at first stellately-scaly, quickly glabrescent, at first rough, finally smooth, often whitish in dry specimens; internodes 6–20cm, sometimes with several, much reduced scattered and quickly deciduous cataphylls. **Leaves** scattered in loose pseudowhorls or sometimes more tightly crowded 3–5 together. **Blade** 70–200 x 50–100mm, elliptic or broadly-elliptic, more rarely ovate; apex obtuse or rounded; margin entire, flat or slightly revolute; base broadly tapering to rounded, more rarely sub-cordate, densely covered with brown fragile scales on both sides when young, glabrescent on both sides at maturity except along the mid-vein. **Scales** deeply stellately divided, dendroid, each on top of a paler permanent epidermal tubercle. Mid-vein as broad as the petiole at the base, weakly raised above in the proximal ½, becoming slightly impressed distally, strongly prominent in the proximal ½ beneath; lateral veins 7–11 per side, straight, curved and less visible towards the edge, anastomosing, slightly impressed above in fully mature leaves, somewhat raised beneath, often obscure on both sides, reticulation inconspicuous. **Petiole** 10–35 x 2–5mm, rounded, without a groove, densely scaly, rough in later stages.

Flower buds (see p.327) to 50–110 x 40–50mm, ovoid, the bracts tightly appressed, dark purple. Bracts to 75 x 30mm; outer bracts ovate, the inner ones obovate-spathulate, rough outside with minute stiff hairs or their remaining warty bases. Bracteoles to 50 x 1–4mm, linear-spathulate, often divided into teeth distally, sub-densely

Rhododendron konori var. *konori*.

hairy, white. Inflorescence of 4–10 flowers in an open umbel, the flowers horizontal to half-hanging. Pedicels 4–15 x 2–4mm, densely brown stellately scaly, sometimes hairy below the calyx. Calyx 6–10mm in diameter, distinctly oblique, shortly (1–2mm) irregularly and obtusely 6–7-lobed, sometimes with one or more lobes up to 15mm, stellate-scaly outside and often with some stiff hairs, whitish ciliate or fringed on the margin. **Corolla** 80–190 x 70–150mm, tubular below, expanded, funnel-shaped, towards the lobes, fleshy, pure white, or pink, often with pink spots at the bases of the lobes, sweetly and powerfully scented; tube 60–110 x 6–15 x 10–20mm, cylindrical, or sometimes slightly 7-angled, laxly scaly or glabrous outside, densely retrorse hairy inside; lobes 40–80 x 30–60mm, 6 or 7, spreading, obovate-spathulate to sub-circular, often sinuous distally. **Stamens** 12 or 14, unequal, lying on the lower side of the flower, mostly exserted for 10–20mm; filaments white, densely hairy and linear proximally, glabrous and almost filiform in the distal ⅓; anthers 8–15 x *c*.1.5mm, orange or yellowish, linear-oblong. Disc densely white-hairy. Ovary 10–15 x 4–7mm, sub-cylindrical, somewhat tapering towards the base, densely covered with yellowish, stiff, forwardly directed hairs which cover the numerous scales, abruptly tapering distally; style 40–85mm, white to reddish, rapidly elongating during and after flowering, attaining the length of the corolla in later stages, densely hairy and laxly stellate-scaly in the proximal ½, gradually more scaly and less hairy in the following ¼, then exclusively scaly, finally glabrous in the distal ⅕–¼; stigma 5–7mm in diameter, yellow, globose, shortly 6–7-lobed. **Fruit** 40–120 x 12–18mm, fusiform, widest a little below the middle, gradually tapering to the apex, rough with persistent hairs and numerous minute tubercles and surmounted by the persistent style; stigma lobes to 2 x 1mm. Capsule irregularly splitting from the top, the valves twisting after the outer coat has been shed. Seeds narrowly fusiform, flattened, 6–10mm, without tails 1.75mm, the longest tail 5mm.

Indonesia, New Guinea (W), from the Vogelkop Peninsula in the west throughout the main ranges to **Papua New Guinea** where it reaches the easternmost tip of the island; also recorded from Fergusson Is., New Britain and New Ireland. Epiphytic in montane forest, or terrestrial at forest margins and other open areas on burned open summits, also on peat bogs, swamps or marsh. A common and widespread species, 750–2500m. *Fl.* Jan.–Dec.

Introduced into cultivation in the 1960s, probably first distributed from the Department of Forests in Lae. It performs well in cultivation with its large white or pale pink, beautifully and powerfully scented flowers. Rather large for pot cultivation it grows best if given space in an open

bed. Although spectacular, flowers in cultivation never match the proportions of those seen in the wild, where the best plants often grow high in large old trees shedding plate-sized corollas to the ground. *Rhododendron konori* has been introduced into horticulture from various places in New Guinea, especially from the Arfak Mts, where it grows in abundance around the Anggi Lakes. It apparently hybridises there locally with *R. asperum*, which is often found in the same places. These hybrids have smaller, 6- or 7-lobed corollas and more ovate and more shortly petioled leaves than are found in typical *R. konori*. It is possible that most or all forms of *R. konori* in the Arfak Mts with such smaller corollas and smaller fruits are due to introgression of *R. asperum*, though the leaves may be typical of *R. konori*. In one place with abundant *R. konori* and *R. laetum*, growing together, Sleumer (1966) recorded a fruiting specimen which was apparently intermediate in character between these species.

Var. **phaeopeplum** (Sleumer) Argent

Type: Eyma 4818, 29 March 1939. New Guinea (W), Wissel Lake region, Enarotali-Kugapa-Egogitoagapa-Enarotali (L, A, BO, K).

Derivation: Greek – *phaos* – dusky; *peplos* – cover. Alluding to the dark-coloured covering of scales.

Synonym: *R. phaeopeplum* Sleumer, Reinwardtia 1960. 5: 92.

Differing from the type in being small in all its parts. Leaves up to 100 x 50mm, with a petiole up to 15 x 3mm. Inflorescence up to 6-flowered. Corolla up to 90mm long; tube up to 45mm long, anthers 6–7mm.

Indonesia, New Guinea (W), Wissel Lakes region and Arfak Mts, above the Wajori R. Heathland and open, fern-covered ridge within the *Nothofagus–Castanopsis* forest, 1300m.

Rhododendron konori var.*phaeopeplum* is a small form of *R. konori*, and possibly in the Wissel Lakes region a hybrid of *R. konori* with a related species of the same subsection with smaller flowers, possibly *R. rappardii*. A number of natural, intermediate hybrids have been observed with the 5-lobed, orange-red-flowered *R. zoelleri*, which is abundant in the same place. These exhibited pale pink, 5- and 6-lobed corollas on the same plant, longer, more acuminate, thinner, glossy leaves, on which the epidermal tubercles are much less distinct than in species of section *Phaeovireya* in general, and longer, more slender pedicels. A few specimens of *R. zoelleri*, typical except for the white corollas with a yellowish colour, at least at the tube, were found in the same place; these are probably due to a slight introgression with *R. phaeopeplum* (Sleumer 1966).

Ross Eudal

Rhododendron leptanthum.

65. Rhododendron leptanthum F.Muell.
Trans. R. Soc. Vict. n.s. 1889. 1(2): 24.
Type: McGregor 1889. New Guinea (E), Southeastern part, Central District, Summits of Owen Stanley Range (MEL).
Derivation: Greek – *leptos* – thin; *anthos* – flower. Thin flowered.

Synonym: *R. warianum* Schltr., Bot. Jahr. 1918. 55: 151.

Shrub to 3m, with thick roots and often hanging branches. Twigs *c*.1.5mm in diameter, slender, densely covered with red-brown, stellate scales when young, glabrescent and a little rough in older parts; internodes 2–12cm. **Leaves** mostly 3–4 together in tight pseudowhorls. **Blade** 25–65 x 14–30mm, ovate or broadly elliptic; apex broadly acute, obtuse or rounded; margin entire, flat or weakly revolute; base rounded, to sub-cordate; equally sub-densely scaly on both sides. **Scales** small, deeply stellately divided and shortly dendroid, each on top of minute paler, often nearly white tubercles beneath, the tubercles less distinct on the upper surface, quickly glabrescent above, more slowly beneath. Mid-vein weakly impressed above, strongly prominent beneath; lateral veins 5–7 per side, straight, anastomosing near the edge, slightly impressed above, somewhat raised beneath, reticulation lax, visible above, smooth to distinctly

raised or inconspicuous beneath. **Petiole** 2–5 x 2–3mm, grooved above, densely brown-scaly.

Flower buds ovoid, to 14 x 8mm, predominantly green with all the bract tips appressed, with a few brown scales outside near the apices and along the midline of the bracts especially near the base of the bud. Bracts to 12 x 6mm, ovate to spathulate; outer smaller ones sub-subulate, upper ones mucronate. Bracteoles to 15 x 2mm, linear-spathulate, glabrous. Inflorescence 2–5-flowered, in open one-sided umbels, the flowers semi-erect to half-hanging. Pedicels 7–15 x 1.5–2mm, pale green but densely brown-scaly. Calyx to 5mm in diameter, a low circular disc, or very shortly obtusely 5-toothed. **Corolla** 25–35 x 25–35mm, tubular, zygomorphic, deep pink; tube 25–30 x 7–8 x 10–13mm, curved, laxly to sub-densely, stellately scaly outside, glabrous inside; lobes 12–15 x 10–15mm, broadly spathulate to sub-circular, mostly emarginate, often with scales on the central basal areas outside. **Stamens** clustered on the upper side of the corolla, exserted *c*.8mm; filaments red, narrowly linear, glabrous or with some scattered hairs; anthers *c*.1.6 x 1mm, brown or dark purple. Disc glabrous. **Ovary** 5–6 x 2–3mm, elongate-conical, densely brown-stellate-scaly, gradually tapering distally; style held on the upper side of the corolla tube, pink, stellate scaly almost to the top; stigma broadly club-shaped, becoming exserted to *c.*6mm, positioned on the upper side of the tube. **Fruit** 30–40 x 4–6mm, fusiform, often curved, densely brown stellately scaly. Seeds 8mm, without tails *c.*1mm, the longest tail 4mm.

Papua New Guinea, Madang to Milne Bay Districts. Terrestrial on rocks or exposed cliff faces, epiphytic on big branches of high trees or growing on fallen trunks in mossy forest. Sometimes common. 1370–2250m. *Fl.* Jan.–Oct.

The first recorded introduction of this species was from seed collected at Edie Creek above Wau which was sent by John Womersley to Edinburgh in 1961. Other introductions were made in the later 1960s by Paddy Woods and Michael Black and this species was introduced to Australia by L.A. Craven in 1966. *Rhododendron leptanthum* performs well in cultivation but is exceedingly variable. The best forms were introduced by Paddy Woods; these are compact and slow growing but produce a profusion of the bright pink flowers over a long period, usually in the northern spring or early summer. Forms agreeing with the description of *R. warianum* were collected by John Sandham but apart from the extreme leaf shape and general vigour these plants are no different to *R. leptanthum* as conceived here.

---

66. **Rhododendron melantherum** Schltr.

Bot. Jahr. 1918. 55 : 152.
Type: Ledermann 12161. New Guinea (NE), Schrader Mts (B†, no lectotype designated).
Derivation: Greek – *melas* – black; *antherae* – anthers. Alluding to the very dark colour of the anthers.

Much-branched shrub to 50cm. Twigs spreading, densely leafy, densely reddish brown-scaly in the young parts, the internodes short. **Leaves** 24–40 x 12–17mm, opposite, elliptic, sub-sessile, the apex obtusely acuminate; base tapering, laxly reddish-brown-stellate-scaly beneath, glabrescent above. **Petiole** 2–4mm, reddish-brown scaly.
 Flowers solitary. Pedicels *c.*15mm, slender, densely reddish-brown-scaly. Calyx *c.*2.5mm in diameter, reddish-brown-scaly, very shortly 5-lobed. **Corolla** tubular, strongly zygomorphic, dark blood red, slightly curved and dilated to *c.*10mm diameter at the apex, sparsely shortly hairy outside, glabrous inside, 27mm long, lobes *c.*7mm in diameter, obovate-sub-circular, truncate-obtuse. **Stamens** *c.*23mm; filaments filiform, sparsely hairy; anthers 2.5mm, oblong, blackish red. **Ovary** oblong, slightly 5-grooved lengthwise, densely reddish-brown hairy; style filiform, shortly finely hairy, almost equalling the stamens in length; stigma globose, 5-lobed.

Papua New Guinea, Schrader Mts, once found in mountain forest at 2070m. *Fl.* June.

No type material is known to be preserved; this description is drawn from Sleumer's (1966) translation of the original. This remains an imperfectly known species.

---

67. **Rhododendron neobritannicum** Sleumer

Blumea 1973. 21 : 361.
Type: Croft & Katik NGF 15558, 15 May 1973. New Britain, Kandrian subdistrict, Mt Klangal (summit), 25 miles NNE of Gasmata, 800m (L, LAE).
Derivation: Named after the island of New Britain from where it comes.

Shrub to *c.*30cm. Twigs 0.5–1mm in diameter, very slender, stellately scaly with brown scales, when young, later glabrescent; internodes 2–8cm. **Leaves** in pseudo-whorls, 2–4 together. **Blade** 20–50 x 5–20mm, narrowly to broadly elliptic; apex gradually tapering, broadly acute to obtuse; margin flat or a little revolute; base tapering; densely brown scaly on both sides when young. **Scales** deeply stellate, fragile; with a small centre from a minute tubercle. Mid-vein smooth above, raised below; lateral veins 5–6 per side, obscure on both sides, without reticulation. **Petiole** 2–4mm, slender, initially stellately scaly.
 Bracts to 8mm, ovate acuminate; outer ones narrowly ovate, subulate, outside densely stellately scaly, without hairs. Bracteoles *c.*10 x 1.5mm, almost linear, slightly broadened distally, sub-glabrous. Inflorescence 2–3-flowered, flowers half-hanging to hanging. Pedicels 5–9 x *c.*1mm, slender, brown-stellate-scaly, without hairs. Calyx *c.*3mm in diameter, obliquely saucer-shaped, hardly lobed, stellately scaly outside. **Corolla** 15mm, tubular, a little expanded at the lobes, slender, red or purple; tube *c.*10 x 2.5 x 3.5mm, glabrous on both sides, slightly 5-lobed at the base; lobes *c.*5 x 5mm, sub-circular. **Stamens** not exserted; filaments glabrous; anthers *c.*1mm long. Disc very shortly hairy. **Ovary** *c.*4 x 1.5mm, cylindrical, very densely brown stellate-scaly, without hairs, tapering distally; style *c.*6mm, scaly at the base, then distally shortly, grey-patently hairy, almost to the apex; stigma club-shaped. **Fruit** *c.*20 x 4mm, narrowly fusiform, scaly.

Papua New Guinea, New Britain, Kandrian subdistrict, Mt Klangal; Pomeo subdistrict, Mt Lululua; Talsea subdistrict, Mt Talawe, Mt Tangis, 800–1585m. Epiphytic in *Castanopsis* or *Notho-fagus* dominated montane forest.

Sleumer (1973) notes the similarity of this species to *R. rarum*. It is distinguished as the leaves are widest in the middle, the corolla is glabrous and the anthers are much smaller. Never known to have been cultivated.

---

68. Rhododendron neriifolium Schltr.

Bot. Jahr. 1918. 55: 149.

Type: Ledermann 11777. New Guinea (E), Northern part, Sepik R. region, Mt Schrader (B†).

Derivation: Latin – *Nerium oleander* L., the oleander (Apocynaceae); *folium* – leaved. The leaves being of similar shape to those of the oleander.

Shrub. Twigs elongate, flaccid, rounded, laxly foliate, densely stellately scaly. **Leaves** opposite. **Blade** 35–70 x 5–9mm, very narrowly ovate or nearly linear; apex acute; margin entire; base broadly tapering, nearly rounded; scaly on both sides initially, glabrescent above, more persistently scaly beneath. **Petiole** 2–3mm.

Inflorescence of solitary flowers. Pedicels to 5mm, densely stellately scaly. Calyx 2.5–3mm in diameter, disc-shaped, densely stellately scaly, very shortly 5-lobed. **Corolla** 27–33mm, tubular, bright pink-red to purplish, zygomorphic and slightly curved; tube densely stellately scaly outside, glabrous inside; lobed to *c.*⅕, lobes subcircular, erecto-patent. **Stamens** to 25mm, very slender; filaments filiform, laxly hairy; anthers *c.*2mm, oval. **Ovary** *c.*6mm, oblong, densely stellately scaly; style *c.*6mm, slender, laxly hairy; stigma globose, 6-lobed.

Papua New Guinea, Schrader Mts, in mountain forest, epiphytic at 2070m. *Fl.* May–June.

The type material was destroyed in Berlin and this species has still to be recollected. The description given is from Sleumer's (1966) translation of the original diagnosis. It would be surprising if the leaves were really opposite; this presumably relates to a very poor specimen either growing weakly or having lost most of its leaves in handling. Otherwise the only good character separating this species from *R. rarum* is the very short pedicels. The short style would seem to be a less reliable character although emphasised by Schlechter when describing this species. It could reflect the fact that the flowers were very young when collected. Kores (1982) notes *R. rarum* as being reported from the West Sepik District which if true means the distribution of this species comes very close to if not overlapping that of *R. neriifolium* and would cast doubt on the validity of this species.

69. Rhododendron opulentum Sleumer

Reinwardtia 1960. 5: 85.

Type: Brass 12001, Jan. 1939. New Guinea (W), Northern part: 15km SW of Bernhard Camp, Idenberg R. (A, L).

Derivation: Latin – *opulentus* – sumptuous; no doubt an impressive plant.

Shrub to 1m. Twigs semi-rounded, the tips densely brown stellate-scaly, the older parts glabrescent and rough with minute tubercles; internodes 10–20cm. **Leaves** laxly spiral. **Blade** 60–100 x 30–40mm, broadly elliptic; apex shortly acuminate, sub-acute or sub-obtuse; margin slightly wavy or revolute; base very broadly tapering to rounded; when young densely brown-scaly above and beneath, mature blades glabrescent except along the mid-vein, densely, minutely tubercled and very rough to the touch. **Scales** minute, deeply stellately divided, shortly dendroid, each on top of a minute pale persistent epidermal tubercle. Mid-vein thick, flattened, a little raised and impressed in the lower part above, prominent beneath; lateral veins *c.*10 per side, dense, irregular, straight below, anastomosing near the margin, slightly prominent on both sides, veins laxly prominently reticulate, finer reticulation obscure. **Petiole** *c.*10 x 2.5mm, flattened, at first densely scaly, rough when the scales have gone.

Bracts to 45 x 20mm; middle and inner bracts spathulate, densely white hairy both in and outside. Bracteoles to 30 x 2mm, linear, very densely whitish hairy, with partly appressed hairs. Inflorescence of 7–8 flowers in an open umbel. Pedicels 8–10 x *c.*1.5mm, densely appressed-hairy and laxly stellately scaly, with fragile scales. Calyx *c.*4mm in diameter, oblique, circular, obscurely 5–6-lobed, densely hairy and scaly outside. **Corolla** 90–100 x 40–50mm, elongate-tubular below, expanded above, fragrant, pink at the tube, shading to white at the lobes; tube 60–70 x 4–5 x *c.*8mm, cylindrical, glabrous outside, densely covered with long retrorse hairs almost to the mouth inside; lobes 25–30 x 18–25mm, broadly obovate to sub-circular, glabrous. **Stamens** exserted to *c.*10mm; filaments linear and densely covered with retrorse hairs below, more laxly hairy distally, filiform and glabrous in the ultimate ¼; anthers *c.*6 x 1.2mm, elongate-oblong, the base obtuse. Disc white hairy. **Ovary** 10–12 x *c.*2.5mm, elongate-cylindrical, very densely stellately scaly and laxly short-hairy (the hairs mostly hidden by the scales), gradually tapering distally; style 50–60mm, thick below, very densely stellately scaly and without hairs in the proximal 30–40mm, more slender and completely glabrous distally; stigma large, globose, distinctly 5-lobed.

Indonesia, New Guinea (W), Bernhard Camp, Idenburg R. and Snow Mountains region E of the Baliem Valley, found as a frequent epiphyte on large trees in mossy forest at 1500–1800m. *Fl.* Jan, Oct.

Not known in cultivation.

70. Rhododendron phaeochitum F.Muell.

Trans. R. Soc. Vict. n.s. 1889. 1(2): 23.
Type: MacGregor *s.n.*, 1889. New Guinea, SE, Milne Bay District, Mt Musgrave (MEL, L, fragment).
Derivation: Greek – *phaios* – dark or dusky; *chiton* – a tunic. Alluding to the dense brown covering of scales.

Shrub, *c.*1m. Twigs *c.*2mm in diameter, slender, densely dark brown stellate-scaly at first, glabrescent and rough later; internodes 3–8cm. **Leaves** 3–4 together in pseudo-whorls or more loosely crowded in tight spirals. **Blade** 40–100 x 25–55mm, elliptic or mostly obovate-elliptic; apex rounded, obtuse often apiculate; margin entire, slightly revolute; base broadly tapering or rounded; initially covered with a dense, dark reddish brown covering, of stellate scales on both sides, becoming smooth above but remaining scaly for a longer time beneath, ultimately glabrescent there also, but remaining distinctly rough to the touch. **Scales** small, deeply divided, sub-sessile but each on top of a minute epidermal tubercle, very fragile. Mid-vein slightly impressed above, thick and prominent beneath; lateral veins 5–7 per side, straight below, irregularly curved-ascending and anastomosing in the upper part, faintly prominent when young, a little impressed above in fully mature leaves, prominent beneath, reticulation dense and conspicuous, visible on both sides. **Petiole** 5–8 x 1–1.5mm, not or only weakly and obscurely grooved, densely brown, stellately scaly.

Flower buds to 25 x 13mm, ovoid to ovoid-cylindrical, acutely to obtusely pointed, smooth with all the bracts tightly appressed, predominantly green and glabrous except for the marginal fringes of brown stellate scales. Bracts to 15 x 8mm, ovate to obovate-spathulate, the basal triangular and brown scaly outside, upper ones obtuse, glabrous except for the marginal scales. Bracteoles to 15 x 1mm, linear-spathulate, sub-glabrous. Inflorescence of 2–5 flowers in one-sided umbels, hanging to half-hanging. Pedicels 14–25 x *c.*2mm, densely stellately scaly (sometimes apparently with hairs as the scales can be very pale), green. Calyx *c.*3mm in diameter, reduced to an almost circular disc, which may be irregularly dentate, densely stellate-scaly. **Corolla** tubular below, expanded distally, zygomorphic, pink to deep red, or cream; tube 30–40 x 5–8 x 10–16mm, curved, brown scaly outside, shortly patently white hairy inside; lobes 16 x 13mm, scaly outside except near the margins, gradually reflexed so that the tips are almost perpendicular, overlapping *c.*halfway. **Stamens** exserted to *c.*20mm, clustered together on the upper side of the flower, slightly unequal; filaments dark red, sparsely to densely, patently hairy in the proximal ⅓–½; anthers 2.5–3 x *c.*1mm, purple, oblong. Disc densely white-hairy at the upper margin. **Ovary** 5–7 x 2–3mm, cylindrical, densely and exclusively pale brown-stellate-scaly, tapering distally; style on the upper side of the corolla tube, pale brown-stellately scaly and sometimes very laxly hairy at least in its proximal ½, often to nearly the top, glabrous near the tip; stigma broadly obconical-globose, dark purple, at first below the mouth of the flower, becoming exserted, often beyond the anthers.

Papua New Guinea, West Sepik District, above Telefomin; Western Highlands, Nondugl; Southern Highlands; Enga Province; Simbu (Chimbu) District; Eastern Highlands District, Goroka region; Central District, Mt Musgrave. **Indonesia**, New Guinea (W), recorded from around Wamena. Epiphytic or terrestrial on ridges (including limestone ridges), 2135–2560m. *Fl.* April–Dec.

Rhododendron phaeochitum (pink form).

Rhododendron phaeochitum (white form).

The first reliable introduction in Edinburgh was the attractive albino form introduced by G.A.C. Herklots which was collected in 1964. A pink form of this species was introduced by Michael Black in 1968; his collection flowered for Mr Geoffrey Gorer in September 1977 who provided the flowering material which was figured in *Curtis's Botanical Magazine* (Hunt 1978). The species grows well in cultivation, flowering profusely in irregular flushes. Not all the collections have good colour, some being a rather pale dingy pinkish-orange, but there are good pink forms and the albino form is very striking as the orange-brown scales show brightly against the creamy white corollas which contrast to the dark green but very scaly foliage. The original collection of this species was bright red and this colour form does not appear to be cultivated.

The species is still not clearly distinguishable from *R. beyerinckianum* although as understood here *R. phaeochitum* has larger flatter leaves as well as hairy filaments and disc.

71. Rhododendron phaeochristum Sleumer

Blumea 1963. 12: 95.
Type: Sleumer & Vink 4465, 26 Jan. 1962. New Guinea, (NW), Anggi Gigi Lake (L, A, CANB, G, K, LAE, UC).
Derivation: Greek – *phaeo* – dusky; *christum* – like *christi*. A phaeovireya with similarities to *R. christi*.

Shrub to 4m. Twigs slender, the tips with a dense brown covering of stellate scales; internodes 2–10cm. **Leaves** 4–6 together in pseudowhorls. **Blade** 30–80 x 20–40mm, elliptic to obovate-broadly elliptic; apex obtuse or sub-acuminate; margin slightly revolute at the very edge; base tapering; covered with fragile brown stellate scales initially, early glabrescent with age above, less so below especially on the veins. **Scales** dendroid, with a deeply stellately divided marginal zone, depressed towards the minute centre, which is prolonged downwards into a very slender stem, which rests on a distinct epidermal tubercle. Mid-vein narrowly impressed above, thickly prominent proximally below, less so distally; lateral veins 6–9 per side, irregular, curved-anastomosing before the margin, very slightly impressed or often obscure above, hardly prominent beneath. **Petiole** 8–14 x 1.5–2mm, densely scaly initially.

Flower buds sub-globose, 10–15mm in diameter. Bracts to 12mm, thin, the outer ones ovate, densely stellate-scaly at the midline outside and with a fragile scaly fringe; inner ones sub-spathulate, glabrous. Bracteoles *c*.10 x 1–1.5mm, sub-spathulate-linear, glabrous. Inflorescence of 2–4-flowered open umbels. Pedicels *c*.10mm, slender, densely stellately scaly. Calyx *c*.2.5mm in diameter, obliquely rimmed, minutely 5-lobed, scaly outside. **Corolla** 30–40mm, tubular, curved, expanded at the lobes, zygomorphic, pale to deep red; tube 15–20 x 3 x 5mm, glossy and densely covered with golden scales outside, laxly hairy inside; lobes *c*.10 x 8mm, sub-spathulate-obovate. **Stamens** slightly exserted; filaments linear, densely to laxly hairy in the proximal ¾, glabrous distally; anthers *c*.2 x 1mm, obovate-oblong, dark purple to almost black, the base obtuse. Disc prominently hairy only on the upper margin. **Ovary** 5 x 2.5mm, sub-cylindrical, densely covered with brown stellate scales and paler, appressed hairs, tapering distally; style *c*.12mm, slightly hairy at the base, glabrous distally; stigma club-shaped. **Fruit** 20–25 x 4–5mm, fusiform, densely scaly and hairy.

Indonesia, New Guinea (W), Vogelkop Peninsula, Tamrau, Nettoti and Arfak Mts. Common in the Arfak Mountains around the Anggi Lakes in the understory of *Nothofagus* forest, 1800–2550m, often growing sterile. *Fl.* Jan.

Not known in cultivation.

A natural hybrid of *R. phaeochristum* apparently with *R. culminicola* var. *angiense* was found once in the Arfak Mts near Lake Anggi Gita at 1900m. In general appearance, the stellate scales and in the flowers it displays characters of *R. phaeochristum*, but in the wider, more obovate and blunt leaves, with a less dense covering of stellate scales and no trace of epidermal tubercles, it has the characters of *R. culminicola* var. *angiense*.

72. Rhododendron phaeops Sleumer

Reinwardtia 1960. 5: 90.
Type: Brass L.J. 12658, Feb. 1939. New Guinea (W), Northern part, 18km SW of Bernhard Camp, Idenburg R. (A, L).
Derivation: Greek – *phae* – dark; *opsis* – aspect. An allusion to its dark appearance.

Shrub to 1m. Twigs 2–3mm in diameter, rounded, the tips stellate-scaly, later densely minutely warty and rough to the touch after the scales have gone; internodes 3–6cm. **Leaves** 3–4 together in pseudowhorls. **Blade** 50–80 x 30–50mm, broadly elliptic or ovate-elliptic; apex shortly tapering, obtuse; margin shortly revolute; base very broadly tapering to nearly rounded; stellate-scaly initially on both sides. **Scales** small, fragile, dendroid, each on top of a persistent epidermal tubercle, quickly becoming glabrescent but rough with the tubercles on both sides especially beneath. Mid-vein as thick as the petiole, above prominent and grooved along the midline in its proximal ⅔, impressed distally; lateral veins 6–8 per side, irregular, straight below, obscurely curved-anastomosing before the margin, very slightly impressed above, prominent beneath. **Petiole** 10–15 x *c.*2mm, grooved above, densely scaly.

Inflorescence of 2–3 flowers. Pedicels 15–20 x *c.*1mm, densely brown-stellate-scaly. Calyx 5–6mm in diameter, disc-shaped, densely scaly, without hairs, with 5 distinct, irregular, elongate-triangular sub-acute teeth, which are white-ciliate and spreading to 2–4mm. **Corolla** 55–60mm, zygomorphic, tubular below, gradually widened upwards, red; tube *c.*50 x 6 x 15mm, curved, densely brown stellate-scaly outside, with white long retrorse hairs inside; lobes 15–20 x 12–15mm, broadly spathulate to sub-circular, scaly outside except near the margins, glabrous inside. **Stamens** unequal; filaments 45–55mm, linear, wider and densely patently hairy proximally, narrower and glabrescent to glabrous distally; anthers 5–5.5 x *c.*2mm, brown, broadly oblong. Disc glabrous. **Ovary** *c.*7 x 3mm, obconical-cylindrical, densely covered with sub-appressed, yellowish, stiff hairs which cover the scales, abruptly contracted distally; style thick, densely hairy and laxly scaly below, more laxly patently hairy but more densely scaly distally, glabrous at the upper 5mm below the globose stigma.

Indonesia, New Guinea (W), Bernhard Camp, Idenburg R., *c.*139°E 3°30′S, one collection epiphytic in mossy forest at 2150m. *Fl.* Feb.

Not reported since the original collection and never cultivated.

73. **Rhododendron prainianum** Koord.
Nova Guinea 1909. 8: 187.
Type: Versteeg 1661, 25 Aug. 1907. New Guinea, SW Noord River, on top of 'Resi' ridge, 900m (BO, K, L, U).
Derivation: Named after Sir David Prain, 1857–1954, one time superintendent of the Calcutta Botanic Garden, professor of botany at the medical college in Calcutta and president of the Linnean Society of London.

Shrub to 2m. Twigs *c.*1.5mm in diameter, rounded, slender, few-branched, at first very densely covered with brown, stellate scales, glabrescent below; internodes 2–6cm. **Leaves** 3–6 together in pseudowhorls. **Blade** 50–100 x 4–7mm, linear, sub-sessile, straight; apex gradually tapering, sub-acute; margin very slightly or not revolute; base shortly tapering; initially scaly on both sides, silvery, early glabrescent and rough above, brown and more persistent

beneath. **Scales** with the marginal zone stellately divided, dendroid, with a small centre, each on top of a minute epidermal persistent tubercle. Mid-vein strongly impressed above, prominent beneath, lateral veins not visible. **Petiole** 3–4 x 2mm, not or only very slightly grooved in the distal part, densely scaly.

Flower buds to 15 x 6mm, narrowly ovoid with the points of the bracts erect or slightly spreading. Bracts to 15 x 6mm; the outer ovate, subulate-acuminate, stellate-scaly outside mainly at the apex and fringed with stalked scales. Bracteoles 10–15mm, linear, laxly scaly. **Flowers** solitary or mostly in twos, rarely 3 or 4, hanging. Pedicels 9–12 x *c.*1mm, very slender, densely scaly. Calyx *c.*2mm in diameter, cup-shaped, glabrescent outside, with obscure teeth. **Corolla** 25–27 x *c.*12mm, zygomorphic, membranous, pale purple, without scent, glabrous in and outside (see note below); tube 15–18 x 5 x 6mm, cylindrical, curved; lobes 6–8 x 5–7mm, spreading, obovate-spathulate to sub-circular. **Stamens** 25–28mm; filaments linear below, filiform distally, glabrous; anthers 1.5 x 1mm, broadly oblong. Disc finely shortly hairy on the upper margin. **Ovary** *c.*3–4 x 1–2mm, elongate-conical, very densely brown-stellate-scaly, gradually tapering distally; style 15–20mm, scaly in the proximal ½–⅓, sometimes with a few short hairs in the middle, glabrous distally; stigma shortly obconical. **Fruit** 22 x 3mm, fusiform, densely brown scaly.

Rhododendron prainianum.

Indonesia, New Guinea (W), Hellwig Mts; Orion Mts; Star Mts, Sibil R. Valley; Mt Jaya. Epiphytic or terrestrial on poor clayey soil, disturbed roadside shrubberies, 900–1300m. *Fl.* May–Aug.

Introduced into cultivation in 2000 from Mt Jaya, these plants differ from the original description in having scattered scales on the outside of the corolla tube and hairs on the inside of the corolla tube and on the filaments but the general form and ecology of the plants is similar to that of the type. It is a pretty species with its pale purple, hanging flowers and very scaly, linear leaves but is not particularly showy. It has not been in cultivation long enough to really know how it will perform.

74. Rhododendron rappardii Sleumer

Reinwardtia 1960. 5: 93.
Type: F.W. Rappard 898, 27 Oct. 1955. New Guinea (W), Enarotali, Wissel Lake (L).
Derivation: Named after the collector, who was stationed in the Dutch East Indies for many years.

Shrub to 2.5m. Twigs *c*.2mm in diameter, rounded, sub-densely covered with fragile, brown, stellate scales, initially becoming glabrescent but then covered with numerous minute tubercles and rough to the touch, the older parts often whitish; internodes 4–10cm. **Leaves** 3–5 together in pseudowhorls. **Blade** 40–75 x 25–50mm, broadly elliptic, to nearly rounded; apex broadly tapering, obtuse or rounded; margin entire, slightly or not revolute; base broadly tapering or rounded; brown-scaly on both sides initially, the scales fragile, small, irregularly stellately divided, dendroid, each on a minute epidermal tubercle, very early glabrescent, the surface smooth above, finally glabrescent also beneath, but permanently rough with the numerous minute tubercles. Mid-vein raised and grooved above proximally, becoming very narrow and impressed distally, thick and obtusely prominent beneath; lateral veins 5–8 per side, rising at an acute angle, straight below, less conspicuous towards the margin, minutely impressed in fully mature leaves above, not or only slightly raised beneath, reticulation indistinct. **Petiole** 6–15 x *c*.2mm, rounded, scaly.

Flower buds to 28 x 18mm, ovate, smooth, the apex broadly acute. Bracts 10–15 x 7–10mm; outer bracts ovate, obtuse, scaly in the middle outside, otherwise shortly papillate-hairy; inner ones to 30 x 15mm, elliptic to spathulate, densely and long-hairy on both sides. Bracteoles to 25 x *c*.1mm, linear, laxly hairy. Inflorescence a 5–8-flowered open umbel. Pedicels 5–12 x *c*.1mm, densely brown-stellate-scaly, sub-densely or laxly hairy at least below the calyx. Calyx 2–3mm in diameter, oblique, disc-shaped, small, scaly and shortly hairy outside, ciliate, very shortly 5-lobed. **Corolla** 40–50mm, narrowly funnel-shaped, regular, white or pink; tube *c*.35–40 x 3–4 x 6–8mm, very sparsely stellately scaly or glabrous outside, densely covered with long retrorse hairs inside, straight, gradually widened towards the mouth; lobes 12–18 x 7–12mm, irregular, obovate-spathulate. **Stamens** exserted to 6–9mm; filaments linear, long hairy below, glabrous and filiform distally; anthers 3.5–4 x *c*.1mm, elongate-oblong, the base with two minute points. Disc low, hairy. **Ovary** 6–8 x 2.5–3mm, cylindrical, gradually tapering distally, densely covered with appressed, stiff, yellow, hairs which cover the scales; style nearly as long as the stamens, thick proximally, densely patently hairy and laxly scaly in the proximal ¾, becoming less densely hairy and finally glabrous distally; stigma globose.

Indonesia, New Guinea (W), Wissel Lakes region. In primary or secondary forest, on steep slopes, 1750–2300m, terrestrial on peaty or clayey soil or stony clay, derived from limestone or sandstone, locally common. *Fl.* Jan., March, May, Oct., apparently flowering abundantly in May.

A tentative hybrid with *R. rosendahlii* is recorded by Sleumer in the Leiden herbarium. Not known to be in cultivation.

75. Rhododendron rarum Schltr.

Bot. Jahr. 1918. 55: 150.
Type: Schlechter 18719, Nov. 1908. New Guinea (E), Central part, Bismarck Mts (B†, P, L, fragment).
Derivation: Latin – *rarum* – rare. According to Hunt (1971) named for 'its sparsely branched and loosely leafy habit, not as might be supposed because it is uncommon'.

Slender much-branched shrub to 1.5m. Twigs 1–2mm in diameter, rounded, tips densely brown-scaly, older parts glabrescent, somewhat rough; internodes 2–10cm. **Leaves** 2–5 together in pseudowhorls, often very different in size in the same whorl, with some very reduced leaves between them. **Blade** 25–60 x 6–15mm, narrowly elliptic to narrowly ovate-elliptic, usually broadest in the proximal ⅓; apex gradually long-acuminate, acute but often with the extreme point obtuse or rounded; margin entire or weakly and irregularly sinuate, flat when fresh or slightly revolute especially near the base when dry; base rounded or broadly tapering; with sparse silvery scales above and sparse brown scales below, quickly glabrescent above, more persistently scaly beneath but eventually also glabrescent there, old leaves a little rough to

Rhododendron rarum.

the touch on both sides. **Scales** deeply stellately divided, dendroid, each on top of a minute, persistent, epidermal tubercle. Mid-vein impressed above and prominent beneath; lateral veins obscure. **Petiole** 2–4 x 0.75–1mm, slender, minutely grooved above and densely scaly.

Flower buds to 12 x 7mm, ovoid, acute. Bracts to 10 x 6mm; outer bracts with spreading tips or these sometimes incurved, subulate, densely scaly outside; inner bracts broadly ovate, abruptly subulate, densely brown scaly outside in a broad stripe which expands distally, all bracts marginally scaly and glabrous inside. Bracteoles to 10mm, linear to filiform, scaly in the distal ½. Inflorescence of solitary or paired flowers, rarely more in the wild, although the close proximity of flower buds can give the appearance of 3–4-flowered umbels. **Flowers** hanging or half-hanging. Pedicels 7–10 x *c*.1mm, densely stellately scaly. Calyx *c*.2mm in diameter, small, disc-like, not or very shortly obtusely lobed, scaly. **Corolla** 25–35 x 20–25mm, pink to dark red, distinctly zygomorphic; tube 20–28 x 4–6 x 8–9mm, curved, densely stellately scaly and without hairs outside, glabrous or very laxly hairy inside; lobes 8–12 x 8–13mm, broadly obovate to sub-circular. **Stamens** clustered on the upper side of the corolla, slightly unequal, exserted to *c*.7mm; filaments narrowly linear, pink to red, glabrous proximally, laxly patently hairy in the middle, glabrous distally; anthers *c*.2 x 1mm, oblong, brown

to purplish-black. Disc glabrous or scaly on the upper margin. **Ovary** *c*.6 x 2–2.5mm, sub-cylindrical, densely stellately scaly, gradually tapering distally; style held on the upper side of the tube, pink, scaly in the proximal 1–2mm and with semi-appressed distally pointing hairs to within 1–2mm of the apex; stigma remaining well short of the mouth of the flower even when receptive, club-shaped, purple. **Fruit** 30–40 x 4–5mm, narrowly oblong, the valves curving back and often twisting, the placentae breaking away from the base of the column and curving outwards. Seeds *c*.4mm including the tails.

Papua New Guinea, widespread along the Central and Bismarck Ranges: Western, Southern and Eastern Highlands, West Sepik District. Primarily an epiphytic species of the lower moss forest, it was reported as common, growing terrestrially on road cuts by van Royen & Kores (1982). 1585–3350m. *Fl.* April–Nov.

Introduced into the Royal Botanic Garden Edinburgh in 1961 from material sent by the Department of Forests in Lae. It was grown at Strybing from material collected by Professor Sleumer in 1965 and this was distributed to Kew. This has proved to be an easy and resilient species which, although it can look extremely untidy, with a bit of care makes a fine hanging basket plant. It flowers very freely several times a year and often throws additional odd flowers. It has been used extensively in hybridising and many fine progeny have been produced. Michael Black commented that it should be grown above eye level to appreciate its elegance.

It has not been possible to check a record from the West Sepik District which is outside the main area of distribution of this species and overlaps with the very similar *R. stelligerum*. It is possible that this is a misidentification.

76. Rhododendron revolutum Sleumer
Reinwardtia 1960. 5: 74.
Type: Brass 9528, Aug. 1938. New Guinea (W), Lake Habbema (L, A).
Derivation: Latin – *revolutus* – rolled back, alluding to the strongly revolute margins to the leaves.

Low shrub to 40cm. Twigs *c*.1.5mm in diameter, rounded, the tips densely stellate-scaly and rough; internodes 1–4cm. **Leaves** 4–6 together in pseudowhorls at the upper 2–3 nodes. **Blade** 10–14 x 4–7mm, narrowly ovate; apex shortly acuminate, sub-acute; margin very strongly revolute, often to the mid-vein when dry; base truncate-rounded; densely brown-scaly on both sides, initially early glabrescent and rough above, scaly for longer beneath. **Scales** irregularly and deeply stellately divided, the minute centre extended downwards into a stem-like foot, each scale on top of a thick persistent epidermal tubercle. Mid-vein very slightly impressed above, obscure beneath as are the lateral veins. **Petiole** 0.5–1mm, thick and scaly.

Bracts to 10 x 5mm, ovate-subulate, outer scaly outside; inner ones narrowly ovate-acuminate, with fragile, marginal scales, whose bases give a ciliate appearance to the margin when the scales have gone, glabrous otherwise, on both sides. Bracteoles *c.*10mm, filiform, laxly long-hairy and scaly. Inflorescence of solitary or paired flowers. Pedicels 12–20 x *c.*1mm, very densely brown-stellate-scaly. Calyx 3–4mm in diameter, obliquely disc-shaped, densely brown-stellate-scaly, the lobes obtuse, *c.*1mm. **Corolla** 15–22mm, tubular-funnel-shaped, bright pink; tube 9–14 x 3–4 x 5–6mm, densely stellately scaly outside, glabrous inside; lobes sub-spathulate-circular, wrinkled, 7–9mm in diameter, laxly scaly outside from the base to the middle, otherwise glabrous. **Stamens** unequal, hardly exserted from the mouth; filaments linear, slightly dilated above the base, glabrous; anthers *c.*1.3mm, oblong-elliptic. Disc low, glabrous. **Ovary** *c.*5 x 3mm, ovoid-conical, densely stellately scaly, the apex obtuse or abrupt distally; style *c.*1.5 x 0.4–0.5mm, columnar, glabrous; stigma thick-obconical, slightly 5-lobed. **Fruit** *c.*8 x 4mm, ovoid-ellipsoid, densely stellate-scaly, the style persistent and the stigma distinctly 5-lobed.

Indonesia, New Guinea (W), Lake Habbema. Restricted to crevices and sandy niches on sterile limestone slopes, 3225m. *Fl.* Aug.

Known only from the type collection and never cultivated.

77. Rhododendron rhodochroum Sleumer

Reinwardtia 1969. 5: 87.
Type: Brass 9572, Aug. 1938. New Guinea (W), Lake Habbema (A, L, fragment).
Derivation: Greek – *rhodo* – rose or rosy-red; *chrom* – colour. Alluding to the colour of the flowers.

Shrub. Twigs 5–7mm in diameter, rounded or obtusely angular at the upper internodes, tips very early glabrescent and rough; internodes 4–13cm. **Leaves** spirally arranged and densely aggregated together in the upper ⅓ of the upper 3–4 internodes, or 3–5 together in pseudowhorls. **Blade** 30–75 x 16–50mm, broadly elliptic; apex broadly tapering, obtuse, sometimes apiculate; margin revolute in dry specimens; base slightly cordate, brown stellate-scaly on both sides when young, fragile and

quickly falling above, more slowly beneath, eventually glabrescent on both sides but remaining rough to the touch. **Scales** minute, sub-sessile, each on top of a paler permanent epidermal tubercle. Mid-vein above: impressed proximally, flat in its distal part above; beneath very prominent proximally, less so apically; lateral veins 8–10 per side, spreading, faintly raised on both sides, disappearing towards the margin, often inconspicuous beneath. **Petiole** 2–4 x 1.5–2.5mm.

Bracts to 15 x 8mm, membranous, ovate-elliptic to obovate, obtuse, the outer ones scaly outside, the inner ones glabrous. Bracteoles to 15mm, linear, glabrous. Inflorescence a 3–8-flowered open umbel. Pedicels *c.*20 x 1mm, densely brown-stellate-scaly. Calyx disc-shaped, reflexed, densely scaly outside, the lobes sub-obtuse, 1–1.5mm, not ciliate. **Corolla** 45–55mm, tubular, somewhat curved and zygomorphic, pink; tube 33–40 x 5–6 x 9–10mm, sub-densely stellate-scaly outside, laxly hairy inside; lobes 10–15 x 10–13mm, spreading, broadly obovate. **Stamens** *c.*10mm, unequal, exserted from the tube; filaments linear below, sub-densely hairy at the base, laxly so in the middle, glabrous and filiform distally; anthers 3–3.5 x 1.3mm, obovate-oblong, obtuse at the base. Disc glabrous below, hairy at the upper margin. **Ovary** 6–8 x *c.*3mm, ovoid-conical, densely hairy and stellately scaly, abruptly contracted distally; style densely patently hairy and laxly scaly in the proximal ½, glabrous distally, as long as the stamens or slightly exceeding them; stigma thick, oblique, globose, distinctly 5-lobed.

Indonesia, New Guinea (W), Lake Habbema, at 3225m, common in more open mossy thickets on peat ridges, associated with *R. haematophthalmum. Fl.* Aug.

Apparently not recollected since the original collection. Never cultivated.

78. Rhododendron rubellum Sleumer

Reinwardtia 1960. 5: 94.
Type: Brass 4517, 6 Sept. 1933. New Guinea (E), Central District, Murray Pass, Wharton Range (L, A, BM, BO).
Derivation: Latin – *rubellus* – reddish, alluding to the flower colour.

Erect branching tree to 5m. Twigs 3–5mm in diameter, rounded, densely stellately scaly, glabrescent on older parts; internodes 3–8cm. **Leaves** 4–5 together in pseudowhorls. **Blade** 40–100 x 25–40mm, broadly elliptic, or slightly obovate; apex shortly acuminate, apiculate; margin flat or slightly revolute; base broadly tapering or rounded to slightly sub-cordate, immature ones densely brown-scaly with fragile scales and early glabrescent, leaving the leaves rough with the persistent tubercles above; covered for a longer time beneath with a nearly woolly scaly covering but later leaving the undersurface also rough. **Scales** large, narrowly stellately divided to form dendroid, stellate hairs, each on top of an epidermal tubercle. Mid-vein flat or minutely impressed above, as wide as the petiole and very prominent proximally, gradually less so distally beneath; lateral veins 4–8 per side, at an acute angle, straight below, curved and anastomosing before the margin, forming a lax network with the veins, with indistinct reticulation above but very distinctly so below. **Petiole** 10–17 x 1.5–2mm, grooved above, densely scaly.

Bracts 15–22 x 8–10mm; the outer bracts ovate, sub-obtuse; the inner ones spathulate, both densely hairy on both sides, or minutely hairy or even glabrous. Bracteoles 10–15 x 1–2mm, linear to very narrowly spathulate, laxly to densely patently hairy. Inflorescence a 3–8-flowered, open umbel, the flowers horizontal to half-hanging. Pedicels 8–15 x 1–2mm, densely brown, stellately scaly, but without hairs except immediately below the calyx. Calyx deeply divided into irregular triangular lobes, to 2mm, densely, shortly-hairy and scaly outside and often with a longer fringe of hairs. **Corolla** 40–65 x 30–40mm, tubular, zygomorphic, bright red; tube 30–45 x 6–8 x 10–15mm, very laxly scaly or glabrous outside, with patent or retrorse hairs inside, straight below, curved and gradually dilated upwards; lobes 12–20 x 10–16mm, semi-erect or spreading, irregular, the upper two much larger than the lower three, obovate-spathulate, sometimes nearly circular. **Stamens** exserted to 8mm, unequal, irregularly arranged all round the mouth; the filaments red, linear and densely patently hairy proximally below, gradually less so distally becoming completely glabrous for 6–10mm; anthers 2–5 x 1–1.25mm, elongate-oblong, the base obtuse. Disc glabrous at least at the base. **Ovary** 8–10 x 2.5–3mm, elongate-cylindrical, gradually tapering distally, very densely hairy in the lowest 1mm (which may be the upper margin of the disc), elsewhere densely brown-scaly and hairy with the scales more numerous than the hairs and clearly visible; style as long or a little longer than the corolla tube, laxly hairy and sparsely scaly in the lower ⅓–⅔, glabrous distally; stigma thickly conical-sub-globose. **Fruit** 30–35 x c.6mm, fusiform, densely brown hairy and scaly. Seeds filiform, 3–4mm, with a very narrow tail at both ends.

Papua New Guinea, Wharton and Owen Stanley Ranges, Mt Piora, Mt Victoria, Mt Amorwange, Mt Scratchley. In forests, usually as part of the understory in closed canopy stands of moss forests or more rarely along the margins of alpine grasslands, said to be common at the Murray Pass (Wharton Range). 2050–3100m. *Fl.* June–Sept.

Van Royen & Kores (1982) noted that additional collections from more widespread localities have shown this to be a variable species. It was introduced into cultivation in 1976 via the Wau Ecology Institute from material said to have been collected from the Mt Victoria area. This introduction grows well, is very compact in habit, and has good bronze colour on the new leaves which persists for some time eventually passing to rich dark green. The apiculate leaves are distinctive, the apiculus showing up as a pale green point on the otherwise dark-coloured new leaves. Flowering tends to be once a year in May or June in Edinburgh but is quite prolific. The cultivated plant differs from the original type description in having non-hairy flower buds and much smaller stamens but amendments to the description (van Royen & Kores 1982) cover at least the variation in the flower buds.

79. Rhododendron solitarium Sleumer
Blumea 1963. 12: 94.
Type: Womersley & Thorne NGF 12253, June 1960. New Guinea (E), Morobe District, Edie Creek (L, LAE).
Derivation: Latin – *solitarius* – by itself, alluding to the rare, solitary nature of the original find.

Erect shrub, sprawling, one- or few-stemmed, to 1.5m. Twigs covered with dense dark-brown, stellate scales, which disappear quickly in the wild; internodes 4–7cm. **Leaves** 4–6 together in pseudowhorls. **Blade** 65–120 x 35–60mm, broadly elliptic, or elliptic, sometimes sub-obovate-elliptic; apex rounded or broadly obtuse occasionally slightly retuse, often very shortly mucronate; margin slightly sinuate, flat or weakly recurved; base broadly tapering to rounded; mature leaves glabrescent above, remaining scaly for longer below especially on major veins. **Scales** dendroid, with the marginal zone stellately divided; the small centre deepened and protracted downwards into a short foot, which sits on top of an epidermal tubercle. Mid-vein raised and rapidly tapering for 10–15mm above, then becoming grooved and impressed for the remainder of the proximal ½, finally narrowly impressed distally to the apex; beneath very strongly raised throughout its length; lateral veins 7–9 per side, irregular and often deeply forked, wide-spreading, anastomosing quite a distance before the edge, dissolving into a coarse network of veins, all veinlets deeply impressed above, sharply prominent beneath, the leaves distinctly bullate, dark green above, yellowish-green below. **Petiole** 10–20 x 3–4mm, not or sometimes very weakly grooved above, densely brown-scaly initially, often becoming pink with age as the scales disappear.

Flower buds to 20 x 12mm, ovoid, densely brown scaly, the outermost bracts spreading out, others appressed. Bracteoles 10–15 x 1–2mm, linear to sub-spathulate, with a fragile scaly fringe. Inflorescence of 4–6 flowers in an open or one-sided umbel. Pedicels *c.*15 x 1mm, densely brown-scaly. Calyx *c.*3mm in diameter, obliquely rimmed, the lobes sometimes elongate. **Corolla** 50–80 x 40–45mm, trumpet-ventricose, expanded towards the lobes, white; tube 40–75 x *c.*4–6 x *c.*7–12mm, curved, densely brown, stellately scaly outside, densely covered with retrorse hairs inside; lobes *c.*15–20 x 15–20mm, obovate-spathulate, scaly outside, except near the margins. **Stamens** *c.*50mm, at first clustered on the lower side of the mouth becoming exserted from the throat to *c.*10mm, and irregularly spreading; filaments linear, laxly hairy in the proximal ¾, glabrous distally; anthers 3–3.5mm, oblong, the base obtuse. Disc glabrous below, hairy on the upper margin. **Ovary** *c.*10 x 2.5mm, sub-cylindrical, densely covered with yellowish hairs and scales, tapering gradually distally; style densely to laxly hairy and scaly in the proximal ¾, glabrous distally, lying on the lower side of the tube and becoming exserted to 20mm. **Fruit** *c.*30 x 7mm, fusiform, the valves irregularly twisting and the placentae breaking away from the central column at the top. Seeds variable, 3.5–5mm, without tails *c.*1mm, the longest tail to 2.4mm, the tails often broad with irregularly divided margins, crimped especially distally.

Papua New Guinea, Morobe District, Edie Creek and Merri Creeks; common on Mt Kaindi. At present known only from this very small area. Growing terrestrially on eroded gold workings, on open, *Vaccinium* shrubbery and grass-covered slopes, at 1850m. *Fl.* June.

Introduced into cultivation in Edinburgh by Paddy Woods from Mt Kaindi in 1968, there have doubtless been other introductions and it is now widely grown although not all plants grown under this name are this species. *Rhododendron solitarium* is easily grown, and has very distinctive and attractive, slightly bullate leaves with a clear reticulation of anastomosing veins. The pure white flowers are scented and produced in abundance.

80. Rhododendron spondylophyllum F.Muell.

Trans. R. Soc. Vict. n.s. 1889. 1(2): 23.
Type: MacGregor *s.n.*, 1889. New Guinea (E), Owen Stanley Range, Mt Knutsford (MEL).
Derivation: Greek – *sphondulos* – a vertebra; *phyllum* – leaf. Possibly the rigid branches looking like backbones.

Synonym: *R. cyatheicolum* Sleumer, Reinwardtia 1960. 5: 86.

Shrub with rigid branches, to 40cm. Twigs 2–5mm in diameter, rounded, the tips densely stellately scaly, older parts rough; internodes 3–8cm. **Leaves** 3–5 together in pseudowhorls at the upper 1–2 nodes. **Blade** 20–40 x 12–25mm, ovate; apex shortly and obtusely acuminate; margin distinctly revolute; base rounded to cordate, almost sessile; youngest leaves densely reddish-brown, stellately scaly on both sides becoming smooth above but rough from the tuberculate scale bases below. **Scales** irregularly divided at the margin, dendroid, each on top of a small permanent paler-coloured tubercle. Mid-vein distinctly grooved and impressed above, prominently raised beneath; lateral veins up to 6 per side or obscure. **Petiole** 0.5–1 x 1mm.

Bracts to 15 x 8mm, membranous; outer ones ovate, apiculate, with a prominent keel and scaly at the apex outside, otherwise glabrous apart from the fringe of scales; inner ones ovate-oblong to obovate or truncate-spathulate, glabrous. Bracteoles to 15 x 1mm, narrowly linear below, sub-spathulate at the apex, laxly hairy. Inflorescence a 3–5-flowered umbel. Pedicels 6–20 x 0.7–0.8mm, densely stellately scaly, not hairy at all. Calyx 3–5mm in diameter, disc-shaped, very shortly obtusely 5-lobed, wavy, scaly and sparsely hairy outside, ciliate. **Corolla** 25–45mm, broadly tubular, zygomorphic, pink; tube *c.*18–30 x 4–6 x 6–10mm, minutely stellately scaly and with a few hairs outside, sparsely sub-patently hairy inside, a little curved; lobes 8–13 x 8–10cm, obovate to sub-circular, half-erect to spreading, scaly outside in the proximal ½ except near the margins. **Stamens** as long as the corolla; filaments linear below, densely hairy in the proximal ⅓–½, glabrescent and filiform distally; anthers 2–3 x *c.*1mm, sub-obovate-oblong, the base very shortly appendaged. Disc glabrous. **Ovary** 4–6 x 2–4mm, ovoid-conical, densely yellowish hairy, the hairs pointing distally, and covering the scales, abruptly contracted distally; style densely hairy and sparsely scaly proximally, becoming more sparsely hairy and scaly distally eventually becoming glabrous for 6–8mm, as long as or a little longer than the corolla; stigma globose.

Papua New Guinea, Mt Knutsford, Owen Stanley Range; Mt Victoria; Wharton Range, Murray Pass. Said to be a common epiphyte on grassland tree-ferns, at 2840m on the Murray Pass. *Fl.* June–Sept.

Van Royen & Kores (1982) reduced *R. cyatheicolum* as a synonym under this name. Sleumer (1966) separated the species at couplet 32 (p.502) with *R. cyatheicolum* having longer flowers (more than 4cm vs. less than 2.8cm) and a leaf size difference which overlapped considerably. The shorter flowers of the *R. spondylophyllum* type specimen may well be at least partly due to poor preservation; otherwise the two descriptions are very similar and it seems safe to include *R. cyatheicolum* under *R. spondylophyllum*.

Not known in cultivation.

81. Rhododendron stelligerum Sleumer

Blumea 1961. 11: 115.
Type: Kalkman 4471, 22 July 1959. New Guinea (W), Star Mts, Mt Antares, *c*.3000m (L, K).
Derivation: Latin – *stellula* – star; *igerum* – bearing. With a covering of stars – the stellate scales.

Erect, much-branched shrub to 1.5m. Twigs 1.5–2mm, the tips densely covered with brown stellate scales, older parts glabrescent; internodes 1.5–7cm. **Leaves** 4–5 together in pseudowhorls. **Blade** 20–45 x 3–8mm, sub-linear, to narrowly elliptic; apex sub-acute; margin entire, strongly revolute; base tapering; very densely covered with brown stellate scales, glabrescent and remaining rough to the touch above at maturity, more persistently scaly beneath. **Scales** overlapping, the marginal area wide, deeply and irregularly stellately divided into narrow filiform lobes; centre large, dark brown, tapering downwards into a short stem, or foot, each scale on top of a minute, persistent epidermal tubercle. Mid-vein hardly visible above, obtuse and strongly prominent beneath; lateral veins inconspicuous. **Petiole** 4–6 x *c*.1mm, very densely scaly.

Flower buds ovoid-oblong, *c*.10mm. Bracts to 10 x 5mm, outer bracts broadly subulate, inner ones ovate, narrowed into an acumen of 2–3mm, slightly keeled and scaly in the upper part outside, innermost ones ovate-oblong, obtuse, glabrous but all densely fringed with scales. Bracteoles to 10mm, filiform, laxly scaly with fragile scales. Inflorescence of 2–3 flowers, rarely solitary. Pedicels 12–16 x 0.7–1mm, entirely covered with golden stellate scales. Calyx *c*.2.5mm in diameter, disc-shaped, shortly 5-lobed, or with one or two lobes elongated up to 8mm, densely scaly outside. **Corolla** tubular below, gradually sub-campanulate, expanded upwards, curved, zygomorphic, deep pink; tube 20–32 x 5–6 x 7–9mm, sub-densely covered with golden stellate scales and white

hairs outside; lobes 7–12 x 6–8mm, spreading, broadly spathulate or obovate, with scales at the base outside. **Stamens** exserted from the tube to *c*.7mm, unequal; filaments linear, 1mm wide below, 0.5mm wide in the upper part, glabrous; anthers 2–2.5 x 1.5mm, obovate-oblong. Disc slightly prominent, glabrous. **Ovary** *c*.5 x 2.5mm, sub-cylindrical, densely covered with deeply stellately divided golden scales, but no hairs, gradually narrowed distally; style covered with dense or more laxly distributed scales in the proximal ¾, glabrous distally; stigma shortly 5-lobed. **Fruit** 20–25 x 4mm, sub-cylindrical, slightly curved, densely stellate-scaly, not hairy, splitting into 5 twisted and sub-reflexed valves. Seeds very narrow, almost filiform, 4mm, long-tailed at both ends.

Indonesia, New Guinea (W), Star Mts, Mt Antares. **Papua New Guinea**, West Sepik District, Star Mts, Sirius Range. Reported to be common in semi-alpine shrub vegetation, on Mt Antares. 3000–3050m. *Fl.* July.

Not known in cultivation. Wild hybrids between *R. stelligerum* and *R. delicatulum* were reported by Sleumer from the Star Mts. This species is very similar to *R. rarum* and replaces it further to the west.

82. Rhododendron stolleanum Schltr.

Bot. Jahr. 1917. 55: 143.
Type: Ledermann 12626. New Guinea (E), Upper Sepik R., Camp Felsspitze, *c*.141°30′ E 4°10′ S (B†).
Derivation: Named after Herr Stoll who participated in the expedition on which this plant was collected.

Much-branched shrub to 1m. Twigs rounded, scaly and hairy initially. **Leaves** opposite, narrowly to very narrowly ovate. **Blade** 40–80 x 12–32mm; apex acute or obtuse; base broadly tapering or rounded; sparsely brown-scaly above, covered beneath with a brown scaly covering initially. **Petiole** 3–4mm.

Umbels 2–4-flowered. Pedicels 13–15mm, slender, densely scaly-hairy. Calyx *c*.3mm in diameter, saucer-shaped, very shortly and bluntly 5-lobed. **Corolla** *c*.25mm, tubular, 5-lobed *c*.halfway, glabrous outside, minutely shortly hairy inside, lilac, the lobes obliquely obovate-oval, obtuse, glabrous on both sides. **Stamens** *c*.20mm long; filaments filiform, sparsely shortly hairy or almost glabrous; anthers *c*.1.5mm, oblong. **Ovary** *c*.8mm, narrowly oblong, very densely and shortly stellate-scaly-hairy; style subulate, glabrous; stigma obliquely globose, 5-lobed.

Papua New Guinea, Upper Sepik R. region: camp 'Felsspitze', *c*.141°30′ E 4°10′ S, epiphytic in low mountain forest.

The holotype was destroyed in Berlin and no isotype has as yet been found; the description is derived from Professor Sleumer's translation of the original which was incomplete. Sleumer (1966) noted: 'The position of *R. stolleanum* both in and within the *subsect. Phaeovireya* thus remains somewhat doubtful; yet most of the characters given are those of *R. dielsianum*'. The essential key difference between these species lies in whether the corolla is completely glabrous outside (*R. stolleanum*) or sparsely to more densely scaly (*R. dielsianum*). This difference could easily be accounted for by the scales having been lost in processing of *R. stolleanum*.

83. Rhododendron superbum Sleumer
Reinwardtia 1960. 5: 76.
Type: Clemens 12322, 19 June 1941. New Guinea (E), Mt Saruwaged, A-mieng, on Yaneng R. (a tributary of the Buso R.), 1500–1800m (A).
Derivation: Latin – *superbus* – superb, alluding to the magnificent flowers.

Ssp. superbum

Stiff shrub to 6m. Twigs 5–7mm in diameter, rounded, pale green, densely, fragilely, brown-stellate-scaly, the older parts glabrescent, rough; internodes 5–10cm. **Leaves** 4 together in pseudowhorls or spirally arranged. **Blade** 75–120 x 45–80mm, broadly ovate, broadly elliptic, sometimes obovate-elliptic; apex broadly tapering and shortly acuminate or obtuse to rounded; margin entire, flat; base broadly tapering, truncate to rounded or slightly cordate, young ones densely covered on both sides with small, golden scales quickly becoming glabrescent above, more slowly so beneath, eventually rough on both sides. **Scales** sub-dendroid, irregularly stellately divided at the margin, each on top of a distinct persistent epidermal tubercle. Mid-vein broadly raised at the base, grooved in the proximal ½ above, narrow and impressed distally, beneath broadly raised proximally narrowing and becoming level before the apex; lateral veins 5–8 per side, the two lowest almost from the base of the blade, the upper ones spreading at about 45°, all straight proximally, curved

Rhododendron superbum ssp. *superbum*.

before the edge and anastomosing, a little prominent on both sides, no distinct reticulation visible. **Petiole** 15–30 x 3–5mm, grooved only distally above otherwise smooth and flattened above, brown-scaly and becoming glaucous white with age.

Flower buds to 35 x 25mm, broadly ellipsoid, with a rounded apex, smooth, with all the bracts appressed, green to deep purple. Bracts ovate, tough, densely covered with coarse, thick, hairs and rough to the touch outside. Bracteoles to 50 x 5mm, linear to linear-spathulate, laxly hairy. Inflorescence an open, 3–6-flowered umbel, the flowers horizontal to half-hanging. Pedicels 12–24 x 2–4mm, densely brown, stellate-scaly, sometimes with white hairs especially distally. Calyx 7–9mm in diameter, a low, cup-shaped, disc, scaly outside, with rounded or broadly pointed lobes up to 2mm, distinctly shortly fringed, rarely much larger and petaloid. **Corolla** 55–140 x 70–120mm, funnel- or widely trumpet-shaped, fleshy or waxy in texture, white to cream or very light yellow, sometimes faintly flushed with pink, and shades to deep pink, strongly scented; tube 65–75 x 10–12 x 20–25mm, gradually broadening from the base upwards, laxly scaly to glabrous outside, covered with white, retrorse, dense hairs in the lower ½ inside, glabrous otherwise; lobes 40–50 x 30–35mm, 6–7, spreading horizontally, broadly obovate or spathulate, glabrous. **Stamens** 12 or 14, exserted to 12mm, unequal, clustered on the lower side of the flower; filaments green, linear, *c.*1mm wide at the base, very densely patently hairy below, less so, or even glabrous and narrower in the upper ½–¾; anthers 8–9 x *c.*1.5mm, linear-oblong, white, the cells minutely lobed at the base. Disc *c.*1mm high, glabrous to sparsely hairy. **Ovary** 10–12 x *c.*4mm, elongate-conical, densely covered with brown, stellate scales, somewhat abruptly narrowed distally; style 55–65 x *c.*2mm, red or green, lying on the lower side of the tube but curving upwards as the flower ages to present the stigma in a central position when it is receptive, completely glabrous, or with just a few scales at the base; stigma rounded, 7–8mm in diameter, obscurely 6–7-lobed. **Fruit** *c.*50 x 13mm, cylindrical, shortly narrowed at both ends, widest above the middle. Seeds 7–8mm including the tails.

Papua New Guinea, from Mt Giluwe in the north to Mt Albert Edward in the south on the Central Ranges. It is also known from the Finisterre and Saruwaket Mts and there are records from the outlying islands of New Ireland (Hans Meyer Range), and the Louisiade Archipelago. Generally epiphytic on the upper branches of large trees, apparently with preference just below the true moss forest level; terrestrial on Mt Michael and Mt Giluwe, in low shrubberies and on the edge of cloud forest, 1525–3050m, in Uinba (Minj–Nona Divide) recorded in fallow native gardens at 1970m. *Fl. fr.* April–Sept. in the wild.

Hybridising in the wild with *R. hellwigii* where these species overlap to give deep pink intermediate forms. It is possible that all the really pink forms of *R. superbum* are of hybrid origin.

First introduced into cultivation by Professor Sleumer who distributed seed in 1961 from Marafunga near Goroka; this collection is currently still growing in the Royal Botanic Garden Edinburgh. It was introduced into cultivation in Australia by L.A. Craven in 1966 from near Aseki in the Morobe District and there have been several subsequent introductions, notably by Michael Black, Paddy Woods, Lou Searle and John Sandham. In cultivation it usually flowers in April or May; in Scotland, it is easy to cultivate and will flower quite young but flowers most freely when it is established and fairly large in size when it gives an exquisite display of its large, powerfully scented flowers.

Stonor (1952) described this [as *R. devriesianum vel. aff.*] as growing commonly, but individually, its huge, lily-like flowers making glowing spots of colour among the greens of the innumerable other epiphytes. He stated: 'This wonderful Rhododendron has a rather faint, but exquisite scent, a little reminiscent of the Regale Lily'; he thought this and other high-epiphytic *Rhododendrons* with a delicious scent like *R. agathodaemonis* 'are pollinated by the Lory parrots', some of which live in moss-forests, these being among the few birds with a sense of smell.

Ssp. **ibele** Argent *ssp. nov.*
Type: Argent, Mendum & Smith 19930918, 27 May 2004. Indonesia, Irian Jaya, Ibele Valley near Wamena (BO, E).
Derivation: Named after the river valley where this was first collected.

A ssp. *superbo* corollae tubo brevissimo, disco dense pilis erectis albis piloso et squamis in ovario rotundatis nec lacerato-acutis differt.

Twigs *c.*5mm in diameter, pale green, slightly glaucous, with dense brown scales which quickly fall off. **Leaves** in loose pseudowhorls, 4–10cm apart.

Flower buds green, 35 x 25mm, ovate with a broadly pointed apex, all bracts appressed, the outer broadly ovate or obovate to sub-circular, with the apex splitting to become emarginate, appressed hairy on both sides, and with very sparse small brown scales outside, fringed with scales. Inner floral bracts white, spathulate, hairy on both sides and fringed with scales. Bracteoles white, linear to narrowly spathulate, slightly broadened upwards to 3mm wide, hairy on both sides and fringed with scales.

Inflorescence of 2–3 flowers, held horizontally or half-hanging. Pedicels *c.*16 x 4mm, densely brown scaly and white hairy, becoming densely hairy also distally just below the flower. **Flowers** 75 x 108mm, white, powerfully carnation-scented, mostly 6-lobed, but occasionally 5; tube 35 x 12 x 19mm, straight, green fading to cream; lobes 45 x 40mm, the sides somewhat reflexed overlapping to *c.*⅓, spreading to the horizontal. **Stamens** at first loosely clustered on the lower side of the mouth, spreading irregularly as the flower ages, exserted to 25mm; filaments green to cream, patently hairy in the proximal ½; anthers 8–9mm, white becoming pale brown. Disc green, densely hairy with erect white hairs on the upper side, only sparsely hairy on the side. **Ovary** densely scaly, without hairs; style scaly for *c.*1mm at the base otherwise completely glabrous; style and stigma green, lying on upper side of tube, the stigma at the mouth of the flower on opening, exserted to *c.*25mm with age and strongly curving upwards.

Indonesia, New Guinea (W), Ibele Valley.

This collection keys out in Sleumer (1966) to *R. superbum* but differs in the very short corolla tube, the densely hairy disc and the totally different, rounded, not laciniate pointed scales on the ovary. It is otherwise very similar. It was found while searching for *R. gardenia* in the type locality of this species and was at first thought to be *R. gardenia* but that species has the ovary covered by long simple hairs as well as the scales. This species was growing with *R. inundatum* and a hybrid between these species was collected. It is tempting to think that the distinctive rounded scales of this subspecies might be due to introgression with *R. inundatum*.

84. Rhododendron thaumasianthum Sleumer
Blumea 1963. 12: 98.
Type: Eyma 4984, 31 July 1939. New Guinea (W), Wissel Lake region, Bivouac on Voorrug-Steenlijst, hehlling voortop (L, BO).
Derivation: Greek – *thauma* – a wonder; *anthum* – flower. A wonderful flower.

Synonym: *R. magnificum* Sleumer, Reinwardtia 1960. 5: 84, non K.F.Ward, J. Bot. 1935. 73: 247.

Shrub. Twigs flattened at the ultimate internodes (10cm), densely covered with fragile brown-stellate scales, becoming glabrescent. **Leaves** laxly spirally arranged in the upper ½ of the upper internode, the highest 2 leaves sub-opposite or 3 in a pseudowhorl. **Blade** 80–130 x 40–

70mm, elliptic or sub-ovate-elliptic; apex obtuse, nearly rounded; margin distinctly revolute; base sub-truncate to rounded; young leaves scaly on both sides, quickly glabrescent above, more slowly so beneath, at maturity very densely covered with pale tubercles, that make them rough on both sides. **Scales** small, stellately divided to dendroid, each on top of a distinct epidermal tubercle. Mid-vein as thick as the petiole below, gradually narrower towards the apex of the lamina, slightly impressed above, prominent beneath; lateral veins *c.*8 per side, straight and clearly raised below, disappearing upwards on both sides, no distinct reticulation. **Petiole** 20–25 x 3–4mm, a little flattened, grooved above, densely scaly and minutely warty.

Outer bracts *c.*20 x 10–15mm, ovate, obtuse, rough with numerous, stiff, short hairs both in and outside, middle ones obovate, 25–40 x 20–30mm and similarly rough, innermost ones 40–70 x 25–30mm, spathulate, covered with longer, stiff, appressed hairs at the base outside, minutely tubercled upwards. Bracteoles *c.*50 x 2mm, linear-spathulate, sub-densely hairy. Inflorescence 3–5-flowered. Pedicels 6–15 x 2–2.5mm, brown-stellate-scaly, not hairy. Calyx disc-shaped, membranous, very short, wavy, obscurely lobed, scaly outside, glabrous inside, the lobes very laxly and shortly whitish ciliate. **Corolla** *c.*90mm, funnel-shaped, fleshy, colour not known (white or pinkish?); tube 50 x 8 x 15mm, straight, laxly stellately scaly outside, densely covered with retrorse hairs in the proximal ½ inside; lobes *c.*40 x 20–25mm, 7, obovate-spathulate. **Stamens** 14, 70–80mm long; filaments linear and densely patently long-hairy proximally, becoming more laxly hairy, glabrous distally; anthers 10–11 x 1.5mm, linear-oblong, the base obtuse. Disc densely white-hairy. **Ovary** *c.*2mm long, *c.*5mm diameter below, 2.5mm diameter in the upper part, cylindrical, densely hairy and scaly below, constricted upwards in form of a bottle-neck and exclusively scaly there; style *c.*65mm appearing abruptly joined to the ovary due to the thick scaly covering at its base, completely glabrous above the base, blackish when dry; stigma thick-globose, 7-lobed.

Indonesia, New Guinea (W), Wissel Lakes, apparently epiphytic, known only from the type collection.

Sleumer (1966) commented that this species was 'similar to *R. konori*, but [the] style [was] completely glabrous'. Awaiting further collections but it seems very likely that this will turn out to be just a variant of *R. konori*.

85. Rhododendron truncicola Sleumer

Reinwardtia 1960. 5: 91.

Type: Cruttwell 540, 11 June 1954. New Guinea, PNG. Mt Dayman, Maneao (K, L, fragment).

Derivation: Latin – *truncus* – the trunk of a tree; *colus* – living on. Alluding to the fact that it was described living epiphytically on tree trunks.

Small shrub. Twigs slender, 1.5–2.5mm in diameter, scaly at the tips at first, otherwise minutely rough from the scale bases; internodes 2–4cm. **Leaves** 3–4 together in pseudowhorls at the upper nodes. **Blade** 30–45 x 16–27mm, elliptic or broadly elliptic; apex obtuse to rounded, occasionally minutely retuse; margin entire, narrowly revolute; base broadly tapering to truncate or rounded, above glabrescent or with the remains of scales and with minute tubercles; below more persistently scaly especially along the mid-vein. **Scales** stellate, sub-sessile on top of pale persistent epidermal tubercles. Mid-vein flat or slightly impressed above, slightly prominent beneath especially towards the base of the blade, much more slender than the petiole; lateral veins *c*.6 per side, irregular, straight below, anastomosing with each other before the margin, forming a lax network which is equally raised on both sides when dry, thick, rigid and rough to the touch. **Petiole** 7–10 x *c*.3mm, pale cream, weakly grooved above, densely scaly.

Flower buds 20 x 11mm, pale-green, ellipsoid, the margins of the bracts tightly appressed but the bract tips 'hooded' with the apex of the 'hood' standing out so that the bud has a lumpy appearance. Bracts to 15 x 6mm, ovate to spathulate, the margins only with brown dendroid scales otherwise glabrous, apiculate. Bracteoles to 15mm, filiform with a few long translucent cilia along the edges sometimes with a reduced dendroid scale on the top. Inflorescence a *c*.3-flowered umbel, the flowers half-hanging except where held by the leaves into horizontal or semi-erect positions. Pedicels 10–15 x *c*.0.6mm, pink, densely brown stellate-scaly, without hairs. Calyx disc-shaped, hardly lobed, *c*.2.5mm in diameter, densely scaly and sparsely hairy outside, sparsely ciliate on the margin. **Corolla** 30–35 x 29mm, zygomorphic, tubular, pink; tube 20–25 x 5–10 x 10–13mm, curved, laxly scaly outside, with a few white hairs within; lobes 10–15 x 10–15mm, broadly obovate-spathulate, half overlapping except not or hardly overlapping between the upper 3 and the lower 2, with a few sparse scales outside. **Stamens** at first tightly clustered on the upper side of the flower, exserted to 5mm, later to 10mm and becoming irregularly arranged, (sometimes with 12 stamens); filaments linear, laxly patent-hairy below, glabrous in the upper ⅓; anthers *c*.2.5 x 1mm, dark purple, broadly oblong, the cells very shortly apiculate at the base. Disc glabrous below, hairy at the upper margin. **Ovary** *c*.4 x 1.8mm, cylindrical, densely scaly and laxly hairy, abruptly contracted distally; style held on upper side of the tube, below the anthers on opening, laxly patently hairy and densely scaly in the lower ⅓, glabrous distally; stigma thickly conical-globose, becoming exserted beyond the anthers to *c*.15mm.

Papua New Guinea, Mt Dayman, Mt Maneao and Mt Simpson, Milne Bay District, at *c*.2135m. *Fl*. June.

Introduced into cultivation in New Zealand by Michael Cullinane in 1988, from Mt Simpson where it was growing at 2025m. So far it has flowered in January and April in the UK. A pretty compact species with delightful bright pink flowers.

Rhododendron truncicola.

86. Rhododendron tuberculiferum J.J.Sm.

Med. Rijksherb. 1915. 25: 4.

Type: Pulle 1045, 10 Feb. 1913. New Guinea (W), South-western part, top of Wichmann Mts (BO, lectotype, K, L, U).

Derivation: Latin – *tubercularis* – tubercules; *feram* – to bear. The rhododendron bearing tubercles.

Shrub to 1.5m. Twigs 2–3mm in diameter, rounded, at first with dendroid, stellate scales, the older parts glabrescent and covered in tubercles; internodes 1.8–11cm. **Leaves** 5–7 crowded towards the upper nodes, or in pseudowhorls. **Blade** 17–48 x 10–21mm, ovate, ovate-elliptic or broadly elliptic; apex obtusely acuminate or obtuse, sometimes apiculate; margin weakly to strongly recurved; base rounded-obtuse to slightly cordate, sub-sessile; densely brown-scaly on both sides when very young. **Scales** stellate, sub-sessile or sub-dendroid, each on top of a minute persistent epidermal tubercle, quickly glabrescent especially above, distinctly tuberculate and

Nova Guinea

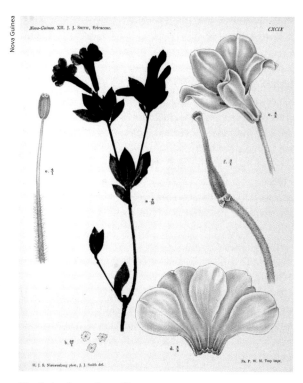

Rhododendron tuberculiferum.

rough to the touch on both sides. Mid-vein impressed above, prominent beneath; lateral veins obscure. **Petiole** 1–4 x 1.5–2mm, at first densely scaly, later rough with tubercles.

Bracts to 18 x 6mm; outer bracts triangular, subulate-acuminate at the apex, the inner ones ovate-acuminate to spathulate and shortly apiculate or obtuse, glabrous on both sides, sub-denticulate. Bracteoles to 20 x *c.*1mm, linear, glabrous. Inflorescence of 2–6 flowers in an umbel. Pedicels 15–30mm, slender, densely scaly. Calyx *c.*4mm in diameter, disc-shaped, oblique, scaly outside, very shortly obtusely 5-lobed. **Corolla** 38–45mm, zygomorphic, tubular below, funnel-shaped towards the mouth, red; tube 25–32 x 4–6 x 8–10mm, densely scaly outside, laxly hairy in the lower ⅔ of the tube inside, glabrous distally; lobes 9–12mm in diameter, 5 (rarely 6), scaly outside except at the margins, sub-circular, retuse. **Stamens** 10, (rarely 12), sub-equal, 28–35mm; filaments linear, laxly hairy proximally, less so upwards, glabrous distally; anthers *c.*3 x 1mm, oblong, the base obtuse. Disc minutely hairy, or practically glabrous. **Ovary** *c.*7 x 2.5mm, elongate-conical, abruptly contracted distally, very densely scaly, with some hairs between the scales in the upper part; style *c.*17mm, with some patent hairs at the base, glabrous distally; stigma globose.

Indonesia, New Guinea (W), Wichmann and Hubrecht Mts, in open places at 3000–3100m. *Fl.* Feb.

Only known from two old collections. Never cultivated.

87. **Rhododendron evelyneae** Danet
Adansonia 2005. 27(2): 270.
Type: Danet 4193, 8 Dec. 2002. Indonesia, Papua, Mt Jayawijaya east to Mt Yonowe (LYJB, BO, CANB, E, L, LAE, MAN, P).
Derivation: Named after the author's mother, Evelyne Danet.

Erect shrub to 2m. Twigs cylindrical, 2–4mm in diameter, densely scaly and warty after the scales have fallen. **Leaves** erect, in pseudowhorls of 4–6 together, with some cataphylls along the internodes. **Blade** 20–60 x 10–30mm; apex acute to obtuse, with a hooked point that often falls early to leave a small callosity; margin entire, strongly revolute, the sides often being bent into a tube; base rounded to cordate; upper side at first densely scaly and rough, the scales quickly falling then remaining rough from the scale bases, green; lower side densely and more persistently scaly and warty. **Scales** orange-brown, irregularly stellate, the centres small from a stalk mounted on an acute persistent protuberance. Mid-vein slightly impressed above and prominent below. **Petiole** 1–3mm, grooved above, rigid and rugose.

External bracts triangular to ovate, caudate to cuspidate at the apex, scaly and rough and shortly hairy outside, scaly on the margin, glabrous inside; internal bracts to 25 x 20mm, obovate-obcordate to broadly spathulate-obcordate, apiculate or mucronate at the apex, glabrous or with a few hairs outside. Bracteoles 15mm, linear, broadened to spathulate distally, sub-glabrous. Inflorescence of 3–7 hanging flowers, without scent. Pedicels 20–30 x *c.*1.5mm, shortly hairy and densely scaly, rough with papillae. Calyx obliquely discoid, *c.*4mm in diameter, sub-entire, shortly hairy and densely scaly. **Corolla** 30–40 x *c.*25mm, pink, tubular; tube 23–31 x 7 x 12mm, straight or a little curved, sometimes slightly laterally compressed, hairy and scaly outside, distinctly hairy inside; lobes 7–12mm in diameter, half-spreading to spreading, overlapping to *c.*½, broadly elliptic to sub-circular, rounded or a little retuse at the apex, scaly outside except near the margins. **Stamens** irregular, exserted to *c.*5mm; filaments pink, shortly hairy at the base; anthers *c.*3 x 1.5mm, deep purple, oblong, with rounded bases to the cells. Disc 10-lobed, glabrous except at the top where it is densely short-hairy. **Ovary** *c.*5 x 3mm, ovoid, tapering to the style, densely short-hairy and scaly, the white hairs covering the reddish-brown scales; style red or pink, slightly exserted from the mouth of the flower, shortly hairy up to halfway; stigma 5-lobed. **Fruit** 20 x 8mm, ellipsoid-oblong, grooved, hairy and scaly, the valves a little or not curving on dehiscence. Seeds 4–5mm including the tails.

Indonesia, New Guinea (W), at the watershed between Mt Yonowe and Mt Jayawijaya, on the Longimik lateral moraine at 3140–3190m. Known at present only from the type collection.

Close to *R. spondylophyllum* but differing chiefly in: the longer petiole, 1–3mm (1mm); the pedicels scaly and hairy (scaly only) and the style shortly hairy in the basal ⅓ (hairy and scaly for *c.*⅔). Not known in cultivation.

88. Rhododendron kawir Danet
Adansonia 2005. 27(2): 273.
Type: Danet 4247. Indonesia, Papua, Mt Jayawijaya at Nambulaga near Dimba village (LYJB, L, MAN, P).
Derivation: Derived from the local name attributed to this species by the inhabitants of Dimba.

Erect shrub to 4m. Twigs cylindrical, 3.5–5mm in diameter, scaly when young, rough with scale bases after the scales have fallen, whitish-green. **Leaves** in tight pseudowhorls of 6–8 together. **Blade** 60–100 x 30–55mm, mostly elliptic, occasionally ovate to obovate; apex obtuse but cuspidate or apiculate; margin entire, weakly revolute; base obtuse or rounded, occasionally acute and a little decurrent on the petiole; upper side sparsely scaly, dark green and slightly rough; underside moderately scaly, yellowish-green, scabrous with epidermal tubercles when the scales have gone. **Scales** reddish-brown, subcircular to sub-stellate; centre relatively small, sessile or prolonged into a stalk which is fixed to the top of a small epidermal tubercle which remains after the scales have fallen. Mid-vein depressed above, raised below; lateral veins 10–15 per side, a little depressed above and a little raised below, reticulation obscure. **Petiole** 7–23mm, rigid, sub-cylindrical with a groove on the upper side, scaly, whitish-green.

External bracts triangular to ovate, cuspidate to rounded at the apex, scaly and hairy outside, scaly at the margin and hairy inside; internal bracts to 45 x 6mm, elliptic to linear-spathulate, truncated to rounded at the apex, sparsely and shortly hairy on both sides, the margin scaly at the apex. Bracteoles *c.*38mm, linear, broader at the apex, sub-glabrous. Inflorescence of 4–10 semi-erect, scented flowers in an open umbel. Pedicels 7–10 x 1.5–

2mm, densely scaly, rough. Calyx *c.*5mm in diameter, obliquely disc-shaped, sub-entire to obscurely 5-lobed, sparsely scaly outside, fringed with scales on the margin. **Corolla** 70–77 x *c.*45mm, the tube pink, the lobes white, trumpet-shaped; tube 46–55 x 4–6 x 7–11mm, slightly curved, sparsely scaly-papillose outside and hairy inside; lobes 23–25 x 16–17mm, obovate to elliptic, rounded or retuse at the apex, reflexed to the horizontal or a little beyond, overlapping *c.*halfway. **Stamens** unequal, exserted to 20mm from the mouth; filaments white, densely hairy at the base becoming less so upwards and glabrous for a few millimetres distally; anthers *c.*5 x 1.5mm, yellow, narrowly oblong, the cells rounded at the base. Disc 10-lobed, densely hairy. **Ovary** *c.*8 x 3mm, narrowly oblong, tapering to the style, densely hairy and densely scaly; style pink, exserted from the mouth, scaly in the basal ½; stigma 5-lobed.

Indonesia, New Guinea (W). Known only from the type collection made in the valley at Nambulaga near Dimba village, near Mt Jayawijaya. Growing at 2280m altitude at the edge of secondary forest with other ericaceous pioneers.

Said to be similar to *R. rappardii* and *R. opulentum*. *Rhododendron rappardii* differs in having shorter flowers up to 55mm long, anthers which are pointed at the base not rounded and a style which is both hairy and scaly in the basal ½. *Rhododendron opulentum* differs with its prominent reticulation which can be seen on both sides of the leaves; it also has hairy pedicels and a calyx and a corolla which is glabrous outside and a style with hairs not scales in the basal part.

89. Rhododendron tintinnabellum Danet
Adansonia 2005. 27(2): 268.
Type: Danet 4319, 15 Jan. 2004. Indonesia, New Guinea, Papua, summit ridge of Mt Sendanihanegen (LYJB, BO, CANB, E, L, LAE, MAN, P).
Derivation: Latin – *tintinnabellum* – little bell, alluding to the flower shape.

Erect shrub to 1.3m. Twigs cylindrical, 1–2mm in diameter, at first very densely scaly, later densely warty from the scale bases after the scales have fallen. **Leaves** erect, in tight pseudowhorls of 3–6 leaves near the tips of the twigs. **Blade** 6–33 x 3–13mm, narrowly elliptic; apex acute to apiculate; margin entire, strongly revolute giving a linear or narrowly oblong appearance; base acutely tapering, the upper side dark green, matt, at first densely scaly but the scales quickly falling leaving a rough densely papillose surface, the lower side densely and more persistently scaly. **Scales** dense, reddish, irregularly stellate, the centre relatively small, from a stalk attached to a small, pointed, persistent, epidermal protuberance. Mid-vein slightly impressed above, prominent below, lateral veins not visible, very leathery and rigid. **Petiole** 1–5mm, strong, rigid, flattened and grooved above, at first densely scaly, later only papillose from the scale bases.

External bracts triangular to ovate, the apices cuspidate to apiculate, scaly and papillose near the apex outside, scaly at the margin, glabrous inside; inner bracts broadly obovate to obovate spathulate, to 11 x 8mm, emarginate and apiculate at the apex, glabrous or scaly or glabrous near the apex externally, scaly on the margins and glabrous internally. Bracteoles to 10mm, linear-spathulate, rounded or mucronate at the apex, sub-glabrous. Inflorescence of 1–2 hanging flowers. Pedicels 10–20 x *c*.1.5mm, densely scaly. Calyx *c*.4mm in diameter, rounded, obscurely 5-lobed, very densely scaly outside. **Corolla** white, campanulate, 17–24mm; tube 10–13 x 7–8 x 9–10mm, the sides straight, scaly-papillose outside, glabrous inside, slightly 5-grooved at the base; lobes 7–11 x 10–12mm, sub-circular to elliptic, apex rounded, spreading or recurved, overlapping to halfway, scaly outside to the margins near the base, glabrous distally. **Stamens** erect, regularly disposed within the mouth of the flower, dimorphic; filaments white, glabrous; anthers *c*.2 x 1mm, brown, oblong to obovoid. Disc 10-lobed, glabrous. **Ovary** *c*.5 x 3mm, conical, very densely scaly; style *c*.2mm, green, glabrous, included within the tube; stigma 5-lobed. **Fruit** *c*.12 x 5mm, sub-conical, 5-grooved, densely scaly, the valves a little twisted and recurved on dehiscence. Seeds 3mm including the tails.

Indonesia, New Guinea (W). Known only from the original collection from the summit ridge of Mt Sendanihanegen between 3470 and 3510m. In montane shrubbery at the transition to the sub-alpine zone.

Said to be close to *R. revolutum* but differing in that the leaves are longer and narrower, the petiole usually much longer, the margins of the corolla lobes are scaly near the base, and the flower is broader and white in colour. Not yet cultivated.

Rhododendron x gilliardii Sleumer
Reinwardtia 1960. 5 : 88.
Type: E.T. Gilliard *s.n.*, July 1950. New Guinea (E), Central Highlands: Mt Hagen (A).
Derivation: Named after the American collector, E.T. Gilliard.

Papua New Guinea, Western Highlands, Mt Hagen, once found near timber line, 2285–3655m. *Fl.* July.

Considered to be a hybrid between *R. macgregoriae* and an unknown species. This plant has not been recollected despite the site being well visited. Described as similar to *R. macgregoriae* in the size and the form of leaves and flowers, but differing in having stellate scales on distinct tubercles, which are typical for section *Phaeovireya*. Kores (1982) suggested a strong resemblance to material tentatively identified as *R. macgregoriae* x *R. dielsianum*; Sleumer (1973) had suggested the possibility of it being *R. beyerinckianum* x *R. macgregoriae*.

Rhododendron x schoddei Sleumer
Blumea 1963. 12 : 95.

= *R. christi* x *R. beyerinckianum* (see van Royen & Kores 1982: 1679).

SECTION V: *Malayovireya* (Sleumer) Argent *stat. nov.*

Type: *R. malayanum* Jack.
Subsection *Malayovireya* Sleumer, Blumea 1958. Suppl. IV: 48.
Section *Lepipherum* G.Don, *sensu* H.F.Copel., Phil. J. Sc. 1929. 40(2): 136, *pro parte typo excluso.*

Fruit not peeling an outer layer before splitting. Flower bud scales (sterile bracts or perulae) fringed with simple white hairs. Filaments hairy from the base or glabrous. Anthers introrse. Flowers various. Style–ovary junction tapering. Scales very variable in size, lobed, with a swollen centre which in the largest scales is dark coloured. Scales usually at least touching, mostly forming a coherent layer over the lower epidermis of the leaf.

A small but distinctive section with all but four of the species being found on the island of Borneo. This is one of the most distinctive sections with its densely scaly leaves and stems and white ciliate margins to the bracts. Some of the species are endemics with very restricted distributions while others are widespread with complex patterns of variation.

Key to all species

1	Leaves linear	2
+	Leaves not linear	4
2	Leaves less than 5x as long as wide, flowers yellow. Scales up to one diameter apart, few overlapping	**97. lineare**
+	Leaves more than 5x as long as wide, flowers white. Scales dense and overlapping	3
3	Flowers white, the tube less than 5mm long (Borneo)	**95. himantodes**
+	Flowers pink or purple, the tube more than 10mm long (Sumatra)	**102. vinicolor**
4	Petiole up to 4mm, not longer than wide	5
+	Petiole more than 4mm, at least 2x as long as wide	6
5	Flowers densely scaly outside on the tube and lobes, corolla tube up to 12mm	**93. fallacinum**
+	Flowers glabrous outside or sparsely scaly, totally without scales on the lobes, corolla tube more than 12mm	**92. durionifolium**
6	Largest leaves less than 10mm wide, the blade more than 3x as long as wide	7
+	Largest leaves more than 10mm wide, the blade less than 3x as long as wide	8
7	Scales not all overlapping, at least some epidermis visible on mature leaves, flowers yellow	**97. lineare**
+	Scales dense and overlapping, without any epidermis visible on mature undamaged leaves, flowers purple or greenish-white	**99. micromalayanum**
8	Flowers wider than long	**94. fortunans**
+	Flowers longer than wide	9
9	Flowers yellow or orange	10
+	Flowers red, purple or greenish-white	13
10	Leaf apex rounded or retuse (Peninsular Malaysia)	**101. obscurum**
+	Leaf apex acutely pointed (Borneo, Philippines)	11
11	More than 10 flowers per umbel, leaves mostly more than 25mm wide, rugose with the lateral veins strongly raised below	**90. acuminatum**
+	Mostly fewer than 8 flowers per umbel, leaves mostly less than 25mm wide, if with more flowers and larger leaves, then the leaves smooth, the lateral veins not raised below	12

12 Flowers uniformly coloured, style about as long as the ovary (Philippines) _____ **91. apoanum**
+   Flowers bicoloured yellow and orange, style twice as long as the ovary _____ **96. lamrialianum**

13 Largest leaves less than 12mm wide _____ 14
+   Largest leaves more than 15mm wide _____ 15

14 Stamens exserted from the mouth of the flower, style twice as long as the ovary (Borneo) _ **99. micromalayanum**
+   Stamens included within the mouth of the flower, style about as long as the ovary (Philippines) ___ **91. apoanum**

15 Leaf apex rounded or retuse (Peninsular Malaysia) _____ **101. obscurum**
+   Leaf apex acutely pointed (Borneo, Philippines) _____ 16

16 Flowers with the stamens included within the mouth of the flower, style as long as the ovary _____ **91. apoanum**
+   Flowers with the stamens exserted from the mouth, style twice as long as the ovary or more _____ 17

17 Flowers less than 3cm long, in umbels of 1–5 (Widespread excluding the Philippines) _____ **98. malayanum**
+   Flowers more than 4cm long, in umbels of more than 8 (Philippines) _____ **100. nortoniae**

Key to species from Thailand and the Malay Peninsula

1 Leaf apex acute or acuminate _____ **98. malayanum**
+ Leaf apex rounded or retuse _____ **101. obscurum**

Key to species from Sumatra and Java

1 Leaves linear (Sumatra only) _____ **102. vinicolor**
+ Leaves not linear _____ **98. malayanum**

Key to species from the Philippines

1 Flowers more than 4cm long _____ **100. nortoniae**
+ Flowers less than 3cm long _____ **91. apoanum**

Key to species from Sulawesi, Seram and Buru

1 Corolla tube hairy outside at least at the base _____ **98. malayanum** var. **pubens**
+ Corolla tube glabrous or with scales only outside _____ 2

2 Filaments hairy in the lower ½ _____ **98. malayanum** var. **pilosifilum**
+ Filaments glabrous _____ **98. malayanum** var. **malayanum**

90. Rhododendron acuminatum Hook.*f.*

Ic. Pl. 1852. *t.*886.

Type: Low *s.n.* Malaysia (Borneo), Sabah, Mt Kinabalu (K, CGE).

Derivation: Latin – *acuminatus* – tapering from inwardly curved sides to a narrow point, referring to the acuminate leaves.

Small shrub or shrub to 6m. Twigs short, spreading, rounded to obtusely angular especially towards the end of each internode; upper internodes 3–7cm, densely dark-scaly at the ends, silvery on older parts. **Leaves** 3–6 close together at the upper nodes or condensed in pseudo-whorls. **Blade** 60–120 x 25–60mm, ovate or elliptic-ovate; apex shortly-acuminate, obtuse; margin flat or slightly revolute; base mostly rounded, sometimes very broadly tapering, densely scaly on both sides initially, glabrescent above, pits where the scales were attached remaining visible; beneath permanently covered. **Scales** overlapping with broad central cushions and wide irregularly lobed margins, the largest dark-brown, almost black, the smaller paler brown. Mid-vein strongly impressed above, thick and rigid beneath, continuing the petiole and gradually narrowing distally; lateral veins 6–8 per side, wide-spreading, from right angles to 45°, straight or slightly curved to the margin, distinctly anastomosing, deeply depressed above, strongly prominent beneath, veins laxly reticulate and distinctly impressed above, not or only slightly raised beneath, the whole surface deeply rugose; dark green and glossy above, brown beneath. **Petiole** 12–28 x 2–4mm, almost rounded in section, grooved above, densely scaly.

Flower buds to 20 x 12mm, broadly ovoid, smooth. Bracts to 20 x 13mm, ovate, truncate at the base, obtuse at the apex, greenish but covered all over with minute, fine, brownish or greyish hairs and scaly outside along the median line and towards the apex outside, but glabrous towards the thin margin, the margin itself fringed with white hairs and occasional scales. Bracteoles to 15mm, linear to filiform, sub-spathulate-dilated at the top, patently hairy. **Flowers** 6–15 in an open umbel, hanging or half-hanging. Pedicels 8–12mm, thick, densely scaly and also finely hairy between the scales. Calyx *c.*2.5mm in diameter, a low scaly ring, or shallowly 5-lobed, densely scaly. **Corolla** 34 x 22mm, tubular or narrowly funnel-shaped, orange or red; tube 20 x 5–6 x 6–7mm, sub-densely to sparsely or occasionally glabrous outside, shortly sub-densely hairy in the lower ½ inside, straight, cylindrical, the base slightly 5-pouched; lobes 12 x 7–9mm, half-spreading, not overlapping, with a few well-spaced scales outside. **Stamens** arranged irregularly all round the flower,

Louise Olley

Rhododendron acuminatum.

exserted to *c.*10mm, very slightly dimorphic; filaments linear, flattened nearly to the top, densely white-patent-hairy in the proximal ⅓; anthers 2.5–2.8 x 1mm, pale brown, without basal appendages. Disc glabrous. **Ovary** *c.*6 x 2mm, cylindrical, densely brown-scaly, gradually tapering to the thick style, which is scaly in its proximal ½ and lies on the lower side of the tube; stigma *c.*1.5mm in diameter, rounded, sometimes distinctly lobed. **Fruit** 25–34 x 4–5mm, cylindrical, longitudinally grooved, shortly tapering at both ends, densely scaly, splitting to the base, with the valves strongly curving back. Seeds 5–6mm, without tails 1mm, the longest tail 2.8mm.

Malaysia (Borneo), Sabah, Mt Kinabalu and one record from Mt Alab in the Crocker Range. Terrestrial in mossy forest and open shrubberies, especially on ridges, occasionally as an epiphyte but always in well-illuminated situations. Occurring from 1830 to 3350m, common on Mt Kinabalu but subject to fluctuations in the size of the populations as it is a species which appears to be very adversely affected by droughts in El Niño years. Recorded as flowering throughout the year; its main flowering appears to be between Feb. and April.

The only natural hybrid recorded is with *R. fallacinum*, a solitary intermediate plant without flowers growing within the zone of overlap between these two species on Mt Kinabalu. It would be surprising if hybrids with *R. lamrialianum* did not also occur but these may be difficult to recognise without flowers. In cultivation this species appears difficult – most records of it growing successfully when checked have proved to be *R. rugosum* which although with superficially similar leaves has quite different dendroid scales. Of the many introductions to the Royal Botanic Garden Edinburgh just one has grown successfully, although very slowly. It flowered for the first time in 1997.

Rhododendron acuminatum is quite distinct amongst section *Malayovireya* species. The orange to red, more or less hanging flowers are produced in a moderate-sized umbel, the leaves are long-petiolate and strongly rugose, the veins deeply impressed on the upper leaf surface and strongly protruding beneath. These vegetative characters are sufficient to separate this species from *R. fallacinum* which grows together with *R. acuminatum* in part of its range on Mt Kinabalu. The flowers of *R. acuminatum* are very sparsely covered (if not glabrous) with much smaller scales than *R. fallacinum* and the limp, slightly hanging disposition of the flowers in *R. acuminatum* is quite different. The flower buds are unusual in this section in often having occasional scales on the margins amongst the simple hairs. The variation in this character needs further observation.

91. Rhododendron apoanum Stein

Gartenflora 1885. 34: 194, *t.*1196.

Type: Schadenberg, Feb. 1882. Philippines, Mindanao, Mt Apo (B†, neotype Elmer 11386 the same locality L, A, BM, E, K, NY).

Derivation: Named after Mt Apo where it was first collected, the highest mountain in the Philippines.

Erect shrub to *c.*1m, commonly branching from the base and branching profusely above as well. Twigs rounded, densely covered with dark-brown scales but these becoming paler and giving the stems a grey appearance with age. **Leaves** 3–6 together in loose pseudowhorls, 2–7cm apart. **Blade** 30–110 x 10–40mm, elliptic to obovate-elliptic, variable in shape and size; apex shortly acuminate, sub-acute or obtuse; margin flat or slightly revolute, often irregularly somewhat crenate or dentate in the distal part; base broadly to narrowly tapering, dull silvery-green above often with a somewhat bluish tinge from a distance, initially densely scaly on both sides, those above predominantly silvery but with visible brown centres to the largest scales, glabrescent with age; below, densely and persistently brown-scaly, but often with narrow areas of the leaf surface visible

between the scales. **Scales** with broad striate flanges and large swollen centres, the largest scales well spaced, with large dark centres. Mid-vein slightly impressed above, very prominent beneath in the lower part of the lamina; lateral veins 6–7 per side, irregularly spreading, the upper ones straight, all anastomosing, very slightly depressed above in fully mature leaves, somewhat raised or only faintly visible beneath, reticulation hardly visible. **Petiole** 9–15 x 2–3mm, weakly grooved distally, densely brown-scaly.

Flower buds to 17 x 12mm, ovate, broadly pointed, with all bracts firmly appressed, purple or green. Bracts ovate to sub-circular, glabrous except for the fringe of simple white hairs and a patch of overlapping brown scales on the outside near the apex, which often extend down the middle line. **Flowers** 6–15 in an open umbel. Bracteoles filiform, shortly patently hairy and with a few scales especially towards the apex. Pedicels 7–11 x *c.*1mm, densely scaly. Calyx *c.*2mm in diameter, disc-shaped, covered in brown scales. **Corolla** 16–20 x 16–20mm, pinkish-orange; tube 13–18 x 4–7 x 5–9mm, straight, often somewhat 5-angled, glabrous or very laxly scaly outside, at least at the sinuses of the lobes; lobes 4–7 x 5–11mm, spreading horizontally or sometimes a little reflexed, broadly rounded or emarginate. **Stamens** at first clustered in the centre of the flower later spreading irregularly round and reaching or slightly exceeding the mouth of the tube; filaments linear, flat, glabrous; anthers broadly oblong, *c.*1.7mm. Disc green, glabrous or with a few scales on the upper side. **Ovary** 4–5 x *c.*2mm, sub-ovoid-conical, densely scaly; style as long as or shorter than the ovary, thick, scaly at the base, glabrous in the upper ½; stigma thick, rounded. **Fruit** 20–25 x 3–4mm, spindle-shaped. Seeds 5–6mm, without tails 0.8–0.9mm, the longest tail 3mm.

Rhododendron apoanum.

Philippines, Mindanao, Davao Province, Mt Apo, Mt McKinley. Bukidnon Province, Mt Lipa, Katanglad Mts. Agusan Province, Mt Urdaneta. Mostly epiphytic in moss forest on peaks and ridges, 1380–2930m, common on Mt Apo. *Fl.* March, May–Oct.

Copeland (1929) discusses the existence of two forms which had been suggested by Elmer (1911), one having slightly larger, entire, spreading leaves, the other with smaller leaves, 'feebly dentate towards the apex, and tend[ing] to ascend strictly'. He concludes 'that not even a varietal distinction can be made' as the flowers are identical. In cultivation in Edinburgh there are two forms with differently coloured flower buds – purple and green – but with no other visible difference. This species might be regarded as an extreme variant of the *R. malayanum* complex but it is distinct in the smaller flowers which have a regular, circular or slightly 5-sided tube, not the laterally compressed tube characteristic of *R. malayanum*, as well as a shorter style. It is distinct from the only other *Malayovireya* so far known from the Philippines – *R. nortoniae* – by the much shorter flowers which are only ½ as long as in that species. *Rhododendron apoanum* was described and figured in the *Gartenflora* (Stein 1885) but the colour plate would appear to have been painted from a herbarium collection with directions from the collector as to the colours; there is no indication that it was cultivated. It took over 100 years to realise the horticultural promise of this species when it was finally introduced to cultivation via Edinburgh in 1993 from material collected on Mt Apo. It is one of the easiest species of this section to grow and flowers freely several times a year, the small size of the flowers being made up for by the freedom with which they are produced and the very attractive bluish-green aspect of the foliage.

---

92. Rhododendron durionifolium Becc.

Malesia 1878. I: 202.

Type: Beccari 3230. Malaysia, Sarawak (Borneo), Batang Lupar, Mt Tiang Laju (Fl, P).

Derivation: Latin – *Durio*, the genus of fruit trees in the family Bombacaceae; *folium* – leaf. Alluding to the similarity of the scales on the leaf to those of a durian.

Ssp. **durionifolium**

Shrub or small tree to 3m. Twigs rounded, thick, initially entirely covered in the younger parts with brown to dark golden scales; internodes 3–16cm. **Leaves** 3–5 in pseudowhorls, in the apical part of the stem. **Blade** 70–170 x 20–65mm, ovate to ovate-elliptic; apex long-acuminate to shortly caudate; margin flat or narrowly reflexed especially when dry, mostly irregularly wavy, sometimes minutely toothed; base rounded to cordate or auriculate; with very thin silvery scales above which leave small pits as they disappear, entirely and persistently covered with the orange-brown scales beneath. **Scales** with broad striate flanges and large swollen centres, the largest darker and forming clearly visible spots. Mid-vein distinctly impressed above, very broad and prominent beneath for at least ¾ of its length; lateral veins 6–9 per side, straight and spreading below, curved and anastomosing towards the edge, smooth or slightly impressed above in mature leaves only, indistinct beneath, veins laxly reticulate and mostly minutely impressed on the upper side only; silvery green when dry above turning green when wet, coppery orange-brown beneath. **Petiole** 1–4 x *c*.3mm, densely scaly, without a groove when fresh, but mostly very short or almost lacking.

Flower buds 20–25 x 12–15mm, smooth, ovoid. Bracts to 20 x 12mm, the outer fully appressed, ovate, obtuse to sub-apiculate, the base truncate, often with minute hairs outside, scaly along the upper outer side near the middle, finely white ciliate along the margins, the inner ones spathulate. Bracteoles to 15mm, filiform, papillose-hairy, often sub-spathulate and very short-ciliate at the apex. Inflorescence an open, or more rarely, a complete umbel of 10–35 flowers. **Flowers** erect to spreading. Pedicels 10–15 x *c*.1mm, densely scaly. Calyx a very low, disc-like ring. **Corolla** 24–30mm, yellow? to orange, or red, tubular to narrowly funnel-shaped; tube *c*.5 x 5 x 8mm, mostly completely glabrous, rarely with a few (apparently rapidly falling) scales on the lower part of the tube outside, glabrous or slightly hairy at the base of the tube inside, straight, often somewhat pouched at the base; lobes *c*.12 x 8mm, spreading, obovate to nearly rounded, overlapping in the basal ⅓, as long as the corolla tube. **Stamens** *c*.20mm, spreading all round the mouth, slightly unequal; filaments linear, flattened and densely whitish hairy in the basal ⅓, filiform and glabrous distally; anthers 2.5–3.5 x 0.5–0.8mm, brown, oblong, often curved. Disc glabrous. **Ovary** 5–8 x *c*.1.5mm, elongate-conical, densely scaly, gradually tapering distally; style 7–10mm, thick and scaly in the proximal ½, glabrous distally; stigma rounded or slightly 5-lobed, lobes enlarging into separate club-shaped spreading parts as the fruit develops. **Fruit** 25–45 x 3–4mm, cylindrical, often somewhat curved, densely scaly, slightly 5-ribbed, the valves curling right back. Seeds 6mm, without tails 0.7mm, the longest tail 2.6mm.

Malaysia (Borneo), Sarawak and Sabah. **Indonesia**, C and SE Borneo. Widespread, growing both terrestrially and epiphytically in moss forest, low shrubberies and on bare sandstone rocks, locally common, 800–2400m. *Fl.* May, Aug.–Nov.

Rhododendron durionifolium
ssp. *sabahense*.

This species is extremely variable throughout its entire range but may be known amongst the section *Malayovireya* by its short petioles and the relatively long, tubular, mostly orange-red flowers which are without scales or only slightly scaly at the base and aggregated together into umbels of 10 or more. I have never seen yellow-flowered specimens and this report may be an error although there are occasional purplish-pink-flowered populations which are similar in colour to many of the forms of *R. malayanum*. A puzzling aspect of this species is the variable shape and size of the flowers. A population in a peat swamp area in southern Sabah had three distinct size classes of flower – large, intermediate and small – which did not appear to intergrade and were all growing together. It is closely related to *R. fallacinum*, which is maintained in this account although distinguished with difficulty from the complex variation that occurs in *R. durionifolium*. *Rhododendron fallacinum* usually has a shorter corolla tube and the flowers are densely scaly outside, with scales occurring right up onto the backs of the corolla lobes. Slender forms of ssp. *sabahense* approach *R. malayanum* in form but the petioles do not get quite as long as in that species, the flowers are more numerous from a single flower bud and *R. durionifolium* never normally produces lateral inflorescences. *Rhododendron acuminatum* could also be confused but apart from occurring at higher altitude, this species has more strongly puckered leaves with the lateral veins deeply impressed on the upper side and like *R. malayanum* it has much longer petioles than *R. durionifolium*.

Ssp. **sabahense** Argent, A.Lamb & Phillipps
Notes RBG Edinb. 1984. 42(1): 119.
Type: A. Phillipps SAN 93169, May 1981. Malaysia, Sabah (Borneo), Sipitang District, Long Pasia Track (SAN).
Derivation: Latin – *Sabah* – the country; *ensis* – place or origin. Coming or originating from Sabah.

Differing from the type subspecies in the more slender, narrowly elliptic to elliptic leaves, 90–160 x 20–50mm, with a tapering base; longer petioles: 4–7mm; leaves which are greener and more quickly glabrescent above and flowers predominantly pink or red rather than orange in colour.

This subspecies occurs above 900m in fairly uniform populations on Mt Lumarku, Mt Lotung and near Long Pasia, in the Sipitang District. With its red or pink flowers and long corolla tubes it would be suitable for bird pollination but this has not been observed. The only hybrid seen is with *R. micromalayanum* on Mt Lumarku and in the Long Pasia region. This subspecies has been cultivated since 1980. It grows slowly but has most attractive flowers.

93. Rhododendron fallacinum Sleumer
Reinwardtia 1960. 5: 99.
Type: Clemens 32714. East Malaysia, Sabah (Borneo), Mt Kinabalu (L, A, BM, BO, E, NY).
Derivation: Latin – *fallax* – deceptive or fallacious, because of a deceptive resemblance to *R. durionifolium* which allowed it to go unrecognised for many years.

Shrub or small tree to 6m. Twigs rounded, rough with a dense covering of dark brown scales; internodes 2–10cm.

Leaves 3–6 in tight pseudowhorls and with small, slender scale leaves arranged along the stems but these soon falling off. **Blade** 80–160 x 30–55mm, sub-sessile, ovate, or ovate-elliptic; apex shortly to long acuminate or sub-caudate, acute; margin irregularly wavy, flat; base rounded to auriculate; densely silvery scaly above, only disappearing gradually; beneath densely overlapping coppery-brown-scaly. **Scales** variable in size, strongly lobed, the broad margins striate; the centres large and darker especially those of the largest scales. Mid-vein slightly impressed in the proximal ½ above, strongly raised below for most of its length and especially at the base; lateral veins 8–12 per side, wide-spreading, distinctly indicated but not raised or impressed on the upper surface, slightly raised or very obscure on the lower side. **Petiole** to 4 x 4mm, very short, rarely longer than broad, densely brown-scaly, not or only weakly grooved above in the fresh state.

Flower buds broadly ovoid with the bud scales appressed. Bracts densely scaly in a broad central band on the outer side of each bud scale and conspicuously fringed with white hairs on the margins. Bracteoles to 15mm, filiform and papillose below, spathulate and long hairy above. Inflorescence of 15–35 flowers in a complete or sometimes open umbel. **Flowers** standing erect to horizontal. Pedicels 15–35 x *c*.1mm, densely brown-scaly. Calyx a low, scaly ring. **Corolla** 18–25 x 30–37mm, bright orange, without scent; tube 7–12 x 5 x 5mm, densely scaly outside; lobes 16 x 16mm, widely spreading, overlapping to *c*.halfway and with a triangular area of scales on the outside. **Stamens** at first standing erect centrally in the mouth of the flower, later reflexing back away from the stigma against the corolla lobes; filaments 12–16mm, slightly broader proximally and hairy in the basal ½; anthers 3–4mm, brown. **Ovary** 5.5–7 x 1.5–2mm, densely scaly; style 8–12mm, scaly at the base otherwise glabrous; stigma 5-lobed, to 3mm in diameter. **Fruit** to 35 x 4mm. Seeds 6mm, without tails 0.9mm, the longest tail 3.5mm.

Malaysia (Borneo), Sabah, Mt Kinabalu, Mt Trus Madi and the Crocker Range. Sarawak, Mt Mulu. Mostly terrestrial, less commonly epiphytic in mossy forest in damp shady places, but also on open exposed ridges, often common, from 1220 to 2600m. *Fl. fr.* Jan.–Dec.

It was noted by Sleumer (1966) that 'sterile specimens [were] hardly distinguishable from those of *R. durionifolium*'. In fact this species is not clearly distinguished from *R. durionifolium* but is retained here at present. Flower size is extremely variable (see under *R. durionifolium*) and pedicel length varies enormously as it elongates after the flowers open, even before the corolla has fallen. This leaves only relative scalyness of the corollas and corolla

tube length to distinguish between these two species. As conceived here *R. fallacinum* has flowers with a relatively short and extremely scaly tube, with the scales extending up onto the backs of the lobes, while *R. durionifolium* flowers are longer and vary from completely glabrous outside to moderately scaly on the basal ⅔ of the tube only. This is the commonest of the malayovireyas in Sabah and is easily recognised by its very heavily scaly, bright-orange flowers. *Rhododendron acuminatum*, which is sometimes confused with this species, has orange flowers which are much less scaly, occurs at higher altitude and has long-petiolate, rugose, leaves.

Rhododendron fallacinum has been collected in flower in most months of the year but probably flowers best in the wild from February to April. Pollinators might be expected to be butterflies with the bright display of orange-red flowers with short floral tube and prominently displayed anthers, but Scarlet Sunbirds (*Aethopyga mystacalis* Temminck) have been seen visiting the flowers. Several hybrids have been recorded with this species in Sabah: x *stenophyllum* occurs on Mt Alab – it has narrow linear leaves and broad dark scales but has not been seen with flowers; x *rugosum* occurred on the Mesilau Spur, Kinabalu – it has a mixture of scale types and handsome red flowers; x *lamrialianum* occurs commonly on Mt Trus Madi and has been seen above the Mesilau Cave – it has

Rhododendron fallacinum.

intermediate-sized leaves but has not been seen in flower; and x *acuminatum*, also from the Mesilau Spur, is known only in vegetative form from its intermediate leaves.

Rhododendron fallacinum has been in cultivation since 1980 from a series of introductions to Australia, New Zealand and the UK. Its handsome flowers and coppery-coloured foliage make it a most attractive plant, but like several of the other malayovireyas it is slow and difficult both to grow satisfactorily and to propagate. The plants seem difficult to 'settle' but when this occurs they can be really splendid.

94. Rhododendron fortunans J.J.Sm.
Bull. Jard. Bot. Buit. III, 1920. 1: 401, *t*.49.
Type: Molengraaf 3436 B, 6 Oct. 1984. Indonesia, (Borneo), Central Kalimantan, Schwaner Mts, B. Raja (BO, L).
Derivation: Latin – *fortunatus* – prosperous, lucky or happy; presumably the collector was happy to find such an attractive plant.

Shrub to 2m. Twigs *c*.1.5mm in diameter, densely and persistently brown-scaly; internodes 2–7cm. **Leaves** 3–5 together in a loose pseudowhorl, or, especially the smaller ones, spirally and evenly arranged along the stems. Blade 25–130 x 6–40mm, narrowly elliptic to elliptic; apex acute or acuminate, the extreme tip rounded; margin revolute especially in the smaller leaves; base acutely tapering, scaly on both sides initially, silvery-scaly but glabrescent above with age although leaving dark pits from scale attachments; beneath completely covered with overlapping brown scales. **Scales** very variable in size, the largest *c*.0.2mm in diameter, with pale brown, broad flanges and large, dark brown, centres. Mid-vein very broad beneath, gradually decreasing distally; lateral veins 5–10 per side, wide-spreading almost to a right angle or in small leaves not visible, clearly anastomosing; distinctly impressed above, prominent beneath, with lax reticulation; lamina markedly bullate. **Petiole** 5–12 x 2–3mm, grooved above, somewhat flattened, densely scaly.

Flower buds ovoid, large. Bracts to 24 x 12mm, ovate to obovate-spathulate, the outer ones all over finely hairy, scaly in the upper outer part, the inner ones scaly only externally, all fringed with simple white hairs. Bracteoles to 16mm, linear below, spathulate distally, ciliate. Inflorescence of 10–13 flowers in a complete or open umbel. Pedicels 15–20mm, thick, densely scaly. Calyx oblique, small, cup-shaped, shortly obtusely 5-lobed, densely scaly. **Corolla** 15 x 20mm, widely funnel-shaped, white, without

scent; tube 3–6 x 3 x 6mm, shortly funnel-shaped, very densely brown-scaly, densely hairy inside except where the filaments are inserted; lobes 9–12 x 9–12mm, glabrous inside, brown-scaly in the lower ½ outside. **Stamens** *c*.9mm; filaments white, linear, glabrous at the very base then hairy to the apex; anthers *c*.3mm, purple-brown, the cells divergent below, each bearing a basal conical obtuse lobe. Disc glabrous. **Ovary** 2.5 x 1.7mm, conical, densely scaly, gradually tapering distally; style 2.5mm, thick, glabrous; stigma thick, rounded. **Fruit** brown, shortly cylindrical, 18–23 x 3mm.

Indonesia, C Borneo, top of Bukit Raya in the Schwaner Mts, 1500–2300m, common. *Fl.* Oct., Dec.

This is an interesting species repeatedly collected on Bukit Raya but not yet introduced into cultivation. The flowers are, as far as can be compared from dry specimens, identical with those of *R. himantodes* but the leaves are markedly different. They are not linear in shape, but elliptic and markedly bullate, with very prominent lateral veins which give *R. fortunans* a very different appearance to that of *R. himantodes*. The very wide range of leaf sizes in different specimens of this species is curious and field observations are needed to explain these differences.

Rhododendron fortunans.

95. Rhododendron himantodes Sleumer

Bot. Jahr. 1940. 71: 145.

Type: Clemens 31818, 3 March 1993. East Malaysia, Sabah, (Borneo), Mt Kinabalu, Kina Taki River (BM, A, BO, E, K, L, NY). Derivation: Greek – *himas* – a strap, alluding to the narrow strap-shaped leaves.

Var. **himantodes**

Shrub to 2m. Twigs slender, rounded, smooth or somewhat rough with the dense covering of brown scales; internodes 1–5.5cm. Older branches with raised leaf scars at intervals. **Leaves** in pseudowhorls of 12–25 or regularly spirally arranged. **Blade** 15–120 x 2–6mm, linear; apex acute or sometimes rounded at the extremity; margin somewhat irregular but otherwise entire, slightly reflexed, becoming strongly so when dry; base tapering, densely scaly, becoming glabrescent above or with silvery patches of scale remains; below persistently brown scaly with overlapping scales. **Scales** variable in size with broad striate, lobed flanges; large darker brown centres. Mid-vein deeply impressed above, prominently raised beneath; lateral veins obscure. **Petiole** 2–6 x 1mm, densely brown-scaly, slightly grooved in the distal part.

Flower buds (see p.327) to 14 x 10mm, ovoid-conical, broadly pointed. Bracts ovate to obovate-spathulate, spotted brown with scales but with broad, green, scale-free, lateral areas, the margins finely white ciliate. Bracteoles to 8mm, narrowly linear, glabrous or laxly scaly. Inflorescence of 8–15 horizontal or semi-erect flowers in a complete umbel. Pedicels 20–30 x *c*.1.25mm, pale green but densely scaly. Calyx a low disc or minutely 5-lobed, densely scaly. **Corolla** 7–12 x 20–25mm, white with prominent brown scales, without scent; tube 3–4 x 3.5 x 5mm, deeply longitudinally grooved and weakly funnel-shaped, white but covered in brown scales outside and densely but very shortly hairy within; lobes 8–10 x 7–10mm, wide-spreading, white, conspicuously brown-speckled outside with scales that sometimes form distinctive but irregular radial lines inside. **Stamens** wide-spreading, irregularly arranged around the corolla but mostly towards the lower side; filaments 5mm, white, hairy especially towards the base; anthers 2.5–3 x *c*.0.3mm, dark brown. Disc glabrous. **Ovary** 3.5–5 x 1.5–2mm, conical, entirely covered by scales, gradually tapering distally; style green, passing to yellow, glabrous, on opening almost straight, 2mm, growing to 7mm and curving downwards through 90° from just above the ovary; stigma hardly broadened from the style, green, 1mm in diameter. **Fruit** 15–20 x 4mm, narrowly fusiform or slightly curved, scaly. Seeds 6–8mm, without tails 1mm, the longest tail 2.5–3.5mm.

Sidney Clarke

Rhododendron himantodes var. *himantodes*.

Malaysia (Borneo), Sabah, Mt Kinabalu, Mt Trus Madi, Mt Alab and in the Long Pa Sia area. Sarawak, G. Mulu National Park (Mt Mulu and Mt Api), Mt Murud. **Indonesia** (Kalimantan), Mt Kongkemul (Kangkemul). Epiphyte in large trees in mossy montane forest on Mt Kinabalu where it can be very difficult to spot even when in flower as the small plants are often obscured by other leaves and branches. Terrestrial on mountain ridges of the correct altitude where the vegetation is sufficiently open; abundant on the summit ridge of Mt Api in the Mulu National Park, Sarawak where it occurs on the deep peat overlying limestone in an open sub-montane shrubbery. 1300–2000m.

This dainty species is very distinct with its narrow strap-shaped leaves and short, white, but brown-scaly flowers with highly contrasting chocolate brown anthers. It is unlikely to be confused with any other rhododendron. *Rhododendron stenophyllum* has similarly narrow leaves but it is a much less scaly plant with glossy green leaves and orange or red flowers. *Rhododendron vinicolor* with similar strap-shaped leaves has purple flowers and does not occur in Borneo. It could possibly be confused with *R. lineare* but this species, apart from having bright yellow flowers, usually has much shorter leaves, is much greener in appearance and has the scales well spaced on the underside of the leaf, not dense and overlapping as in *R. himantodes*. The flowers would appear to be very similar to *R. fortunans* but that species has broad, deeply wrinkled leaves with distinct lateral veins.

The flowering time is not well established. It has been collected in flower in most months of the year and was flowering abundantly in the Mulu National Park, Sarawak in April 1978, but more regular observation is needed. No hybrids of this species with others have yet been reported, although growing as it usually does alongside several other *Rhododendron* species it would be surprising if hybrids did not occur occasionally. It was first introduced into cultivation in Edinburgh by Bill Burtt and Paddy Woods in 1962 but this introduction did not persist and it was reintroduced in 1978 and several times subsequently to both Britain and New Zealand. It flowers regularly in cultivation, usually just once a year, and its unusual foliage and delicate flowers make it stunningly attractive, especially as it usually flowers in the depths of winter in the UK. It grows slowly, however: one of the original plants is less than 1m high at 25 years old. It often aborts its flower buds when growing in pots in Scotland unless provided with supplementary lighting, although the plants growing in open beds flower well without it.

Var. **lavandulifolium** Sleumer
Reinwardtia 1960. 5: 97.
Type: Endert 4257. Indonesia, East Borneo, W Kutei, Mt Kemul (L, A, BO, SING).

Leaves 30–45 x 2mm. Flowers only seen in bud, reported to be very light yellow.

Known only from the type locality in mountain forest, 1800m. *Fl.* Oct.

It is doubtful if the flowers on this variety really are yellow and would not have opened the normal white. Sleumer (1973) doubted the significance of the variety as forms with small leaves have been collected elsewhere, notably on Mt Api in Sarawak, and are almost certainly due to greater exposure. It would be interesting to get further collections from Mt Kongkemul which might rule out the colour difference.

---

96. **Rhododendron lamrialianum** Argent & Barkman
The New Plantsman 2000. 7(4): 209.
Type: Argent 84/12 (19841164), March 1984. E Malaysia, Sabah, G. Trus Madi, east ridge (SAN, E).
Derivation: Named in honour of Datuk Lamri Ali, Director of Sabah Parks, who supported field work on rhododendrons in Sabah.

Synonym: *R. variolosum auct. non* Becc.; Sleumer, Reinwardtia 1960. 5: 105, *pro parte*; Blumea 1963. 12: 101; Flora Malesiana 1966. 6(4): 536 var. *andersonii, pro parte*. Argent *et al.*, Sabah Parks Publ. 1988. 8: 88.

Ssp. **lamrialianum**
Compact shrub to 1m. Twigs rounded, brown, slightly rough with a dense covering of scales. Vegetative buds obscure, rounded, to 2mm. **Leaves** in pseudowhorls of 4–5 together with small, scale leaves on the stems between, these quickly falling off. **Blade** 45–80 x 12–30mm, elliptic; slightly acuminate, with an acute apex which is often rounded at the extreme point; margin flat and entire; base broadly tapering; densely scaly above initially with pale scales but quickly glabrescent; underside with persistent scales which are less dense than is typical for the section, only occasionally touching and with areas of the lower leaf surface showing. **Scales** large, dark brown, with a large centre in relation to the paler marginal zone, very dissimilar in size. Mid-vein impressed above and strongly raised beneath throughout its length; lateral veins 3–5 per side, wide-spreading, slightly impressed above, raised below for about ⅓ the distance from the mid-vein to the edge in the fresh state (further when dried); dark-green above and dark-brown beneath. **Petiole** 15–25 x 2–2.5mm, grooved above, very densely covered in brown scales.

Flower buds (see p.327) to 20 x 12mm, ovoid, smooth, but somewhat irregularly imbricate, brown, with scales outside. Bracts fringed with brown scales for most of the perimeter but with white hairs near the apex. Outer bracts externally with brown scales, these extending to the margin in the upper part but leaving a narrow to broad green margin in the proximal ½, also minutely hairy; internally glabrous or minutely hairy in the distal ⅓. Inflorescence of 2–5 flowers in open umbels, (up to 10-flowered in cultivation). **Flowers** tubular-funnel-shaped, half-hanging to hanging. Pedicels 5–10 x 1mm, densely brown-scaly. Calyx a low scaly ring or with short triangular lobes. **Corolla** 25–28 x 18–21mm, bicoloured with orange lobes and a yellow tube, without scent; tube 15–18 x 5–6 x 7–8mm, mostly glabrous in the proximal ¼, prominently scaly distally, with a few scales often following longitudinal lines, glabrous within; lobes 8–9 x 8–9mm, half-spreading, not or only slightly overlapping, with the smallest lobes on the lower side of the flower, all lobes with occasional scales on the outer sides, sometimes forming a distinct triangle with the apex near the tip of the lobe. **Stamens** slightly dimorphic, arranged irregularly all round the mouth of the flower; filaments 18mm, somewhat swollen and hairy in the proximal ⅓; anthers 2.5mm, brown. **Ovary**

Rhododendron lamrialianum ssp. *lamrialianum*.

5 x 2mm, densely brown-scaly; style 15mm, densely scaly in the proximal ½, glabrous distally; stigma only slightly broader than the style, 1mm in diameter. **Fruit** to 32 x 4mm, becoming erect as it develops, densely brown-scaly, splitting to the base, with the valves strongly curving back, without first shedding the outer layer. Seeds 6.5mm, without tails 1.2mm, the longest tail 2.6mm.

    Malaysia (Borneo), Sabah, known only from Mt Trus Madi, E ridge and above Kidukaruke.

Ssp. **gunsalamianum** Argent & Barkman
The New Plantsman 2000. 7(4): 214.
Type: Mitchell & Smith 312 (19952748), 12 Oct. 1995. East Malaysia, Sabah, Mt Kinabalu (SAN, E).
Derivation: Named in honour of Ansow Gunsalam who has accompanied many scientists on field visits in Sabah; a lively companion, an acute observer and free thinker.

    Differing from the type subspecies in the taller laxer habit, up to 1.5m. Corolla tube glabrous or only sparsely scaly outside and densely white hairy in the proximal ½ within.

    Malaysia (Borneo), Sabah, Mt Kinabalu, occurring from 2150 to 2700m as an epiphyte in moderately shady situations in the tall montane valley forest, often occurring high up in trees but apparently not competing successfully on open ridges where many of the other *Rhododendron* species such as the closely related *R. acuminatum* do so well. It is characteristic of the zone usually dominated by the climbing bamboo *Racemobambos gibbsiae* (Stapf) Holttum and becomes much more conspicuous after one of the mass flowerings and death of most of these bamboos. At this time the forest takes on a much more open aspect for a year or two before the bamboo again begins to dominate the sub-canopy. *Fl.* Nov.–Jan., possibly throughout the year.

    This species is easily known from all other rhododendrons in section *Malayovireya* by its bicoloured, red and yellow flowers, and in having only a small area of the bract margins near the apex with simple hairs, otherwise the bracts are fringed with scales. *Rhododendron variolosum* Becc. (now considered a hybrid) included, in the past, materials now separated as *R. lamrialianum* and is only reliably reported from southern Sarawak. It is highly likely that *R. lamrialianum* is the product of a hybridisation event in the past which would account for the anomalous marginal indumentum of both scales and hairs, but it behaves as a good species on Kinabalu and Trus Madi and on both mountains it is common in its own distinctive ecological niche. *Rhododendron acuminatum* could easily be supposed to have been one parent but the other is not obvious. Professor Sleumer (1966) attributed the Kinabalu forms of this species to *R. variolosum* Becc. var. *andersonii* (Ridl.) Sleumer, saying: 'almost certainly a natural hybrid of *R. malayanum* with a yellow-flowered species of series *Javanica*'. The type of *R. andersonii* comes from Mt Rumput in southern Sarawak and appears very similar to Beccari's *R. variolosum*, differing only in the hairy filaments and the slightly hairy corolla tube inside. Ridley's species appears to be very similar to Beccari's and it is highly likely that they are both hybrids between *R. jasminiflorum* and *R. malayanum*. *Rhododendron lamrialianum* is very different from the southern Sarawak plants, having considerably shorter leaf blades and the distinctive bicoloured flowers. The pattern of distribution from southern Sarawak to Sabah is also an unlikely one with no other parallel in the family.

    Rhododendron lamrialianum is closely related to *R. acuminatum* from which it differs in its smaller, smoother leaves, the bicoloured flowers, and having fewer flowers in the umbel. It also had different ecology, being essentially an epiphyte of lightly shaded situations whereas *R. acuminatum* is a terrestrial plant of open ridges. In its small leaves *R. lamrialianum* is similar to *R. micromalayanum* Sleumer but differs from that species in the scales on the leaves being less dense and in flower colour, *R. micromalayanum* being pale-purple or green, never bicoloured or with orange pigmentation. *Rhododendron micromalayanum* also has a different distribution pattern.

    The only hybrids recorded are with *R. fallacinum* on Mt Trus Madi. These hybrid plants are locally common, usually have intermediate-sized leaves, long petioles, pure orange flower colour and totally ciliate bract margins. It would be surprising however if hybrids between this species and *R. acuminatum* did not occur from time to time, but the different flowering times and very different habitats does no doubt effect good isolation of these two species.

Rhododendron lamrialianum has been cultivated since 1984, the earliest known introduction being to the Royal Botanic Garden Edinburgh. It grows slowly but forms attractive scaly plants, which in the type subspecies are very compact, the plants so far introduced remaining after 20 years less than 30cm high. Although young plants usually flower only once a year, older plants may frequently produce several successive crops of flowers throughout the year. The dainty bicoloured flowers, heavily speckled with brown scales in the type subspecies, can be produced in abundance and make this a very colourful and appealing plant. Subspecies *gunsalamianum* by contrast produces long lanky growth which is less desirable in cultivation.

97. Rhododendron lineare Merr.

J. Str. Br. R. As. Soc. 1917. 76: 108.
Type: Native Collector, B.S. 1161. Sarawak, without locality (PNH†, K).
Derivation: Latin – *linearis* – a long and narrow parallel-sided shape, alluding to the leaves.

Shrub to 2m. Twigs slender, rounded, densely brown-scaly; internodes 1.5–6cm. **Leaves** 3–7 together in loose pseudowhorls or spirally arranged. **Blade** 18–30 x 4–7mm, linear to narrowly elliptic, gradually tapering in the distal ⅓, the extreme apex obtuse; margin flat or revolute in dry specimens slightly irregular; base broadly tapering to rounded, silvery scaly but quickly glabrescent above, the surface then green; densely brown-scaly beneath. **Scales** large, of a more uniform size than is typical of species in this section; although larger ones are present, the majority are spaced about one diameter apart with relatively few overlapping. Mid-vein strongly impressed above, slightly prominent beneath (more so in dry specimens); lateral veins obscure. **Petiole** 2–4 x 1mm, grooved above, densely scaly.

Flower buds 7–15 x 4–6mm, ovoid; apex obtuse, bracts all closely appressed. Outer bracts narrowly ovate, inner ones obovate to sub-spathulate, with a broad triangular area of dense brown scales in the centre outside and with green, glabrous marginal areas, margins white ciliate. Bracteoles narrowly linear, ciliate at the top, to 12mm. Inflorescence of 2–6 flowers in an open umbel, the flowers held horizontally to half-hanging. Pedicels 8–10 x 1mm, covered with brown scales. Calyx *c*.2mm in diameter, small, oblique, disc-shaped, obscurely lobed, densely scaly. **Corolla** 22 x 27mm, bright yellow but with prominent orange-brown spots from the large scales

Mary Mendum

Rhododendron lineare.

outside; tube *c*.10 x 5 x 11mm, but constricted in the middle to 4mm where it is longitudinally fluted, covered in prominent brown scales outside, glabrous inside, straight; lobes 15 x 11mm, brown scaly outside in a broad roughly triangular area from the tube and tapering distally, spreading to *c*.45°, the upper lobes overlapping to ⅓, the two lower, not overlapping. **Stamens** loosely and irregularly arranged all round the flower, or on the lower side; filaments pale yellow, filiform above, dilated towards the base, densely white-patent-hairy in the proximal 3mm; anthers brown, exserted to *c*.10mm, *c*.3 x 0.5mm, cells pointed at the base. Disc thick, glabrous. **Ovary** 4–5 x 1.5–2mm, sub-cylindrical, densely scaly, gradually tapering distally; style thick, translucent pale yellow and almost as long as the corolla, scaly in the proximal ½, glabrous distally; stigma thick, pale yellow, curved to the lower side of the flower, 5-lobed. **Fruit** 15–25 x 3–3.5mm, cylindrical, densely brown-scaly; valves reflexing back against the pedicel and often twisting; placentae splaying out and often breaking away from the base. Seeds 58–63mm, without tails 0.9–1mm, the longest tail 25–27mm, the tails very slender, filiform, sometimes crimped.

Widespread in western Borneo. Presently recorded from: **Malaysia**, Sarawak, Mt Buri, Mt Dulit, Mt Lupar, Bt Sagan, Mt Mulu.

Brunei, Bt Bedawan. A high epiphyte in dipterocarp and mossy forest, occasionally on moss-covered ground, 360–1230m. *Fl.* June–Oct.

A dainty species in cultivation, first introduced in 1982 from Mt Buri in Sarawak by Ian Sinclair. It is of weak growth but always admired with its relatively large bright yellow flowers which are prominently spotted with large brown scales outside. It flowers irregularly about twice a year in spring and autumn with the flowers opening in succession.

98. Rhododendron malayanum Jack

Mal. Misc. 1822. 2: 17.

Type: Jack *s.n.*, Mt Bunko, 915m (destroyed, not yet lecto-typified).

Derivation: Of Malaya – a general term for a wide area of the SE Asian archipelago at the time and indicating the place of origin.

Synonyms:

Vireya tubiflora Blume, Bijdr. 1826. 855.
R. malayanum var. *axillare* J.J.Sm., Ic. Bog. 1919. 4: 74.

Var. **malayanum** f. **malayanum**

Erect shrub or small tree to 5m. Twigs rounded, slender, brown, with the tips very densely covered with flat, rounded or lobed persistent scales, quite distinct to the naked eye; internodes 2–10cm. **Leaves** 3–6 together in tight pseudowhorls. **Blade** 40–190 x 10–40mm, elliptic, or narrowly ovoid, variable in shape and size, tapering at both ends; apex mostly gradually shortly acuminate, the extreme point obtuse with a small gland, entire or indistinctly and irregularly denticulate in the upper ½; margin often slightly revolute especially proximally; base acutely tapering, scales very dense, silvery and glabrescent above, brown and forming a coherent, persistent overlapping layer beneath. **Scales** with the marginal zone thin, brown, becoming silvery with age, irregularly and mostly deeply crenate or lobed; centre dark-brown to almost black, large in relation to the marginal zone, leaving a small dark pit when the scale has gone. Mid-vein impressed above, prominent beneath proximally, less so distally; lateral veins 5–8 per side, irregular, mostly straight, anastomosing before the margin, obscure above, slightly raised beneath, reticulation obscure. **Petiole** 10–22 x 2–3mm, grooved above, semi-rounded in section, densely scaly.

Flower buds both terminal and lateral, narrowly ellipsoid, to 15 x 6mm, the bracts fully appressed, totally brown-scaly except for the white, ciliate, margins and sometimes glabrous in a marginal strip. Bracts ovate-triangular or ovate to spathulate, densely scaly outside, glabrous green inside and densely white ciliate on the margins. Bracteoles to 15mm, filiform, slightly dilated at the apex, sometimes with a few small scales and with sparse white hairs in the upper ½ which become denser towards the apex. Pedicels slender, 6–10mm, moderately short-hairy, the hairs often completely covered by the scales. **Flowers** in open umbels of 1–5 which hang vertically down, without scent. Calyx oblique, small, 5-lobed, densely scaly, the lobes obtuse, sometimes up to 1mm. **Corolla** 15–30 x 17–22mm, waxy and glossy, bright red or purplish, to pink, or in albino forms greenish-white; tube 17–23 x 4–5 x 5–5.5mm, cylindrical, straight or slightly curved but laterally compressed, and often deeply grooved at the base, slightly dilated distally, sub-densely to sparsely scaly outside, glabrous inside; lobes 7–10 x 5mm, not or only very slightly overlapping at the base, mostly half-spreading. **Stamens** exserted to 6mm, unequal, loosely clustered on the lower side of the flower and turning downwards as the flower ages; filaments linear, nearly filiform above, glabrous; anthers 1.2–1.6mm, broadly oblong. Disc without hairs but covered with scales on the upper side. **Ovary** 4–5 x 1.5–2mm, oblong-conical, densely scaly, tapering distally; style 10–20mm, slender, equalling or slightly longer than the stamens and lying on the lower side of the corolla, mostly scaly in the proximal ¼–⅓, rarely so to ½, or glabrous except at the very base, green or white; stigma shortly club-shaped, hardly wider than the style. **Fruit** 22–33 x 3–4mm, fusiform, brown-scaly, the valves splitting and curling right back against the pedicel, the placentae breaking away from the base and weakly spreading. Seeds 7.5mm, without tails 0.8mm, the longest tail 3.5mm.

Thailand (the extreme south). **Malaysia**, Peninsula; Sarawak, Sabah (Borneo). **Indonesia**, Kalimantan (Borneo), Sumatra, W Java, Sulawesi, Maluku.

This was the first vireya to be described, is the most widespread species in the subgenus and is subtly variable. *Rhododendron vinicolor* might be considered an extreme form differing in its linear leaves but otherwise having identical flowers, and *R. micromalayanum* similarly has identical flowers although smaller leaves (however, this leaf size can be approached in high altitude exposed forms of *R. malayanum* from both the Malay Peninsula and Seram). Professor Sleumer was mistaken to assert (1966) that only the Bornean forms produced lateral inflorescences; those in the Malay Peninsula often produce these also, both in the wild and in cultivation, and this character is not considered of great significance. Thus

Rhododendron malayanum var. *malayanum*.

var. *axillare* has been included within the type variety. An odd form from West Malaysia has produced both terminal flowers and lateral inflorescences from bare leafless stems, thus being ramiflorous. The flowers of *R. malayanum* are recorded as constantly somewhat larger in Sulawesi compared with those of other islands, although it must be noted that *R. nortoniae* (Philippines) essentially differs from this species only in its larger flowers. The best colour forms of *R. malayanum* come from West Malaysia where it is decidedly montane in its ecology and occurs with deep reddish-purple glossy flowers which, although small, can be produced in great profusion in cultivation, making it an attractive plant when in full flower. In Borneo it can also be montane in its ecology but large-leafed forms come down almost to sea level in the heath (kerangas) forests, usually on peaty accumulations over white sand, where it can be a common and dominant feature of the vegetation. These large-leafed forms (forma *latifolium*) often have truncate or rounded leaf bases; they are undoubtedly different in physiology and have proved difficult to cultivate successfully. This species was one of the earliest in cultivation, although we are lacking precise records of its first appearance and the provenance of the plants first grown. It was one of the parents of the early 'Veitch' hybrids, and Henslow (1891) lists the horticultural hybrid 'Little Beauty' made by crossing a complex vireya hybrid with *R. malayanum* (probably of West Malaysian origin) which resulted in an improved type of *R. malayanum* which has long since disappeared from cultivation.

Wild hybrids are not recognised as common but see under var. *pilosifilum*, *R.* x *hybridogenum* and *R.* x *wilhelminae*. The hybrid between *R. malayanum* and *R. vinicolor* was collected on Mt Bandahara, exactly intermediate in leaf shape and growing between the two parent species. It is now thought that *R. variolosum* in southern Sarawak is the hybrid between *R. malayanum* and *R. jasminiflorum*.

Key to the varieties and forms of *R. malayanum*

1   Flowers shortly hairy outside _____ var. **pubens**
+   Flowers glabrous or with scales only outside ____ 2

2   Filaments glabrous _____ var. **malayanum** 3
+   Filaments hairy at least at the base _ var. **pilosifilum**

3   Leaves narrowly tapering at the base _ f. **malayanum**
+   Leaves broadly tapering to rounded at the base ____
_____ f. **latifolium**

Var. **malayanum** f. **latifolium** Sleumer
Reinwardtia 1960. 5: 103.
Type: Endert 3978. Borneo, SE Kalimantan, W Kutei, top of Mt Kemel, 1800–1850m (A, BO, L).

Synonym: *R. malayanum* var. *axillare* J.J.Sm. f. *ovatum* Sleumer, Reinwardtia 1960. 5: 103.

Leaves broadly elliptic to ovate, the base rounded, the apex shortly obtusely tapering, base truncate-obtuse, 90–150 x 40–80mm.

Malaysia (Borneo), Sarawak. **Brunei**. **Indonesia**, C and SE Kalimantan. 200–1500m. *Fl.* April, Oct.

Var. **pubens** Sleumer
Reinwardtia 1960. 5: 102.
Type: Stresemann 14, 2nd Freiburger Molukken Expedition (L, A).

Corolla shortly hairy both inside and out, 30mm. Filaments hairy proximally. Leaves 80–120 x 25–50mm.

Indonesia, Maluku, W Seram, Ora Mts, rare on steep limestone ridge, one record at 1000m. *Fl.* May.

Var. **pilosifilum** Sleumer
Reinwardtia 1960. 5: 102.
Type: Toxopeus Aa, Maluku, Buru, Kunturun (BO, L).

Synonym: *R. malayanum* var. *infrapilosum* Sleumer, Reinwardtia 1960. 5: 103.

Filaments laxly to sub-densely hairy in the proximal ½.

Malaysia (Borneo), Sarawak. **Indonesia**, Kalimantan (Borneo) near the Sarawak border; Maluku, C Seram and Buru, on peat moor and light summit forest on limestone at 1075–1830m. *Fl.* Oct.–March.

The Bornean forms at least would suggest that var. *pilosifilum* represents hybrids with *R. durionifolium* or *R. fallacinum*: both species have hairy filaments and broad rounded leaf bases which could account for the broader leaf characteristics. The Kinabalu record of Sleumer (1966) has not been traced and has been discounted (Argent *et al*. 1988). A hybrid between this variety and *R. ruttenii* was collected above the village of Kanikeh in the Manusela National Park, Seram.

99. Rhododendron micromalayanum Sleumer

Blumea 1973. 21: 364.
Type: Nooteboom & Chai 2279, 28 April 1970. Borneo, Sarawak, Kalabit Highlands, Mt Batu Lawi summit (L, SAR). Derivation: Greek – *micro* – little or small; *malayanum* – of Malaya. The small species related to *R. malayanum*.

Erect to spreading shrub to 1.2m. Twigs rounded, minutely rough with the dense covering of dark-brown overlapping scales. **Leaves** 5–7 together in tight pseudo-whorls; 2–6cm apart. **Blade** 25–40 x 7–12mm, narrowly elliptic with an obtusely pointed to rounded apex; margin entire but slightly uneven, flat; base tapering; quickly glabrescent above; densely persistently scaly below, the scales partially overlapping or the gaps between scales less than the width of the smaller scales. **Scales** with a broad lobed and striate flange and large darker, swollen centre. Mid-vein impressed above, very prominent beneath; lateral veins 2–4 per side, wide-spreading, almost to the perpendicular, hardly distinct beneath, but moderately distinct and impressed above. **Petiole** 5–7 x 1.5mm, distinctly grooved above, densely dark-brown scaly.

Flower buds narrowly ellipsoid, smooth, green, with brown scales only in the basal ⅓, imbricate. Bracts: the basal with brown scales outside, upper ones glabrous but all finely fringed with white hairs. Inflorescence of 1–4 flowers hanging vertically downwards. Pedicels 15 x 1mm, green and densely covered in brown scales. Calyx a low, brown, scaly disc. **Corolla** 26 x 18mm, purplish-pink, pale pink or greenish-white, without scent; tube 20 x 6 x 8mm, cylindrical, fluted and a little swollen at the base, laterally flattened, with scattered brown scales outside, glabrous inside; lobes 10 x 7mm, wide-spreading, with or without scales outside. **Stamens** irregularly arranged with

more on the lower side of the corolla; filaments 24mm, glabrous, tapering from base to apex; anthers 2 x 1mm, pale orange-brown. **Ovary** 5 x 2mm, densely scaly; style 17mm, scaly in the proximal 4mm, otherwise glabrous, tapering upwards; stigma 1.5mm in diameter, green. **Fruit** 20–37 x 4mm, distinctly fluted and slightly curved, with the remains of the stigma curved upwards, opening lantern-like, the outer skin not peeling back. Seeds 5–6mm, without tails 0.7–0.8mm, the longest tail 3mm, distinctly wavy.

Malaysia (Borneo), Sarawak, Mt Api, Mt Mulu, Mt Murud and Mt Batu Lawi. Sabah, Mt Lumarku. Epiphytic in mossy forest or terrestrially on open ridges at suitable altitudes from 800 to 2000m. Flowers intermittently throughout the year and can probably always be found with at least a few flowers where it occurs in any quantity.

Hybrids recorded in the wild are with *R. durionifolium* ssp. *sabahense* on Mt Lumarku and with either *R. durionifolium* or *R. fallacinum* on Mt Mulu in Sarawak. In cultivation it is a neat, free-flowering species and is amongst the easiest of the malayovireya rhododendrons to grow.

The small leaves covered underneath in overlapping scales, alpine habit and umbels of mostly 1–2 purplish pink or greenish-white, hanging flowers which are prominently scaly outside make this species quite distinct. *Rhododendron lamrialianum* is probably most likely to be confused, with its similar small leaves, but the scales on the undersides of the leaves are much more widely spaced with parts of the lower epidermis visible, whereas in *R. micromalayanum* they are densely overlapping and completely obscure the leaf surface. Flower colour in the two species is completely different, *R. lamrialianum* having bicoloured orange and yellow flowers. Some forms of *R. malayanum* outside Borneo can have leaves as small

Rhododendron micromalayanum.

and can grow in alpine situations but they usually then have darker maroon-coloured flowers from less imbricate flower buds which are scaly up to the top. *Rhododendron micromalayanum* differs anatomically from all forms of *R. malayanum* so far sampled in having a double palisade layer in the leaves, *R. malayanum* having a single palisade layer.

100. Rhododendron nortoniae Merr.

Phil. J. Sc. 1906. 1: Supp. 220.

Type: Clemens 500, April 1906. Philippines, Mindanao, Lanao, Lake Lanao Camp Keithley (PNH†, E, fragment, L, fragment).

Derivation: Named after Mrs J.B. Norton (née Jesse Baker), 1877–1938, at the request of the collector for having largely inspired her interest in botanical work.

Synonym: *R. catanduanense* Merr. in H.F.Copel., Phil. J. Sc. 1929. 40: 149, pl.2.

Epiphytic shrub. Twigs rounded, brown, densely covered with dark brown scales. **Leaves** in tight pseudo-whorls; up to 12cm apart. **Blade** 70–150 x 15–35mm, narrowly elliptic; apex acuminate with a long, slender acute apex; margin entire, narrowly recurved when dry; base tapering; glabrescent above, densely and persistently scaly below, the scales touching and slightly overlapping. **Scales** variable in size, brown, with broad striate flanges and large brown centres, the largest with conspicuously very dark centres. Mid-vein impressed above, prominent beneath; lateral veins 5–6 per side, distant, ascending, slightly impressed above and raised beneath, reticulation obscure. **Petiole** 10–14 x 2mm, densely scaly.

Bracts to 10–17mm, ovate to elliptic-ovate, sub-acute, glabrous outside, ciliate on the margins. Bracteoles filiform. Inflorescence in *c.*12-flowered umbels, the flowers hanging. Pedicels 10–20mm, patently short-hairy, not scaly (but described only in fruit). Calyx 3mm in diameter, disc-like, obscurely and obtusely lobed with shortly ciliate lobes. **Corolla** 40–45mm, tubular, red; tube 35 x 6–7 x 6–7mm, cylindrical, slightly curved, glabrous outside, hairy inside along the 5 main veins; lobes 8–10 x 6–8mm, broadly obovate to nearly rounded. **Stamens** slightly unequal, as long as the corolla or slightly exserted; filaments filiform, densely brown-hairy in the proximal ⅓; anthers 3.5mm, oblong, (in the Negros specimen only 2mm). Disc glabrous. **Ovary** narrowly cylindrical, densely scaly; style elongated, filiform, densely scaly in the proximal ½, glabrous distally, nearly as long as the corolla; stigma conical. **Fruit** 4–8 x 3–4mm, cylindrical, slightly

curved, densely brown-scaly. Seeds 6–7mm, without tails 1mm, the longest tail 3.5mm.

Philippines, Mindanao, near Lake Lanao, 800m; Catanduanes, Mt Mariguidon, 270m; S Negros, Dumaguete, Cuernos Mts.

Doubtfully specifically distinct from *R. malayanum* but with larger flowers and more in the umbel than is usual in that species at least in the wild. It is also described with glabrous bracts, apart from the marginal fringe of white hairs, which if true would be another distinguishing character, but this description may have resulted from describing inner bracts if the outer were missing. The leaves are very similar to those of *R. malayanum* and *R. apoanum*. It remains a poorly known species and apparently has not recently been recollected. Sleumer (1966) noted that there were small differences between the known specimens, each from three different localities.

101. Rhododendron obscurum Sleumer

Reinwardtia 1960. 5: 104.

Type: Strugnell F.M.S. 22344. West Malaysia, Pahang, on top of G. Benom (KEP).

Derivation: Latin – *obscurus* – meaning indistinct, from the fact that the author originally thought this was a hybrid.

Shrub to 3m. Twigs 2mm in diameter, sub-densely, minutely, reddish-brown scaly; internodes 2–3cm. **Leaves** 3–4 in pseudowhorls at the upper 2 or 3 nodes. **Blade** 45–65 x 20–30mm, elliptic-obovate; apex rounded or mostly slightly retuse; margin entire; base broadly tapering, scaly initially on both sides, at maturity glabrescent above, subdensely and persistently scaly beneath. **Scales** minute, with the thin marginal zone variously indented; centre a little impressed, large and of dark-brown colour typical of the section. Mid-vein narrow and impressed above, as thick as the petiole beneath at the base and very prominent, gradually less so distally; lateral veins 7–9 per side, curved and anastomosing towards the margin, minutely impressed above, somewhat raised or nearly invisible beneath, without reticulation. **Petiole** 6–8 x *c.*2mm, grooved above, densely scaly, a little flattened.

Bracts 7 x 4mm, ovate-acuminate, hairy on both sides, white-ciliate round the margins. Inflorescence a 3-flowered umbel. Pedicels 14–18mm, slender, laxly scaly. Calyx 2.5mm in diameter, oblique, disc-shaped, very shortly or not lobed, scaly outside. **Corolla** 26–30mm, tubular, slightly curved, gradually widened to the mouth, pink, or orange-red; tube 20 x 3–4 x 6mm, laxly scaly outside, glabrous inside; lobes 7–10 x 4–5mm, obovate, suberect. **Stamens** unequal, the longer ones nearly as long as the corolla; filaments linear, glabrous; anthers 1–5 x 0.7mm. Disc glabrous. **Ovary** 4 x 1.5mm, elongate-conical, densely scaly, gradually tapering distally; style slender, exserted; stigma rounded. **Fruit** 10mm.

Malaysia, Malay Peninsula, Pahang, top of Mt Benom. Reported as common in open *Leptospermum* woodland, 2050–2105m. *Fl.* March, May.

Described as common on the summit of Mt Benom by Whitmore, who made only the second known collection of this species from the type locality. This caused Sleumer (1973) to revise his opinion of the status of this plant as a true species rather than the hybrid that he suspected it was when it was first described.

102. Rhododendron vinicolor Sleumer

Reinwardtia 1960. 5: 98.
Type: Steenis 9928, 21 March 1937. Indonesia, Sumatra, Atjeh, Gajo Lands on the confluence of the rivers Kapi and Aoenan (L, A, BO, K, SING).
Derivation: Latin – *vinicolor* – wine coloured, the flowers on the collecting label of the type being described as wine-red.

Shrub to 80cm. Twigs 3–4mm in diameter, rounded, dark brown with a dense rough covering of scales; internodes 5–10cm. **Leaves** 8–10 together, in loose pseudo-whorls, often with up to 4 leaves at some distance below the pseudowhorl. **Blade** 50–120 x 4–8mm, linear; apex gradually tapering, the extreme point rounded and often deflexed; margin irregular, distinctly revolute when living, strongly so when dry; base narrowly tapering; subpersistently silvery scaly above with occasional dark spots visible from the centres of the largest scales; densely and persistently brown scaly below. **Scales** variously sized, with broad striate, lobed flanges, and broad swollen centres; the largest with very dark brown swollen centres. Mid-vein impressed above, strongly raised beneath throughout its length; lateral veins not visible, reticulation obscure. **Petiole** 5–10 x 1–2mm, grooved above, densely brown-scaly.

Flower buds to 12 x 6mm, predominantly brown. Bracts to 12 x 5mm, smoothly appressed, ovate, densely brown-scaly outside with a narrow green glabrous, or minutely appressed hairy border and a white-ciliate margin; outer bracts densely appressed white-hairy inside, inner ones less densely hairy. Bracteoles to 10 x 1mm, narrowly subulate, glabrous. Pedicels 8–12 x 0.75mm, green, slender, laxly scaly. Calyx minute, disc-like, densely scaly.

Corolla 22–24 x 16mm, reddish-purple, without scent; tube 18 x 4 x 5mm, cylindrical, laterally compressed, slightly keeled on the upper side and grooved in the basal ½, curved, laxly and inconspicuously scaly outside, glabrous inside; lobes 7 x 5mm (the upper three), 7 x 4mm (the lower two), the three upper overlapping to *c*.⅓, the two lower hardly overlapping, spreading horizontally, broadly elliptic to obovate, scaly in a broad central band outside. **Stamens** 17–19mm, clustered in a group on the lower side of the flower, exserted to *c*.4mm; filaments linear, filiform distally, slightly unequal, glabrous; anthers *c*.1.5mm, broadly obovate. Disc glabrous. **Ovary** *c*.4 x 1.5mm, obconical-cylindrical, densely scaly, gradually tapering distally; style 8–12mm, glabrous, scaly at the base or up to the proximal ⅓, green, lying on the lower side of the tube; stigma shortly club-shaped and obscurely lobed. **Fruit** *c*.22 x 3.5mm, fusiform, brown-scaly. Seeds 5.5–6.5mm, without tails 0.8mm, the longest tail 3mm.

Indonesia, Sumatra, Atjeh Province: Mt Lembuh region; Tapanuli, near Sidikalang; Mt Bandahara, above Lawe Peunaggalan; Northern Province: Karo District, near Brestagi. Mostly epiphytic in sub-montane mossy forest ridges and on old volcanic vents, also on peat overlying limestone. 1100–1500m. *Fl.* Feb.–March.

In the wild found hybridising with *R. malayanum*, the leaves of the hybrid being intermediate in shape between the two parents which were both growing locally on Mt Bandahara.

Introduced into cultivation in 1999, it grows easily and is one of the bizarre-looking narrow-leafed species, although the flowers are not nearly as showy as those of *R. himantodes* or *R. stenophyllum*.

Rhododendron vinicolor.

Rhododendron x **andersonii** (Ridl.) Argent
Type: J. Anderson 179. Borneo, Sarawak, G. Rumput (K, SING).
Derivation: Named after James Webster Anderson, one time curator in the Gardens Department of the Straits Settlements 1910–1917, collector of this variety.

Synonyms:
R. andersonii Ridl., Kew Bull. 1914. 209.
R. variolosum Becc. var. *andersonii* (Ridl.) Sleumer, Reinwardtia 1960. 5: 105.

Filaments densely patently hairy in the proximal ⅓. Corolla sometimes hairy inside at the base of the tube, of a pink to deep red colour.

Malaysia (Borneo), southern Sarawak.

The Central Borneo specimens need further evaluation. The type specimen coming from southern Sarawak agrees well with the suggestion that this is a hybrid between *R. jasminiflorum* and *R. malayanum*, the hairy filaments being inherited from *R. jasminiflorum*. A recent living collection by David Binney from southern Sarawak agrees well with the description of this variety, although it has its leaves clearly arranged in pseudowhorls and the flower buds have no simple hairs on the margins of the bracts as one might expect.

Rhododendron x **hybridogenum** Sleumer
Reinwardtia 1960. 5: 106.
Type: Sow F.M.S. 29345, 16 Oct. 1932. Malaysia (Malay Peninsula), Pahang, Cameron Highlands (KEP).
Derivation: Latin – *hybridogena* – of hybrid origin.

Leaves 4 together in pseudowhorls. **Blade** 45–60 x 20–29mm, sub-ovate-elliptic; apex acuminate; margin irregularly indented, slightly revolute proximally; base rounded to slightly cordate, above densely covered with small scales or their remains, very densely and persistently scaly beneath. **Scales** small, often touching, with a narrow marginal zone, variously lobed, the centre slightly impressed, relatively large and dark brown. Mid-vein broad at the base, abruptly narrowed and slightly impressed above, less prominent distally beneath; lateral veins 6–10 per side, slightly curved, inarching at the margin, weakly depressed above and slightly raised beneath, without visible reticulation. **Petiole** densely scaly, somewhat flattened, 4–6 x 2mm.

Bracts ovate-acuminate, apiculate, hairy outside, scaly towards the top, obscurely ciliate at the margin. Pedicels 10–20 x 0.5mm, scaly, and laxly short-patent-hairy. **Corolla** 30mm, tubular, said to be yellowish, outside laxly scaly and in the proximal ½, laxly patently hairy, inside finely hairy; tube *c.*20 x 3 x 4mm; lobes *c.*10 x 5–6mm, obovate-spathulate, spreading. **Stamens** unequal; filaments linear, densely hairy proximally, less so towards the middle, narrower and glabrous distally. **Ovary** 5 x 2mm, very densely scaly, with occasional hairs; style scaly and laxly patent-hairy in the proximal ⅔, glabrous distally.

Malaysia (W), Pahang, Cameron Highlands. Once found. *Fl.* Oct.

Rhododendron hybridogenum is considered to be a natural hybrid between *R. malayanum* and *R. jasminiflorum* var. *punctatum* (Sleumer 1966). It is intermediate between these two species, which commonly grow together in the Cameron Highlands.

Rhododendron x **variolosum** Becc.
Type: Beccari P.B. 2430. Borneo, Sarawak, Mt Poi (Fl).
Derivation: Latin – *variola* – small pox, alluding to the impressed scales leaving 'pock marks'.

Synonym: *R. variolosum* Becc., Malesia 1878. I: 206.

Shrub or tree to 1.6m. Twigs rounded, the youngest densely scaly, older ones glabrescent; internodes 2–12cm. **Leaves** in loose pseudowhorls close together in the upper part of the upper nodes. **Blade** 70–160 x 20–55mm, narrowly elliptic; apex gradually tapering, acute, the extreme point rounded; margin narrowly revolute; the extreme base obtuse before decurrent to the petiole; glabrescent and shining above when mature, often with a few persisting scales, smooth; beneath densely covered with persistent scales. **Scales** typical of the section but the larger ones sparse and less different in size than in *R. malayanum*, smaller ones well spaced initially, but some touching or overlapping, all distinctly impressed. Mid-vein deeply impressed above, strongly raised beneath; lateral veins 10–12 per side, straight, curved and anastomosing before the margin, all slightly impressed above, prominent beneath. **Petiole** 10–25 x 2–3mm, grooved above, flattened, densely scaly.

Flower buds oblong-ellipsoid, acuminate. Bracts to 15 x 7mm, ovate-elliptic to sub-spathulate; the outer ones sharply acuminate, scaly upwards outside. Bracteoles to 10mm, filiform, glabrous. Pedicels 10–20mm, slender, densely scaly. Calyx 3mm in diameter, disc-shaped, oblique, wavy, obscurely lobed, densely scaly. **Corolla** 25–30mm, pink or red, laxly scaly or glabrous outside, glabrous inside; tube 12–15 x 3–4 x 6mm, cylindrical, straight, lobed at the base; lobes 11–15 x 6–8mm, obovate-spathulate, rounded-obtuse, spreading. **Stamens**

17–20mm, unequal; filaments linear, glabrous; anthers 2 x 0.7mm, almost rectangular. Disc glabrous. **Ovary** 5 x 1.5mm, elongate-conical, densely scaly, deeply 5-ribbed, gradually tapering distally; style thick, as long as the stamens and scaly in its proximal ⅔, glabrous distally; stigma shortly 5-lobed.

Malaysia (Borneo), Sarawak, Mt Pueh (Poi), terrestrial or epiphytic, 1500m.

See discussion of the status of this taxon under *R. lamrialianum.*

Rhododendron x **wilhelminae** (Hochr.) Sleumer
Candollea 1925. 2: 493.
Type: Hochreutiner 1966. Indonesia, Java, G. Salak, W slope towards G. Bunder (G).
Derivation: Named after Queen Wilhelmina of the Netherlands, 1880–1962.

Shrub to 2m. Twigs somewhat flattened at the ends, scaly; internodes 5–8cm apart. **Leaves** 4–5 together in pseudowhorls (one leaf often inserted a little below the pseudowhorl). **Blade** 80–100 x 26–37mm, ovate-elliptic; apex acuminate, acute; margin slightly recurved, especially proximally; base tapering; scaly on both sides initially, glabrescent and shining above with age, persistently scaly beneath. **Scales** flaky, dense but spaced 1–3 times their own diameter, with a narrow light brown marginal zone that is irregularly lobed; centre relatively large, dark-brown. Mid-vein slightly impressed above, prominent beneath; lateral veins 8–10 per side, slightly raised beneath only, reticulation obscure. **Petiole** 8–15 x 2mm, flattened, scaly.

 Flower buds 17 x 5mm, elongate-ovoid. Bracts to 15 x 7mm, elliptic-ovate, sub-obtuse, glabrous on both sides apart from the white-ciliate apex. Bracteoles linear. Inflorescence a 4-flowered umbel. Pedicels 12–16mm, thick, densely scaly and finely patently hairy. Calyx oblique, very shortly sub-acutely lobed, or occasionally with one lobe elongated up to 2mm. **Corolla** *c.*35 x 25mm, tubular-funnel-shaped, bright red; tube 18 x 4–5 x 6mm, practically glabrous outside; lobes 15 x 10mm, obovate-spathulate. **Stamens** to 26mm, very unequal; filaments linear proximally, somewhat broadened above the base, densely patently hairy in the proximal ⅓, narrower and glabrous distally; anthers 2.5 x 0.5mm, elongate-obovate. Disc hairy on the upper margin, glabrous below. **Ovary** *c.*4 x 1.5mm, sub-cylindrical, densely scaly and laxly finely patently hairy; style *c.*22mm, sub-densely patently hairy for *c.*2mm proximally, glabrous distally; stigma distinctly 5-lobed.

Indonesia, W Java, Mt Salak, the W slope towards Mt Bunder. Only a single collection known, found in a shrubbery near the crater at 1350m. *Fl.* Oct.

Hochreutiner, the author and collector of this species, pointed out that the characters of *R. wilhelminae* were a combination of those of *R. javanicum* and *R. malayanum*, which both are found on Mt Salak, and suggested it was a natural hybrid between these species. The fact that it does not appear to have been recollected despite the accessibility of the locality would support this conclusion.

SECTION VI: *Albovireya* Sleumer

Reinwardtia 1960. 5: 107

Type: *R. album* Blume.

Section *Zygomorphanthe* Schltr., Bot. Jahr. 1918. 55: 145, *pro parte typo excluso*.

Fruit irregularly peeling an outer layer before splitting. Flower bud scales (sterile bracts or perulae) fringed with scales (multicellular trichomes). Filaments hairy from the base or glabrous. Anthers introrse. Flowers various. Style–ovary junction abrupt to tapering. Scales deeply lobed, mostly pale coloured. Scales usually at least touching, mostly forming a coherent layer over the lower epidermis of the leaf.

Sleumer (1966) commented that it was doubtful if *Albovireya* is a natural entity or whether it should be merged into *Euvireya*. Certainly the relationships between the West Malesian species and those from New Guinea are not likely to be great, and the densely scaly form is likely to be the result of parallel evolution. Merging *Albovireya* into *Euvireya*, however, makes this group even more unwieldy, and the species included here can usually be identified as belonging to *Albovireya* without too much trouble. The scales although dense are rarely as dark as those of *Malayovireya*, and the fringe of scales on the bracts rather than hairs works well. The leaves often have a silvery appearance on the upper side due to the greater persistence of the scales there than in the euvireyas, and this gives them a distinctive look.

Key to species from West Malesia

1	Ovary with scales only, no simple hairs	2
+	Ovary with scales and simple hairs	5
2	Flowers tubular, the tube distinctly longer than the lobes	3
+	Flowers campanulate, the tube as long as or shorter than the lobes	4
3	Leaf base tapering, corolla tube narrowed distally	**107. zollingeri**
+	Leaf base broadly tapering to rounded, corolla broadening distally	**110. lagunculicarpum**
4	Flowers orange, filaments glabrous (Sumatra)	**103. aequabile**
+	Flowers creamy-white, filaments hairy at the base (Java)	**106. album**
5	Corolla up to 12mm (Sumatra)	**105. cernuum**
+	Corolla more than 18mm (Sulawesi)	6
6	Petiole more than 10mm, style hairy to beyond the middle	**104. lampongum**
+	Petiole less than 8mm, style glabrous or hairy at the base only	7
7	Leaves up to 30mm wide, flower tube up to 18mm	**108. arenicola**
+	Leaves more than 30mm wide, flower tube more than 22mm	**109. pudorinum**

Key to species from New Guinea

1	Ovary scaly and hairy	2
+	Ovary scaly only without simple hairs	4
2	Corolla tube scaly outside, style scaly and/or hairy in the basal ⅓	3
+	Corolla tube glabrous outside, style glabrous	**113. giulianettii**
3	Flowers red and yellow, lateral veins 2–4 per side	**116. versteegii**
+	Flowers red, lateral veins obscure	**114. comptum** var. **trichodes**
4	Petiole up to 3mm	5
+	Petiole more than 4mm	6
5	Leaves with 4–6 lateral veins per side, style shorter than the ovary	**115. yelliotii**
+	Leaves without visible lateral veins, style longer than the ovary	**114. comptum**
6	Petiole up to 12mm, anthers *c.*2.5mm	**111. correoides**
+	Petiole more than 15mm, anthers *c.*3.5mm	**112. proliferum**

103. Rhododendron aequabile J.J.Sm.

Bull. Jard. Bot. Buit. III, 1935. 13: 451.

Type: Docters van Leeuwen 3985, 29 Jan. 1920. Sumatra, Mt Singgalang (BO, A, L, SING).

Derivation: Latin – *aequabilis* – uniform or consistent; a rather obscure reference.

Synonym: *R. album* (*non* Blume) Ridl., J. Fed. Mal. St. Mus. 1917. 8: 58.

Large shrub or tree to 4m. Twigs thick, rounded, densely dark-brown scaly; internodes 3.5–16cm. **Leaves** 6–9 together in tight pseudowhorls at the upper 2 or 3 nodes. **Blade** 40–90 x 20–40mm, elliptic; apex shortly acuminate or apiculate, sub-acute to obtuse; margin broadly revolute (the leaves somewhat convex); base tapering, glabrescent at maturity above, or with a few small silvery scales remaining, very densely dark-brown persistently scaly beneath. **Scales** entire, with a broad marginal flange and moderately large, dark centre, dense with many touching or slightly overlapping. Mid-vein impressed over its entire length above, strongly prominent beneath; lateral veins 5–10 per side, spreading, straight below, anastomosing towards the edge, slightly but distinctly depressed above, weakly raised beneath or indistinct. **Petiole** 18–22 x 2–3mm, distinctly grooved above in the distal ½, densely brown-scaly.

Flower buds spherical, brown, but with long, wide-spreading, protruding, broadly subulate bract apices, and a long acute point. Bracts broadly ovate, long acuminate, densely brown-scaly in the upper ½ outside, green near the base, inside brown-scaly for a broad band near the margins and densely scaly on the acumen. Bracteoles to 10mm, filiform, with just a few scales. Inflorescence of 5–10 flowers held horizontally in a compact, open umbel. **Flowers** 15–18 x 34–40mm, orange, without scent. Pedicels 10–14 x 2–3mm, orange, thickened distally, often curved, densely scaly with some long stalked scales but without hairs. Calyx 3–4mm in diameter, small, oblique, disc-shaped, angular, densely scaly outside. **Corolla** campanulate; tube 11–15 x 7–10 x 16–20mm, laxly to sub-densely inconspicuously scaly outside, glabrous inside; lobes 12–15 x 17–21mm, obovate-circular, rounded, slightly retuse, or sometimes subdivided into miniature lobe-like structures, spreading horizontally or reflexed back, with some scales outside near the base, overlapping to *c.*halfway. **Stamens** regularly arranged all round the mouth of the flower, very slightly dimorphic; filaments 10–13mm, pink, linear, glabrous; anthers *c.*2 x 1mm, oblong, dark brown, exserted to *c.*2mm. Disc glabrous. **Ovary** *c.*4 x 3.5mm, conical-ovoid, densely scaly, without

Rhododendron aequabile.

hairs, abruptly contracted distally; style 8–10mm, glabrous; stigma 2–3mm in diameter, centrally placed in the mouth, rounded to weakly 5-lobed. **Fruit** ellipsoidal, 14–17 x 6–7mm, smooth, densely brown-scaly. Seeds 4mm including the tails.

Indonesia, Sumatra, West Coast to Benkulen: Mt Singgalang, Mt Kerintji, W side of Barisan Range and Mt Pesagi. In dense sub-alpine forest, 2300–2870m. *Fl.* Jan.–June, *fr.* May–June.

First introduced into cultivation by Dr Willem Meijer who collected seed from the type locality which was distributed by the Rijksherbarium in 1957 and grown successfully at Kew, where it was figured in *Curtis's Botanical Magazine* (Hunt 1974). It was also collected by Peter Valder in 1975 (see History chapter); progeny from his plants are now widely cultivated. This species is one of the easiest of the albovireyas and has most attractive deep bronze new foliage. The bright orange flowers can be disappointing when the plants are young, often being overtopped by new foliage, but as the plant matures the flowers become more prominent and often give a wonderful display of colour. Flowering appears to be irregular in cultivation, often with two good flowerings a year and sometimes the occasional odd branch flowering out of synchrony with the rest of the plant.

104. Rhododendron lampongum Miq.

Fl. Ind. Bat. 1860. Suppl. 1: 251, 585 (description).

Type: Teysmann 4479, Sumatra, west coast, Lampong, G. Radja Bas(s)a (U, BO, L, fragment).

Derivation: Named after the province of Lampung at the southern tip of Sumatra.

Synonym: *Azalea lamponga* (Miq.) O.Kuntze, Rev. Gen. Pl. 1891. 2: 387.

Shrub. Twigs robust, rounded, tips densely brown-scaly, glabrescent below; internodes 3–11cm. **Leaves** 5–6 together in pseudowhorls. **Blade** 40–95 x 20–45mm, narrowly ovate to elliptic; apex shortly to sub-caudately acuminate, broadly acute; margin revolute in dry speci-mens; base tapering, dark green above, brownish green underneath, practically glabrous above at maturity, dark brown or reddish-scaly beneath. **Scales** very dense, touch-ing and overlapping with broad lobed flanges and small centres, leaving small pits when they disappear. Mid-vein strongly impressed above, very prominent beneath; lat-eral veins *c.*8 per side, irregular, spreading, straight below, anastomosing towards the edge, slightly impressed above in mature leaves, minutely or not raised beneath, visible above only. **Petiole** 10–25 x 1.5–3mm, semi-rounded, grooved above, densely scaly.

Flower buds ovate-apiculate as in *R. album.* Bracts to 16 x 6mm; outer bracts ovate, abruptly and longish api-culate or subulate, inner ones elliptic-spathulate, obtuse, all scaly outside. Bracteoles to 15mm, linear, laxly scaly. Pedicels 10–15mm, thick, densely brown-scaly and laxly short-hairy. Calyx *c.*4mm in diameter, obtusely shortly 5-lobed, densely scaly. **Corolla** 18–20mm, campanulate, yel-low; tube *c.*15 x 3–4 x 6–7mm, laxly scaly outside; lobes broadly obovate-spathulate, spreading, 7–9 x 6–8mm. **Stamens** 14–16mm; filaments linear, patently long-hairy in the proximal ⅓, glabrous distally; anthers 2 x 1mm, broadly oblong. Disc glabrous at the base, densely hairy upwards. **Ovary** *c.*4 x 2mm, obovoid-cylindrical, taper-ing at the base, densely scaly and patently hairy, gradu-ally narrowed distally; style nearly as long as the corolla, slender, scaly and patently hairy in the proximal ⅓, con-spicuously hairy in the middle, glabrous in the distal ⅓ stigma indistinctly lobed. **Fruit** (sub-mature) *c.*18 x 3mm, obovoid-fusiform, long-tapering to the base, broadest in the upper ⅓, sub-densely scaly and patently hairy.

Indonesia, Sumatra, Padang Highlands: Mt Gombak; Lam-pongs: Mt Radja Bassa, in low forest, 1370–2330m. *Fl.* Nov.

Not apparently recently recollected or cultivated.

105. **Rhododendron cernuum** Sleumer

Reinwardtia 1960. 5: 111.
Type: Rappard 63, 12 Aug. 1963. Sumatra, Benkulen, Mt Belirang (BO, L).
Derivation: Latin – *cernuus* – slightly drooping, presum-ably alluding to the habit of the flowers.

Shrub to 1m. Twigs spreading, tips reddish-brown-scaly; internodes 1.5–8cm. **Leaves** 4 together in pseudo-

whorls. **Blade** 40–90 x 10–17mm, narrowly elliptic; apex shortly, to long acuminate; margin slightly revolute when dry; base tapering, glabrescent above with age, the remaining scales flat and not impressed, densely and persistently scaly beneath. **Scales** flat, with many touch-ing or slightly crenate overlapping, forming a continu-ous layer, the marginal zone wide in relation to the small darker centre, deeply and irregularly to moderately lobed; centres impressed. Mid-vein impressed above, thick and prominent beneath; lateral veins 6–8 per side, straight and spreading, sometimes minutely depressed above, obscure beneath. **Petiole** 6–15 x *c.*1.5mm, semi-rounded, scaly.

Outer bracts to 8 x 5mm, ovate to sub-spherical, abruptly subulate-tapering at the apex, densely scaly outside; inner ones ovate to sub-spathulate, obtuse. Bracteoles to 6mm, filiform, laxly scaly. Inflorescence *c.*5-flowered, an open umbel, the flowers half-hanging. Pedi-cels 10–15mm, slender, densely scaly. Calyx *c.*2.5mm in diameter, sub-oblique, almost cup-shaped, the margin spreading or reflexed, irregularly, shortly and obtusely 5-lobed. **Corolla** 10–12mm, broadly campanulate, yel-low; tube *c.*8 x 2–3 x *c.*10mm, sub-densely scaly outside; lobes 5–6 x 4–5mm, broadly obovate, shortly retuse or irregularly crenate distally, scaly outside except near the margins. **Stamens** nearly as long as the corolla; filaments linear, long patently hairy in the proximal ⅓, glabrous dis-tally; anthers 1.7mm. Disc prominent, very shortly hairy at the upper margin, glabrous below. **Ovary** *c.*2.5 x 1.7mm, ovoid-conical, densely patently hairy and scaly, abruptly contracted distally; style 4–5mm, scaly at the extreme base, glabrous distally; stigma large, 5-lobed.

Indonesia, S Sumatra, near Bengkulu (Benkulen): Mt Kaba (Mt Belirang). Mt Belirang does not appear on modern maps. Belerang is the Indonesian for sulphur, and the local people har-vest sulphur on Mt Kaba and often call it Mt Belerang. It seems most likely that Belirang and Kaba are one and the same place. *Rhododendron cernuum* is reported growing on a dry sulphur-stone slope at 1500m and is said to be rare. *Fl.* July–Aug.

Apparently known from only two specimens, not recently recollected or ever cultivated.

106. **Rhododendron album** Blume

Cat. Hort. Buitenz. 1823. 72.
Type: Zippelius *s.n.* Indonesia, Java, Mt Salak, Megame(n)dong (A, L).
Derivation: Latin – *albus* – white, alluding to the flower colour but not apt.

Synonym: *Vireya alba* (Blume) Blume, Bijdr. Fl. Ned. Ind. 1826. 855.

Rhododendron album.

Shrub to 1m. Twigs 3–4mm in diameter, rounded, densely covered with brown scales; internodes 1.5–8cm. **Leaves** 4–5 together in dense pseudowhorls. **Blade** 40–100 x 12–30mm, narrowly elliptic, acuminate; apex acute; margin entire, flat or slightly revolute, markedly so in dry specimens; base acutely tapering; moderately silvery scaly above initially, becoming glabrescent in the mature state; dull with dense, golden-brown scales beneath. **Scales** flat, with many touching or slightly overlapping each other, forming a continuous layer, the marginal zone wide in relation to the small darker centre, deeply and irregularly crenate to moderately lobed, disappearing in old leaves leaving depressed scale centres or small pits. Mid-vein distinctly impressed for the entire length above, and grooved near the base, strong and prominently raised beneath for almost the entire length; lateral veins 6–10 per side, irregular, spreading, straight below, anastomosing towards the margin, slightly raised above when dry, obscure beneath. **Petiole** 10–25 x 2–2.5mm, grooved above, very densely brown-scaly.

Flower buds 10–13 x 5–7mm, green, with dense brown scales, sub-spherical but with a distinct *c.*3mm apiculus, the bracts all appressed but sometimes with a few basal, linear ones, spreading, but inwardly curling and with cataphylls around the base; basal bracts triangular, very densely brown-scaly outside and with dense scales inside at the apex, other bracts ovate, densely brown-scaly outside and with a fringe of scales along the margins, glabrous inside. Bracteoles to 10mm, linear, scaly. Inflorescence 8–13-flowered in an open umbel, the flowers semi-erect to half-hanging. Pedicels 15–20 x *c.*1.25mm, slender, pink, densely scaly, the scales on short stalks and minutely, patently hairy. Calyx disc-shaped or

triangularly lobed, the lobes 1–2mm, covered with, and fringed with, scales. **Corolla** 13–18 x 18–27mm, campanulate, cream or very pale yellow, without scent; tube 8–11 x 4–6 x 11–15mm, brown-scaly outside, glabrous inside except for a few long hairs near the base; lobes 8–10 x 9–13mm, sub-circular, erect or semi-erect and half overlapping, scaly outside except near the margins. **Stamens** exserted to *c.*4mm, at first, with the anthers curved inwards towards the centre of the flower, later regularly wide-spreading around the mouth, *c.*11mm; filaments linear, patently hairy in the basal ⅓, glabrous above; anthers *c.*1.8mm, broadly oblong. Disc hairy or glabrous. **Ovary** *c.*3 x 1.5mm, conical, densely scaly, with a mixture of purple-coloured and brown scales but without simple hairs, tapering distally; style 6–7mm, thick, mostly deflected to the lower side of the flower, curving towards the centre as the flower ages, scaly in the proximal ½ with both purple and brown scales, glabrous distally; stigma thick, deeply 5-lobed. **Fruit** 15–20 x 4–5mm, densely scaly, the valves curling back, the placentae weakly spreading and breaking away from the base. Seeds 5–6mm, without tails *c.*1mm, the longest tail 2.5mm.

Indonesia, W Java, Mts Salak, Gedeh, Telaga above Puntjak and Telaga Warna and vicinity, reported from C Java (Kedu: Dieng, coll. Junghuhn), but not recollected there recently. Epiphytic in montane forest, 1200–1700m, locally common. *Fl.* Sept.–Jan.

First brought back from Java as a living plant by Mr Henshall, a collector for Mr Rollison of Tooting Nursery in London. It flowered in November 1856 in Britain and was figured in *Curtis's Botanical Magazine* (*t.*4972) in 1857, where it was described as 'an exceedingly pretty species'. It was lost to cultivation subsequently and reintroduced into cultivation in Edinburgh in 1988. This species grows and flowers freely. The flowering in cultivation is irregular, usually with one major flowering which can take place between February and May but often with occasional flowers at any time of the year. The foliage is attractive, pale and scaly, and the plant has a demure charm.

107. Rhododendron zollingeri J.J.Sm.

Ic. Bog. 1910. 4: 73, *t.*322.
Type: Zollinger 1684, 16 June 1845. Java, Besuki, Hijang (Jang) plateau, Argopuro (BO, lectotype, BM, Fl, L, fragment, P).
Derivation: Named after the collector of this species, Heinrich Zollinger (1818–1859), a Swiss botanist who made extensive collections in Java and other Indonesian islands.

Rhododendron zollingeri.

Synonyms:

R. tubiflorum (*non* Blume) Mor., Syst. Verz. 1846. 42.

R. album (*non* Blume) Zoll., Syst. Verz. 1854. 2: 137.

R. malayanum (*non* Jack) Koord., Junghuhn Gedenkb. 1910. 185.

Much-branched, erect shrub or tree, to 4m. Twigs slender, rounded, densely reddish scaly when young; internodes 2–10cm. **Leaves** 4–6 together in tight pseudo-whorls but commonly with an odd leaf inserted apart from the others. **Blade** 30–70 x 10–22mm, narrowly ovate to obovate or elliptic or narrowly elliptic; apex shortly acuminate, sub-acute or sometimes obtuse, often apiculate with a small protruding gland; margin flat and entire, or slightly revolute when dry; base broadly to narrowly tapering; initially scaly on both sides, glabrescent above at maturity, the scales leaving small pits; persistently scaly beneath. **Scales** small, dense to overlapping, pale yellowish-brown, rounded or lobed, marginal zone broad, the centre small and impressed, with occasional much larger scales distributed irregularly. Mid-vein impressed above, prominent beneath, reddish in fresh specimens; lateral veins 5–7 per side, the lower ones steeply ascending, upper ones more spreading, curved, indistinctly anastomosing, faintly impressed above, minutely, but visibly raised beneath. **Petiole** 2.5–5 x 1–1.5mm, semi-rounded, grooved above, scaly.

Bracts to 8 x 4mm, ovate to obovate, obtuse, thin, scaly outside towards the apex, glabrous otherwise. Bracteoles to 6mm, filiform, glabrous. Inflorescence terminal but often with some axillary, a 3–8-flowered open umbel, the flowers horizontal to half-hanging. Pedicels 10–15mm, slender, densely scaly. Calyx *c.*3mm in diameter, cup-shaped, oblique, irregularly 5-lobed, often with 2 narrowly triangular acute lobes, up to 2mm, the other

ones smaller, all densely scaly. **Corolla** 14–15 x 9mm, tubular, red or orange; tube *c.*10 x 3–6 x 3–5mm, sub-densely scaly outside, glabrous inside, variable in shape, cylindrical or sometimes contracted distally; lobes *c.*4 x 4mm, sub-circular, scaly outside except near the margins, erect and overlapping to *c.*¾. **Stamens** nearly as long as the corolla tube; filaments linear, glabrous; anthers *c.*1 x 1mm, broadly obtusely obovate. Disc glabrous. **Ovary** 3–4 x 2–2.5mm, conical, 5-ribbed, densely brown-scaly, abruptly contracted distally; style 4–5mm, glabrous, with a 5-lobed stigma. **Fruit** 15–18 x 5–6mm, thick-fusiform or sub-cylindrical, sometimes slightly curved in the upper part, densely scaly, the style persistent. Seeds 2.7–3mm, without tails *c.*0.8mm, the longest tail *c.*1mm.

Indonesia, C and E Java; Kedu, Besuki, Madiun, Lesser Sunda Is. (Bali, Flores, Lombok), C and SW Sulawesi. **Philippines**, Luzon, Prov. Benguet: Mt Bandschan, Mountain Province Banaue to Bontoc. Bare open slopes or ridges, exposed summits, volcanic rocks or crater walls, in fern-grass – and scrub-vegetation or open forest, in *Casuarina* forest, on dry places, on sandy, stony or ashy soil, also near solfataras, common locally, 1200–3090m. *Fl. fr.* predominantly in the dry season, April–Oct.

Recently introduced into cultivation from Sulawesi but not a very spectacular plant, with small dull red or orange flowers. This is one of the few vireyas to have a wide distribution over several islands and apparently shows little variation.

---

108. Rhododendron arenicola Sleumer

Reinwardtia 1960. 5: 113.

Type: Eyma 955, 24 June 1937. Indonesia, Sulawesi, Enrekang, Batubóllong-Madjadja, NNW of Madjadja, 2900m (BO, L).

Derivation: Latin – *arenicola* – sand dwelling, alluding to the fact that it was first collected on a dry sandy ridge.

Erect shrub to 2m. Twigs rounded, densely pale-brown-scaly; internodes 3–8cm. **Leaves** scattered in the upper ½ of the upper 1–2 internodes. **Blade** 20–40 x 15–26mm, elliptic, broadly elliptic or rarely sub-ovate-elliptic; apex obtuse to very shortly acuminate or apiculate, with a blunt terminal gland; margin minutely crenulate, not or only very slightly revolute; base sub-truncate to rounded; very densely reddish brown-scaly beneath at least initially the scales forming a continuous layer. **Scales** lobed or rounded with a broad marginal flange, centres variable, slightly impressed, becoming glabrescent and then densely pitted. Mid-vein flat above, slightly prominent beneath; lateral veins 5–7 per side, the lower 2–3 from, or from slightly above, the base, the remainder straight at first, curving distally and obscurely anastomosing, faintly impressed above, slightly raised beneath, somewhat rugose above when mature. **Petiole** 3–4 x 2–3mm, not grooved above, flattened, scaly.

Flower buds broadly ovoid, *c.*15 x 10mm. Bracts to 15 x 10mm; outer bracts ovate, inner ones sub-spathulate, blunt, with white silky hairs and also scaly along the midline outside. Bracteoles to 3mm, slender. Inflorescence 7–13-flowered, in an open umbel, hanging, without scent. Pedicels 15–25 x *c.*1mm, densely brown-scaly but without hairs. Calyx disc-shaped, *c.*3.5mm in diameter, densely scaly outside, the margin wavy and spreading, indistinctly, bluntly 5-lobed. **Corolla** 23–27 x 20–27mm, tubular-campanulate, pink; tube 12–18 x 6–7 x 9–11mm, a little pouched at the base, laxly to sub-densely scaly outside and with a few simple hairs outside at the base and a few inside near the base only; lobes 12 x 11mm, broadly obovate to nearly rounded, retuse or irregularly crenulate, spreading almost to the perpendicular, overlapping to *c.*halfway. **Stamens** regularly arranged in a circle, just included or slightly exceeding the corolla tube in length, weakly dimorphic; filaments 1–3mm, white, filiform, glabrous or with some sparse hairs near the base; anthers 18 x 1.2mm, brown, oblong. Disc glabrous or with dense long hairs on the upper side. **Ovary** 4–5 x 3–4mm, green, thick, conical, abruptly contracted to the style, covered with patent or somewhat distally pointed white hairs which obscure dense silvery scales; style 4–6mm, thick, glabrous; stigma large, sub-conical, distinctly 5-lobed, centrally placed.

Indonesia, SW Central Sulawesi, Latimodjong Range. On open sandy ridges, 2600–3000m. *Fl.* June.

Introduced into cultivation by Galloway and Smith from Mt Rantemario where it was common at 2700m. It flowered for the first time in cultivation in Edinburgh in December 2003 with most attractive pale pink flowers. Plants in cultivation tend to be less scaly than those from the wild, with dense but not overlapping scales on the undersides of the leaves.

---

109. Rhododendron pudorinum Sleumer

Reinwardtia 1960. 5: 112.
Type: Eyma 646, 16 June 1937. Celebes, Enrekang, between Pokapindjang and Tinábang (L, BO, K).
Derivation: Latin – *pudor* – modest or shameful, alluding to the colour of the corolla being like a blush.

Tree to 4m. Twigs 5–7mm in diameter, angular to rounded, densely brown-scaly, early glabrescent;

internodes 12cm or more, with conspicuous rounded lateral buds. **Leaves** laxly spirally arranged. **Blade** 50–90 x 30–55mm, broadly elliptic to nearly rounded or obovate-elliptic; apex shortly (5mm) acuminate or apiculate or blunt; margin entire or obscurely crenulate, slightly revolute; base broadly tapering, truncate or rounded, sometimes a little decurrent; glabrescent and impressed-punctate above when mature in dry specimens, very densely, to overlapping, reddish-brown-scaly beneath, irregularly scattered over the surface a few much larger scales. **Scales** rounded, lobed or stellate, with broad pale brown marginal flanges and small dark brown impressed centres. Mid-vein thick and prominent near the base, gradually flattened and sometimes grooved above, flat or weakly raised beneath; lateral veins 5–6 per side, steeply ascending and only slightly prominent above and below, the larger ones narrowly grooved above, laxly reticulate, veinlets almost obscure above, more visible beneath. **Petiole** 5–8 x 3–4mm, flattened without a groove when fresh, initially scaly.

Flower buds *c.*20 x 15mm, broadly ovoid. Bracts to 13mm; outer bracts sub-circular, inner ones broadly spathulate, obtuse with silky hairs on both sides and scaly outside. Bracteoles *c.*10 x 2mm, linear-spathulate, densely long-hairy. Inflorescence an 8–15-flowered umbel. Pedicels 20–25 x *c.*0.8mm, densely scaly, without hairs. Calyx *c.*4mm in diameter, disc-shaped, thick-membranous, wavy and indistinctly lobed at the margin, densely scaly outside, fringed by scales which project beyond the margin. **Corolla** *c.*40 x 30mm, pink; tube 22–25 x 4–6 x 7–8mm, straight, cylindrical but flaring just below the lobes, laxly to very laxly scaly outside, glabrous inside; lobes 11–14 x 10–12mm, broadly obovate to nearly rounded, often slightly retuse. **Stamens** somewhat longer than the corolla tube, unequal; filaments linear below, filiform distally, glabrous; anthers *c.*2.5mm, broadly sub-obovate-oblong. Disc thick, glabrous. **Ovary** *c.*5 x 3mm, obconical, very densely covered with sub-patent, short yellowish hairs which cover scales, shortly contracted distally; style *c.*20–25mm, hairy and scaly at the base, glabrous otherwise, thick; stigma weakly lobed. **Fruit** 25–30 x *c.*6mm, sub-cylindrical, the apex acuminate, the base tapering, slightly thicker in the upper ⅓, densely hairy and scaly.

Indonesia, Sulawesi, Latimodjong Range: Mt Pokapindjang and its spur to Tinabang. In low forest and open sub-alpine shrubberies, 2500–3000m. *Fl.* June.

Introduced into cultivation in 1998 by David Binney but not well tested; it grows slowly and has not yet flowered. A distinctive feature of the plants is that the scaly covering on the underside of the leaves is much less dense along the mid-vein and major lateral veins; this makes these veins more distinctive than they would be otherwise. In cultivation the plants are less scaly than they are in the wild and vegetatively this species approaches *R. impositum*, but that species has very small, widely spaced scales whereas *R. pudorinum* even in cultivation has at least some of the scales touching each other.

110. Rhododendron lagunculicarpum J.J.Sm.

Bot. Jahr. 1937. 68: 200.

Type: Kjellberg 3922, June 1929. Celebes, Enrekang, B. Pokapindjang (S, L, fragment).

Derivation: Latin – *lagunuli* – a small bottle; Greek – *carpo* – relating to the fruit. Alluding to its bottle-shaped fruit but not especially apt.

Much-branched shrub or tree, to 2m. Twigs 1–2.5mm in diameter, erect or erecto-patent, the tips densely covered with scales, the lower parts rough to the touch with scale stalks; internodes 4–11cm. **Leaves** in loose pseudo-whorls, with 7–12 leaves, in the upper ⅓ or ½ of the internode. **Blade** 10–25 x 6–16mm, sub-circular to elliptic, rarely sub-ovate-elliptic; apex obtuse to rounded, with a small glandular point; margin flat or slightly revolute, crenulate with impressed scales; base broadly tapering to rounded; glabrescent above, but often densely pitted, not rough to the touch, undersurface densely scaly, the scales mostly touching and overlapping. **Scales** of two sizes: small silvery scales with small impressed centres which leave pits after they have fallen and regularly scattered amongst them, larger, brown, scales, with large swollen centres. Mid-vein impressed in a narrow groove above, somewhat raised beneath, sometimes becoming indistinct distally; lateral veins 4–6 per side, irregularly spreading and curved-ascending, anastomosing, slightly

Rhododendron lagunculicarpum.

depressed above, faintly raised beneath. **Petiole** 2–4 x 1–1.5mm, grooved above, scaly.

Flower buds to 12 x 8mm, ovoid, smooth or with the tips of the bracts slightly spreading. Outer bracts ovate to sub-circular-ovate, sub-acuminate, with a narrow raised keel, inner ones ovate to spathulate, obtuse, thin, scaly outside towards the apex, all fringed with scales. Bracteoles linear-spathulate, glabrous, up to 8mm. Inflorescence an open umbel of 4–6 flowers, the flowers horizontal or half-hanging. Pedicels 10–13mm, densely covered with sessile, or very shortly stalked scales. Calyx 3–4mm in diameter, oblique, disc-shaped, scaly outside, wavy and irregularly minutely lobed, sometimes with one lobe longer than the others. **Corolla** 17–20 x 10–12mm, yellow or orange, elongate-campanulate; tube 10–13 x 4–5 x 7–8mm, straight, densely scaly outside, glabrous inside; lobes 4–5 x 4–5mm, not or hardly reflexed, overlapping to *c*.¾, scaly except near the margins, irregularly crenate and often retuse. **Stamens** arranged all round the mouth, exserted to *c*.2mm; filaments linear but expanded near the base, glabrous, 10–12mm; anthers sub-orbicular, *c*.1mm. Disc glabrous. **Ovary** 3–4 x 2.5–3mm, broadly ovoid-conical, densely silvery scaly, abruptly contracted distally; style 3–4mm, glabrous, stigma shortly 5-lobed, centrally placed. **Fruit** 13–15 x 6–7mm, ellipsoid to obovoid-fusiform, conspicuously 5-ribbed, densely brown-scaly, becoming erect on the pedicels which elongate to 22mm, the style not elongating. Seeds 3–3.5mm, without tails 0.9mm, the longest tail *c*.1.5mm.

Indonesia, Sulawesi, Latimodjong Range: Mt Pokapindjang and its spurs; Mt Rantemario, locally common in short sub-alpine forest and mountain heath vegetation, 2800–3000m. *Fl. fr.* March, June but probably continuously.

Introduced into cultivation by David Binney in 1998, it is a straggly plant which flowers irregularly with its smallish orange or yellow flowers. Cultivated plants are less scaly than they are in the wild, with quite substantial spaces between the scales; they also tend to have longer petioles which might cause confusion with *R. zollingeri* but *R. lagunculicarpum* retains the broadly tapering to rounded leaf bases which distinguishes them from the narrowly tapering bases of *R. zollingeri*. *Rhododendron lagunculicarpum* is very similar to *R. correoides* from New Guinea, having a similar arrangement of scales on the leaves and similar colour variants. *Rhododendron correoides* is distinguished from this species by its style which is longer than the ovary (reflecting a longer flower), and the flower bud morphology appears from the limited material examined to be different, with *R. correoides* having much longer, subulate pointed bracts.

111. Rhododendron correoides J.J.Sm.

Med. Rijksherb. 1915. 25: 2.

Type: Pulle (Versteeg) 2435, 7 Feb. 1913. W New Guinea, Hubrecht Mts (lectotype) (L, BO, K, U).

Derivation: Resembling *Correa*, Australian trees in the Rutaceae.

Synonym: *R. coniferum* Wernham, Trans. Linn. Soc. London, II, Bot. 1916. 9: 97.

Shrub with erect branches, to 4m. Twigs round to angular, at first densely covered with scales, which give a grey appearance; internodes 1–8cm often with conspicuous rounded lateral buds. **Leaves** either scattered in loose, or crowded in distinct 5–7-leafed, pseudowhorls. **Blade** 20–35 x 8–17mm, elliptic or sub-obovate, rarely ovate-elliptic; apex broadly obtusely tapering, sometimes rounded, apiculate with a small terminal gland; margin thickened and crenulate by impressed scales; base very broadly tapering to rounded, densely scaly initially on both sides, glabrescent later above and then with a pitted surface; very densely and more persistently scaly beneath. **Scales** overlapping with broad transparent, lobed marginal zones which eventually disappear and small to moderately sized centres which are impressed, leaving pits. Mid-vein slightly impressed above, bluntly raised beneath especially in the proximal part, disappearing distally, or sometimes entirely inconspicuous; lateral veins 3–5 per side, curved-ascending, faintly impressed or often obscure above, indistinct beneath. **Petiole** 3–12 x *c.*2mm, semi-rounded, grooved above, densely scaly.

Buds 15–20 x 8–11mm, narrowly ovate with a slender acute apex and with spreading tips. Bracts to 20 x 10mm; outer bracts ovate-acuminate, sub-acute with a few scales outside near the midline and margins, glabrous elsewhere but often with a greyish waxy deposit; inner ones narrowly ovate to obovate-spathulate, membranous and shiny, glabrous. Bracteoles 10–15mm, linear-sub-spathulate, glabrous. Inflorescence an open, 3–5-flowered umbel, the flowers hanging vertically, occasionally half-hanging. Pedicels 10–20 x *c.*1mm, very densely scaly, without hairs, forming an angle with the calyx. Calyx 2.5–3mm in diameter, very shortly cup-shaped, oblique, densely scaly outside, obscurely lobed. **Corolla** 20–32 x 20–25mm, tubular below, slightly dilated distally, yellow or orange, without scent; tube 12–22 x 4–8 x 6–12mm, sub-densely or laxly scaly outside, glabrous inside; lobes 6–11 x 8–9mm, broadly elliptic to sub-circular, semi-erect, overlapping to halfway, scaly outside away from the margins. **Stamens** unequal, irregularly clustered around the mouth of the flower; filaments linear, glabrous; anthers

Rhododendron correoides (orange form).

2–2.5 x 1.3–2mm, broadly obovate-oblong. Disc glabrous. **Ovary** *c.*4 x 2.5–3mm, conical, densely scaly; style thick, scaly at the very base, glabrous otherwise, as long as the corolla, becoming exserted; stigma thick, 5-lobed. **Fruit** *c.*15–20 x 4–5mm, sub-cylindrical, apex long-tapering, base shortly tapering, becoming erect before maturity. Seeds 4–4.8mm, without tails 1mm, the longest tail *c.*2.1mm, one tail often much broader than the other.

Indonesia, New Guinea (W), the Main Range from Mt Jaya (Carstensz), Hubrecht and Orange Mts to Mt Trichora (Wilhelmina).

Rhododendron correoides (yellow form).

Sub-alpine forest, marginal forest shrubberies and in open vegetation, also on ridge crests, commonly on mossy or peaty soil, locally abundant, 3100–4300m. *Fl. fr.* Feb., Aug.–Dec.

Introduced into cultivation in 1993 by Paul Smith, it grows weakly as a leggy shrub in Edinburgh although flowering regularly. It is one of the species used in the Mt Jaya mine to recolonise disturbed ground and spoil heaps as it grows well at high altitude. It is not a spectacular plant, the flowers being rather small. It comes in two colour forms, yellow and orange, although intermediates may occur.

112. Rhododendron proliferum Sleumer

Blumea 1963. 12: 101.
Type: Sleumer & Vink 4372, 21 Jan. 1962. W New Guinea, Arfak Mts, Mt Gwamongga near Sujrerei, Anggi Gigi Lake (L, A, CANB, K, LAE, UC).
Derivation: Latin – *prolificus* – bearing progeny, possibly due to its being largely described in fruit.

Erect, few-branched shrub to 2m. Twigs 4–6mm in diameter, purplish, obtusely angular, the tips very densely and persistently scaly; internodes 3–10cm. **Leaves** 8–12 together in pseudowhorls, erect, or a little spreading, (the uppermost whorl concealing the inflorescence or infructescence). **Blade** 60–105 x 20–50mm, sub-spathulate-obovate or obovate-elliptic; apex broadly tapering to almost rounded, margin entire, slightly convex; base tapering and somewhat decurrent, young leaves covered by scales on both sides, becoming glabrescent above, very densely and sub-persistently scaly beneath. **Scales** sub-equal, overlapping, brown to reddish-brown and shining; marginal zone thin and wide, irregularly sub-stellately angular; centre small and impressed, leaving dark pits when the scales have gone. Mid-vein narrowly impressed above, thick and obtusely prominent beneath; lateral veins 7–9 per side, the lower ones acutely spreading, the upper ones spreading at a wide angle to the mid-vein, obscurely inarching before the margin, faintly impressed above, a little prominent or obscure beneath, without reticulation. **Petiole** 15–20 x *c.*3mm, flattened and grooved above, very densely scaly.

Bracts to 40 x 20mm, numerous, thin, purplish, persistent for a long time; outer ones elongate-triangular to ovate-acuminate and scaly outside; inner ones elongate-elliptic to spathulate. Inflorescence a 4–10-flowered umbel. Pedicels 25–32 x *c.*1mm, densely scaly. Calyx *c.*5mm in diameter, slightly oblique, saucer-shaped, shortly 5-lobed. **Corolla** (only known in a withered state on young fruit) tubular below, expanded at the lobes, apparently slightly zygomorphic and red when fresh, *c.*30mm long, scaly at the base of the tube outside, otherwise glabrous; tube *c.*20 x 4–5mm; lobes *c.*5 x 5mm, obovate. **Stamens** *c.*27mm, with linear filaments, narrower upwards, glabrous; anthers *c.*3.5 x 1.5mm, sub-obovate-elliptic, the base obtuse. Disc prominent, glabrous. **Ovary** in a developed state (or young fruit) very densely covered with reddish stellate scales, tapering distally; style 20–25mm, scaly at the base, glabrous distally; stigma 2–2.5mm in diameter, sub-peltate. **Fruit** 20–25 x 6–8mm, thick-fusiform, with 5 thick ribs, densely scaly.

Indonesia, New Guinea (W), Arfak Mts on Mt Gwamongga, Anggi Gigi Lake, known only from the imperfect type collection. Terrestrial in dense sub-mossy forest, on a steep slope below the summit, 2550m, apparently rare. *Fr.* Jan.

113. Rhododendron giulianettii Lauterb.

In K.Schum. & Lauterb., Nachtr. 1905. 338.
Type: Giulianetti *s.n.*, 1896. E New Guinea, Owen Stanley Range, Mt Scratchley (B†, K, MEL).
Derivation: Named after the collector, who was one time travelling government agent for the collecting of natural history objects and was shot at Mekeo, New Guinea in 1901.

Synonym: *R. papuanum* (*non* Becc.) C.H.Wright, Kew Bull. 1899. 104.

Shrub to 3m. Twigs *c.*1.5mm in diameter, slender, densely covered with shortly stalked scales in the younger parts, rough with the stalks after the scales have gone and with conspicuous rounded lateral buds. **Leaves** spreading, spiral, mostly at the upper ⅓ of the internodes which are 2–8cm apart. **Blade** 15–20 x 7–12mm, glossy dark green above, brown beneath, elliptic to ovate-elliptic, sometimes nearly rounded; apex broadly tapering, obtuse to rounded, not apiculate; margin slightly revolute; base rounded, abruptly contracted, densely scaly on both sides initially, early glabrescent above, the flat scales leaving small, shallow pits on the upper surface, very densely overlapping, brown-scaly beneath. **Scales** translucent or pale brown, with broad lobed flanges and small impressed centres; scattered at fairly regular intervals are much larger, darker brown scales, with large swollen centres which gives the underside of the leaf a spotted appearance. Mid-vein narrowly impressed above, moderately to strongly raised beneath; lateral veins 2–3 per side, spreading, irregular, indistinctly anastomosing, slightly depressed above, obscure below. **Petiole** 2–3 x *c.*1mm, flattened, and somewhat winged by the decurrent blade in the distal ½, grooved above, scaly.

Flower buds to 10 x 7mm, deep red, broadly ovoid, the tips and margins appressed. Bracts to 10 x 7mm, ovate, obtuse, outer ones scaly outside, inner ones larger, glabrous, not hairy. Bracteoles to 10mm, filiform, glabrous. Inflorescence 1–4-flowered, the flowers held horizontally. Pedicels 10–14mm, thick, densely brown-scaly. Calyx 3–4mm in diameter, obliquely disc-shaped, the margin wavy, densely scaly outside. **Corolla** 28–35 x 15–18mm, red, completely glabrous both outside and inside; tube 20–25 x 4–5 x 7–10mm, cylindrical, straight, flaring slightly at the mouth; lobes *c.*10 x 10mm, nearly circular, spreading, often retuse. **Stamens** 25–30mm, unequal; filaments linear, but dilated below, glabrous; anthers 2.6–3 x *c.*1mm. Disc glabrous. **Ovary** 5 x 2.5mm, conical, densely shortly patently hairy and scaly, gradually tapering distally; style *c.*24mm, thick, glabrous except for scales at the base; stigma broad-conical, the lobes inconspicuous.

Papua New Guinea, Owen Stanley Range: Mt Scratchley, English Peaks near Lake Omha, Mt Victoria, 3050–3960m.

This species has been confused with *R. comptum* but differs in the spreading leaves, the more rounded leaf shape, the usually visible lateral veins and the completely glabrous corollas outside. It would also appear to have larger flowers with a different disposition but this needs to be confirmed with more observations. Not known to have been cultivated.

114. Rhododendron comptum C.H.Wright

Kew Bull. 1899. 103.
Type: Giulianetti *s.n.*, 1896. New Guinea, Owen Stanley Range, Mt Scratchley (K).
Derivation: Latin – *comptus* – adorned, presumably alluding to the plant being covered with flowers.

Var. **comptum**

Low erect shrub with several branches arising independently from subterranean stems. Twigs 2–3mm in diameter, firm, angular and longitudinally striate, densely covered with sessile scales initially, glabrescent and smooth with age, often with conspicuous lateral buds; internodes 2–8cm. **Leaves** loosely spirally arranged, mostly in the upper ½ of the internode, sometimes over the whole length, semi-erect. **Blade** 18–30 x 5–9mm, narrowly elliptic to elliptic or obovate-elliptic; apex shortly tapering, sub-apiculate, or sometimes nearly rounded;

margin minutely crenulate by impressed scales, not revolute; base tapering, densely scaly on both sides initially, glabrescent and shining above with age, below more persistently scaly. **Scales** very dense, touching and often overlapping each other, flat, thin, small, brown initially, becoming silvery with age; centre impressed, leaving a pitted surface when the scales have gone. Mid-vein a little impressed above, and slightly and obtusely raised beneath, obscure apically; lateral veins not visible. **Petiole** 0.5–2 x *c.*1.5mm, flattened and grooved above, scaly.

Outer bracts to 20 x 10mm, ovate-elliptic, subacuminate, inner ones elliptic to elliptic-obovate, scaly on a broad midline outside, glabrous elsewhere. Bracteoles linear, glabrous, *c.*15mm. Inflorescence 3–5-flowered, the flowers hanging vertically. Pedicels very densely scaly, without hairs, 12–18 x 1–1.5mm. Calyx *c.*3.5mm in diameter, shortly cup-shaped, oblique, forming an angle with the pedicel, densely scaly outside, obscurely and bluntly lobed, sometimes with one lobe more distinct. **Corolla** tubular below, campanulate distally, *c.*28 x 20mm, bright red; tube 15–18 x 4–5 x 6–7mm, laxly scaly outside, glabrous inside; lobes 7–9 x 7–9mm, sub-circular, spreading. **Stamens** within the mouth; filaments linear, light yellow, glabrous; anthers 1.3–1.5mm, inwardly curved, light brown, obovate to sub-orbicular. Disc glabrous. **Ovary** 3–4 x 2.5–3mm, very densely scaly, conical, tapering or somewhat abruptly contracted distally; style as long as the corolla, thick, scaly proximally for ¼–⅓, glabrous distally; stigma large, 5-lobed. **Fruit** *c.*15 x 6mm, ovoid.

Papua New Guinea, Owen Stanley Range: Mts Scratchley, Victoria and Albert Edward, 3000–4000m.

Not known to be cultivated and likely to be difficult. The species is fairly distinctive, with its scattered elliptic leaves with no obvious lateral veins but often drying with oblique lateral folds on the undersides of the blades. This has been confused with *R. giulianettii* but that species has much broader leaves in relation to length, with rounded rather than tapering bases. *Rhododendron giulianettii* also commonly (but not always) has leaves with 1–2 lateral veins per side, visible.

Var. **trichodes** Sleumer

Reinwardtia 1960. 5: 111.
Type: Brass 4346. New Guinea, Central Dist., Mt Albert Edward (L, A, BO).
Derivation: Greek – *tricho* – hairy, alluding to the hairy ovary which distinguishes this from the type variety.

Differing only in that the ovary is hairy, as well as densely scaly. Described with bright red flowers. Fruit

10–12 x 6–7mm, becoming erect with persistent styles. Seeds 20–25mm, without tails 0.9mm, the longest tail 0.9mm.

Papua New Guinea, Mt Albert Edward, cliffs in open grassland and terrestrial on a steep, boggy slope, 3600–3800m. *Fl.* April–July.

---

115. Rhododendron yelliotii Warb.

Bot. Jahr. 1892. 16: 25.
Type: Hellwig 312, 14 Oct. 1888. Papua New Guinea, Finisterre Mts (B†), lectotype from the same locality; Schlechter 19153 (P).
Derivation: Named after Herr Yelliot, member of the Finisterre Expedition on which this was first collected and who contributed greatly to the success of the expedition.

Synonyms:
R. saruwagedicum Foerster, Fedde Rep. 1914. 13: 222.
R. saruwagedicum Foerster var. *alpinum* Sleumer, Flora Malesiana 1966. I, 6(4): 487, f.5.
R. yelliottii Warb. *loc. cit.* (orthographic error).

Erect, much-branched and mostly compact shrub or tree, to 12m. Twigs 1–2mm in diameter, rounded, slender, densely covered with stellate scales, the largest ones brown and distinctly stalked, the many smaller ones silvery and sessile; rough after the scales have gone. **Leaves** regularly spirally arranged, densely to laxly covering the twigs. **Blade** 7–25 x 5–15mm, broadly-elliptic to ovate-elliptic, rarely ovate or obovate; apex mostly broadly obtuse, sometimes rounded, the terminal gland small but usually protruding; margin cartilaginous, distinctly irregularly crenulate, slightly revolute; base rounded or truncate-sub-cordate, greyish dark green and shining above, pale brownish, silvery or pale yellow beneath, glabrous or very laxly scaly above at maturity, very densely scaly beneath. **Scales** pale yellow to brown, mostly small, touching each other, and forming a coherent layer initially, marginal zone lobed, the centre small and deeply depressed, a few scattered much larger and deeper brown scales can give the surface a spotted appearance. Mid-vein slightly impressed above, clearly obtusely raised beneath; lateral veins 4–6 per side, straight below, curved towards the margin and anastomosing distally, very slightly impressed above, faintly raised beneath. **Petiole** 1–3 x *c.*1mm, a little flattened, grooved above, densely scaly.

Flower buds *c.*8 x 5mm, ovoid, pale green to brown, smooth, densely scaly and very shortly, to long hairy. Outer bracts to 8 x 5mm, ovate, sub-acute, inner ones spathulate, obtuse, all scaly outside and with short hairs, also scaly towards the tips inside and fringed with scales. Bracteoles to 8mm, linear-sub-spathulate, crimped, glabrous or laxly hairy apically. Inflorescence of 3–5 flowers in an open umbel, the flowers hanging to half-hanging. Pedicels 8–13 x *c.*1mm, slender, densely covered with sub-sessile scales, without hairs. Calyx 2.5–3.5mm in diameter, disc-shaped, oblique, very densely scaly outside, irregularly obtusely 5-lobed. **Corolla** 13–16 x 8–10mm, cylindrical, zygomorphic, pale to deep red, without scent; tube 10–12 x 4–5 x 5–7mm, straight or a little curved, densely yellowish scaly outside, glabrous inside; lobes 3–5mm in diameter, sub-erect, overlapping *c.*halfway, unequal, sub-circular, often shortly retuse and irregularly crenulate. **Stamens** irregularly arranged, slightly exserted; filaments narrowly linear, glabrous; anthers *c.*1mm, sub-globose. Disc glabrous. **Ovary** *c.*5 x 2.5mm, ovoid-conical, densely scaly, broadly tapering distally; style 3–4mm, centrally positioned or irregularly displaced to one side, glabrous; stigma 5-lobed. **Fruit** 12–15 x 5–6mm, with a persistent short style. Seeds 2mm, without tails *c.*0.8mm, the longest tail 0.8mm.

Papua New Guinea, Star Mts, Finisterre Mts, Mt Saruwaged region, Mt Wilhelm, Kubor Range, Mt Michael, Mt Giluwe, Mt Dickson, Mt Albert Edward, Murray Pass and the Owen Stanley Range. Epiphytic in montane forest, but mostly terrestrial at the forest margins, on steep slopes or exposed rocks or grassland above the forest line, often along streams, 1300–3680m. *Fl. fr.* throughout the year.

Often confused with *R. inconspicuum*; for differences see under that species. I have followed van Royen & Kores (1982) in treating this species in a broad sense and including *R. saruwagedicum* as a synonym. I have not seen the type material to examine the bud scales. All the material to hand shows the bract margins fringed with scales, not ciliate, as is described for *R. yelliotii*, although, with hairs present on the outside of the bracts, it often looks as if the bracts are ciliate. The fact that Sleumer's (1966) description of the bracts (perulae) of *R. sarawagedicum* did not mention a ciliate margin is further evidence that this species does not belong in *Discovireya*. There is a great deal of variation in the many specimens, much of it due to the very broad altitudinal range ascribed to this species: the high altitude forms have very small leaves as might be expected. A specimen collected by Vinas & Thomas (LAE 59673) from the north valley of Mt Capella (Star Mts) has stalked scales on the ovary and very irregularly toothed leaf margins but there are no bracts present in the specimen seen. This may represent a hybrid or an undescribed species.

Rhododendron yelliotii was introduced into cultivation in Edinburgh by John Sandham in 1986 from material from Mt Wilhelm. It is very similar to *R. inconspicuum* but less floriferous and slower growing, differing mainly in the hairy and scaly bracts. It is not especially attractive, the small scaly flowers being dull red and not at all showy. In cultivation the scales tend to be less dense than is the case in most of the wild collected specimens.

116. Rhododendron versteegii J.J.Sm.

Med. Rijksherb. 1915. 25: 2.

Type: Pulle (Versteeg) 2573, 18 Feb. 1913. W New Guinea, Oranje Mts, S ridge of the Quarles Valley, 4000m (L, BO, K, U).

Derivation: Named after the collector, Gerard Martinus Versteeg, Medical Officer in the Dutch East Indies army who was attached to two New Guinea expeditions.

Erect shrub to 1m, with arching branches sometimes appearing from below ground. Twigs rounded, densely covered with sessile scales, early glabrescent and smooth, with conspicuous rounded lateral buds; internodes 2–12cm. **Leaves** spiral or in loose pseudowhorls in the upper ½–⅔ of the internodes. **Blade** 15–35 x 8–20mm, elliptic or broadly elliptic, sometimes slightly obovate, or rarely ovate-elliptic; apex obtuse to rounded, sometimes with a shortly protruding apical gland; margin flat or weakly revolute when dry, minutely crenulate; base truncate, rounded, or broadly tapering, very densely scaly on both sides initially, glabrescent above, scaly for a longer time beneath. **Scales** forming a coherent layer, irregularly stellate, slightly overlapping, marginal zone wide; centres small and impressed leaving pits after the scales have gone. Mid-vein narrowly grooved above in the proximal ½, thick and obtusely prominent in the proximal ½ beneath, often becoming obscure distally; lateral veins 2–4 per side, often obscure. **Petiole** 2–3 x 1–2mm, flattened and grooved above, scaly.

Bracts to 19 x 8mm; outer bracts ovate-elliptic, sub-acuminate or obtuse, inner ones elliptic to elliptic-spathulate, membranous, scaly along the outside mid-line, otherwise glabrous. Bracteoles to 16mm, linear to linear-sub-spathulate, glabrous. Inflorescence of 3–8 flowers, in an open umbel. Pedicels 9–20 x *c.*1mm, very densely brown scaly but without hairs. **Flowers** 30–40 x 30–35mm, hanging to half-hanging. Calyx 4–5mm in diameter, oblique, disc-shaped, densely scaly, obtusely 5-lobed, sometimes with one or more lobes larger and more elongate. **Corolla** funnel-shaped, red and yellow, in an irregular pattern, the yellow mostly on the lobes where the surface has been recently exposed as the flower finally opens; tube 18–22 x 4–5 x 6–8mm, laxly to sub-densely scaly outside, glabrous inside, somewhat angular, slightly pouched at the base; lobes 10–14 x 10–13mm, obovate to sub-circular, half-spreading, and overlapping to *c.*halfway, scaly outside near the base except near the margins. **Stamens** exserted to *c.*4mm, unequal; filaments linear, glabrous; anthers *c.*2.5 x 1mm, obovate-oblong. Disc prominent, green, glabrous. **Ovary** 5–6 x 2.5–3mm, shortly conical, very densely scaly and patently hairy (the hairs obscuring the scales), abruptly contracted distally; style slender, as long as the corolla, densely scaly and laxly to sparsely hairy in the lower ⅓–⅖, or almost completely glabrous; stigma globose, distinctly 5-lobed. **Fruit** 13–20 x 5–6mm, oblong-conical, 5-ribbed, densely scaly and hairy, broadest below the middle, held erect.

Indonesia, New Guinea (W), Mt Carstensz and Mt Trichora and vicinity. Grassy edges of *Podocarpus* forest, alpine grassland or boggy slopes, scattered through open mossy shrubberies on exposed ridges, 3200–3950m, sporadic, but locally common, in wet shallow sandy or peaty soil. *Fl.* continuously.

First brought into cultivation to Edinburgh by Ian Edwards in 1991, but this plant subsequently died. It grew slowly and did not have the brilliantly coloured flowers that it did in the wild, the flowers being pale orange with a green cast. It is being used extensively around the Mt Jaya (Carstensz) mine in New Guinea in the rehabilitation of disturbed land, where it is one of the most favoured species, growing well at high altitude and flowering continuously.

Rhododendron versteegii.

SECTION VII: *Euvireya* (H.F.Copel.) Argent *stat. nov.*

Type: *R. javanicum* (Blume) Benn.
Subsection *Euvireya* H.F.Copel., Phil. J. Sc. 1929. 40(2): 137. Including subsection *Solenovireya* H.F.Copel., Phil. J. Sc. 1929. 40(2): 136.

Fruit peeling an irregular outer layer at maturity. Flower bud scales (sterile bracts or perulae) fringed with multicellular trichomes (scales). Filaments hairy from the base or glabrous. Anthers introrse. Flowers various, often large (mostly more than 15mm long) and showy, mostly funnel-shaped or trumpet-shaped. Scales (multicellular epidermal trichomes) thin with small centres, moderately to deeply stellately lobed occasionally sub-dendroid or dendroid. Scales well spaced with the lower epidermis of the leaf clearly visible between them.

Subsection i: *Linnaeopsis* (Schltr.) Sleumer
Bot. Jahr. 1949. 74: 541

Type: *R. linnaeoides* Schltr. (= *R. anagalliflorum* Wernham).
Series i *Linnaeoidea* Sleumer, Reinwardtia 1960. 5: 134.
Section *Linnaeopsis* Schltr., Bot. Jahr. 1917. 55: 144, *f.2*.

Leaves small, the majority of well-developed leaves less than 1cm long. Stomata on the abaxial (lower) leaf surface only. Small creeping or erect shrubs.

Key to the species

1	Ovary hairy and scaly	2
+	Ovary scaly only	6
2	Pedicels more than 15mm, the flowers standing well above the foliage	**123. xenium**
+	Pedicels less than 15mm, the flowers not well clear of the foliage	3
3	Erect plants with spirally arranged leaves	4
+	Prostrate or compact cushion plants	5
4	Filaments glabrous, style with hairs to at least halfway	**130. womersleyi**
+	Filaments laxly hairy at the base, style hairy at the base only	**129. capellae**
5	Flowers predominantly white, funnel-shaped with erect lobes, the lobes up to 7mm	**127. anagalliflorum**
+	Flowers predominantly pink or red, campanulate with spreading lobes more than 12mm	**128. rubineiflorum**
6	Erect shrubs	7
+	Prostrate or mat-forming shrubs	10
7	Leaves spirally arranged	8
+	Leaves in distinct pseudowhorls	9
8	Leaf bases rounded, style glabrous	**126. disterigmoides** ssp. **astromontium**
+	Leaf bases acutely tapering, style hairy	**131. gracilentum**
9	Corolla more than 25mm, style *c.*15mm	**118. schizostigma**
+	Corolla less than 23mm, style up to 9mm	**126. disterigmoides** ssp. **disterigmoides**
10	Bracts hairy outside	11
+	Bracts scaly or glabrous outside	12

11 Corolla tube up to 10mm, disc glabrous ⸺ **124. parvulum**
+ Corolla tube more than 20mm, disc hairy on the upper margin ⸺ **122. muscicola**

12 Style hairy to at least halfway ⸺ **131. gracilentum**
+ Style glabrous or with hairs at the base only ⸺ 13

13 Style more than 10mm ⸺ 14
+ Style less than 5mm ⸺ 15

14 Pedicels less than 6mm, corolla glabrous outside ⸺ **125. oxycoccoides**
+ Pedicels more than 10mm, corolla sparsely scaly outside ⸺ **121. coelorum**

15 Pedicels less than 4mm, corolla tube less than 8mm ⸺ **117. caespitosum**
+ Pedicels more than 6mm, corolla tube more than 10mm ⸺ 16

16 Leaves in pseudowhorls ⸺ **120. microphyllum**
+ Leaves spirally arranged ⸺ **119. pusillum**

117. Rhododendron caespitosum Sleumer

Reinwardtia 1960. 5: 137.
Type: Brass 9039, Aug. 1938. New Guinea, Mt Wilhelmina, Habbema Lake (A, L).
Derivation: Latin – *caespitosus*, growing in tufts like grass, generally of low growing plants.

Prostrate, cushion-forming, low shrub, forming vertical patches up to 2cm in depth and 20cm in diameter, extending by prostrate, elongate, not, or sparsely, branched stoloniform shoots which root freely into the substrate. These eventually become erect and branch freely. Twigs *c*.1mm in diameter, covered in shortly stalked sub-stellate, brown scales at first, these falling and leaving a minutely warty surface with scale stalks up to 0.2mm high. **Leaves** spirally arranged along the elongate shoots, densely crowded towards the erect branch tips. **Blade** 3–6 x 2–3mm, elliptic; apex shortly acuminate, broadly acute to obtuse or rounded; margin entire or sub-crenulate with a broad and only faintly demarcated sub-cartilaginous edge; base tapering, laxly to sub-densely scaly at first on both sides but these scales disappearing quickly from the upper surface. **Scales** orange-brown, with a broad and deeply incised marginal zone. Mid-vein only visible when fresh, all veins obscure after drying. **Petiole** 1–2 x *c*.0.5mm, weakly grooved above when fresh.

Flower buds brown, 5–6 x *c*.3mm. Bracts long acuminate, the tips standing away from the bud, glabrous outside but with scales along the margins. Bracteoles *c*.4mm, filiform. **Flowers** solitary, horizontal to half-hanging. Pedicels 2–3 x *c*.1mm, densely scaly. Calyx a low disc, densely white-scaly. **Corolla** 12 x 7mm, pale pink; tube 7 x 5 x 4mm, cylindrical but contracted just below the lobes, densely scaly outside, glabrous inside; lobes 3 x 3.5mm, without scales, semi-erect to horizontally spreading, overlapping to *c*.⅔. **Stamens** 6mm, curving distally so that the anthers fill the upper part of the tube; filaments white, glabrous; anthers 1–1.1mm, brownish-purple. Disc glabrous. **Ovary** 5 x 3mm, densely white-scaly, abruptly contracted distally; style 2–2.5mm, glabrous, reddish-brown; stigma *c*.1mm in diameter, dark pink. **Fruit** 11 x 5mm, erect, broadly fusiform and densely brown-scaly, the pedicels elongating to 5–6mm, on ripening the outer layer irregularly peeling back and then the valves splitting to *c*.45°. Seeds 1.8–2.2mm, without tails to 0.8mm, the longest tail to 0.7mm.

Indonesia, New Guinea (W), Mt Trichora (Mt Wilhelmina), Lake Habbema vicinity. Growing in the high open valleys dominated by tree-ferns and forming cushions on their trunks, 2400–3500m. Probably protected from frost and with optimal shading by growing usually about mid-way up the tree-fern trunks (Argent *et al.* 1999). *Fl.* Aug.–Sept.

Rhododendron caespitosum.

Debbie White

This species was first collected by Leonard Brass on the Third Archbold expedition to the Snow Mountains, Netherlands New Guinea 1938–1939, in August 1938 and was recollected by the Trekforce expedition to the same area in October 1992 and most recently by Hansjörg and Margot Brentel. Living plants were brought back to Edinburgh in 1992 and flowered for the first time in December 1996. The flowers were remarkable for vireyas in that the corolla lobes opened in strong light but tended to close again when it was dull and cold. The plants do not grow strongly and the original collections have since died but been replaced by collections from Austria. This species appears to require high levels of both light and humidity, and the best growth so far has been obtained in closed cases where, although the light levels must be lower than in their native habitat, the humidity can be kept much higher than in the open greenhouse. Low light levels are probably the reason that the plants are so reluctant to flower in cultivation.

118. Rhododendron schizostigma Sleumer
Reinwardtia 1960. 5: 63.
Type: Brass 9567, Oct. 1938. New Guinea (W), Lake Habbema, 3225–3345m (A, BO, L).
Derivation: Greek – *schizo* – split, deeply divided, alluding to the deeply lobed stigma.

Shrub to 1.5m. Twigs erect, slender, tips laxly scaly with stalked scales, lower parts covered with the scars and thick leaf-cushions of the fallen leaves. **Leaves** densely spiral. **Blade** 5–14 x 3–8mm, ovate, elliptic-ovate or elliptic; apex shortly acuminate or acute with a small terminal gland; margin slightly cartilaginous, flat, crenulate where marginal scales are attached; base sub-truncate, rounded, or broadly tapering; very laxly scaly and early glabrescent above, laxly and persistently scaly beneath. **Scales** circular or nearly so; margin entire or sub-entire; centre mostly small, not or weakly impressed. Mid-vein minutely or not impressed above, slightly raised beneath; lateral veins obscure or 1 or 2 per side faintly visible. **Petiole** 1–2 x c.2mm, laxly scaly.

Bracts to 13 x 8mm, ovate-acuminate, membranous, glabrous or laxly scaly outside along the mid-vein, glossy, the margin crenulate with sunken glands distally, entire proximally. Bracteoles 6–10 x 1–2mm, linear-sub-spathulate, glabrous. **Flowers** solitary or in pairs. Pedicels 10–14mm, thick, densely covered with sub-sessile scales. Calyx minute, oblique, disc-shaped with an undulate margin, laxly scaly outside. **Corolla** 25–32mm, tubular, dark to light red; tube 16–22 x 3–4 x 8–10mm, laxly scaly proxi-

mally, almost glabrous distally, glabrous inside; lobes 6–8 x 4–6mm, broadly elliptic to sub-circular, erect or slightly spreading, overlapping to c.¾, margin undulate. **Stamens** c.25mm, unequal; filaments linear, glabrous, somewhat dilated towards the base, filiform distally; anthers 1.5–1.7 x c.1mm, brown, broadly sub-obovate-elliptic. Disc glabrous, the lobes thick and a little prominent. **Ovary** c.4 x 2mm, obliquely ovoid-conical, very densely scaly, without hairs, abruptly narrowed distally; style c.15mm, glabrous; stigma gradually thickened or conical, its numerous lobes irregularly club-shaped.

Indonesia, New Guinea (W), Lake Habbema and Hubrecht Mts. **Papua New Guinea**, Mt Auriga. Usually terrestrial in open vegetation, near Lake Habbema said to be plentiful in shrubberies with thick ground moss, or on peaty ridges, 3100–3450m. *Fl.* Feb., Aug.

Not known in cultivation.

119. Rhododendron pusillum J.J.Sm.
Med. Rijksherb. 1915. 25: 1.
Type: Versteeg (Pulle) 2499, 17 Feb. 1913. New Guinea (W), Oranje Mts Meer-bivouk, 3600m (BO, K, L, U).
Derivation: Latin – *pusillus* – very small, alluding to the habit of the plant.

Synonym: *R. candidapiculatum* Wernham, Trans. Linn. Soc. London, II, Bot. 1916. 9: 96.

Dwarf spreading shrub to 50cm. Twigs 1–1.5mm in diameter, densely covered with sessile and shortly stalked brown scales, older parts warty. **Leaves** densely spirally arranged at the ends of the twigs. **Blade** 4–10 x 2–5mm, ovate-elliptic; apex shortly acuminate, sub-acute, often with a paler apiculus; margin distinctly crenulate at least in the distal ½, flat, cartilaginous and paler than the lamina; base tapering or almost rounded, laxly scaly on both sides initially, becoming glabrescent above, more persistently scaly beneath. **Scales** irregularly stellate, flat, not or slightly impressed. Mid-vein slightly impressed above, raised beneath, often obscure; lateral veins obscure. **Petiole** 1–2mm.

Flower buds 10–12 x c.5mm, ovoid. Bracts to 12 x 6mm, membranous, ovate-acuminate, shortly subulate or apiculate, outer scaly outside, inner ones completely glabrous. Bracteoles to 8mm, linear. Inflorescence a solitary flower or up to 3 together hanging from an erect pedicel. Pedicels 6–20mm, densely covered with stalked stellate scales (without hairs). Calyx 2–3mm in diameter, disc-shaped, shortly sub-acutely 5-lobed, densely scaly. **Corolla** 15–23mm, tubular to sub-campanulate, slightly oblique, red, turning to orange with age; tube 10–16 x 3–4 x 5–6mm, laxly scaly proximally, or mostly glabrous

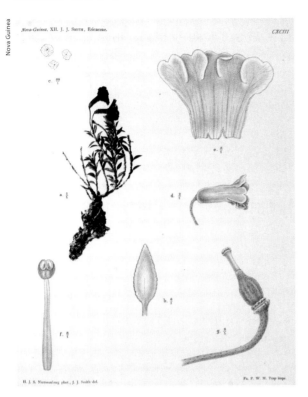

Rhododendron pusillum.

outside, glabrous inside; lobes 5–9 x 5–9mm, semi-erect or spreading, obovate to sub-circular, slightly retuse. **Stamens** unequal, ½ as long as the corolla; filaments linear, glabrous; anthers *c*.1.2mm, sub-orbicular, black. Disc glabrous. **Ovary** 3–4 x *c*.2mm, ovoid-conical, abruptly contracted distally, densely stellate-scaly; style 2–4mm, columnar, glabrous; stigma globose, 5-lobed.

Indonesia, New Guinea (W), Main Range from Mt Carstensz, where it is said to be frequent, to the Oranje Mts. Growing in alpine grassland, margins of sub-alpine forest, on exposed sandstone, in shallow sandy soil or on peaty soil at the base of rocks, 3200–3900m, locally common. *Fl.* Sept.–Feb.

Not known to have been cultivated.

120. Rhododendron microphyllum J.J.Sm.

Bull. Jard. Bot. Buit. II, 1912. 8 : 51.
Type: de Kock 89, March 1911. New Guinea (S), Mt Goliath, 3200m (BO, lectotype, L, fragment).
Derivation: Greek – *micro* – little or small; *phyllum* – leaf. The small-leafed rhododendron.

Synonym: *R. minimifolium* Wernham, Trans. Linn. Soc. London, II, Bot. 1916. 9 : 98.

Slender prostrate shrub to 30cm, rooting along the branches. Twigs *c*.1mm in diameter, rounded, at first covered in reddish-brown stalked, stellate scales, becoming glabrescent, the scale stalks leaving a warty surface; internodes 0.6–5cm. **Leaves** 3–6 together in tight pseudowhorls. **Blade** 4–9 x 2–6mm, broadly elliptic to obovate-elliptic, sometimes sub-circular; apex broadly acute, obtuse, to rounded, often apiculate; margin narrowly cartilaginous, sub-crenulate with impressed scales; base broadly tapering; laxly scaly on both sides initially, glabrescent above, persistently scaly beneath. **Scales** irregularly stellately lobed, flat, impressed. Mid-vein slightly impressed above, somewhat raised beneath or obscure; lateral veins obscure. **Petiole** 1–3mm, grooved.

Flower buds to 7 x 4mm, green, narrowly ovoid, acutely pointed, terminal and often lateral. Outer bracts

Rhododendron microphyllum.

to 6 x 3mm, subulate or ovate-elliptic, appressed or the shorter outermost slightly spreading, densely scaly outside; inner ones broader, ovate-acuminate, glabrous dorsally or nearly so, at first shortly glandular-fringed with a row of scales. Bracteoles *c.*5mm, filiform. **Flowers** solitary, hanging. Pedicels 6–17mm, slender, densely covered with reddish-brown, dendroid, or deeply stellate scales, (without hairs). Calyx *c.*3mm in diameter, obliquely disc-shaped, weakly obtusely 5-lobed, densely stellate-scaly outside. **Corolla** 18–28 x *c.*17mm, broadly tubular, sub-campanulate, purplish red or pale red; tube 12–22 x *c.*4 x 6–8mm, laxly to sub-densely, stellately scaly outside, glabrous inside; lobes 5–8 x 5–7mm, sub-circular, spreading, scaly on the proximal ½, overlapping up to ⅓. **Stamens** clustered on the lower side of the mouth, unequal, not exserted; filaments linear, glabrous; anthers *c.*1.5mm, as broad as long. Disc glabrous. **Ovary** *c.*4 x 2mm, cylindrical-conical, densely stellate-scaly, abruptly contracted distally; style *c.*3.5mm, shortly columnar, thick, glabrous or with some sparse sub-patent hairs at the base; stigma globose, distinctly 5-lobed. **Fruit** (immature) fusiform, 15 x 2.5mm, densely scaly.

Indonesia, New Guinea (W), Main Range from Mt Jaya (Carstensz) to Mt Goliath and Mt Wilhelmina (Trichora), Lake Habbema. Epiphytic on moss-covered trees in sub-alpine forest, locally common. *Fl.* March–April, Aug.

Not known to have been cultivated.

121. Rhododendron coelorum Wernham
Trans. Linn. Soc. London, II, Bot. 1916. 9: 96.
Type: Kloss *s.n.* New Guinea (S), Mt Carstensz, 3200–3810m (BM).
Derivation: Latin – *caelestis* – heavenly; no doubt an impressive plant.

Prostrate shrub to 15cm. Twigs *c.*1mm in diameter, covered with stalked stellate scales, becoming glabrescent, laxly warty. **Leaves** spirally arranged, not aggregated into pseudowhorls. **Blade** 6–12 x 4–8mm, ovate or elliptic; apex broadly acute to obtuse, sometimes with a protruding gland; margin entire to sub-crenulate, cartilaginous, narrowly revolute; base broadly tapering to rounded; quickly glabrescent above, more persistently but laxly scaly beneath. **Scales** irregularly obtusely stellate-lobed, slightly or not impressed. Mid-vein impressed above and raised beneath, or almost smooth; lateral veins obscure. **Petiole** *c.*1–1.5 x 1mm, grooved above, scaly.
Flower buds to 13 x 7mm, ovate, acute with the bract tips spreading out, almost glabrous. Bracts to 10 x 5mm,

Rhododendron coelorum.

ovate, glabrous outside except for a few scales near the acute points outside. **Flowers** 1–2, horizontal to hanging. Pedicels 10–17 x 0.5mm, sub-densely stellate-scaly, with or without hairs. Calyx *c.*2.5mm in diameter, disc-shaped, obscurely 5-lobed. **Corolla** 25–30 x 14–18mm, pink to red, without scent; tube 20–25 x 4–5 x 10–12mm, tubular, slightly expanded upwards, very sparsely scaly outside, glabrous inside, oblique; lobes 5–7 x 5–7mm, sub-circular, half-spreading. **Stamens** unequal, exserted to *c.*3mm; filaments linear, glabrous; anthers sub-orbicular, *c.*1.5mm. Disc prominent, glabrous. **Ovary** sub-cylindrical, densely scaly, *c.*3–6 x 2mm, gradually tapering distally; style glabrous, nearly as long as the corolla; stigma obconical-globose. **Fruit** 18–22 x *c.*2.5mm, fusiform.

Indonesia, New Guinea (W), Mt Jaya (Carstensz), Lake Habbema, at 2600–3810m. *Fl.* Jan., Oct.

Still a poorly known species but distinctive in its prostrate habit and spirally arranged leaves. Sleumer (1973) commented that it might have to be united with *R. schizostigma* and *R. disterigmoides* but both of these species have a much more vigorous erect habit. Not known to have been cultivated.

122. Rhododendron muscicola J.J.Sm.
Nova Guinea 1936. 18: 93, *t.*19, 1.
Type: Docters van Leeuwen 10907, Oct. 1926. New Guinea (N), Nassau Mts, W side, 2600m (BO, L).
Derivation: Latin – *muscus* – moss; *cola* – inhabiting. Living amongst mosses, alluding to the habitat.

Spreading shrub to 10cm. Twigs 1–1.5mm in diameter, rounded, the youngest parts densely covered with stellate scales on stalks and with occasional hairs, older parts warty with the scale stalks; internodes 1–6cm. **Leaves**

5–7 together in well-marked pseudowhorls. **Blade** 6–12 x 3–8mm, narrowly to broadly elliptic, sometimes obovate; apex shortly acuminate, sub-acute to obtuse, or rounded; margin flat, entire or minutely crenulate; base tapering; laxly scaly and quickly glabrescent above, laxly and more persistently scaly below. **Scales** variably sized, rounded to stellate, impressed. Mid-vein impressed above and slightly raised below or obscure; lateral veins mostly obscure, sometimes with one at an acute angle. **Petiole** 1.5–2 x 1mm, grooved above, scaly with minute scales and occasional short hairs.

Flower buds to 8 x 4mm, green becoming brown before opening, smooth with all bracts appressed. Bracts to 8 x 3.5mm, broadly ovate to broadly elliptic, covered with semi-appressed hairs outside and a few scales near the centre line distally and on the margin near the apex. Bracteoles *c.*8mm, filiform, with a few scales near the apex. **Flowers** solitary, rarely in pairs, hanging vertically. Pedicels 8–10 x 0.8mm, red, densely scaly with stalked scales and a few hairs. Calyx *c.*2.5mm in diameter, obliquely cup-shaped, 5-lobed, densely scaly. **Corolla** 25–28 x 18mm, dark red, without scent, narrowly funnel-shaped; tube 20–22 x 3–4 x 6–8mm, weakly curved, laxly silvery scaly outside, glabrous inside; lobes *c.*6 x 6mm, circular, overlapping to ⅓. **Stamens** loosely clustered on the lower side of the mouth, exserted to *c.*2mm; filaments linear, red, glabrous; anthers of two sizes, *c.*0.8 x 0.6mm and *c.*1.4 x 0.9mm. Disc with some hairs and scales at the upper margin. **Ovary** *c.*5 x 2mm, oblong-conical, longitudinally 5-grooved, densely silvery, stellate-scaly, gradually tapering distally; style *c.*8mm on opening, elongating to 15mm as the flower ages, with some sparse, spreading, yellowish hairs or scales at the base, elsewhere glabrous, or glabrous all over; stigma minute, *c.*1mm in diameter. **Fruit** 25 x 4mm, fusiform, curved, outer layer peeling away and the valves curling back. Seeds 6–7.5mm, without tails *c.*0.7mm, the longest tail 3.5mm, tails laxly crimped.

Indonesia, New Guinea (W), Nassau Mts, W side; Mt Jaya (Carstensz); Snow Mts region, E of the Baliem Valley. Mossy forest at 1750–2600m. *Fl.* Oct.

Cultivated from seed collected on Mt Carstensz by Dr Geoffry Atherton in 1993, germinated by Graham and Wendy Snell in Maleny, Australia and subsequently distributed from there. It is a small, low growing species with intensely dark red flowers produced in abundance. There are some small discrepancies between the type description and the living plants. The chief one is that the styles are in fact very short when the flower first opens and it has scales at the base not yellowish hairs. The anthers are very distinctive in being of two quite distinctly different sizes, not the usual dimorphism of stamens being of different filament lengths. Sleumer (1966) described the bracts as ciliate, following J.J. Smith's type description, but recent collections which agree very closely with the type description in other respects have bract margins which are scaly. However, the scales have long stalks which remain after the scales have fallen, giving the impression of a ciliate margin. Similarly the hairs reported on the pedicels are probably always scale stalks.

123. Rhododendron xenium Gillian Brown & Craven
Novon 2003. 13: 26.
Type: Hope, ANU 10847, 13 Dec. 1971. Indonesia, West Papua, limestone hill at S end of Carstensz meadow, Mount Jaya, 3540m (CANB, BO).
Derivation: Greek – *xenium* – gift for a guest, alluding to the long pedicel that makes the flower more accessible to visiting birds.

Prostrate shrub to *c.*20cm. Twigs rounded, moderately to densely scaly. **Leaves** spirally arranged. **Blade** 3–8 x 2–4.5mm, ovate to ovate-elliptic; apex shortly acuminate; margin entire, slightly revolute; base broadly tapering. Mid-vein impressed above in the proximal ½–⅔, inconspicuous; lateral veins obscure, initially scaly on both sides, quickly glabrescent above, persistently, sub-densely to laxly scaly below. **Scales** irregularly lobed, brown, sessile. **Petiole** 1–1.6 x 0.5mm, flat, scaly.

Flower buds 4.5–6.5 x *c.*2.5mm. Bracts ovate, acuminate, sparsely scaly outside and fringed with stalked scales, inner bracts narrower and more shortly acuminate. Inflorescence a solitary flower, horizontal to semi-erect. Pedicels 15–31 x 0.6–0.9mm, densely scaly and hairy. Calyx *c.*2mm in diameter, 5-lobed, the lobes up to 1.5mm,

Rhododendron xenium.

scaly and hairy, margin with stalked scales. **Corolla** 15–20 x 13–15mm, red, sub-campanulate; tube 9–14 x 3.5–5 x 6–8mm, slightly curved, scaly outside, glabrous inside; lobes 5.5–8.5 x 6.5–8.5mm, wide-spreading, circular to circular-obovate, scaly outside in the lower middle part, overlapping for ¼–½. **Stamens** arranged all round the mouth, exserted to *c.*3mm; filaments 10–11mm, glabrous except for a few hairs at the base; anthers 1.2–1.6 x *c.*1mm. Disc 10-lobed, with dense, erect, white, hairs on the upper margin. **Ovary** 3–4 x *c.*2mm, sub-cylindrical, densely covered in short white hairs over a sub-dense to lax layer of scales, broadly tapering distally; style 4.3–8.4mm, hairy in the proximal ¼–½, glabrous distally; stigma globose, 5-lobed. **Fruit** 15–20 x *c.*3.5mm, fusiform.

Indonesia, New Guinea (W), Mt Jaya (Carstensz), Carstensz Meadow. Growing in peaty crevices on limestone slopes and cliffs. 3520–3540m.

Distinct in its very long pedicels which are reminiscent of *R. saxifragoides*. It is a very pretty species not yet in cultivation and probably difficult to cultivate due to the high elevation at which it is found.

124. Rhododendron parvulum Sleumer
Reinwardtia 1960. 5: 139.
Type: Eyma 5203, 9 Sept. 1939. New Guinea (W), Wissel Lake Region, slope and summit of Moetaro (BO, L).
Derivation: Latin – *parvus* – little, small or puny; *ulum* – the diminutive. Alluding to the small, weak nature of the plant.

Small, weak shrub. Twigs slender, 0.6–1mm in diameter, densely covered at first with dark, brown, shortly stalked scales, minutely warty and rough to the touch; internodes 1.2–4cm. **Leaves** 2–4 together in pseudowhorls. **Blade** 6–12 x 3–8mm, broadly elliptic to sub-obovate-elliptic; apex obtuse to round; margin pale, sub-cartilaginous, entire or sub-crenulate with impressed scales; base broadly tapering or rounded, laxly to sub-densely scaly on both sides when young, glabrescent above, more persistently scaly beneath. **Scales** irregularly stellate, flat, slightly impressed. Mid-vein and lateral veins not visible. **Petiole** 1mm, slender, scaly.

Bracts to 6 x 2.5mm, narrowly ovate-acuminate, distinctly sub-densely appressed-hairy, fringed initially with scales along the margin. Inflorescence of solitary or paired flowers. Pedicels 7–10mm, slender, densely covered with shortly stalked, deeply stellate-incised scales and very short slender sub-patent hairs. Calyx 2mm in

diameter, disc-shaped, deeply obtusely 5-lobed, scaly outside. **Corolla** 10–12mm, tubular; tube *c.*8 x 2.5 x 3.5mm, sub-densely stellate-scaly outside, glabrous inside; lobes *c.*4 x 4mm, spreading, sub-circular, scaly outside in the proximal ½. **Stamens** exserted to *c.*2mm, unequal; filaments filiform, glabrous; anthers *c.*1mm, obovate. Disc glabrous. **Ovary** *c.*2 x 1.2mm, obconical-cylindrical, densely stellate-scaly, gradually tapering distally; style *c.*3.5mm, slender; stigma club-shaped-sub-globose.

Indonesia, New Guinea (W), Wissel Lakes region: summit of Mt Mutaro (Moetaro). Known only from the type collection. *Fl.* Sept.

Never cultivated.

125. Rhododendron oxycoccoides Sleumer
Reinwardtia 1960. 5: 139.
Type: Brass 12184, Jan. 1939. New Guinea (N), Idenburg R., 18km from Bernard camp, 2100m (A, L, fragment).
Derivation: With leaves like those of *Vaccinium oxycoccus* (cranberry).

Shrub. Twigs 0.5–1mm in diameter, densely brown-stellate-scaly, at first glabrescent and smooth later. **Leaves** laxly spirally arranged. **Blade** 3–7 x 2.5–4mm, ovate, shortly acuminate, sub-acute or obtuse; margin thickened, flat or slightly recurved; base broadly rounded; initially scaly on both sides, quickly glabrescent above, more persistently scaly below. **Scales** irregularly stellately lobed, not or only slightly impressed. Mid-vein and lateral veins obscure. **Petiole** 0.5–1mm, slender.

Bracts to 15 x 5mm, membranous, ovate-elliptic, inner ones long subulate-acuminate, glabrous and shining. **Flowers** solitary. Pedicels 4–6mm, slender, densely stellate-scaly. Calyx *c.*2.5mm in diameter, disc-shaped, margin wavy, scaly outside. **Corolla** 25–27mm, slightly zygomorphic, pink, thin; tube 18–20 x *c.*3 x *c.*5mm, cylindrical, glabrous both inside and out; lobes 5–7 x 5–7mm, spreading, sub-circular. **Stamens** exserted to *c.*3mm, unequal; filaments linear, glabrous; anthers 1–1.2mm, hardly longer than broad. Disc prominent, glabrous. **Ovary** *c.*3.5 x 2mm, sub-cylindrical, densely scaly, gradually tapering distally; style *c.*14mm; stigma globose.

Indonesia, New Guinea (W), Idenburg R., Bernard Camp, *c.*139°E 3°30′S. Epiphytic in stunted, mossy forest on an exposed summit, 2100m. *Fl.* Jan.

Known only from the type collection. Never cultivated.

126. **Rhododendron disterigmoides** Sleumer

Reinwardtia 1960. 5: 140.

Type: Brass 9022, Aug. 1938. New Guinea (N), Mt Wilhelmina, Lake Habbema, 3225m camp (A, L, fragment).

Derivation: Like a *Disterigma*, a genus of South American Ericaceae.

Ssp. **disterigmoides**

Shrub to 80cm, with strong erect branches. Twigs 1.5–2mm in diameter, when young covered with reddish-brown, stalked, stellate scales, later glabrescent. **Leaves** sub-densely spirally arranged. **Blade** 6–10 x 4–6mm, ovate; apex acuminate, apiculate, acute; margin thickened and pale, distinctly revolute, crenulate with impressed scales; base rounded to sub-truncate; glabrescent above, persistently laxly scaly beneath. **Scales** small, irregularly stellate-incised, weakly or not impressed. Mid-vein obtusely prominent beneath, obscure above; lateral veins obscure. **Petiole** *c.*1mm.

Inflorescence 2–4-flowered, flowers half-hanging to hanging. Pedicels 8–12mm, slender, densely shortly stalked, stellate-scaly, without hairs. Calyx *c.*2.5mm in diameter, shortly cup-shaped, shortly obtusely 5-lobed, densely scaly outside. **Corolla** 22–23mm, tubular, deep red; tube *c.*17 x 4 x 7mm, laxly to sub-densely scaly outside, glabrous inside; lobes *c.*8 x 8mm, sub-circular, with a few scales outside. **Stamens** exserted to *c.*2mm, unequal; filaments linear, glabrous; anthers *c.*1.8 x 1mm, broadly obovate-oblong. Disc glabrous. **Ovary** 4–5 x *c.*2mm, sub-conical-cylindrical, densely scaly gradually tapering distally; style 8–9mm, glabrous, columnar; stigma club-shaped-globose.

Indonesia, New Guinea (W), Lake Habbema. A common terrestrial in shrubberies and on peaty ridges, 3225m. *Fl.* Aug.

Ssp. **astromontium** Argent

Folia Malaysiana 2003. 4(2): 101–128.

Type: Vinas LAE 67036, 7 April 1975. Papua New Guinea, West Sepik District, Telefomin Subdistrict, Ridge-top, west of Tel Basin 2.5km E of Mt Capella, 3800m (LAE, A, BISH, CANB, E, K, L, SYD).

Derivation: Latin – *aster* – a star; *montes* – mountains. Alluding to the Star Mountains where it has been collected.

Erect shrub to 1m. **Leaves** shiny dark green above, light green with brown scales below, arranged in distinct pseudowhorls. Flower buds to 10 x 4mm, outer bracts broadly elliptic, with long points, inner bracts ovate, acuminate, also with long slender subulate points, completely glabrous except for a dense fringe of scales around the bract margins. Pedicels pink. **Corolla** deep red with white scales. **Stamens** pink with white pollen. **Ovary** brown.

Papua New Guinea, West Sepik District, Telefomin subdistrict, Ridge top W of Tel Basin, 2.5km E of Mt Capella. **Indonesia**, New Guinea (W), Star Mts, Mt Antares, 3380–3800m. *Podocarpus–Phyllocladus* woodland with *Gahnia* tussocks dominating the ground layer, locally common.

Differing from the type subspecies chiefly in the distinctly pseudowhorled leaf arrangement.

Rhododendron disterigmoides was described from the Lake Habbema area in West New Guinea, not a great distance from the locality of this subspecies. The type of ssp. *disterigmoides* was described incompletely in that the flower buds were not collected. It is possible that flower bud characters from the type area will show sufficient difference from those of this new subspecies to warrant that this taxon be raised to specific level. Apart from the difference in leaf arrangement there are some other minor differences: the leaves of this subspecies are less revolute, the margins being so only in the proximal ⅓, the apices are often obtuse rather than acute to acuminate, and the leaf bases are often broadly tapering rather than rounded or sub-truncate. This subspecies has been confused in the past with *R. pulleanum*. It is easily distinguished on the marginal bud scale indumentum which is of simple hairs in *R. pulleanum*, not scales.

127. **Rhododendron anagalliflorum** Wernham

Trans. Linn. Soc. London, II, Bot. 1916. 9: 94.

Type: Kloss *s.n.* New Guinea (W), Ascent to Mt Carstensz Camp VIb (BM).

Derivation: Latin – *Anagallis* (Primulaceae); *florum* – flower. With flowers like an *Anagallis* (pimpernel).

Synonym: *R. linnaeoides* Schltr., Bot. Jahr. 1917. 55: 144, *f.*2.

Dwarf prostrate or creeping shrub to 15cm. Twigs very slender, 0.5–0.7mm in diameter, densely covered with shortly stalked dendroid or sub-sessile stellate scales at first, warty in the older glabrescent parts; internodes 0.5–2.5cm. **Leaves** 3–5 together in tight pseudowhorls at the upper 3–4 nodes. **Blade** 3–7 x 1–2.5mm, elliptic or sub-obovate; apex sub-acute or obtuse; margin entire, flat; base broadly tapering, initially scaly on both sides, glabrous above at maturity, laxly and more persistently scaly beneath. **Scales** brown, flat or slightly concave; marginal zone rounded or obtusely lobed; centre small, slightly impressed. Mid-vein visible only near the base above and

Debbie White

Rhododendron anagalliflorum.

slightly impressed there, slightly raised and visible for a greater length beneath; lateral veins obscure. **Petiole** 0.5–1 x 0.3mm, not grooved, brown-scaly.

Flower buds to 6 x 3mm, narrowly ovoid with an acute apex, pale brown or pink, laxly scaly outside, the bract tips slightly spreading. Bracts narrowly ovate-acuminate, laxly scaly outside and along the margins. Bracteoles 4–5mm, linear. Pedicels 6–7 x 0.75mm, very slender, densely covered with dendroid stellate scales and sparse white hairs. **Flowers** solitary. Calyx *c.*2mm in diameter, obliquely cup-shaped, shortly obtusely 5-lobed. **Corolla** 13–18 x 12–14mm, funnel-shaped, white flushed with reddish purple near the base; tube 5–7 x 3–5 x 5–7mm, laxly scaly outside, glabrous inside; lobes 6–7 x 4–5mm, elliptic, semi-erect or half-spreading, not overlapping. **Stamens** distinctly dimorphic, regularly arranged all round the mouth, the longest exserted to 1.5mm; filaments 8 and 6.5mm, pink, linear, glabrous; anthers *c.*0.7 x 0.4mm, oblong. Disc densely hairy along the upper margin. **Ovary** *c.*1.8 x 1mm, broadly sub-ovoid-cylindrical, densely covered with short, spreading hairs, less densely scaly between the hairs; style *c.*1.5 x 0.2mm, sparsely hairy at the base or to halfway; stigma green, thick-globose. **Fruit** 12–15 x *c.*2mm, fusiform, pink, shortly hairy and scaly. Seeds 3–4mm including the tails.

Indonesia, New Guinea (W), Mt Carstensz. **Papua New Guinea**, Bismarck Mts and Wahgi–Jimmy Divide. New Britain: Mt Lululua, in the Pomio subdistrict. In montane forest, open grassland or alpine shrubberies, epiphytic on moss on trees, or trailing over fallen logs, 1190–3500m. *Fl.* Jan.– Dec.

This species was for some time confused with *R. rubineiflorum* (for differences see under that species). It was introduced into cultivation in Australia by L.K. Searle and D.B. Stanton in 1972 (Craven 1980). It grows well like a delicate alpine and flowers continuously when established. It has been used very successfully in hybridising using the trailing habit to produce some lovely plants which work very well in hanging baskets.

128. Rhododendron rubineiflorum Craven
Notes RBG Edinb. 1980. 38(1): 141, *f.*1.
Type: Pullen 227, 28 July 1957. Papua New Guinea, W Highlands District: upper Minj River valley on the Minj–Nona divide (CANB).
Derivation: Latin – *rubineus* – ruby red; *florus* – flower. The ruby-red flowered rhododendron.

Synonyms:
R. anagalliflorum auct. non Wernham, Sleumer, Reinwardtia 1960. 5: 136.
R. rubiniflorum Craven in van Royen & Kores, The Alpine Flora of New Guinea 1982. 3: 1606 (orthographic error).

Low shrub to 20cm. Twigs 0.75–1.5mm in diameter, covered with shortly stalked stellate scales and with very short white hairs, warty in the older glabrescent parts; internodes 1–4cm. **Leaves** 4–7 together in tight pseudo-whorls, with fragile cataphylls along the internodes. **Blade** 5–10 x 2–6mm, elliptic to ovate; apex broadly acute to obtuse; margin flat and entire; base broadly tapering to rounded, initially scaly on both sides, glabrous above at maturity, laxly but more persistently scaly beneath. **Scales** brown, flat rounded to sub-stellately lobed and slightly impressed, with small centres. Mid-vein impressed in the proximal ⅓ above, smooth and indistinct beneath; lateral veins not visible. **Petiole** 1–2 x *c.*0.5mm, not grooved above, densely brown-scaly and with very short white hairs.

Flower buds to 6 x 3mm, narrowly ovoid with an acute apex, pale brown or pink, laxly scaly outside, the bract tips slightly spreading. Bracts narrowly ovate-acuminate, laxly scaly outside and along the margins. Bracteoles 4–5mm, linear. Pedicels 7–12 x *c.*1mm, slender, densely covered with dendroid-stellate scales and sparse

Eve Bennett

Rhododendron rubineiflorum.

white hairs. **Flowers** solitary or occasionally paired, held horizontally or half-hanging. Calyx obliquely cup-shaped, shortly obtusely 5-lobed, *c.*2mm in diameter, densely scaly. **Corolla** 15–20 x 25–35mm, broadly campanulate, red or pink; tube 10–12 x 7–8 x 9–10mm, laxly to moderately densely transparently scaly outside, glabrous inside; lobes 13–15 x 10–13mm, elliptic, spreading to reflexed, over-lapping to *c.*¼. **Stamens** distinctly dimorphic, regularly arranged all round the mouth, the longest exserted to 1.5mm or all slightly included within the mouth; filaments 8 and 6.5mm, pink, linear, glabrous; anthers 0.7–1.2 x 0.4–0.6mm, oblong, dark-purplish-brown. Disc densely hairy along the upper margin. **Ovary** *c.*3 x 2mm, broadly sub-ovoid-cylindrical, gradually contracted distally, densely covered with short, patent hairs, less densely with scales between the hairs; style 4–4.5 x 1.5mm, sparsely hairy at the base or to ⅔ and sparsely scaly near the base; stigma *c.*2mm in diameter, green or red, globose. **Fruit** 12–15 x *c.*2mm, fusiform, pink, shortly hairy and scaly. Seeds 3–4mm including the tails.

Indonesia, New Guinea (W), Mt Carstensz, Kemarong Valley. **Papua New Guinea**, Star Mts, Upper Ambun Valley, Kubor Mts, Minj–Nona Divide, Mt Hagen, Gumine, Mt Wilhelm, Mt Otto, Mt Piora, Sarawaket Mts, Busu–Tamunac area, Mt Amungwiwa, Bull-dog Road, Mt Ne, Mt Giluwe, Mt Bosavi, Wharton Mts, Murray Pass, Mt Victoria and the Owen Stanley Mts. In alpine shrubberies and upper montane forest, epiphytic or at the base of trees. 2600–3400m. *Fl.* Jan., April–July.

Collected by Graham Smith and others in 1986, and flowering for the first time at Pukeiti, New Zealand in 1990, it is now widely distributed and has been used in hybridising. This species remained included within, and confused with, *R. anagalliflorum* until Craven (1980) described it and clearly showed how it differed.

Rhododendron rubineiflorum is apparently much more common and widespread than *R. anagalliflorum*; it is a larger, more vigorous plant with much longer internodes up to 4cm long (up to 2.5cm in *R. anagalliflorum*). The corolla is very differently shaped and coloured: funnel-shaped, with erect lobes, up to 18mm long and very pale, almost white in *R. anagalliflorum*; broadly campanulate, with spreading lobes, 17–25mm long and bright red in *R. rubineiflorum*. A delightful species, with its very large bright red flowers contrasting with the small leaves and delicate habit, it is not difficult to cultivate.

129. Rhododendron capellae Kores
Blumea 1978. 24: 181, *f.*1.
Type: Croft & Hope LAE 68056, 29 May 1975. Papua New Guinea, W Sepik Province, Star Mts, summit region of Mt Capella (LAE, A, BRI, CANB, CANU, E, K, L).
Derivation: Named after the mountain on which it was found.

Terrestrial, erect, branching shrub, *c.*50cm. Twigs erect, slender, rounded, 1–2mm in diameter, tips laxly scaly, gla-brescent below. **Leaves** crowded especially at the tips of the new shoots. **Blade** 8–15 x 3–6mm, elliptic or obovate; apex abruptly acuminate; margin thickened and a little paler than the lamina, sub-crenulate where impressed scales are, or have been, slightly or not revolute; base acutely tapering, dark green above, lighter green below, sub-densely scaly on both sides initially, glabrescent and shiny above at maturity, persistently scaly below. **Scales** the marginal zones entire and somewhat irregu-lar, impressed with thickened centres. Mid-vein impressed above, raised beneath; lateral veins obscure. **Petiole** 2–3mm, slender, flattened, laxly scaly.

Outer bracts 6–10mm, ovate-acuminate, subulate or apiculate, laxly scaly and very laxly hairy; inner bracts broader, obovate, apiculate and very laxly scaly outside. Inflorescence of solitary flowers or in twos. **Flowers** half-hanging to hanging. Pedicels 12–15mm, slender, scaly. Calyx membranous, with 5 broadly triangular lobes 0.5–1mm. **Corolla** 25–30mm, tubular, slightly dilated near the mouth, bright red, glabrous inside; tube cylindrical, 17–20 x 3–4 x 5–7mm, slightly curved, laxly scaly outside, glabrous inside; lobes 6–7 x 4–6mm, half-spreading, broadly obovate, scaly proximally outside. **Stamens** almost equal in length, exserted to *c*.3mm; filaments linear, laxly hairy in the proximal ¼, glabrous distally; anthers obovate, *c*.1.5 x 1mm. Disc glabrous except for a minutely hairy upper margin. **Ovary** cylindrical-conical, densely covered with long white hairs and sub-densely scaly, *c*.5 x 1.5mm, tapering distally; style just shorter than the corolla tube with a few hairs at the base, glabrous distally; stigma club-shaped-globose.

Papua New Guinea, West Sepik Province, Star Mts, summit region of Mt Capella in sub-alpine shrubbery at 3800m. *Fl.* May.

Transferred from *Pseudovireya* (*sensu* Sleumer 1966) as the bract margins are scaly, not hairy. At present known only from the type collection and not in cultivation. Said to be closely related to *R. pulleanum* (Kores 1978) but *R. capellae* has much less warty twigs, much longer, subulate outer bracts and an ovary which is both hairy and scaly. It would appear to be closer to *R. womersleyi* but differs in the more slender subulate bracts in addition to the characters used in the key.

130. Rhododendron womersleyi Sleumer

Reinwardtia 1960. 5: 136.
Type: Womersley NGF 8871, 1 Aug. 1956. Papua New Guinea, Central Highlands, Mt Wilhelm, vicinity of Lake Piunde, 3600m (LAE, BRI, K, L).
Derivation: Named after John Womersley, long time Chief of Division of Botany in Lae, Papua New Guinea, collector of the type specimen and rhododendron enthusiast.

Synonym: *R. aff. inconspicuum* Stonor, Rhod. Yearbook 1951. 6: 51, *f*.52.

Stiffly erect shrub to 2m. Twigs 1–2mm in diameter, rounded, tips densely covered with brown, stellate, stalked scales, glabrescent below with the small peg-like bases persisting. **Leaves** densely spirally arranged along the upper part of the twigs. **Blade** 7–14 x 4–9mm, ovate to ovate-elliptic, broadly elliptic or sub-circular; apex shortly acuminate, broadly acute to obtuse or rounded; margin

Ken Grant

Rhododendron womersleyi.

entire or very weakly crenulate from indentations of scale bases, sometimes slightly revolute in the basal ½; base broadly tapering to rounded, sub-densely scaly on both sides initially, glabrescent and often a little shining above at maturity, persistently sub-densely or more sparsely scaly beneath. **Scales** flat, or somewhat domed, with the marginal zone irregularly obtusely stellate-incised to almost entire and circular; centre often broad and slightly domed. Mid-vein distinctly impressed above, weakly prominent beneath; lateral veins not visible. **Petiole** 1–2 x 1–1.5mm, weakly grooved and with dense, short, white hairs above and brown scales mostly beneath.

Flower buds to 12 x 6mm, green often with a pink flush, ovoid but acutely pointed, with the bracts appressed except for the basal, partly leaf-like bracts which are wide-spreading. Outer bracts ovate-acuminate, shortly apiculate, or narrowly pointed, the outermost with a few scales outside; inner ones narrower, glabrous inside and out, except for the margins which are densely fringed with brown scales of which those in the lower parts are long stalked, the more distal ones almost sessile. Inflorescence of 1–4 hanging flowers. Bracteoles *c*.5mm, filiform. Pedicels 15–20 x *c*.1mm, densely covered with very shortly stalked stellate scales and more laxly with short patent white hairs. Calyx disc-shaped, spreading or reflexed, *c*.2.5mm in diameter, lobes broadly triangular, obtuse, scaly and finely hairy, *c.*1mm. **Corolla** 20–25 x 16–20mm, tubular, slightly dilated at the mouth, bright or deep red; tube 15–18 x 5–7 x 8–10mm, almost parallel sided but expanded just below the mouth, laxly stellately scaly outside and patently white hairy especially in the basal ½, glabrous inside; lobes *c.*8 x 9mm, sub-circular, overlapping ½–⅔, curved, the lower ½ almost vertical, the upper ½ widely spreading, with a few scales outside at the base and sometimes along the midline. **Stamens** arranged around the lower ½–⅔ of the mouth, exserted to *c.*5mm; filaments filiform, deep pink, glabrous; anthers 2 x 1mm, oblong, dark purplish-black and with grey pollen. Disc prominent, hairy on the upper margin. **Ovary** 3–4 x 1–1.5mm, sub-cylindrical, densely semi-erect to patently white hairy and sub-densely scaly, gradually tapering distally; style lying on the lower side of the mouth and nearly equalling the corolla in length, covered with spreading white hairs in the lower ½–⅔, glabrous distally; stigma club-shaped or sub-globose. **Fruit** 15–20 x 3–4mm, fusiform, hairy, greyish or purplish when almost ripe. Seeds 4mm including the tails.

Papua New Guinea, Eastern, Western and Southern Highlands; Morobe District: Rawlinson Range. Mostly in open mossy forest or along forest margins, also in grassland above the timber line; mostly terrestrial, rarely epiphytic on mossy trunks. Locally common, 3200–3960m. *Fl.* Feb.–Sept.

Recorded as hybridising with *R. atropurpureum* and *R. commonae* on Mt Wilhelm.

Introduced into cultivation by L.K. Wade in 1966 with a further introduction by J. Vandenberg in 1968. Slightly fickle and prone to sudden death if the temperatures get too high but otherwise a pretty species with a good erect habit.

131. Rhododendron gracilentum F.Muell.

Trans. R. Soc. Vict. n.s. 1889. 1(2): 22.

Type: MacGregor *s.n.* New Guinea (E), Central District, Mt Musgrave, Upper Vanapa Valley, 2240–2745m (MEL).

Derivation: Latin – *gracilis* – slender, alluding to the delicate habit of the plant.

Erect or prostrate shrub with spreading branches, to 60cm. Twigs 1–1.5mm in diameter, sub-densely covered with brown, stellate, shortly stalked scales at first, later glabrescent and warty; internodes 0.5–3cm. **Leaves** 2–7 in tight pseudowhorls, often somewhat recurved. **Blade** 6–18 x 3–6mm, narrowly ovate or narrowly elliptic; apex shortly acuminate, or acute to rounded, occasionally mucronate; margin entire, slightly wavy and weakly revolute; base acutely tapering, dark green and glossy above, distinctly paler beneath, laxly scaly on both sides initially, glabrescent above, persistently scaly beneath. **Scales** irregularly and obtusely stellately divided at the margin; centre not impressed. Mid-vein smooth and inconspicuous above, more distinct and slightly raised beneath;

Rhododendron gracilentum.

lateral veins obscure. **Petiole** 1.5–3 x 0.6–1mm, grooved above, brown-scaly and often with a few white hairs which are scale stalks.

Flower buds to 10 x 4mm, ovoid, smooth, acutely pointed, green or flushed with red. Bracts to 8 x 4mm, ovate, acutely pointed or mucronate, glabrous except for the marginal brown scales. Bracteoles 7 x 1.2mm, spathulate with an irregular margin and hooded apex, glabrous except for a few marginal scales. **Flowers** solitary, or rarely in pairs, hanging. Pedicels 8–16 x *c*.1mm, pink, densely covered with shortly stalked sub-stellate scales and sometimes with a few very short hairs. Calyx membranous, rounded to deeply 5-lobed, stellate-scaly outside, the lobes triangular, sub-acute, to *c*.1mm. **Corolla** 26–33 x 20–25mm, cylindrical, red, or pink, without scent, laxly covered with pale brown scales outside, glabrous inside; tube 18–22 x 6–8 x 9–11mm; lobes 8–11 x 8–10mm, semi-erect to spreading or slightly revolute, obovate to sub-circular. **Stamens** unequal, clustered on the lower side of the mouth, exserted to *c*.3mm; filaments linear, glabrous, pink; anthers *c*.1.5 x 1mm, dark purplish-brown. Disc prominent, glabrous, green. **Ovary** 4–7 x 1.5–2mm, oblong-cylindrical, densely and exclusively scaly, gradually tapering distally; style on the lower side of the mouth, becoming exserted to 4mm, covered with fine patent, white hairs for the proximal ½–¾ of the length; stigma club-shaped, *c*.1mm. **Fruit** 15–22 x 3–4mm, erect, oblique, oblong, a little curved, glabrescent.

Papua New Guinea, Central District: Mt Musgrave; Morobe District: Mt Kaindi and Edie Creek above Wau. Terrestrial in open low vegetation, on dry slopes or clayey ground of old gold mine workings, also epiphytic in *Nothofagus* forest or in summit vegetation, 2000–2745m. *Fl*. May–Oct.

First recorded in cultivation from material obtained by Arnold Teese from Mrs Holnen, wife of the chief engineer of Wau Goldfields. Material was sent to Kew by the Australian Rhododendron Society in 1966 but the origin is unknown. It was introduced into cultivation in Edinburgh by Paddy Woods in 1968 from Mt Kaindi near Wau and this species is now widely grown. Most forms make compact, slow growing plants, which cover themselves in bright red, or pink, flowers, mostly just once a year in May or June (in Edinburgh), although occasional out of season flowers do occur. It has been used for hybridising, the compact growth form, small leaves and relatively large flowers being attractive attributes for breeders.

Subsection ii: *Saxifragoidea* (Sleumer) Argent *stat. nov.*

Type: *R. saxifragoides* J.J.Sm.
Series ii *Saxifragoidea* Sleumer, Reinwardtia 1960. 5: 141.

Cushion forming plant with stomata on both sides of the leaf.

132. Rhododendron saxifragoides J.J.Sm.
Med. Rijksherb. 1915. 25: 3.
Type: Pulle (Versteeg) 2475, 15 Feb. 1913. New Guinea (W), Oranje Mts, Watervalbivak, 3400–3500m (L, BO, K, U).
Derivation: Named after the genus *Saxifraga* from the similarity of its tussock forming habit.

Dwarf shrub, to 15cm, forming tussocks, large cushions or dense mats, up to 1m in diameter, with subterranean spreading woody branches. Twigs thick, those above ground very short, stellate-scaly near the apex which is densely packed with spreading leaves, sometimes more elongate and decumbent, with 2 internodes. **Leaves** 6–10 together in pseudowhorls at the apex and the ultimate node. **Blade** 16–34 x 3–7mm, linear to narrowly elliptic or narrowly elliptic-obovate; apex shortly acuminate, often apiculate or almost mucronate; margin weakly revolute; base gradually tapering; glabrescent above, laxly scaly beneath. **Scales** small, the marginal zone irregularly and often obtusely dentate or angular with the centre impressed. Mid-vein impressed above, obtusely prominent beneath; lateral veins 2–3 steeply ascending on each side, very slightly impressed above, or often inconspicuous, below inconspicuous. **Petiole** 3–7 x 1–2mm, grooved, flat, not clearly distinct from the leaf blade.

Flower buds to 12 x 6mm, ovate to obovate, acutely pointed. Bracts to 15 x 5mm, the outer acutely pointed, green, scaly outside, inner ovate and broadly pointed, pink glossy, glabrous except for the fringe of scales round the margins, often becoming brown on opening, innermost spathulate. Bracteoles 16 x *c*.1mm, linear, glabrous, or with a few short hairs but fringed with scales on long hair-like stalks. **Flowers** solitary, or rarely in twos, half-hanging to hanging. Pedicels erect, red, 25–100 x 2–3mm, laxly to sub-densely scaly, sometimes also laxly covered with short patent hairs. Calyx *c*.6mm in diameter, oblique, disc-shaped, wavy and obtusely 5-lobed (sometimes with longer, irregular lobes up to 2mm), scaly and sometimes shortly hairy, often fringed with hairs. **Corolla** 30–35 x 25–30mm, pink to red, without scent; tube 17–25 x 5–8 x 10–15mm, curved, cylindrical, often grooved, densely stellate-scaly outside, shortly hairy inside; lobes 13–15 x 11–16mm, broadly spathulate or sub-circular. **Stamens** mostly clustered on the upper side of the corolla but often irregularly arranged, exserted to 10mm, sub-equal; filaments linear, laxly patently hairy in the proximal ⅓, glabrous above, red; anthers *c*.2.8 x 1.5mm, broadly oblong-obovate. Disc prominent, glabrous or hairy along the upper margin. **Ovary** *c*.7 x 5mm, conical, tapering distally; style 12–22 x 1–2mm, held on the upper side of the corolla tube, densely hairy with semi-appressed white hairs and obscurely scaly, the hairs covering the scales; style as long as or slightly shorter than the stamens, thick, hairy and scaly in the basal ⅓, then with hairs only to *c*.halfway, glabrous distally; stigma to 3mm in diameter, oblique. **Fruit** 15–20 x 6–8mm, erect, narrowly ellipsoid, shortly hairy and scaly, the outer coat irregularly splitting and then dividing from the apex into 5 valves, the axis and style persistent for a long time, the valves becoming reflexed and twisted, fruit pedicel 60–110mm. Seeds 2.5–3.2mm, without tails *c*.1mm, the longest tail *c*.1.2mm.

Seed heads of *Rhododendron saxifragoides*.

Rhododendron saxifragoides.

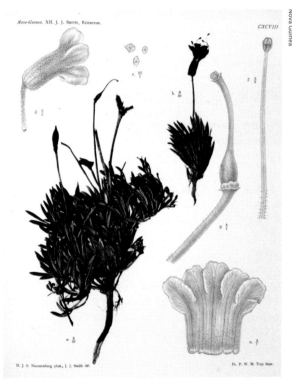

Rhododendron saxifragoides.

Indonesia, New Guinea (W), along the Main Range in suitable habitats; recorded from: Mt Jaya, Mt Wilhelmina, Oranje Mts; Star Mts. **Papua New Guinea**, Star Mts, Western and Southern Highlands: Hagen Range, Mt Giluwe and Mt Sugarloaf. In open alpine grassland, occasionally on shrubby ridges, 3225–4000m; locally abundant and a conspicuous feature in bogs or forest openings, on peaty soil.

Professor R.J. Johns excavated what appeared to be separate plants in a bog on Mt Giluwe and found they were all interconnected by woody rhizomes. In cultivation the plants form extended horizontal branches when growing vigorously; these no doubt become buried by normal upward growth of a bog and thus form the rhizomes. The implication of this is that some of the colonies in the wild must be very old. Recorded flowering in the wild from May to February and probably throughout the year where it is common.

Introduced into cultivation in the 1960s from several sources but mostly growing slowly and flowering intermittently throughout the year. It has however been used as the parent in a number of hybridisations, particularly by Os Blumhart in New Zealand who has produced a range of compact plants that throw their flowers well above the foliage. Several of these have been registered with names prefixed by the word 'Saxon'. Two of these, 'Saxon Blush' and 'Saxon Glow', have been taken up by Dutch growers for mass production as decorative pot plants and registered for plant breeders rights.

Subsection iii: *Solenovireya* H.F.Copel.

Phil. J. Sc. 1929. 40(2): 136

Type: *R. jasminiflorum* Hook.
Subsection *Solenovireya* H.F.Copel.; Sleumer, Bot. Jahr. 1949. 74: 537, *pro parte*.
Series I subseries 7 *apud* Hook.*f.* in Benth. & Hook.*f.*, Gen. Pl. 1876. 2: 600.
Section *Hadranthe* Schltr., Bot. Jahr. 1918. 55: 157, *pro parte typo excluso*.

    Flowers trumpet-shaped (hypocrateriform), white or pale pink, the lobes less than ¼ the length of the tube. Medium to large shrubs with stomata on the abaxial (lower) leaf surface only.

    Maintained at subsectional level as it is defined only on flower shape which is not considered to be a strong taxonomic character.

Key to species from West Malesia

1	Leaves densely hairy both above and below	**135. stapfianum**
+	Leaves sometimes with a few hairs near the base, not hairy all over otherwise with scales	2
2	Leaves up to 6mm wide, more than 5x as long as wide	**133. jasminiflorum** ssp. **chamaepitys**
+	Leaves more than 10mm wide, less than 4x as long as wide	3
3	Leaves distinctly rugose with distinct red venation visible underneath and extending to the lateral veins	**136. alborugosum**
+	Leaves smooth, venation green or sometimes with red coloration on the main vein only near the base	4
4	Petiole distinctly longer than broad	5
+	Petiole as long as broad or shorter	11
5	Largest leaves more than 80mm	6
+	Largest leaves less than 80mm	8
6	Leaves up to 3x as long as wide, the apex obtuse to rounded	7
+	Leaves more than 3x as long as wide, the apex broadly acute	**138. lambianum**
7	Leaf bases mostly cordate, corolla tube up to 30mm	**141. mogeanum**
+	Leaf bases broadly tapering, corolla tube more than 30mm	**140. pseudotrichanthum**
8	Scales on top of persistent epidermal tubercles	9
+	Scales from a smooth surface or slightly impressed	10
9	Corolla tube densely scaly outside, flower buds with the bract tips reflexed	**134. edanoi**
+	Corolla tube laxly scaly only outside, flower buds with the bract tips appressed	**133. jasminiflorum** ssp. **oblongifolium**
10	Petiole up to 3mm, pedicels up to 12mm (Sulawesi)	**142. amabile**
+	Petiole more than 5mm, pedicels more than 15mm (Maluku)	**144. ruttenii**
11	Pedicels more than 15mm	12
+	Pedicels less than 15mm	13
12	Leaves with a conspicuous cartilaginous margin, stigma long exserted when receptive, flower buds with broad, spreading tips to bracts	**137. suaveolens**
+	Leaves without a conspicuous cartilaginous margin, stigma remaining within the mouth of the flower, flower buds with erect, narrowly subulate tips	**139. niveoflorum**
13	Corolla tube more than 50mm (Sulawesi)	**143. radians**
+	Corolla tube less than 45mm	14

14	Corolla tube densely scaly outside, flower buds with reflexed tips to the bracts	**134. edanoi**
+	Corolla tube laxly scaly outside, flower buds smooth with appressed tips to the bracts	**133. jasminiflorum**

Key to species from New Guinea

1	Ovary without visible hairs	2
+	Ovary clearly hairy with the hairs overtopping any scales	5
2	Petiole more than 10mm	**162. natalicium**
+	Petiole less than 8mm	3
3	Pedicels up to 10mm, scaly only	**161. multinervium**
+	Pedicels more than 10mm, scaly and hairy (the hairs sometimes minute)	4
4	Pedicels up to 15mm, corolla tube more than 50mm	**151. roseiflorum**
+	Pedicels more than 15mm, corolla tube up to 35mm	**150. rhodosalpinx**
5	Petiole up to 2x as long as broad, leaf base rounded to auriculate	6
+	Petiole more than 2x as long as broad, leaf base various, mostly tapering	11
6	Inflorescence 1–2-flowered, pedicels more than 25mm	**164. oliganthum**
+	Inflorescence more than 3-flowered, pedicels less than 25mm	7
7	Pedicels less than 10mm, anthers 5–7mm	**157. carringtoniae**
+	Pedicels more than 12mm, anthers less than 5mm	8
8	Pedicels hairy and scaly, largest leaf blade more than 80mm, disc glabrous	**165. pleianthum**
+	Pedicels scaly only, largest leaf blade less than 70mm, disc hairy	9
9	Style hairy and/or scaly at the base for up to 5mm (up to ⅒)	**156. carrii**
+	Style hairy and/or scaly at the base for at least 25mm (½–⅔)	10
10	Leaf reticulation obscure above, corolla tube up to 65mm, lobes up to 12mm wide	**166. tuba**
+	Leaf reticulation very distinct above, corolla tube mostly more than 65mm, lobes more than 15mm wide	
		167. rhodoleucum
11	Corolla tube less than 50mm	12
+	Corolla tube more than 50mm	20
12	Filaments with retrorse hairs	**163. retrorsipilum**
+	Filaments with patent or distally pointing hairs	13
13	Most leaves more than 25mm wide	14
+	Most leaves less than 25mm wide	17
14	Pedicels less than 8mm	15
+	Pedicels more than 10mm	16
15	Corolla up to 35mm, anthers 1–2mm	**44. gideonii**
+	Corolla more than 40mm, anthers 3–4mm	**145. brachypodarium**
16	Pedicels laxly shortly hairy (W New Guinea)	**147. cinerascens**
+	Pedicels scaly only (Papua New Guinea)	**168. loranthiflorum**
17	Pedicels more than 15mm	**155. armitii**
+	Pedicels less than 11mm	18
18	Pedicels less than 4mm, corolla tube more than 8mm wide	**149. oreadum**
+	Pedicels more than 4mm, corolla tube up to 4.5mm wide	19

19 Leaves elliptic to obovate, pedicels less than 8mm ———— **145. brachypodarium**
+   Leaves ovate to ovate-elliptic, pedicels more than 8mm ———— **154. archboldianum**

20 Pedicels less than 10mm ———— 21
+   Pedicels more than 10mm ———— 24

21 Corolla tube more than 100mm ———— **152. syringoideum**
+   Corolla tube less than 80mm ———— 22

22 Petiole less than 10mm, pedicels less than 4mm ———— **149. oreadum**
+   Petiole more than 10mm, pedicels more than 5mm ———— 23

23 Anthers with a long tail-like appendage (more than 1mm) at the base of each cell, inflorescence 6–9-flowered ———— **146. carstensense**
+   Anthers with a short basal apiculus only, inflorescence 8–22-flowered ———— **160. goodenoughii**

24 Anthers more than 7mm ———— **148. macrosiphon**
+   Anthers less than 6mm ———— 25

25 Petiole *c.*twice as long as broad ———— **165. pleianthum**
+   Petiole more than 3x as long as broad ———— 26

26 Corolla tube more than 70mm ———— **153. majus**
+   Corolla tube less than 65mm ———— 27

27 Pedicels scaly only or with a few hairs below the calyx only, corolla lobes more than 15mm ———— **155. armitii**
+   Pedicels scaly and hairy throughout, corolla lobes less than 14mm ———— 28

28 Petioles less than 12mm, disc glabrous ———— **158. cruttwellii**
+   Petioles more than 18mm, disc hairy ———— **159. hartleyi**

---

133. Rhododendron jasminiflorum Hook.
Bot. Mag. 1850. *t.*4525.
Type: Peninsula Malaya, Johore, Mt Ophir, Lobb *s.n.* cultivated from seed (K).
Derivation: With flowers like that of a *Jasminum* (Oleaceae), noted for their sweetly scented flowers.

Synonyms:
R. elongatum Blume, Fl. Jav. Pl. inéd. 1863–83. *t.*7 B, *f.*1.
Azalea jasminiflora (Hook.) Kuntze, Rev. Gen. Pl. 1891. 2: 387.

Key to the subspecies

1 Leaves up to 6mm wide ———— ssp. **chamaepitys**
+   Leaves more than 10mm wide ———— 2

2 Corolla tube shortly hairy outside ———— 3
+   Corolla tube without hairs outside or with just a few at the base ———— 4

3 Umbel mostly 2–5-flowered, twigs densely hairy and scaly ———— ssp. **heusseri**
+   Umbel with more than 6 flowers, twigs without hairs ———— ssp. **jasminiflorum**

4 Some leaves broadest in the upper ½, petiole more than 2x as long as broad ———— ssp. **copelandii**
+   Leaves broadest in the middle or lower ½, petiole hardly longer than broad ———— 5

5 Leaves ovate or elliptic, pedicels up to 11mm ———— ssp. **jasminiflorum**
+   Leaves narrowly elliptic, pedicels more than 15mm ———— ssp. **oblongifolium**

Ssp. **jasminiflorum**

Synonyms:

R. jasminiflorum var. *punctatum* Ridl. [*punctata*], J. Fed. Mal. St. Mus. 1909. 4: 42.

R. jasminiflorum var. *maculatum* Ridl. [*maculata*], Fl. Mal. Pen. 1923. 2: 218.

Shrub to 2.5m. Twigs rounded, covered in stellate scales, quickly becoming glabrescent; internodes 2–9cm. **Leaves** 3–5 together in tight pseudowhorls, appearing sub-sessile. **Blade** 25–60 x 10–36mm, broadly obovate-elliptic or elliptic, sometimes sub-circular, usually widest in the middle; apex broadly obtuse, acuminate or rounded; margin entire, revolute especially when dry; base sub-truncate, rounded or weakly cordate; dark green and glossy above, paler and dull beneath, laxly sub-stellately scaly but quickly glabrescent above, laxly and more persistently scaly below. **Scales** stellate to sub-dendroid with a deeply divided margin, each on top of a minute, blunt epidermal tubercle. Mid-vein slightly impressed above, strongly raised beneath; lateral veins *c.*5 per side, straight, often obscure, reticulation not visible. **Petiole** 2–4 x 1.5–2mm, scaly.

Flower buds to 14 x 6mm, ovoid, smooth, green or flushed with purple. Bracts to 10 x 6mm, ovate to obovate-spathulate, obtuse, glabrous or with a few scales outside near the apices and along the margins, glabrous inside. Bracteoles to 10 x 0.6mm, linear, glabrous. Inflorescence 5–15-flowered, an open umbel, the flowers half-hanging to semi-erect, white, or flushed with pink, especially when young, scented. Pedicels 8–11 x *c.*2mm, patently shortly hairy and scaly. Calyx *c.*2mm in diameter, obscurely 5-lobed. **Corolla** 40–50 x 10–14mm, trumpet-shaped; tube 35–43 x 3–4 x 3–4mm, straight, laxly scaly but not hairy outside, laxly hairy almost to the mouth inside; lobes 8–15 x 6–11mm, spreading horizontally, broadly obovate, glabrous or laxly scaly outside. **Stamens** exserted to 4mm, in an irregular group in the centre at first, reflexing back against the corolla lobes in old flowers; filaments linear, laxly hairy for almost the whole length; anthers *c.*1.8 x 1mm. Disc densely shortly hairy. **Ovary** 5 x 2mm, shortly cylindrical, densely hairy and scaly, abruptly contracted distally; style laxly scaly in the proximal ⅓ and laxly hairy almost to the top; stigma shortly obconical, at first below the mouth, later becoming exserted to *c.*10mm. **Fruit** 18–28 x 4–5mm, narrowly ellipsoid.

Malaysia (Peninsula), Johore, Mt Ophir, Mt Ledang. Epiphytic or terrestrial in ridge forest and shrubberies and in open places on rocks, 1100–1500m. *Fl.* Dec.

Cultivated from seeds collected by Thomas Lobb in 1845 (see History chapter) and this or other varieties of the species have probably been in cultivation somewhere ever since. It is a magnificent species that grows and flowers easily, producing a profusion of the scented, white or pale pink flowers mostly once a year in December or January but it can flower in any month of the year.

The material figured for *Curtis's Botanical Magazine* (*t.*4524) in the Kew Herbarium is hairy to above halfway up the outside of the tube so the distinctness of var. *punctatum* is not valid and this variety is included within the type subspecies which probably always has at least a few hairs on the outside of the corolla tube.

Ssp. **chamaepitys** (Sleumer) Argent *stat. nov.*
Basionym: *R. chamaepitys* Sleumer, Bot. Jahr. 1940. 71: 144.
Type: Haviland & Hose 2015, 21 May 1895. Borneo, Sarawak, Mt Lambia, 305m (BM).
Derivation: Greek – *chamae* – on the ground or low growing; *pitus* – a pine tree (*Pinus*). Alluding to the narrow leaves and being like a small pine tree.

Rhododendron jasminiflorum ssp. *jasminiflorum*.　　　　*Rhododendron jasminiflorum* ssp. *jasminiflorum*.

Debbie White

Rhododendron jasminiflorum
ssp. *heusseri.*

Shrub to 1m. **Leaves** 7–10 together in tight pseudo-whorls, linear to narrowly elliptic. **Blade** 30–50 x 5–6mm. **Flowers** white or tinged with pink, scented. Disc glabrous.

Malaysia (Borneo), Sarawak, Mt Lambir. Known only from the summit area of this isolated peak, 300–450m.

Introduced into cultivation by John Dransfield in 1981 but no longer growing. Although very distinctive with its narrow leaves, this appears to be no more than an extreme form of *R. jasminiflorum* at the edge of its range in Borneo.

Ssp. **copelandii** (Merr.) Argent *stat. nov.*
Basionym: *R. copelandii* Merr., Publ. Gov. Bot. 1905. 29: 42.
Type: Copeland 1439, Oct. 1904. Philippines, Mindanao, Davao Province, Mt Apo 2350–3100m (PNH†, A, K, P, US).
Derivation: Named after the collector, H.F. Copeland, who published a landmark account of Philippine rhododendrons in 1929.

Synonym: *R. jasminiflorum* var. *copelandii* (Merr.) Sleumer, Reinwardtia 1960. 5: 130.

Shrub to 2.5m. Twigs 1.5–3mm in diameter, scaly and sometimes very shortly hairy. **Leaves** in tight pseudo-whorls 3–8 together. **Blade** elliptic to obovate-elliptic. **Petiole** 3–8 x 1–2mm. **Corolla** hairy in the proximal ½ only inside, otherwise like ssp. *jasminiflorum.*

Philippines, Mindanao, summit area of Mt Apo, sub-alpine shrubbery, 1900–3100m. *Fl.* March–Nov.

Introduced into cultivation in 1992, it has a somewhat lanky growth form and small inflorescences but has the strongest perfume of any of the subspecies in cultivation and is to be recommended for this alone. The original description describes the twigs as glabrous; the living material in Edinburgh which is from the type locality has minutely hairy stems, which are also brown-scaly. It is very difficult to determine whether the type material has any simple hairs since it is covered with crystals of mercuric chloride.

Ssp. **heusseri** (J.J.Sm.) Argent *stat. nov.*
Basionym: *R. jasminiflorum* var. *heusseri* (J.J.Sm.) Sleumer, Reinwardtia 1960. 5: 129.
Type: Heusser 9a, 10 Aug. 1916. Indonesia, Sumatra, Tapanuli, Lake Toba, Samosir Peninsula, solfataras (BO, BM, BRI, L, PNH).
Derivation: Named after Dr Carl Heusser, the collector, who worked for some years in Medan, Sumatra.

Synonyms:
R. retusum [*non* (Blume) Benn.] Steenis, Arch. Hydrobiol. Suppl. 1932. 11: 18, f.21, 22.
R. longiflorum Lindl. var. *heusseri* J.J.Sm., Bull. Jard. Bot. Buit. III, 1935. 13: 447.

Shrub with densely hairy and scaly twigs. **Leaves** in dense pseudowhorls 3–6 together. **Blade** 35–40 x 20–25mm, ovate, cordate at the base, sub-sessile. **Petiole** 1–2 x 1–2mm. Inflorescence mostly 2–5-flowered, the flowers horizontal to half-hanging. **Corolla** white (see below), sparsely scaly and densely patently short-hairy outside.

Indonesia, Sumatra, Atjeh, Mt Kemiri, Gajolands; East Coast: Sibolangit and near Pematang Siantar; around Lake Toba, especially the Samosir Peninsula. Terrestrial in open rocky places often near volcanic vents, and a high epiphyte in sub-montane rain forest, 750–1500m. *Fl.* May–July.

This subspecies has only recently been brought into cultivation. It typically has only 2–3-flowered inflorescences although the isotype in the British Museum has 7 flowers, that in Leiden 7 and 8, in an inflorescence and the holotype has 3- and 5-flowered inflorescences. It grows slowly and the small inflorescence does not make it a particularly worthwhile horticultural plant. A recent search of the Samosir Peninsula failed to find the multicoloured forms reported by Sleumer (1966); these would appear to be hybrids with *R. longiflorum* as intimated in that account. Populations elsewhere have uniformly white flowers.

Ssp. **oblongifolium** (Sleumer) Argent *stat. nov.*
Basionym: *R. jasminiflorum* var. *oblongifolium* Sleumer, Reinwardtia 1960. 5: 130.
Type: Sinclair SF 38353, 23 Feb. 1949. Borneo, Sarawak, Summit Mt Santubong, 760m (SING, BO, K).
Derivation: Latin – *oblongus* – oblong; *folium* – leaf. Alluding to the leaf shape.

Synonym: *R. verticillatum* (*non* Low *ex* Lindl.) Becc., Malesia 1878. I: 204.

Leaves in tight pseudowhorls of 3–6 larger and almost as many smaller. **Blade** 40–75 x 10–28mm, narrowly elliptic; apex obtuse to rounded; base obtuse or truncate-rounded. **Petiole** 4–7mm, grooved above, often red. Bracts glabrous or laxly scaly, shiny. **Corolla** white, laxly scaly but without hairs outside, laxly hairy inside the entire length of the tube.

Malaysia (Peninsula), Pahang; P. Tioman, Mt Rokam, Johore; Mt Blumut. Sarawak (Borneo), Mt Santubong, Mt Bongo, delta of the Sarawak River. Sea level to 1000m.

134. Rhododendron edanoi Merr. & Quisumb.
Phil. J. Sc. 1953. 83: 333.
Type: Edaño PNH 153, 13 May 1947. Philippines, Palawan, Mt Mantalingahan, Brook's Point (A, BM, E, K, L, PNH†).
Derivation: Named after Gregorio Edaño, a Philippine collector employed by the Bureau of Science, Manila.

Ssp. **edanoi**

Shrub to 40cm. Twigs rounded, densely stellate-scaly; internodes 2–5cm. **Leaves** 4–6 together in tight pseudowhorls. **Blade** 25–55 x 15–25mm, elliptic, broadly elliptic or obovate-elliptic; apex obtuse to rounded, often with a pale gland-like spot at the apex; margin entire, narrowly revolute; base broadly tapering to rounded; quickly glabrescent above, densely and sub-persistently scaly beneath. **Scales** stellate, margin deeply divided; centre very small, each on top of a small persistent epidermal tubercle. Mid-vein impressed above, strongly raised beneath throughout its length; lateral veins 3–6 per side, straight, slightly impressed above, obscure beneath; reticulation not visible. **Petiole** 5–7 x *c.*1.5mm, grooved above, densely scaly.

Flower buds to 15 x 8mm, slender, ovoid. Bracts broadly subulate with the upper sides rolled and the tips reflexed, green, with a few scales outside and densely scaly along the margins. Bracts to 15 x 7mm, ovate to elliptic to spathulate, densely scaly outside in the upper ⅓, glabrous elsewhere. Bracteoles to 15mm, linear to sub-spathulate. Inflorescence 7–15-flowered, an open umbel, flowers white, horizontal to half-hanging, scented. Pedicels 9–15 x *c.*1mm, densely stellate-scaly and laxly shortly hairy. Calyx disc-like, oblique, sometimes obscurely 5-lobed. **Corolla** trumpet-shaped, 30–50 x 25–30mm; tube 25–42 x 6–7 x 4–5mm, straight or slightly curved, densely silvery-scaly outside, (the scales turning brown on drying), laxly hairy inside in the proximal ⅓, glabrous distally; lobes 14–16 x 9–11mm, spreading to reflexed, with a few scales outside. **Stamens** irregularly arranged, at different heights well below the mouth of the tube; filaments 24–30mm, linear, sub-densely hairy at the base only, glabrous distally; anthers *c.*1.5–2.5 x 1mm, oblong, the bases with small points. Disc densely hairy. **Ovary** 5–6 x 2–2.5mm, cylindrical, densely scaly and shortly hairy, abruptly tapering distally; style *c.*25mm, becoming exserted up to 7mm, hairy and scaly in the proximal ⅓, laxly hairy in the middle, glabrous in the distal ½; stigma to 1.5mm in diameter, rounded, white or red. **Fruit** 30–40 x *c.*5mm, the valves splitting away from the base or apex and often spirally twisting, the placentae becoming slightly separated curving outwards. Seeds 3.5mm, without tails 0.9mm, the longest tail 1.5mm.

Philippines, Palawan, Mt Mantalingahan, Thumb Peak, Cleopatra Needle, 1500–1725m. In mossy sub-montane forest.

Introduced into cultivation by the Edinburgh/Philippines expedition of 1998. This subspecies is slow growing but forms a neat, compact plant and flowers irregularly, usually in the spring in Edinburgh. For a full discussion of the re-finding and introduction of this species see Argent (2004).

Ssp. **pneumonanthum** (Sleumer) Argent
Gardens Bull. Sing. 2004. 56: 79.
Type: Endert 4522, 23 Oct. 1925. SE Borneo, W Kutei, Mt Kemul, *c.*1700m (L, A, BO, SING).
Derivation: Greek – *pneumon* – lungs; *anthos* – flower. Applying to the inflated-looking corolla tubes, but not particularly apt.

Synonyms:
R. jasminiflorum (*non* Hook.) Ridl., J. Str. Br. R. As. Soc. 1912. 63: 60.
R. pneumonanthum Sleumer, Reinwardtia 1960. 5: 132.

Shrub or small tree to 3m. **Scales** blackish-brown. Lateral veins 5–9 per side, straight or curving away from the mid-vein and disappearing before the edge of the leaf, hardly raised but usually distinct both above and below and without visible reticulation. **Petiole** 1–3 x 3–4mm, dark red, often broader than long and with dark-brown scales, weakly grooved above.

Malaysia (Borneo), Sarawak, Mt Lemakok, Mt Lawai, Mt Murut, Mt Murud. Sabah, vicinity of Long Pasia. **Indonesia**, Mt Kemul, Mt Batu Ajoh, Kayan R. Epiphytic in montane mossy forest, (700)1700–2400m. *Fl.* May–June, Oct.–Nov.

Introduced into cultivation in 1984 by Keith Adams to New Zealand and distributed from Pukeiti; it is now widely grown. It is superficially similar to *R. jasminiflorum* and shares many of the attractive attributes of that species in cultivation. The very much more scaly leaves and flowers will distinguish it, as will the distinctive flower bud morphology.

Rhododendron pneumonanthum has been reduced to a subspecies of *R. edanoi* (Argent 2004). Sleumer (1966) distinguished these two species: 'Corolla tube more or less manifestly and gradually narrowed from the base upwards. Leaves sub-sessile [*R. pneumonanthum*] *vs.* Corolla tube equally wide all over or slightly and gradually widened from the base upwards. Leaves distinctly petioled. [*R. edanoi*]'. An examination of isotypes of the original collection of *R. edanoi* showed that the first character is not a valid difference. Several corolla tubes exhibit quite definite narrowing from the proximal to the distal ends. The corollas from cultivated plants from both Palawan and Borneo in the fresh state all quite clearly taper from base to mouth. After pressing, the tube can appear to at least look parallel sided. There is a difference in petiole length between Bornean and Philippine materials but again there is a good deal of variation even on one plant and this alone would not support maintaining these plants as different species. There is also a very small difference in the scales on the leaves from the two islands –

Rhododendron edanoi ssp. *pneumonanthum.*

those from Bornean materials are darker and more variable in size – but both have essentially the same sub-stellate shape, are tall and are set on pronounced epidermal tubercles. The vegetative habit of the plants in cultivation from the different islands is certainly very different. Both Philippine collections are slow and low growing compared with the tall, 'leggy' and much more vigorous Bornean plants. Differences in habit between different populations of the same species are known elsewhere (*R. burttii* and *R. leptanthum*). The clinching factor in regarding the Bornean *R. pneumonanthum* to be, at best, a subspecies and not specifically distinct from *R. edanoi* is the fact that the distinctive flower bud morphology is identical in plants from both Borneo and Palawan.

135. Rhododendron stapfianum Hemsl. *ex* Prain
Bot. Mag. 1911. *t.*8372.
Type: Haviland 1295. North Borneo, Mt Kinabalu, Penokok, 1065–1525m (K, BM, CAL, SAR, SING, L, fragment).
Derivation: Named after Otto Stapf who first published this species (see below), author of the first flora of Mt Kinabalu and keeper of the Kew Herbarium 1909–1922.

Synonym: *R. lacteum* Stapf, Trans. Linn. Soc. London, II, Bot. 1894. 4: 197, *t.*15 A 1–2.

Shrub to 2m. Twigs *c.*3mm in diameter, rounded, densely patently long, white-hairy and laxly covered with brown scales; internodes 1.5–4cm. **Leaves** in lax pseudo-whorls of 7–10 larger and 2–4 smaller leaves, sometimes sub-spirally arranged. **Blade** 30–55 x 9–20mm, elliptic, often appearing narrowly elliptic as it is strongly revolute; apex broadly acute, obtuse or rounded; margin entire, broadly revolute; base broadly tapering to rounded; densely white hairy and more laxly scaly both above and

Rhododendron stapfianum.　　　　　　　　　　　　　　*Rhododendron stapfianum.*

below. **Scales** with long narrow arms, sub-dendroid but not on raised epidermal tubercles. Mid-vein slightly raised above proximally, and then impressed distally to the apex, weakly raised below; lateral veins hardly visible in the fresh state, about 6 per side, narrowly angled, sometimes visible after drying. **Petiole** 2–5 x 2–4mm, with a shallow groove, densely hairy and scaly.

Flower buds to 30 x 14mm, ellipsoid, pale green, smooth. Bracts broadly ovate to spathulate, densely appressed hairy outside and with a few very small brown scales, brown scaly and with some hairs along the margins, glabrous inside. Inflorescence an open umbel of 7–18 semi- or fully erect flowers. Pedicels 5–8 x 2mm, pale green, densely hairy and with a few pale scales. Calyx a low ring. **Corolla** 50 x 25mm, white, sweetly scented or without scent; tube 40–46 x 5 x 3mm, narrowing gradually from the base upwards, straight or slightly curved, sub-densely hairy and brown scaly outside, glabrous inside; lobes 15 x 9mm, not or hardly overlapping, strongly reflexed, scaly and hairy outside except near the margins. **Stamens** irregularly spread around the flower, exserted to c.10mm before reflexing back against the lobes; filaments white, c.58mm, glabrous; anthers c.1.75 x 1mm, pale-brown. **Ovary** c.8 x 2mm, cylindrical, densely hairy with semi-appressed white hairs and white scales; style 55 x 1mm, white or pale pink, hairy, the hairs spreading at the base, appressed above and with white scales to within 4mm of the apex; stigma hardly expanded, c.1mm in diameter, strongly exserted to 18mm. **Fruit** 30–40 x 6mm, the valves twisting on opening. Seeds 5mm, without tails 1.5mm, the longest tail 2.5mm.

Malaysia (Borneo), Sabah, Mt Kinabalu, Mt Tambuyukon and along the Crocker Range to Mt Alab, Mt Trus Madi, Mt Lotung. Sarawak, Mt Mulu, Batu Lawi. **Indonesia**, Kalimantan from Mt Palimasan. **Brunei**, Temburong R., Tutong R. Mostly epiphytic on

the branches of tall trees in sub-montane forest but occasionally growing terrestrially in disturbances such as road cuttings and landslides, 900–1550m. *Fl.* Jan.–Dec., mainly March–April.

Introduced into cultivation in Edinburgh in 1980, it first flowered in 1982 and has flowered irregularly since. It grows vigorously but has a tendency to 'flop' and become prostrate which it does not appear to do in the wild. A distinctive species with its very hairy leaves and flowers which has not so far been reported as hybridising with any others. It replaces *R. jasminiflorum* in the northern part of Borneo and is in many respects just a very hairy form, but the hairs on all parts are significantly longer than any that occur in *R. jasminiflorum*.

136. Rhododendron alborugosum Argent & J.Dransf.
Notes RBG Edinb. 1989. 46(1): 27.
Type: Dransfield 2910, 24 Oct. 1972. Indonesia (Borneo), South Kalimantan, Mt Halauhalau (G. Besar), Pergunungan, Meratus, Barabai (BO, L).
Derivation: Latin – *albo* – white; *rugosum* – the name of another superficially similar Bornean *Rhododendron* species but differing in the white (or very pale) flower colour.

Shrub to 3m. Twigs smooth, finely longitudinally striated when dry and with scattered dark-brown scales; internodes 5–12cm. **Leaves** 3–5 together in tight pseudowhorls. **Blade** 40–80 x 23–37mm, elliptic, narrowly ovate or obovate; apex broadly acute, obtuse or rounded; margin entire, slightly revolute; base broadly tapering to rounded; laxly silvery scaly but quickly glabrescent and dark green above, persistently laxly scaly and paler below. **Scales** rounded, variable in size, with a broad marginal flange and small centre. Mid-vein distinct, above broad at the base and longitudinally grooved but quickly tapering to a narrow, impressed channel, green; broad and strongly raised throughout its length below, deep reddish-purple; lateral veins 7–9 per side, issuing at an angle of 45–90°, strongly impressed above, almost to the leaf edge, giving a rugose surface, very prominent and red in colour below. **Petiole** 8–12 x 3–4mm, red, weakly grooved above, scaly.

Flower buds to c.20 x 10mm, glossy dark purplish-red, elliptic. Bracts ovate, often with a dark purple median line, the tips of the bracts broadly pointed and reflexed to c.4mm, these tips scaly both inside and out. Inflorescence a 6–10-flowered open or one-sided umbel, the flowers semi-erect to horizontal, white, or pale pink, fragrant. Pedicels red, 12–26 x c.2mm, minutely rough with scales and short simple hairs. Calyx a low lobed scaly and hairy ring, 1–1.5mm high. **Corolla** 40–46 x 35–45mm; tube 35–40 x 9 x 5mm, straight, covered in scales outside, densely short-hairy inside near the base; lobes 18 x 14–18mm, slightly forward pointing or spreading to the perpendicular, overlapping to c.halfway, slightly scaly outside. **Stamens** irregular in length, included c.2mm below the mouth; filaments white or pale pink, tapering slightly distally, hairy throughout their length; anthers c.2.8 x 1.25mm, brown with a finely granular surface and oblique pores. Disc lobed, with short erect hairs. **Ovary** 5.5 x 3.5mm, ovoid to almost conical, tapering slightly towards

both base and apex, densely scaly and covered in short forwardly directed hairs; style 37 x c.1mm, sparsely scaly in the lower ⅓ and with forwardly directed, semi-patent hairs to within 3–4mm of the stigma; stigma irregularly lobed, c.1mm, cream, eventually protruding to 6mm from the mouth of the flower. **Fruit** 17–25 x 4–7mm, narrowly ellipsoid, strongly longitudinally grooved. Seeds 4–4.5mm, without tails c.1.1mm, the longest tail to 1.9mm.

Indonesia, S Kalimantan (Borneo), Pergunungan, Meratus, Mt Halauhalau (G. Besar). It is known only from the mountain on which it was originally collected. It grows in upper montane, mossy forest dominated by *Phyllocladus*, *Drimys* and *Vaccinium* and is common in open islands of scrub amongst bryophytes and lichens on the summit sandstone ridge at 1400–1800m.

Rhododendron alborugosum is a very distinct species. It was originally confused with *R. rugosum* no doubt because of a superficial resemblance in the rugose leaves, but that species has dendroid scales, and pendent, much darker pink flowers. It has also been determined in the past as *R. suaveolens* Sleumer, which has superficially similar flowers, but that species has smooth, much larger leaves, a corolla which is glabrous outside and a much larger umbel of 14–20 flowers.

It has been in cultivation since collected in 1996 by Argent & Wilkie (1996:2356 & 2364–2372), and grows

Rhododendron alborugosum.

and flowers well. Some forms have almost pure white flowers, although the buds are often flushed with pink, while others have a delicate pink blush which remains throughout the life of the flower. This species also has the added advantage of very clean, rigid, rugose foliage with dark red petioles and mid-veins, and looks attractive even when the plant is without flowers.

137. Rhododendron suaveolens Sleumer
Bot. Jahr. 1940. 71: 147.
Type: Clemens 505076, 30 Nov. 1933. BN Borneo, Mount Kinabalu, Gurulau Spur, 1800m (K).
Derivation: Latin – *suaveolens* – sweetly smelling.

Forma **suaveolens**

Shrub or tree to 3m. Twigs 4–5mm in diameter, smooth, rounded, green with a sparse covering of scales; internodes 2–10cm. **Leaves** in tight pseudowhorls of 3–6, variable in size within the pseudowhorl. **Blade** 60–100 x 35–70mm, elliptic, about twice as long as wide; apex rounded, or very obtuse to slightly retuse; margin smooth, with a narrow cartilaginous flat edge; base cordate or occasionally rounded; sparsely scaly but quickly glabrescent above, sparsely scaly beneath. **Scales** small, sub-circular or irregularly lobed with a broad marginal zone and small centre, slightly impressed. Mid-vein 5mm wide at the base, slightly raised both above and below, distinctly grooved on the upper side and quickly tapering within 10mm of the base, beyond which point it is hardly raised either above or below; lateral veins 5–9 per side, pinnate, spreading at 45°, straight or somewhat curved, distinct above, indistinct below; surface smooth, pale-green especially below but with the main vein

prominently dark-red in at least the broad basal part, reticulation obscure. **Petiole** 1–2 x 4–5mm, indistinctly grooved above, laxly scaly.

Flower buds (see p.327) narrowly conical in shape, green, the protective bracts with flat narrowly pointed, reflexed, green tips. Inflorescence a 12–25-flowered complete umbel. Pedicels 15–25 x 1.5mm, sparsely covered in silvery or pale-brown scales and spreading white hairs, often distinctively bright red. **Flowers** stiffly held erect to half-hanging. Calyx an irregular low ring. **Corolla** 35–70 x 20–25mm, pure white or sometimes lightly flushed pink especially on the tube, usually strongly and sweetly scented; tube 35–55 x 6–9 x 3–5mm, distinctly narrowed distally, glabrous outside but with sparse hairs inside; lobes 13 x 10mm, horizontal, or irregularly reflexed back against the tube, overlapping to *c*.½ and 'crimped'. **Stamens** irregularly clustered at or below the mouth of the flower, not exserted; filaments slender, white, about as long as the corolla tube, shortly hairy proximally for 2–3mm; anthers 2 x 1mm, pale-brown. Disc slightly lobed, circular, green with erect white hairs. **Ovary** 9 x 2mm, cylindrical, slightly curved and gradually tapering distally, densely covered in silvery scales but also with erect, white hairs to *c*.halfway; stigma 1.5–2mm wide, irregularly 5-lobed, quickly becoming exserted to *c*.10mm from the mouth of the flower. **Fruit** 30–45 x 3–5mm, cylindrical but curved and narrowed to the persistent style and also ribbed longitudinally. Seeds 5–5.5mm, without tails *c*.1mm, the longest tail 2.5mm often crimped.

Malaysia (Borneo), Sabah, epiphytic and terrestrial, common on the trees and ridges on Mt Kinabalu, Crocker Range and Mt Lumarku, 1200–1700m. *Fl.* Dec.–March.

This is a very attractive and distinctive species with its long, white, usually scented flowers and pale green leaves

Rhododendron suaveolens f. *suaveolens*.

Rhododendron suaveolens f. *roseum*.

Debbie White

Rhododendron lambianum.

with their contrasting red marks at the base. This species was confused with *R. orbiculatum* but was clearly shown to be different by Hunt (1972) in the much narrower flowers with smaller corolla lobes and in having many more flowers in the inflorescence and longer leaves. The lack of hairs on the corolla, leaves and stems will distinguish it from *R. stapfianum*. It is very similar to *R. lambianum* but has consistently narrower flowers and shorter broader leaves. *Rhododendron suaveolens* has been in cultivation since first introduced by Mr and Mrs Allen from a collection they made from Mt Kinabalu in January 1966. It grows and flowers well as a cool greenhouse plant in temperate countries, flowering mostly in the winter months. Not all forms are strongly scented: those from Mt Kinabalu appear to always have strong scent; the slightly smaller-flowered plants collected on Mt Lotung are totally without scent. The cultivar 'Painted Snipe' was named and illustrated (Hunt 1972); this plant is in no way distinctive from the majority of wild plants.

Forma **roseum** Argent, A.Lamb & Phillipps
Notes RBG Edinb. 42(1): 117.
Type: Jukien *s.n.*, April 1981. Sabah, Kinabalu National Park, 1600m (SNP).
Derivation: Latin – *roseum* – rose coloured, with reference to the pink colour of the flowers.

Differing from the type in the uniformly pink colour of the flowers.

This form was first found by Mr Justin Jukian, Senior Park Ranger, near the Kinabalu Park Headquarters in 1980. It has since been reported as common and the predominant form in the Penataran River area of Kinabalu. It has been in cultivation in Edinburgh since 1982 and grows and flowers freely, producing large inflorescences of luridly pink flowers which appeal to some people but not to others.

138. Rhododendron lambianum Argent
Folia Malaysiana 2003. 4(2): 109, pl.2.
Type: Argent & Lamb 19801308, 15 Feb. 1980. Sabah, Gunong Alab, Tuaran District, 1400–1600m (SAN, A, CANB, E, L).
Derivation: Named in honour of Tony Lamb who first found this species, and who has made a major contribution to the knowledge of the Sabah flora during his many years of residence there.

Shrub or small tree to 3m. Twigs 3–4mm in diameter, bright red passing to green, finely but fairly densely scaly; internodes 3–12cm. **Leaves** 3–5 together in loose pseudowhorls. **Blade** 60–120 x 20–45mm, narrowly obovate to narrowly elliptic; apex broadly acute and sometimes tipped with a very small, pale gland; margin entire, slightly irregular, flat or minutely revolute and with a very narrow cartilaginous edge; base rounded from a tapering lower ½; minutely brown scaly above and below, quickly glabrescent above. **Scales** small, sub-circular to irregularly lobed, marginal zone pale brown or silvery; with a small slightly impressed centre. Mid-vein raised above proximally, tapering rapidly from the petiole, faintly grooved when fresh and deep pink for *c.*10mm, becoming impressed in the distal ½; below prominently raised for almost the whole length and tapering gradually; lateral veins 8–12 per side, slender, spreading at *c*.45°, hardly visible below. **Petiole** 2–7 x 3–6mm, not grooved, deep pink, finely scaly.

Flower buds to *c*.4 x 2cm, narrowly ovate, green or reddish-brown, especially the basal bracts, acutely pointed with the bract tips narrow and erect or slightly spreading. Bracts ovate, concave, acuminate, the apical portion inrolled to a subulate point, the margins fringed with scales, otherwise glabrous. Bracteoles to 23mm, linear, glabrous, silvery. Inflorescence of 14–18 flowers in a complete umbel or slightly flat-topped. Pedicels *c*.35 x 1.75mm, bright red, sparsely silvery scaly and minutely patently white-hairy. **Flowers** mostly disposed horizontally, some half-hanging to semi-erect, pink, fading to almost white with age, sweetly scented. Calyx a low almost circular disc with a red margin, scaly. **Corolla** 40–50 x 40–50mm, pale pink; tube 36–42 x 7–10 x 6–7mm, straight, narrowest at about ⅔ of the distance from the base, completely glabrous outside, densely hairy proximally inside, becoming glabrous distally; lobes 17–23 x 16–20mm, spreading horizontally, flat and overlapping to *c*.halfway. **Stamens** arranged regularly all round the mouth of the flower, distinctly dimorphic (about 3mm difference between the longer and shorter); filaments white, shortly patently hairy in the proximal ⅓, glabrous distally; anthers *c*.3mm, pale brown, each cell with a small apiculus at the base. Disc prominent, green, deeply lobed, shortly hairy on the upper surface only. **Ovary** *c*.10 x 3mm, green, sparsely silvery scaly and shortly, white, patently hairy, tapering gradually distally; style white, with just a few scales at the very base, shortly patently hairy in the proximal ⅓ and glabrous distally; stigma *c*.3mm in diameter, pink, disc-like with 5 lobes. **Fruit** *c*.36 x 5mm, green or flushed red, tapering gradually to the style. Seeds *c*.5.5mm, without tails 1.3mm, the longest tail *c*.2.6mm.

Malaysia (Borneo), Sabah, Mt Alab. Sarawak, Mt Mulu, E ridge. Terrestrial or epiphytic in upper montane forest, 1400–1600m. Fl. Feb., June.

This species when first collected on Mt Alab was thought to be a hybrid between *R. suaveolens* and *R. orbiculatum* and was recorded as such (Argent *et al*. 1988). It is florally intermediate between these two species but its foliage was always anomalous in being longer and narrower in proportion than in either of the supposed parents, an unusual attribute for a hybrid. The second collection from the Mulu National Park in northern Sarawak was a long way from the first record and well outside the range of one of the supposed parents (*R. suaveolens*). This second collection has been growing alongside the original now for more than ten years and is identical. This species is still only known from two localities, although two simultaneous collections originally made on Mt Alab show small differences in leaf shape. *Rhododendron lambianum*, although apparently closely related to *R. suaveolens*, is quite distinct: it has broader flowers, fewer in number in the inflorescence, and narrower leaves with a length/breadth ratio of 3:1 or more for the largest leaves (in *R. suaveolens* 2:1 or less). It also has much more distinct petioles which are longer than broad, rounded to broadly tapering leaf bases and a distinctly if broadly acute apex, compared with the rounded apices and cordate to rounded bases from petioles which are broader than long in *R. suaveolens*. It also differs from *R. suaveolens* in flower bud morphology, lacking the broad, green, spreading to reflexed, leafy apices of that species, instead having red, narrow subulate points. From *R. orbiculatum*, a species with a very widespread distribution in Borneo, it differs in having more, smaller flowers in each umbel and distinctly long petiolate narrow leaves. It has been in cultivation since its discovery in 1980 and grows vigorously, flowering profusely usually several times a year.

139. Rhododendron niveoflorum Argent

Folia Malaysiana 2003. 4(2): 115, pl.4, 5.
Type: Burtt & Martin 5380, 27 Sept. 1967 (Cultivated specimen 19672550, collected RBGE, 11 April 2001). Sarawak, G. Murud, *c*.1800m (SAR, A, E, L).
Derivation: Latin – *niveus* – snow white, alluding to the pure snow-white flowers of this species.

Shrub to 80cm. Twigs 3–4mm in diameter, rounded, green, finely brown scaly; internodes 3–15cm. **Leaves** 4–6 together in tight pseudowhorls. **Blade** 50–80 x 25–40mm, obovate, elliptic or broadly elliptic; apex obtuse to rounded, sometimes minutely mucronate; margin entire, flat when fresh, becoming slightly revolute when dry; base rounded to cordate; quickly glabrescent above, more densely, persistently scaly beneath. **Scales** brown, rounded to irregularly lobed, *c*.0.1mm in diameter, weakly impressed into shallow pits. Mid-vein impressed into a narrow groove above, only slightly raised beneath; lateral veins 3–5 per side, inconspicuous, reticulation obscure. **Petiole** 2–3 x 4–5mm, grooved above, green or with a faint reddish flush on the upper side, scaly.

Flower buds (see p.327) *c*.40 x 20mm, green, narrowly ovate, acute, the bracts standing out from the buds at an acute angle with a 'spiky' appearance. Bracts to 30 x 14mm, ovate elliptic below but narrowly acuminate with channelled and inrolled upper margins; margins minutely scaly otherwise glabrous, shiny green in the central and upper parts, translucent towards the lower margins. Inflorescence 9–14 flowers in an open or one-sided umbel. Pedicels *c.*20 x 2mm, dark-pink, pale brown scaly and minutely covered with patent white hairs. **Flowers** half-hanging to semi-erect. Calyx forming a low irregular disc covered with hairs and scales. **Corolla** *c.*50 x 40mm, pure white with a faint sweet scent; tube *c.*40 x 8 x 5mm, distinctly narrowed upwards, glabrous outside, inside covered with moderately dense patent hairs; lobes *c.*19 x 20mm, circular or nearly so, overlapping for at least ½ their length and spreading at right angles or a little reflexed, glabrous. **Stamens** irregularly filling the mouth of the corolla tube but not exserted; filaments white, with some short white patent hairs in the proximal 5mm otherwise glabrous; anthers 2.5–3mm, pale brown, weakly apiculate at the base. Disc green, minutely hairy on the upper side. **Ovary** 6–7 x *c.*3mm, densely white scaly and with short white slightly distally directed simple hairs, gradually tapering; style scaly in the proximal ¼ and with semi-erect hairs in the proximal ½, completely glabrous distally, pink at the base, becoming white; stigma *c.*3mm in diameter, white, rounded, remaining within the mouth of the flower.

Malaysia (Borneo), Sarawak, Fifth Div. Route from Bakelalan to Mt Murud; Mt Murut, Lawas; Mt Api, Fourth Div., summit ridge; Bario, Ulu Baram, path to Kuba'an Pungor Pwan; Secondary Peak of Batu Lawi. Sabah, Mt Lumarku, Sipitang District. Epiphytic in large trees in montane mossy forest, or terrestrial on deep peat, sometimes in ultrabasic areas, 1300–2100m. *Fl.* Jan., June, Sept.

This species is superficially very similar to *R. suaveolens* but differs most conspicuously in the bract shape of the flower buds which in this species have subulate erect points whereas those of *R. suaveolens* have broad, reflexed leafy points. The pedicels are shorter, proportionately broader and with denser scales compared with the longer and more delicate pedicels of *R. suaveolens* which have only a very sparse covering of scales. The stigmas remain completely immersed within the corolla tube in this species, even in old flowers, whereas they become exserted when receptive in *R. suaveolens* although as an artefact of drying they can appear exserted in herbarium specimens of this species. The leaves are much thicker and more leathery in *R. niveoflorum* than in *R. suaveolens*, with the margin hardly showing any sign of a translucent cartilaginous edge whereas in *R. suaveolens* leaves held against the light show a distinct pale translucent cartilaginous margin.

The distributions are at present fairly distinct except for three anomalous collections. *Rhododendron*

Rhododendron niveoflorum.

suaveolens occurs along the western mountain spine of Sabah from Kinabalu along the Crocker Range with just one record from G. Mulu in Sarawak (Burtt & Woods 2140). *Rhododendron niveoflorum* is known from the above listed locations in northern Sarawak with the two doubtful records listed above from Sabah. The fruiting collection (Argent & Lamb 1536) from G. Lumarku near Sipitang has every appearance of being this species and would not be at all surprising given that this area contains many other plants known from northern Sarawak. The collection made by A. Lamb (SNP 0316) from the ridge north of Low's Gulley also appears to be this species, although the damaged flowers were reported as dark pink and there are no bud scales to compare. The type collection has always had pure white flowers in cultivation as reported from the wild (Burtt & Martin 5250); however, another Burtt & Martin collection (5363) from higher up on Mt Murud is described as having flowers flushed with pink from red pedicels. Introduced into cultivation in Edinburgh in 1967 by Bill Burtt and Adam Martin, it grows slowly, its pure white, slightly scented flowers being attractive but not very freely produced on lanky gnarled stems.

140. Rhododendron pseudotrichanthum Sleumer

Blumea 1964. 12: 340.

Type: Endert 444, 21 Oct. 1925. Borneo, Central East, W Kutei, Mt Kemul, 1800m (L, BO).

Derivation: Greek – *pseudo* – false; *trichanthus* – with hairy flower. Named originally for the hairy flowers but since this turned out to be a name that had been used before was prefixed with 'false'.

Synonym: *R. trichanthum* Sleumer, Reinwardtia 1960. 5: 127, *non* Rehder, J. Arn. Arb. 1945. 26: 480.

Shrub. Twigs 2–3mm in diameter, rounded, upper ones densely scaly and laxly hairy; internodes 3–6cm. **Leaves** 3–4 together in pseudowhorls. **Blade** 80–120 x 30–55mm, broadly elliptic to elliptic-oblong, with somewhat unequal sides; apex obtuse to rounded, often minutely retuse; margin sub-revolute; base broadly tapering to nearly rounded; glabrescent above except for some hairs at the base, laxly scaly beneath. **Scales** small, deeply sub-stellate-dentate, flat; centre red-brown, small, slightly impressed. Mid-vein distinctly impressed above, thick and prominent beneath proximally, less so distally; lateral veins 6–8 per side, well spaced, straight below, curved-anastomosing before the margin, slightly impressed above, a little prominent beneath, reticulation indistinct. **Petiole** 6–13 x 2–4mm, glabrous or with some hairs, rough, grooved above.

Bracts to 13 x 10mm, ovate, glabrous, irregularly shortly sub-serrate. Bracteoles *c.*10mm, linear, laxly hairy. Inflorescence 7–10-flowered. Pedicels 20–30mm, densely covered with patent greyish hairs, very laxly scaly. Calyx *c.*2mm in diameter, disc-shaped, inconspicuous. **Corolla** trumpet-shaped, pale red-violet when fresh; tube *c.*35 x 3–4 x 3–4mm, cylindrical, base inflated and 5-lobed, hardly or not widened towards the mouth, densely covered all over with soft greyish hairs outside, also inside in the proximal ½; lobes 10–12 x 5–7mm, obovate-rounded, spreading, densely hairy outside except near the margin, glabrous inside. **Stamens** unequal, as long as the corolla; filaments linear, flattened, densely whitish hairy to the proximal ⅓, glabrous distally; anthers 2.5 x 0.8mm, oblong, base obtuse. Disc with a few scattered hairs. **Ovary** 4–6 x 1.5–2mm, cylindrical, 5-ribbed, densely covered with sub-patent hairs, tapering distally; style slender, *c.*⅔ of the length of the corolla, laxly covered with spreading hairs in the proximal ⅓; stigma narrowly obconical.

Indonesia, Kalimantan, summit of Mt Kemul. In ridge forest, on humus-rich peaty soil, 1800–1850m. *Fl.* Oct.

Known only from the type collection and never cultivated.

141. Rhododendron mogeanum Argent

Folia Malaysiana 2003. 4(2): 111, pl.3.

Type: Mogea 3983. Indonesia, Central Kalimantan, Bukit Raya SE side, upper Katingan (Meddawai) River area, Upper Samba river, *c.*2,000m alt. (BO, L).

Derivation: Named after Dr Joannes Mogea, the collector of this species and former curator of the Herbarium Bogoriense.

Shrub or tree to 4m. Twigs 3–4mm in diameter, rounded, whitish and densely brown-scaly, slowly becoming glabrescent; internodes 3–10cm. **Leaves** 3–6 together in tight pseudowhorls. **Blade** 50–86 x 30–45mm, broadly elliptic, elliptic or obovate; apex rounded and apiculate occasionally broadly pointed or slightly retuse; margin entire, narrowly cartilaginous, markedly revolute when dry; base cordate occasionally rounded or broadly tapering; laxly scaly and quickly glabrescent above, laxly and more persistently scaly below. **Scales** small (up to 0.2mm in diameter), with broad transparent margins and small to medium-sized dark centres which may become raised on circular swellings around the scale centre on older leaves. Mid-vein impressed above, prominently raised throughout its length below, where it is whitish; lateral veins 5–10 per side, slender, the basal 2–3 spreading almost at a right angle, the distal lateral veins spreading at *c.*45°, straight but branching and disappearing before the margin; reticulation obscure. **Petiole** 7–12 x 3–4mm, grooved above, deeply scaly and rugulose.

Inflorescence an umbel with *c.*8 flowers. Pedicels 20–25 x *c.*0.7mm, erect, very densely brown scaly and with just a few, short, white, simple hairs. Calyx a low densely scaly disc. **Corolla** *c.*40 x 25mm, white or faintly pink; tube 25–28 x *c.*3 x *c.*4mm, densely scaly outside and shortly, patently, white-hairy inside; lobes *c.*13 x 10mm. **Stamens** with the anthers in the mouth of the corolla; filaments flattened and hairy in the proximal ¼, filiform and glabrous distally; anthers pale brown, *c.*3mm, sometimes apiculate at the base. Disc hairy on the upper margin. **Ovary** 4 x 1.75mm, scaly and shortly hairy with patent or slightly distally pointing hairs; style sparsely hairy and scaly in the basal ½, glabrous distally.

Indonesia, C Kalimantan (Borneo), Mt Raya, *c.*2000m, in primary upper montane mossy forest.

This species is similar to *R. suaveolens* and *R. niveoflorum* but the material so far collected is not complete and it is not possible to compare the single herbarium collection as completely as one would like. Floral measurements in particular being from dry material are not necessarily strictly comparable as shrinkage varies greatly in the drying process. It appears to have smaller inflorescences with fewer flowers in each umbel than the other two species but clearly has much longer petioles. It apparently replaces the other species of subsection *Solenovireya* on the isolated Bukit Raya and may well be endemic to this mountain.

142. Rhododendron amabile Sleumer

Reinwardtia 1960. 5: 127.
Type: Steup 206, 19 Aug. 1937. Celebes, Central, Masamba, Limbung-Porio, 1700m (L, BO).
Derivation: Latin – *amans* – loving; a lovable rhododendron.

Shrub. Twigs rounded and densely scaly becoming glabrescent; internodes 2.5–9cm. **Leaves** 4 together in pseudowhorls, sub-sessile. **Blade** 25–60 x 12–28mm, broadly elliptic to elliptic; apex broadly tapering, sub-obtuse; margin slightly revolute; base sub-truncate, rounded to sub-cordate; at first scaly becoming glabrescent above, persistently and laxly scaly beneath. **Scales** irregularly dentate at margin, flat, each on top of a minute epidermal tubercle. Mid-vein flat or weakly impressed above, thick and very prominent beneath in the proximal ⅔, less so distally; lateral veins 7–8 per side, straight below, curved-anastomosing near the margin, hardly visible above, somewhat raised beneath, reticulation inconspicuous. **Petiole** 2–3 x *c.*1.5mm, scaly.

Bracts to 14 x 9mm, ovate-acuminate, acute, outer ones scaly and sub-densely covered with hairs outside, inner ones hairy only. Bracteoles to 10 x 1mm, linear to sub-spathulate-linear, laxly hairy. Inflorescence 7–9-flowered. Pedicels 7–12 x *c.*0.5mm, densely scaly and shortly sub-patently greyish hairy. Calyx *c.*2.5mm in diameter, minute, membranous, wavy, irregularly fringed. **Corolla** trumpet-shaped, proximally white, pink-coloured distally; tube 30–33 x 2.5 x 3.5mm, cylindrical, straight, distinctly pouched at the base, laxly short-hairy and scaly outside, the scales completely disappearing by maturity, shortly hairy in the proximal ½ inside, glabrous distally; lobes 10–12 x 7–8mm, slightly spreading, obovate-spathulate, hairy outside at the base, otherwise glabrous, though distinctly ciliolate. **Stamens** slightly exserted; filaments linear, hairy in the proximal ⅓, glabrous distally; anthers 1.8–2 x 0.7mm, oblong, base obtuse. Disc prominently 10-lobed, glabrous. **Ovary** 6–7 x 1.6mm, sub-cylindrical, densely hairy and scaly, abruptly narrowed distally; style hairy and scaly to nearly the top; stigma thick, conical-globose, just below the mouth.

Indonesia, Sulawesi (C), Masamba District near Limbung, *c.*1700m, said to be common in secondary forest on stony and peaty soil. *Fl.* Aug.

Known only from the type collection. Not cultivated.

143. Rhododendron radians J.J.Sm.

Bull. Jard. Bot. Buit. III, 1920. 1: 403, *t.*51.
Type: Rachmat 885, Nov. 1913. Indonesia, Celebes, Central part, G. Sinadji (BO, K, L).
Derivation: Latin – *radians* – spreading or radiating out from a common centre, alluding to the arrangement of the flowers.

Var. radians

Shrub. Twigs rounded, tips laxly hairy and scaly; internodes 3–12cm. **Leaves** 5–12 in tight pseudowhorls. **Blade** 25–55 x 12–25mm, ovate to elliptic, sub-sessile; apex shortly obtusely pointed, sometimes almost rounded; margin entire, narrowly but distinctly revolute; base broadly tapering to cordate, glabrescent above sparsely scaly beneath. **Scales** deeply dentate, each on top of a minute epidermal tubercle, with a persistent dark centre. Mid-vein impressed above, prominent beneath; lateral veins 6–8 per side, distinctly anastomosing, slightly impressed above and prominent beneath in the oldest leaves, often obscure, reticulation inconspicuous. **Petiole** *c.*1–2 x 1–2mm, weakly grooved, laxly scaly and shortly hairy.

Outer bracts to 10 x 8mm, ovate-acuminate, acute; inner ones spathulate, obtuse, laxly silky-hairy on both sides. Bracteoles to 15 x 0.5mm, linear, patently hairy. Inflorescence an open umbel of 7–20, horizontally or half-hanging flowers. Pedicels 7–13mm, thick, densely shortly patently hairy, not scaly, often pink. Calyx small,

Rhododendron radians var. *radians*.

oblique; margin wavy and shortly 5-lobed. **Corolla** 50–75 x 25–30mm, white or very lightly flushed with pink at the lobes; tube 55–72 x 5–6 x 4–5mm, straight, cylindrical, laxly to very laxly scaly and without hairs outside, or with just a few at the base, sub-densely to laxly short-hairy proximally to ¾ inside, glabrous distally; lobes spreading, broadly obovate-spathulate, laxly scaly outside, glabrous inside, 10–13 x 7–9mm. **Stamens** becoming exserted to *c.*10mm; filaments linear, laxly patent hairy for ¾ of their length, filiform and glabrous apically; anthers obovate-oblong, base obtuse, *c.*1.8 x 1mm. Disc glabrous at base, hairy on the upper margin. **Ovary** 5 x 1.8mm, subcylindrical, densely patently hairy and silvery scaly, the scales often hidden by the hairs, abruptly narrowed distally; style laxly patently hairy in the proximal ⅚ and with some scales in the proximal part; stigma rounded, *c.*2mm in diameter, when young, near the mouth of the flower and slightly towards the lower side, becoming exserted to *c.*10mm.

Indonesia, Sulawesi (C), Mt Sinadji.

Var. **minahasae** Sleumer
Reinwardtia 1960. 5: 130.
Type: Boesveld 6. Celebes, Menado: Tondano, Soputan Volcano, 1500–1700m (BO, L).
Derivation: Named after the Minahasa region where it was first found.

Synonym: *R. verticillatum* (*non* Low) Koord., Minah. 1898. 514.

Scales more deeply stellate-incised at the marginal zone, sub-dendroid, each on top of a more distinct minute epidermal elevation than in var. *radians*. Outer bracts obtuse, long hairy at the apex or practically glabrous, somewhat shining. Style hairy and scaly almost to the top.

Indonesia, Sulawesi, (NE) Minahasa area on several volcanoes, (W) Mt Sojol. In low forest, on volcanic grit or sandy soil. 1500–1700m.

Sleumer (1966) notes: 'The corolla of the type specimen from Mt Soputan is given as white and very fragrant by the collector, and other collections from that region also seem to have had white corollas, as far as this can be concluded from the dried material. Only Koorders says, that his specimen, also collected on Mt Soputan, has dark red corollas, but no corollas are preserved in his herbarium. Boesveld, the collector of the type specimen of var. *minahasae*, says on the label, that he has found "a similar *Rhododendron* on Mt Klabat with red corollas" but I have

seen no material from there which would agree with that. It remains open whether var. *minahasae* has always white flowers, or if, possibly, both white- and red-flowered forms exist together'. No recent collections have had red flowers so that red-flowered forms seem highly doubtful. A recent collection from Mt Sojol in west Sulawesi may represent a new taxon. It agrees in most respects with the description of var. *minahasae* but it has rounded scales which are if anything slightly impressed into the leaf surface rather than raised. It could be more closely allied with var. *pubitubum* although it has simple hairs on the outside of the corolla tube near the base. Further collections are needed to understand the variation properly.

Var. **pubitubum** (Sleumer) Argent *comb. nov.*
Basionym: *R. pubitubum* Sleumer, Reinwardtia 1960. 5: 126.
Type: Eyma 1441, 30 July 1937. Celebes (C), Masamba, Tomadu-Singkálong, 2000m (L, BO).
Derivation: Latin – *pubi* – softly hairy; *tubus* – a tube. Alluding to the tubular, hairy flowers.

Differing in the corolla tube being densely hairy throughout its length and with the lobes hairy outside along the middle line.

Indonesia, Sulawesi (C), Masamba District, Tomadu-Singkalong and Limbung. In open places, peaty soil or granite, 1700–2000m. *Fl.* July–Aug.

The isotype of var. *radians* in Leiden actually has hairs on the outside of the corolla tube near the base, and plants collected on Mt Sojol have hairs up to halfway up the outside of the corolla tube. Thus the main distinction between *R. radians* and *R. pubitubum* is not satisfactory and *R. pubitubum* is reduced to varietal status. The plants with hairs up to halfway up the corollas are in cultivation; the fully hairy form is not as far as is known being cultivated.

144. Rhododendron ruttenii J.J.Sm.
Fedde Rep. 1932. 30: 170.
Type: Rutten (Kornasi) 1472, 1 July 1918. Central Ceram, G. Murkele, 1900–2500m (BO, K, L).
Derivation: Named after L. Rutten, a Dutch geologist who also collected many plants, and leader of the expedition that collected this species.

Shrub to 2m. Twigs rounded, smooth, moderately densely brown scaly; internodes 1.7–4.5cm. **Leaves** 4–6 together in tight pseudowhorls. **Blade** 30–80 x 12–45mm, obovate to elliptic; apex broadly tapering, obtuse to

Rhododendron ruttenii.

rounded, sometimes slightly retuse; margin entire, narrowly revolute; base narrowly tapering; laxly scaly initially, glabrescent above, more densely and persistently scaly beneath. **Scales** variable in size, marginal zone narrow to moderately broad, sub-entire to dentate, the centre sometimes relatively large and dark brown, sometimes slightly impressed. Mid-vein impressed above, distinctly raised beneath; lateral veins 3–8 per side, straight below, curved and anastomosing before the edge, slightly impressed above, inconspicuously raised beneath, reticulation obscure. **Petiole** 5–8 x 2–3mm, grooved above, scaly.

Flower buds to 12 x 8mm, green strongly flushed with dark purple, broadly ellipsoid to obovoid, smooth with all bracts appressed and a broad rounded apex, glabrous apart from the fringe of brown, marginal scales. Bracts, the outer broadly triangular, the inner sub-circular, deeply concave, rounded but often splitting to become emarginate. Bracteoles *c.*10mm, filiform, basally *c.*1mm wide, broadening in the distal ½ to *c.*3mm, glabrous. Inflorescence 4–8-flowered, the flowers held stiffly semi-erect to half-hanging, white or very lightly flushed pink at the lobes as the buds open, strongly and sweetly scented. Pedicels 16–20 x *c.*1.75mm, red, densely scaly, and with sparse very small hairs. Calyx small, densely scaly, obliquely disc-shaped. **Corolla** 45–50 x 21–30mm, trumpet-shaped; tube 41–50 x 6–8 x 5–6mm, straight, cylindrical, sparsely covered with small brown scales outside, densely patently short-hairy inside in the proximal ½; lobes 10–13 x 10–12, sub-circular with irregular margins, spreading horizontally on opening, later reflexing, with a few scales outside. **Stamens** at first clustered centrally or slightly to the lower side of the mouth, later reflexing irregularly back against the lobes, becoming exserted to 6mm; filaments filiform, laxly hairy near the base only; anthers *c.*1.5 x 1mm. Disc sparsely hairy in the upper ½ or glabrous. **Ovary** *c.*7 x 2.5mm, cylindrical, gradually tapering distally; style 15–28 x *c.*1mm, white, with thick protruding scales almost to the top and a few hairs; stigma *c.*2mm in diameter, cream. **Fruit** 20–24 x 5–6mm, scaly, purple.

Indonesia, Maluku, C Seram, Mt Murkele, Mt Binaia. Primary forest, abundant on limestone, 1900–2500m. *Fl.* July.

Introduced into cultivation in the Royal Botanic Garden Edinburgh in 1987. It is very similar to *R. jasminiflorum* but has substantially larger flowers. It grows well, flowering irregularly but mostly in late spring with handsome white and well-perfumed flowers. With the type description was the note that the number 1471 had pink flowers. This is likely to be a hybrid with *R. malayanum* which grows commonly with *R. ruttenii*; the pure species probably always has white flowers. This hybrid was observed on Mt Binaia in 1987. The scales are not on small elevations as described by Sleumer (1966).

145. Rhododendron brachypodarium Sleumer
Blumea 1963. 12: 103.
Type: van Royen & Sleumer 7065, 26 Oct. 1961. New Guinea (NW), Tohkiri Mts, East crest 1400m, on path Surerem–Chaquai (L, A, BO, CANB, G, K, LAE, UC).
Derivation: Greek – *brachypodus* – short stalked, alluding to the short-stalked flowers.

Shrub to 3m. Twigs 2–3mm in diameter, densely scaly, greyish often whitish when dry; internodes 2–10cm. **Leaves** reflexed, 4–5 together in tight pseudowhorls. **Blade** 40–80 x 20–40mm, elliptic, obovate-elliptic to obovate; apex broadly tapering, obtuse or rounded; margin entire, wavy, flat or only slightly and narrowly revolute; base more broadly to narrowly tapering; sub-densely scaly on both sides initially, early glabrescent above, more slowly so beneath. **Scales** flat, marginal zone angular or dentate; centre small, slightly impressed. Mid-vein thick, grooved and strongly raised in the proximal ¼–⅓, then smooth or impressed above, beneath, strongly raised and gradually tapering throughout its length; lateral veins 7–10 per side, issuing at *c.*45°, almost smooth often obscure, reticulation obscure. **Petiole** 6–12 x 1.5–2mm, weakly grooved above, densely scaly initially.

Bracts to 20 x 13mm, green when fresh, outer ones ovate, firm, scaly at apex and margin, fringed with scales, inner ones thinner, broadly spathulate, very laxly hairy in the proximal part on both sides, otherwise glabrous. Bracteoles to 18mm, filiform, laxly hairy. Inflorescence an 8–14-flowered open umbel. Pedicels 4–8 x 0.5mm, densely scaly. Calyx *c.*2mm in diameter, oblique, rim-like, obscurely lobed, scaly outside. **Corolla** narrowly trumpet-shaped, pure white, scented, 40–50mm; tube 23–40 x 2–2.5 x 2.5–3mm, straight or curved, densely stellately scaly outside, shortly hairy inside; lobes 10 x 4–5mm, spreading becoming strongly reflexed, obovate, not or hardly overlapping. **Stamens** irregularly centrally grouped, exserted to *c.*10mm; filaments narrowly linear and densely hairy

in the proximal ¾, slender and glabrous distally; anthers 3–4mm, narrowly oblong, base obtuse. Disc slightly prominent, laxly short-hairy. **Ovary** *c.*8 x 1.3mm, narrowly cylindrical, dense white or yellowish hairs covering scales, tapering distally; style exserted from the mouth for *c.*5mm, densely hairy at the base, then more laxly hairy and densely scaly, exclusively scaly for the distal ⅓; stigma obconical, green.

Indonesia, New Guinea (W), Vogelkop Peninsula, Tamrau, Tohkiri and Nettoti Range. Epiphytic or terrestrial in *Castanopsis* and *Nothofagus* forests, also on mossy ridges and valley forest, 1200–2000m. *Fl.* Oct.–Dec.

Not known in cultivation. A distinctive species with extremely narrow flowers (amongst the New Guinea species of this group) reminiscent of *R. jasminiflorum*. The flowers were recorded in the field as becoming fragrant towards the evening.

146. Rhododendron carstensense Wernham
Trans. Linn. Soc. London, II, Bot. 1916. 9: 96.
Type: Kloss B. *s.n.*, 26 Jan. 1913. New Guinea (W), Ascent to Mt Carstensz, 1675–2040m (BM).
Derivation: Named after the mountain on which it was collected.

Shrub. Twigs sub-angular, whitish, smooth, early glabrescent; internodes 7–10cm. **Leaves** 3–4 together in pseudowhorls. **Blade** 65–100 x 40–55mm, broadly elliptic, elliptic to obovate-elliptic; apex obtuse to rounded; margin entire, flat; base shortly and broadly tapering, glabrescent above at maturity, sub-densely scaly beneath. **Scales** small, marginal zone irregularly dentate; centre a little impressed. Mid-vein somewhat impressed above, strongly prominent beneath; lateral veins 8–10 per side, irregular, straight below, curved-anastomosing before the margin, slightly impressed above, hardly prominent beneath, smaller veins laxly reticulate, raised beneath only. **Petiole** 10–15 x *c.*2mm, grooved above.

Bracts to 40 x 18mm, obovate-elliptic, hairy outside in the middle and with longer and appressed hairs in the lower part on both sides. Bracteoles 30–50mm, filiform, hairy. Inflorescence 6–9-flowered. Pedicels *c.*5mm, thick, scaly. Calyx minute, oblique, annular, obscurely 5-lobed. **Corolla** 65–70mm, trumpet-shaped; tube 50–60 x *c.*3 x *c.*6mm, cylindrical, hardly widened upwards, glabrous outside, densely hairy inside in the proximal ½; lobes *c.*17 x 14mm, obovate-sub-circular, glabrous. **Stamens** somewhat exserted from the mouth; filaments linear, densely

Rhododendron brachypodarium.

Leiden

hairy to ⅘, glabrous distally; anthers *c.*6 x 1mm, each cell with a tail-like appendage (1–1.5mm) at the base. Disc sub-glabrous. **Ovary** *c.*7 x 1.8mm, elongate-cylindrical, very densely covered with yellowish hairs, gradually tapering distally; style yellowish hairy in the proximal ⅓, glabrous distally; stigma thick-obconical.

Indonesia, New Guinea (W), Mt Jaya (Mt Carstensz), once collected at 1675–2040m.

Not so far recollected and never cultivated. Very similar to *R. syringoideum*, differing chiefly in the much smaller flowers; it is the older name and would take precedence if the species were amalgamated.

---

147. Rhododendron cinerascens Sleumer
Reinwardtia 1960. 5 : 130.
Type: Eyma 4854, 11 April 1939. New Guinea (W), Wissel Lake region, Upper Ennaro Valley and Puraida ridge, 1755m (L, A, BO, K, SING).
Derivation: Latin – *cinerascens* – becoming ash-grey, alluding to the colour of the twigs.

Shrub to 2m. Twigs rounded, slender, grey, tips laxly scaly; internodes 2.5–10cm. **Leaves** 4–6 together in pseudowhorls. **Blade** 40–55 x 12–23mm, elliptic to obovate; apex shortly obtusely acuminate, rarely rounded; margin entire, flat; base tapering; sub-densely scaly initially on both sides finally glabrescent above, persistently scaly beneath. **Scales** thin, flat, irregularly lobed; centre small, impressed. Mid-vein shallowly impressed above, prominent beneath, especially proximally; lateral veins 6–8 per side, inconspicuous. **Petiole** 6–10 x *c.*1.3mm, grooved above, flattened, scaly initially.

Bracts to 15 x 7mm, ovate to obovate-spathulate, laxly scaly outside and with hairs apically, glabrous internally, ciliate and with scales at the margin. Bracteoles 10–15 x 1mm, filiform to sub-spathulate. Inflorescence 5–7-flowered. Pedicels 9–20 x 0.5mm, densely scaly, laxly and very shortly hairy. Calyx very oblique, a thin, wavy, irregularly 5-dentate rim, one or more teeth elongate to 2–4mm. **Corolla** 50–60mm, trumpet-shaped, white; tube 37–50 x *c.*2.5 x 3–3.5mm, cylindrical, straight or slightly curved, densely scaly, not hairy outside, laxly hairy inside in the proximal ⅓ only; lobes *c.*10 x 6–7mm, spreading, spathulate-obovate, laxly scaly outside, glabrous inside. **Stamens** well exserted from the corolla tube; filaments filiform, hairy in the proximal ½ only; anthers *c.*2.5mm, oblong, base obtuse. Disc shortly hairy at the upper margin. **Ovary** *c.*5 x 1.2mm, elongate-cylindrical, sub-densely

scaly and sub-appressed-hairy, gradually narrowed distally; style exserted for *c.*10mm, scaly and sub-patently hairy for 30mm above the base, otherwise scaly only, nearly to the top; stigma shortly obconical-globose.

Indonesia, New Guinea (W), Wissel Lakes area, in secondary forest amongst *Sphagnum*, 1750m. Two collections. *Fl.* April–May.

An anomalous collection from the Vogelkop (van Royen & Sleumer 7836) keys out to this species but is from much lower altitude (700m). Never cultivated.

---

148. Rhododendron macrosiphon Sleumer
Blumea 1961. 11 : 118.
Type: Kalkman 4353, 2 July 1959. New Guinea (C), Star Mts, 1km east of the mouth of the Minam R. into the Bon R., 1500m (L).
Derivation: Greek – *macro* – long or great; *siphon* – relating to a tube. Alluding to the tube-shaped flowers.

Shrub to 4m. Twigs thick, scaly, often white; internodes 6–9cm. **Leaves** 4–5 together in pseudowhorls. **Blade** 70–100 x 40–60mm, obovate-elliptic; apex broad to very broadly obtuse to rounded, sometimes with an apiculus; margin entire, flat; base tapering, slightly decurrent, glabrescent above with age, densely scaly beneath. **Scales** minute, the thin silvery, fragile marginal zone variously stellately lobed; centre thick, small, deeply impressed, flat. Mid-vein narrowly impressed above; beneath as thick as the petiole and very prominent proximally, decreasing upwards; lateral veins 6–7 per side, irregular, with shorter ones between them, all spreading and anastomosing, strongly impressed above, hardly raised beneath, reticulation faintly impressed above, slightly prominent or sometimes obscure beneath. **Petiole** 20–25 x *c.*3mm, grooved above, densely scaly, semi-rounded.

Inner bracts elongate-spathulate, hairy on both sides, up to 30mm. Bracteoles linear, glabrous, up to 25mm. Inflorescence 8–10-flowered. Pedicels 40–80 x *c.*1.5mm, very densely scaly. Calyx 5–6mm in diameter, obliquely disc-shaped, irregularly 5-lobed, densely scaly outside. **Corolla** tubular below, abruptly expanded to the lobes, white; tube 60–70 x 5–6 x 10–15mm, sub-densely or laxly scaly outside and with dense appressed white retrorse hairs inside; lobes 25–30 x 25–30mm, sub-spathulate-obovate or sub-circular. **Stamens** exserted to 15mm; filaments linear, and densely covered with retrorse hairs proximally, more laxly hairy and slender upwards, glabrous and filiform for the distal 15mm; anthers 7–8 x 1.5mm, elongate-oblong, each cell narrowed into a distinct basal apiculus to *c.*1mm. Disc thick, 10-lobed, more densely hairy at, than between, the lobes. **Ovary** *c.*15 x 3mm, cylindrical, densely covered with coarse yellowish, distally directed hairs which cover scales, gradually tapering distally; style 1.5–2mm diameter proximally, gradually narrowing upwards, hairy for the proximal ⅔, more laxly hairy and scaly distally, glabrous for the ultimate 10mm; stigma *c.*2mm in diameter, globose, with thick lobes.

Indonesia, New Guinea (W), Star Mts: near the mouth of the Minam R. into the Bon R., also from Koruppen Valley (139°38′E 4°28′S). **Papua New Guinea**, Hong Kong Hill, Ok Tedi headwaters, Kiunga, Western District. Originally from a depression on peaty ground in primary forest, also from secondary vegetation, 1500–2000m, locally common. *Fl.* July.

Leaves similar to those of *R. scabridibracteum* in form and nervation. Said to be similar to *R. carringtoniae* and *R. carstensense* but differing in the more dilated corolla tube and larger lobes.

149. Rhododendron oreadum Wernham
Trans Linn. Soc. London, II, Bot. 1916. 9: 98.
Type: Kloss *s.n.* New Guinea (W), Ascent to Mt Carstensz, 1095–1495m (BM, L, fragment).
Derivation: Greek – *oreo* – pertaining to mountains, alluding to the mountainous habitat.

Shrub. Twigs weakly angular, slender, tips sub-densely scaly, glabrescent with age. **Leaves** mostly 3 together in tight pseudowhorls. **Blade** 80–140 x 30–50mm, narrowly ovate to elliptic, broadly elliptic to slightly obovate, sometimes with slightly unequal sides; apex acuminate and acute to obtuse; margin flat; base narrowly tapering; glabrescent above when mature, laxly stellate-scaly beneath. **Scales** thin, irregularly dentate, flat; centre small, faintly impressed. Mid-vein slightly impressed above, prominent beneath; lateral veins 8–12 per side, dense, curved and anastomosing before the margin, obscurely impressed above, raised beneath, reticulation inconspicuous on both sides. **Petiole** 8–10 x 1.5mm, laxly scaly.

Flower buds to 60 x 20mm, imbricate, ellipsoid, smooth. Bracts to 30 x 18mm, ovate to broadly obovate, scaly and shortly hairy outside in the distal ½ and shortly hairy in the distal ½ inside, with longer appressed hairs proximally. Bracteoles to 30mm, filiform, laxly hairy. Inflorescence compact, 8–12-flowered, the flowers erect or semi-erect. Pedicels *c.*2–4 x 1.5mm, scaly. Calyx *c.*2.5mm diameter, obtusely 5-lobed. **Corolla** trumpet-shaped, probably white; tube 45–60 x 3–4 x *c.*11mm, cylindrical, straight, practically glabrous outside, hairy almost to the mouth inside; lobes *c.*20 x 15mm, broadly elliptic

or obovate, glabrous. **Stamens** exserted to 14mm, clustered on the upper side of the flower before collapsing irregularly; filaments linear and densely patently hairy in the proximal ½, gradually glabrescent distally; anthers *c.*4 x 1mm, oblong, base obtuse. Disc shortly hairy on the upper side. **Ovary** 8–10 x 1.7mm, cylindrical, densely covered with long, appressed, distally directed hairs with some scales between them, gradually tapering distally; style *c.*40mm, laxly covered with hairs for the proximal ⅔, glabrous distally; stigma shortly broad-obconical, indistinctly 5-lobed.

Indonesia, New Guinea (W), Mt Carstensz, 1095–1495m.

Not known to have been cultivated.

150. Rhododendron rhodosalpinx Sleumer
Blumea 1961. 11: 121.
Type: Bergman 815, 19 April 1958. New Guinea, Northern Part, Swart R. valley, Kadubaka, 1600–2000m (S, L, fragment).
Derivation: Greek – *rhodo* – rose (the colour); *salpinx* – a war trumpet. Alluding to the rose-coloured corolla tube.

Shrub. Twigs slender, *c.*2mm in diameter, tips densely scaly; internodes 1–4cm. **Leaves** 3–4 together in pseudo-whorls at the upper nodes. **Blade** 30–50 x 15–26mm, elliptic or sub-obovate-elliptic; apex broadly tapering and blunt, or almost rounded, sometimes slightly retuse; distinctly revolute at the margin; base broadly tapering, glabrescent with age above, sub-densely scaly beneath. **Scales** small, marginal zone sub-stellately lobed; centre minute, deeply impressed. Mid-vein very narrowly impressed above, as thick as the petiole and strongly prominent below, gradually decreasing distally beneath; lateral veins *c.*3 per side, a little raised beneath only, or often inconspicuous, without visible reticulation. **Petiole** 4–6 x 1mm, grooved above, slightly flattened, scaly.

Bracteoles linear, *c.*10mm. Inflorescence 3-flowered. Pedicels 17–21 x *c.*0.8mm, sub-densely scaly, minutely patently hairy. Calyx *c.*2.5mm in diameter, sub-obliquely disc-shaped, very shortly and irregularly 5-lobed, scaly outside. **Corolla** trumpet-shaped, apparently red; tube 30–35 x 3–4 x 5–7mm, straight, sub-densely sub-stellately scaly outside, laxly hairy proximally inside; lobes 10–12 x *c.*8mm, obovate, spreading, scaly outside proximally. **Stamens** equalling or slightly exserted from the mouth of the corolla; filaments narrowly linear, patently laxly hairy in the proximal ½, glabrous distally; anthers 2.5 x 1mm, narrowly oblong, base obtuse. Disc glabrous. **Ovary** *c.*6 x 1.7mm, sub-cylindrical, densely covered with scales, which touch or even overlap each other (and possibly hide some short hairs), gradually tapering distally; style slender, as long as the corolla, scaly in the proximal ⅓ and laxly patently short-hairy in the proximal ⅔, glabrous distally; stigma globose, shortly 5-lobed.

Indonesia, New Guinea (W), Swart R. Valley (*c.*138°15′E 3°30′S), at 1600–2000m. *Fl.* April.

Known only from the type collection. This species should possibly not be included in *Solenovireya* on account of flower colour and the large corolla lobes in relation to the tube. Further specimens are badly needed to establish its proper identity.

151. **Rhododendron roseiflorum** P.F.Stevens

Adansonia 1978, ser. 2, 18(1): 55.
Type: Raynal 17672, 11 May 1973. Irian Jaya, S spur of Mt Carstensz, Tembagapura (P, L).
Derivation: Latin – *rosei* – red coloured; *florum* – flower. Alluding to the prominent pink flush on the flowers.

Shrub to 3m. Twigs 1.5–2.5mm in diameter, rounded, often glaucous, sparsely scaly. **Leaves** 3–7 together in tight pseudowhorls. **Blade** 17–85 x 10–29mm, elliptic to ovate; apex tapering to broadly rounded; margin flat to slightly recurved; base shallowly cordate to broadly

Rhododendron roseiflorum.

tapering. **Scales** remotely spaced on both sides, flat, thin with a broad lobed margin and small central area. Midvein impressed above, slightly raised below; lateral veins 4–7 per side curving upwards towards the margin, raised both above and below, reticulation obscure above, below slightly raised, the leaf surface often furrowed. **Petiole** 2–7mm, with sub-persistent scales.

Bracts to 14 x 2mm, with scaly margins, the outer ovate, *c.*5 x 5mm, the apex mucronate, the internal bracts sub-linear, apex rounded. Inflorescence of 5–8, half-hanging flowers in an open umbel. Pedicels 8–15 x 0.4–0.9mm, covered with scales and simple hairs. Calyx *c.*1.8mm in diameter, obliquely disc-shaped, weakly 5-lobed, with scales and hairs outside, inside glabrous. **Corolla** pink, tubular, expanded distally but contracted shortly below the mouth; tube 53–78 x 4.3–8.2 x 3.5–7.5mm, curved, outside sparsely scaly, inside covered with short hairs especially proximally; lobes 7.5–10.5mm, spreading, apex rounded to weakly retuse. **Stamens** clustered together; filaments 65–76mm, densely covered with white hairs in the proximal ½; anthers 2.6–3.5mm, exserted to *c.*10mm. Disc covered with hairs. **Ovary** 7–9.5mm, densely scaly; style 58–82mm, scaly becoming laxly so upwards; stigma 1–1.4mm wide, becoming exserted.

Indonesia, New Guinea (W), above Tembagapura near Mt Jaya (Carstensz) and also in the vicinity of Mt Trichora (Wilhelmina). Terrestrial shrub in open sub-alpine woodland or shrubberies, occasionally epiphytic, 2100–2700m.

Not yet known in cultivation.

152. **Rhododendron syringoideum** Sleumer

Blumea 1963. 12: 104.
Type: Sleumer & Vink 4442, 26 Jan. 1962. New Guinea (NW), Arfak Mts, summit of Mt Saru-mot near Iray, Anggi Gigi Lake, 2350m (L, K).
Derivation: Greek – *syrinx* – a shepherd's pipe, alluding to the shape of the flowers.

Shrub to 2m. Twigs to 5mm in diameter, obtusely angular or laterally compressed, densely brown, stellate-scaly; internodes 5–12cm. **Leaves** 5–6 together in loose pseudowhorls or laxly arranged in the upper ⅓ of the internodes. **Blade** 60–90 x 40–60mm, broadly elliptic or sub-ovate-elliptic; apex broadly obtuse to rounded, sometimes slightly retuse; margin entire, narrowly revolute, especially proximally; base broadly tapering to rounded, or sub-cordate, laxly covered with reddish-brown scales on both sides initially. **Scales** very variable in size, stellate to sub-dendroid, each on top of minute epidermal

Rhododendron syringoideum.

tubercles. Mid-vein thick and prominent, grooved proximally, gradually becoming flat distally above, strongly raised below, gradually less so distally; lateral veins 7–8 per side, irregular, some deeply forked, indistinctly anastomosing before the margin, smooth when fresh, slightly impressed above, prominent below when dry, reticulation obscure. **Petiole** 10–20 x *c.*2mm, weakly grooved above, densely brown-scaly.

Outer bracts ovate to sub-circular, to 20 x 20mm, inner ones to 35 x 18mm, spathulate, innermost ones elongate-spathulate, to 50 x 10mm, all laxly short-hairy outside, internally more densely and longer, appressed hairy. Bracteoles 40–50 x 2–5mm, sub-spathulate-linear, hairy especially along the margin. Inflorescence an 8–14-flowered open umbel. Pedicels 5–7 x 1.5–2mm, laxly scaly. Calyx *c.*5mm in diameter, oblique, rim-like, obscurely lobed. **Corolla** 100–110 x 55mm, trumpet-shaped, pink, strongly scented, weakly zygomorphic; tube 85–105 x 6–9 x 10–15mm, sub-densely scaly outside, hairy for ¾ of the tube inside, straight or slightly curved, strongly angled in the proximal ½, gradually widening for the proximal 65mm, (where curved), then parallel for the remainder; lobes 26–27 x 24–25mm, spreading, oblong-obovate, in two groups: three upper overlapping to ⅔; two lower, widely separated from the upper three, overlapping ⅓–½. **Stamens** exserted to 15mm, grouped on the lower side of the mouth, becoming reflexed back against the corolla lobes with age; filaments linear, hairy for *c.*¾ proximally, narrower and glabrous distally; anthers 5–6 x 1–1.3mm, narrowly oblong, base of each cell apiculate. Disc glabrous. **Ovary** 12–15 x *c.*3mm, elongate-cylindrical, densely covered with white or yellowish appressed hairs, which cover the scales, tapering distally; style exserted to 15mm, pink, densely covered with hairs and scales proximally, becoming less hairy and more scaly, glabrous for

the distal 10mm; stigma *c.*1.5mm in diameter, 5-lobed, green. **Fruit** to 50 x 7mm.

Indonesia, New Guinea (W), Arfak Mts: Mt Saru-mot, Anggi Gigi Lake, Mt Carstensz. Both epiphytic in dense forest and terrestrial in open disturbed *Nothofagus* summit forest or shrubberies, 2200–3000m. *Fr.* Jan.

Introduced into cultivation in the Royal Botanic Garden Edinburgh in 1994 from a collection made by Dr G. Atherton on Mt Carstensz and grown on by Graham Snell in Queensland. It flowered first in February 2001 with beautiful large pink flowers powerfully scented of *Dianthus*. There seems little except corolla size to separate this species from *R. carstensense*, and the fact that large-flowered plants have been found on Mt Carstensz (Mt Jaya) further undermines the credibility of this species. It is maintained at present as we have so few collections. The description above probably differs from Sleumer's type description, mainly because the type collection was already in a partially withered state when collected.

153. Rhododendron majus (J.J.Sm.) Sleumer
Reinwardtia 1960. 5: 120 ('*maius*').
Type: Pulle (Versteeg) 2422, 7 Feb. 1913. New Guinea (W), Hubrecht Mts, 3200m (L).
Derivation: Latin – *maius* – large, alluding to the larger flowers than those of *R. carringtoniae*.

Synonym: *R. carringtoniae* F.Muell. var. *majus* J.J.Sm., Nova Guinea 1917. 12: 511.

Shrub to 2m. Twigs 3–5mm in diameter, rounded, tips laxly scaly; internodes 6–14cm. **Leaves** 6–10 together in well-marked pseudowhorls. **Blade** 50–90 x 22–40mm, elliptic; apex broadly tapering, obtuse; margin slightly revolute; base broadly tapering to rounded; sub-densely minutely impressed-spotted above with age, sub-densely and persistently scaly beneath. **Scales** dark, marginal zone coarsely dentate; centre slightly impressed. Mid-vein weakly impressed above, strongly prominent beneath, though more slender towards the apex of the lamina; lateral veins 9–10 per side, the lower 4–5 slightly curved, upper ones straight, all branched distally and anastomosing with each other and slightly impressed above, prominent beneath; finer reticulation dense and visibly prominent beneath. **Petiole** 4–10 x *c.*1.5mm, scaly.

Flower buds to 30 x 15mm, ovoid, apiculate, reddish-brown, the tips of the bracts spreading to revolute. Outermost bracts narrowly triangular, reflexed becoming rolled back, inner bracts to 20 x 13mm, ovate, broadly reflexed, apiculate densely scaly and shortly semi-appressed hairy in the distal ½ and along the midline outside, densely brown scaly and minutely patently hairy inside in the reflexed apical portion, glabrous below, densely fringed with brown scales, the innermost (floral) bracts narrowly spathulate. Bracteoles 20 x 0.5mm, linear, white with just a few scattered scales. Inflorescence of (5)12–15 mostly horizontal flowers in an open umbel. Pedicels 10–25 x 2mm, thickened distally, sub-densely covered with thin reddish-brown scales. Calyx *c.*6mm in diameter, with irregular, triangular, obtuse or acute teeth, one of them often longer (up to 2mm). **Corolla** 70–90 x 25–30mm, trumpet-shaped, white, or white with a pink tube, sometimes darkening to red at the base, carnation-scented; tube 70–75 x 4–5 x 6–7mm, widest (7–8mm) at about ¾ of the distance from the base, slightly curved, laxly appressed-scaly outside, inside densely retrorse hairy in the proximal part, more laxly so in the upper part; lobes 12–14 x 10–17mm, obovate to circular, irregularly undulate at the margin, reflexing to right angles, the tips slightly more, glabrous except for some scales at the sinuses or the base of the lobes, overlapping ½–¾. **Stamens** at first clustered tightly at the upper side, exserted 7–8mm, later more irregular and spreading; filaments linear, laxly hairy in the proximal ½, gradually less hairy to become completely glabrous distally; anthers 3.5 x 1mm, narrowly oblong, base obtuse. Disc laxly appressed hairy or almost glabrous. **Ovary** 9–12 x 2mm, cylindrical or elongate-conical, tapering gradually distally, densely covered with coarse white or yellowish hairs, which cover the scales; style 50–55mm, densely patently hairy proximally, laxly hairy and scaly in the middle, glabrous in the upper ⅓; stigma globose-conical, crenulate.

Indonesia, New Guinea (W), Hubrecht Mts, Lake Habbema and Mt Jaya. **Papua New Guinea**, Marafunga and a form on Mt Wilhelm with 5-flowered umbels. Terrestrial or epiphytic, in open places or on stream banks within the mossy forest, 2770–3000m. *Fl.* Feb.–Oct.

Cultivated since 1961 from material collected at Marafunga in Papua New Guinea. It grows easily, is vigorous and flowers irregularly. The flowers have a very powerful sweet perfume.

Note: Sleumer's adoption of the name as '*maius*' cannot be maintained under the existing Code and the name reverts to J.J. Smith's original spelling '*majus*'.

154. Rhododendron archboldianum Sleumer

Reinwardtia 1960. 5: 121.

Type: Brass 4855, May–Sept. 1933. New Guinea (E), Central District, Mt Tafa (L, A, BO, NY).

Derivation: Named after Richard Archbold and his daughter Anne, American philanthropists and explorers who financed the expedition on which this plant was collected.

Tall shrub. Twigs rounded, thick, at first sub-densely scaly, later glabrescent; internodes 6–16cm. **Leaves** 5–7 together in pseudowhorls, in which 3–4 leaves are normal, the rest much smaller. **Blade** 40–110 x 20–60mm, ovate to elliptic-ovate, often asymmetrical; apex shortly acuminate, sub-acute; margin entire, sub-revolute proximally; base sub-truncate-rounded or broadly tapering, sometimes sub-cordate, sub-densely scaly on both sides, the scales slowly disappearing above, persistent for a long time beneath. **Scales** flat, small, the margin irregularly deeply dentate; centre not impressed. Mid-vein slightly depressed above, thickly prominent beneath proximally, less so distally; lateral veins 8–11 per side, slightly curved, irregular, anastomosing with each other before the margin, faintly impressed or raised above, raised beneath, reticulation dense, more visible beneath only. **Petiole** 4–12 x 1.5–2mm, grooved above, sub-densely scaly.

Bracts to 10 x 7mm, ovate to broadly obovate, laxly scaly and with hairs outside. Bracteoles to 15mm, narrowly linear, glabrous or laxly scaly. Inflorescence an 8–15-flowered open umbel. Pedicels 8–11mm, densely scaly, obliquely thickened below the calyx. Calyx small, rim-like, wavy, indistinctly 5-lobed. **Corolla** trumpet-shaped, pink; tube 45–50 x *c.*2.5 x 3.5–4.5mm, cylindrical, slightly curved, gradually expanding from the base but then a little constricted below the mouth, laxly to sub-densely scaly outside, densely hairy inside almost to the mouth; lobes 10–12 x 8–12mm, broadly spathulate to nearly circular, laxly scaly outside at the base and in the middle, glabrous inside. **Stamens** exserted; filaments linear below, filiform above, shortly hairy nearly to the top; anthers 3.5–4 x 1mm, oblong, base obtuse. Disc glabrous below, densely hairy on the upper margin. **Ovary** 7–8 x *c.*2mm, cylindrical, gradually tapering distally, densely appressed-hairy and obscurely scaly; style as long as the corolla tube, covered with sub-patent hairs and scales nearly to the top; stigma thick, shortly obconical.

Papua New Guinea, Mts Tafa and Suckling. Usually epiphytic in ridge forests, occasionally terrestrial in clearings, 2400m.

Not known to have been cultivated.

155. Rhododendron armitii F.M.Bailey
Bot. Bull. Queensl. Dep. Agr. 1895. 10: 39.
Type: Armit, 1894. New Guinea, Milne Bay District, Mt Dayman, 2710m (BRI, MEL).
Derivation: Named after the collector William Edington de Margrat Armit, Belgian officer of the Queensland mounted police, who led the Argus expedition to Papua on which this species was collected.

Shrub to 2.5m. Twigs rounded, tips sparsely to sub-densely stellately scaly; internodes 2–12cm. **Leaves** 4–5 in well-marked pseudowhorls. **Blade** 70–100 x 30–60mm, elliptic, broadly elliptic, to sub-obovate-elliptic; apex very shortly obtuse; margin entire, flat or slightly revolute; base rounded or broadly tapering, the extreme base sometimes truncate to slightly sub-cordate; sub-densely scaly on both sides initially, early glabrescent above, more persistently scaly beneath. **Scales** thin, flat, brown, often on minute low epidermal elevations which are still visible as pale spots when the scales have gone, marginal zone thin, irregularly deeply incised; centre very small. Mid-vein impressed above, very prominent beneath especially proximally; lateral veins 8–10 per side, straight basally, sometimes forking, obscurely curved-anastomosing before the margin, smooth above when fresh, (raised when dry), prominent beneath, laxly reticulate, more visible beneath, veinlets obscure. **Petiole** 8–15 x 2.5mm, grooved above, semi-rounded, brown-scaly.

Flower buds to 30 x 12mm, narrowly ovate, acutely pointed, green, the bract tips spreading and recurving, densely hairy and with a few scales outside and fringing the bract margins. Bracts ovate to obovate-spathulate. Bracteoles *c.*20 x 2.5mm, linear-spathulate, laxly hairy. Inflorescence an open one-sided umbel of 5–7 flowers, held horizontally or half-hanging. Pedicels 15–25 x *c.*2mm, sub-densely scaly, sometimes with a few hairs below the calyx, red. Calyx distinct, scaly and laxly hairy outside, glabrous inside, irregularly, deeply 5-lobed, lobes triangular, *c.*3 x 2mm, occasionally subulate up to 7mm, red, fringed often becoming reflexed. **Corolla** 55–60 x 35–40mm, trumpet-shaped, white or pink with white lobes; tube 45–60 x 5–6 x 10–12mm, straight or slightly curved, angled in section and grooved proximally, very laxly scaly or practically glabrous outside, densely long-hairy inside in the proximal ⅓, becoming less densely so and glabrous in the distal ⅓; lobes *c.*15–20 x 14–18mm, broadly obovate to nearly circular, spreading, overlapping to *c.*halfway, glabrous. **Stamens** loosely clustered on the lower side of the mouth, exserted to *c.*6mm, hanging down on the lower side in older flowers; filaments slender, white, densely hairy at the base, becoming less so, and completely

glabrous in the distal ⅓; anthers 3–4 x *c.*1mm, oblong, base obtuse. Disc glabrous or hairy. **Ovary** 10–12 x 2.5–3mm, elongate-conical, 5-ribbed, densely covered with appressed white hairs, which cover some scales, gradually tapering distally; style densely hairy and very laxly scaly in the proximal ½, glabrous and more slender distally; stigma broadly obconical, distinctly 5-lobed, becoming exserted to 12mm.

Papua New Guinea, Mt Dayman, summit; Central/Northern District, Mt Suckling; Milne Bay District, Mt Vineuo, Goodenough Is., 2250–2710m. *Fl.* March, July.

Plants of this name were first introduced to Edinburgh by Paddy Woods in 1968. They grew into tall leggy plants about 2m high which became covered in the delicate pink, scented, tubular flowers, often in the depths of the Scottish winter. They will however flower at almost any time of the year and will flower, though not as well, as small plants.

156. Rhododendron carrii Sleumer
Reinwardtia 1960. 5: 124.
Type: Carr 15266, 27 Jan. 1936. New Guinea (SE), Central District, ascent to Mt Victoria, Main Range NW of 'The Gap', 2440m (BM, A, K, SING).
Derivation: Named after the collector, Cedric Carr, orchid enthusiast and prolific plant collector who spent many years in SE Asia.

Shrub. Twigs rounded, tips glabrous or very laxly scaly; internodes 2.5–9cm. **Leaves** 3–4 together in pseudowhorls at the upper 3–4 nodes. **Blade** 40–60 x 25–55mm, ovate to sub-ovate-rounded; apex broadly and shortly acuminate, obtuse; margin entire, flat; base distinctly sub-auriculate, cordate, sessile or nearly so, superficially glabrous, but laxly covered with minute irregularly stellate scales beneath leaving a minute spot where the slightly impressed centre was. Mid-vein flat or slightly impressed above, grooved in the proximal ½, thick and very prominent beneath proximally, less so distally; lateral veins *c.*10 per side, 2–3 of them from the base of the blade, the others from the mid-vein, all curved-ascending and anastomosing near the edge, prominent on both sides, reticulation dense and clearly visible especially beneath. **Petiole** *c.*1 x 1.5mm.

Bracteoles linear. Inflorescence a 4–5-flowered umbel. Pedicels 13–25mm, thick, sub-densely to laxly thin-scaly, thickened at apex. Calyx *c.*2mm in diameter, oblique, membranous, shortly, obtusely 5-lobed to 1mm, shortly fringed. **Corolla** trumpet-shaped, white; tube 55–60 x *c.*3.5 x *c.*7mm, slightly curved, dilated gradually upwards, laxly sub-stellately scaly outside, with dense retrorse hairs proximally, distally more laxly so with spreading hairs, glabrous below the mouth; lobes 12–15 x 10–15mm, spreading, rounded-obovate, glabrous on both sides. **Stamens** a little exserted; filaments narrow-linear, densely hairy at the base, more laxly and patently so in the middle, glabrous distally; anthers 2.8–3 x 1mm, oblong, base obtuse. Disc densely short-hairy especially above. **Ovary** *c.*10 x 2mm, elongate-conical, densely covered with appressed yellowish hairs and laxly with scales which tend to be hidden by the hairs, gradually tapering distally; style 55–65mm, exserted, laxly hairy and scaly at the base for *c.*5mm only, glabrous distally; stigma thick-conical, crenulate.

Papua New Guinea, Mt Victoria, NW of 'The Gap'. Epiphytic on an open hillside, 2440m. *Fl.* Jan.

Introduced into cultivation by Paul Kores in 1976, it is vegetatively similar to *R. blackii* although without the down-turned basal lobes to the leaves and with much more distinct reticulation; the flowers, being long, tubular and pink, are quite different.

---

157. Rhododendron carringtoniae F.Muell.

Vict. Nat. 1887. 4: 110.
Type: Cuthberson & Sayer *s.n.* New Guinea (SE), Central District, Mt Obree, 1830–2135m (MEL, K).
Derivation: Named after Lady Carrington, wife of the British representative in New Guinea, for her interest in the plants of the colony.

Shrub to 5m. Twigs *c.*4mm in diameter, rounded, tips densely covered with thin brown scales; internodes 2–3cm. **Leaves** 3–5 together in tight pseudowhorls, sometimes with one or two much smaller leaves, also recorded as spiral. **Blade** 40–80 x 25–45mm, obovate to elliptic-obovate, apex rounded or obtuse; margin slightly or not recurved; base broadly tapering but the extreme base rounded or truncate; glabrescent above when fully mature, sub-densely to laxly scaly beneath. **Scales** thin, marginal zone persistent, shallowly and irregularly dentate; centre small, impressed. Mid-vein raised above but grooved proximally for a few millimetres, impressed distally, strongly prominent beneath, but less so towards the apex; lateral veins 6–8 per side, often forked before the edge, anastomosing both among each other and with the stronger veins, laxly reticulate, prominent on both sides. **Petiole** 2–6 x 2–5mm, somewhat flattened and weakly grooved above, scaly.

Flower buds to 40 x 20mm, elongate-ovate, imbricate, yellow-brown, smooth. Bracts to 25 x 15mm, sub-circular to obovate-spathulate, scaly outside and not or only laxly shortly hairy. Inflorescence at first an erect umbel of 5–6 flowers, the tubes closely held together by the bracts, later the flowers spreading and the umbel becoming open. Bracteoles linear. Pedicels *c.*2 x 5–8mm, sub-densely scaly. Calyx *c.*2mm in diameter, rim-like, membranous, irregularly and very shortly 5-dentate, fringed. **Corolla** trumpet-shaped, white, powerfully and sweetly scented; tube 50–70 x 4–4.5 x 5.5–6mm, cylindrical, slightly curved, sub-densely scaly outside, inside with short spreading hairs proximally becoming glabrous above the middle; lobes 10–15 x 6–13mm, obovate to broadly elliptic-circular, spreading, very laxly scaly outside, glabrous inside. **Stamens** exserted to 8mm, arranged all round the mouth; filaments linear, densely covered with spreading hairs below, these gradually thinning to become glabrous distally; anthers 5–7 x 1–1.2mm, sub-obovate-oblong, base of each cell with a distinct spur-like point. Disc densely hairy. **Ovary** *c.*10 x 1.5mm, narrowly cylindrical, slightly tapering towards the base, densely covered with yellowish or whitish, forwardly pointing hairs which cover numerous scales, gradually tapering distally; style 55–65mm, hairy and densely scaly apart from the distal 6mm; stigma conical. **Fruit** narrowly cylindrical, shortly tapering at both ends, with 5 grooves, sub-densely hairy and scaly, *c.*50 x 6mm. Seeds with very narrow appendages.

Papua New Guinea, Owen Stanley Range; Central District: Mt Obree, Mt Victoria; Milne Bay District: Mt Dayman, Mt Suckling. On open hillsides, along rocky river banks and gorges, mostly terrestrial but occasionally epiphytic. 1830–2440m. *Fl.* Jan., June.

Introduced into cultivation by Canon Cruttwell in Australia in 1972 from Mt Suckling and from Mt Dayman in 1974. He regarded this species as 'in the top rank of the tubular (Solenovireya) Rhododendrons' (Cruttwell 1972).

Rhododendron carringtoniae.

158. Rhododendron cruttwellii Sleumer

Reinwardtia 1960. 5: 120.

Type: Cruttwell 525, 11 June 1954. New Guinea (SE), North-eastern District, Mt Maneao, 2590m (K, E).

Derivation: Named after the collector, the Reverend Canon Norman Cruttwell, for most of his life a missionary in Papua New Guinea but also a keen botanist who collected many vireyas.

Tree to 6m. Twigs semi-rounded, laxly to densely scaly; internodes 2.5–14cm. **Leaves** 5–7 together in tight pseudowhorls, with some much smaller than the others. **Blade** 50–100 x 20–40mm, obovate-elliptic or elliptic to broadly elliptic; apex shortly gradually acuminate, obtuse to broadly acute, sometimes with a small terminal gland; margin entire, flat; base broadly tapering, dark green above, paler and dull beneath, glabrescent above, laxly to sub-densely scaly beneath. **Scales** with a broad, thin marginal zone variously dentately divided; centre small, somewhat impressed and more persistent. Mid-vein raised and grooved for a few millimetres proximally otherwise slightly depressed above, raised beneath; lateral veins 8–10 per side, lower ones irregular, distinctly grooved above in the basal part, upper ones more straight and sub-parallel, curved-anastomosing with each other, smooth when fresh, prominent on both sides when dry, reticulation dense and visibly raised on both sides when dry, very distinct underneath when fresh. **Petiole** 6–12 x 1.5–2mm, grooved above, slightly flattened, scaly.

Flower buds to 25 x 15mm, imbricate, green, smooth with the bracts appressed. Bracts to 15 x 10mm, ovate-acuminate, laxly scaly in the middle outside, also with hairs all over the outer and undersurface, glandular-ciliate. Bracteoles to 15mm, narrowly linear, glabrous. Inflorescence 4–9-flowered in erect to spreading umbels. Pedicels 10–15 x 1–1.5mm, laxly patently hairy and scaly especially in the distal ⅓, obliquely thickened below the calyx. Calyx c.2.5mm in diameter, membranous, indistinctly 5-lobed, laxly scaly and hairy. **Corolla** 60–70 x 25–30mm, trumpet-shaped, pure white, scented; tube 50–60 x 4–5 x 8–10mm, slightly curved, a little lobed at the base, sparsely scaly outside, densely hairy in the proximal ½ and glabrous distally inside; lobes 10–13 x 7–12mm, spreading, broadly obovate to sub-circular, glabrous. **Stamens** exserted to 10mm; filaments linear, hairy in the proximal ½, glabrous distally; anthers 2–2.3 x c.1mm, oblong, base obtuse. Disc low, glabrous. **Ovary** 6–7 x c.1.5mm, cylindrical, gradually narrowed distally, densely covered with sub-patent white or greyish hairs, and some obscure scales; style c.60mm, patently hairy and scaly for over ½ its length, becoming scaly only, glabrous for the distal 6–10mm; stigma

exserted to 10mm, conical-globose, crenulate. **Fruit** (immature) to 30 x 5mm, fusiform, often curved.

Papua New Guinea, Maneau Range: Mt Maneao, Mt Yauama and Mt Simpson. Central Province: Mt Albert Edward. Eastern Highlands District: Mt Gahavisuka. In open evergreen forest, margins of valley forest, on moss-covered ground among non-calcareous rocks in shade, 1860–2600m. *Fl.* June–Aug.

First introduced into cultivation by Paddy Woods in 1968 and since lost; later reintroduced in 1974 by Paul Kores from Mt Dayman and widely distributed. An earlier introduction under this name by G. Herklots in 1965, possibly from the Telefomin area, is now considered to be *R. multinervium. Rhododendron cruttwellii* grows easily and can produce an abundance of white, scented flowers, mostly in early summer in Edinburgh but it can flower at any time of the year. The type material in Edinburgh differs from Sleumer's type description in having a densely hairy (not glabrous) disc and having scales as well as hairs on the ovary; further the style is not 'at the base laxly hairy proximally for c.6mm, completely glabrous otherwise' but as described above.

159. Rhododendron hartleyi Sleumer

Blumea 1973. 21: 366.

Type: Hartley 12788, 24 Jan. 1964. New Guinea (E), Morobe District, above Bakaia, 15 miles SE of Garaina (L, LAE).

Derivation: Named after the collector, G. Hartley.

Shrub to c.5m. Twigs c.2mm in diameter, slender, laxly sub-stellately scaly; internodes 2–3cm. **Leaves** 4–5 together in pseudowhorls. **Blade** 45–75 x 15–30mm, narrowly ovate to narrowly elliptic, rarely narrowly sub-obovate; apex gradually tapering, sub-acute; margin entire, slightly revolute; base tapering; obscurely scaly above, distinctly laxly scaly below. **Scales** flat, sub-stellate; centre small, somewhat impressed, finally blackish. Mid-vein slightly impressed above, raised below; lateral veins moderately irregular, 7–8 per side, with a moderately dense, raised reticulation on both sides. **Petiole** 18–25 x c.1mm.

Bracteoles filiform to elongate spathulate, 10–15mm, the apex up to 2mm broad. Inflorescence 6–8-flowered. Pedicels c.15 x 1mm, slender, red, densely, shortly white, patent hairy. Calyx c.2.5mm in diameter, oblique, saucer-shaped, obscurely 5-lobed. **Corolla** tubular, slightly curved, slightly dilated towards the mouth, slender, white, laxly sub-stellately scaly outside, laxly hairy in the proximal ⅓ inside; tube 60–65 x 3–4 x 5–6mm; lobes c.13 x 10mm, obovate, spreading or more or less reflexed, glabrous on both sides. **Stamens** with the filaments hairy for the proximal 20mm, glabrous distally, slightly exserted from the tube; anthers *c.*2.5mm, oblong, the base obtuse. Disc slightly hairy. **Ovary** 5–6 x *c.*1.5mm, cylindrical, slightly greyish-white hairy, tapering distally; style 60–65mm, laxly patently hairy proximally for 10–15mm, laxly patently hairy distally, not scaly; stigma 5-lobed.

Papua New Guinea (E), Morobe District, above Bakaia, 15 miles SE of Garaina. Known only from the type locality, epiphytic in moss forest, at 2745m. *Fl.* Jan.

Said to be 'close to *R. cruttwellii* but sufficiently distinct by more slender and much longer petioles, smaller leaves, and a hairy disk' (Sleumer 1973).

160. Rhododendron goodenoughii Sleumer
Reinwardtia 1960. 5: 131.
Type: W.E. Armit *s.n.*, 1895. New Guinea (SE), Mt Goodenough (MEL, L).
Derivation: Named after the island from which it was collected, which in turn was named after Commodore Goodenough, a British naval sea captain.

Shrub to 2m. Twigs 4–6mm in diameter, rounded, densely, smoothly, brown-scaly; internodes 4–15cm. **Leaves** 4–6 together in tight pseudowhorls. **Blade** 50–100 x 30–60mm, broadly elliptic to obovate; apex very shortly acuminate, broadly obtuse to almost rounded; margin entire, narrowly recurved or flat; base broadly tapering, glabrescent above, sub-densely scaly beneath. **Scales** small, circular to weakly lobed, with a broad margin and small darker brown centre, distinctly impressed. Mid-vein broadly raised and grooved for the proximal *c.*10mm, distally narrowly impressed, beneath broadly raised for most of its length and tapering gradually; lateral veins 7–9 per side, diverging at *c.*45°, straight proximally but curving in the distal ⅓, reticulation obscure. **Petiole** 10–15 x 3–4mm, a little flattened, not grooved above or very faintly in the distal part, scaly initially.

Flower buds to 35 x 20mm, elongate-ellipsoid, distinctly imbricate, yellowish-green, smooth with all tips appressed. Bracts to 25 x 18mm, ovate, obtuse, outer ones densely scaly and very shortly hairy outside, appressed-hairy and scaly near the apex only inside. Bracteoles to 15 x 0.5mm, narrowly linear, hairy throughout. Inflorescence of 8–22 flowers, at first held semi-erect in a tight cluster by the collarette of bracts, these later spreading and falling, so the umbel becomes open with the flowers horizontally displayed. Pedicels 5–10 x 2–3mm, sub-densely scaly, sometimes with a few hairs just under the calyx.

Calyx *c.*2.5mm in diameter, oblique, indistinctly lobed, brown-scaly and hairy. **Corolla** 65–75 x 30–35mm, trumpet-shaped, white, sweetly scented; tube 55–65 x 4–5 x 7–9mm, cylindrical, slightly curved, weakly grooved or angled and sub-glabrous outside but hairy inside, in the proximal ½, tubular and distinctly scaly distally outside; lobes 15–17 x 12–15mm, spreading obliquely, the lower two becoming reflexed, the upper three staying semi-erect, obovate, laxly scaly outside at the base, otherwise glabrous. **Stamens** at first exserted to 18mm, in a tight group on the upper side of the mouth, in later stages spreading more irregularly; filaments linear, white, sub-densely hairy in the lower ⅔, nearly filiform and glabrous distally; anthers 4–6 x 1mm, brown, each cell with a short basal apiculus. Disc sub-glabrous or hairy on the upper side. **Ovary** 8–10 x 2–3mm, elongate-cylindrical, densely covered with appressed, white hairs which cover small silvery scales, gradually narrowed distally; style *c.*50mm, on the upper side of the corolla, green, densely covered with scales and forwardly directed hairs in the lower ⅔, glabrous distally; stigma green, at first deep within the corolla tube, later exserted to *c.*15mm, thick-obconical.

Papua New Guinea, Goodenough Island, Mt Goodenough.

Introduced into cultivation at Kew in 1964 from seed sent by Rev. N.E.G. Cruttwell (1410). It was described (Hunt 1982) as a 'strong grower'. An introduction to the USA was recorded as raised from seed sent to Maurice Sumner about 1970 from New Guinea from an unknown source (Eversole 1985). Another introduction was from Paul Kores (1977); this was widely distributed and is now grown in many parts of the world. It is indeed a vigorous plant in cultivation, flowering prolifically at least once a year and often producing odd flowers between main flowerings. The way the flowers are held erect for some time with a collarette of bracts around the flower tube is distinctive, and the beautiful scent makes this a very desirable species for cultivation for those who have a reasonable amount of space.

161. Rhododendron multinervium Sleumer
Reinwardtia 1960. 5: 117.
Type: Smith NGF 1021, Oct. 1944. New Guinea, Western Highlands, Aiyura, 1830m (L, LAE).
Derivation: Latin – *multi* – many; *nervi* – veining. Alluding to the distinct venation of the leaves.

Shrub or small tree to 3m. Twigs densely scaly initially; internodes 4–6cm. **Leaves** 3–6 together in tight pseudowhorls. **Blade** 40–95 x 25–65mm, obovate-elliptic or broadly elliptic; apex obtuse, or very shortly and abruptly obtusely acuminate; margin entire, flat or slightly revolute proximally; base broadly tapering, sometimes decurrent, scaly initially, glabrescent above with age, densely and persistently scaly beneath. **Scales** small, marginal zone sub-stellately lobed; centre becoming dark. Mid-vein slightly impressed above, weakly grooved in the proximal 10mm, strongly prominent beneath but tapering and flattening gradually from base to apex; lateral veins 10–14 per side, close and parallel to each other, straight proximally, obscurely anastomosing before the margin, with some other less distinct veins between them, all somewhat prominent on both sides, reticulation lax and faintly raised underneath only. **Petiole** 6–8 x *c.*1.5mm, very slightly or not grooved above, scaly, somewhat flattened.

Outer bracts to 12 x 14mm, broadly ovate, inner ones spathulate, all densely scaly distally outside, and along the margins. Bracteoles filiform. Inflorescence 5–8-flowered in an open umbel, the flowers held semi-erect to horizontal or half-hanging. Pedicels 6–10 x *c.*1mm, densely scaly. Calyx *c.*2.5mm in diameter, oblique, disc-shaped, very shortly lobed. **Corolla** 55–75 x 20–25mm, trumpet-shaped, or trumpet-ventricose, white, sweetly scented; tube 40–55 x 3–4 x 7–8mm, straight, often ventricose, broadest at about ⅔ of the distance from the base; outside glabrous or laxly scaly, the scales denser at the bases of the lobes, inside sub-densely hairy in the proximal ½, glabrescent distally; lobes 8–15 x 6–8mm, spreading, obovate-elliptic. **Stamens** exserted to 8mm; filaments linear below and densely, patently, hairy in the proximal ⅔, filiform and glabrous above, unequal; anthers 2.5 x 0.9mm. Disc densely and shortly white-hairy or glabrous. **Ovary** 5–6 x *c.*1.5mm, elongate columnar, shallowly 5-ribbed, very densely covered with thick, almost circular scales, gradually tapering distally; style becoming exserted to 8mm, slender and

Rhododendron multinervium.

glabrous or with a few scales at the base; stigma shortly obconical, crenulate. **Fruit** 30–35 x 4–5mm, elongate-fusiform, sub-densely scaly.

Papua New Guinea, Eastern Highlands: Mt Michael, Mt Otto, Daulo Pass. Simbu District: Engwegl, (Upper Chimbu R. valley), Gembogl. Western Highlands: Aiyura and near Wankl village, Mt Hagen. Sepik District: Telefomin. Terrestrial or epiphytic, on grassy slopes or *Castanopsis* and *Nothofagus* forest, 1370–2050m. *Fl.* April, Aug.–Oct.

Introduced into cultivation independently in the same year, 1965, by M. Black and G. Herklots. It grows to be a large shrub in cultivation, flowering freely, often in the winter months, with its beautiful tubular white flowers which have been variously described as *Vanilla* or Frangipani (*Plumeria*) scented. The original material was described with a hairy disc but recent collections all have glabrous discs. Similar to *R. cruttwellii* but in addition to the difference in indumentum on the ovary the leaves of this species have slender ungrooved lateral veins and obscure reticulation when viewed from the underside.

---

162. Rhododendron natalicium Sleumer
Reinwardtia 1960. 5: 118.
Type: Clemens 4852, 3 Jan. 1937. New Guinea (NE), Morobe District, Ogeramnang (Satelberg region) (A, L, fragment).
Derivation: Latin – *natalis* – relating to birth. 'Gift from nr. 1 for my 64th birthday'. Presumably collected by a special field companion for Mary Clemens.

Shrub. Twigs flattened, sub-densely scaly; internodes 7–15cm. **Leaves** 4 together in pseudowhorls. **Blade** 70–100 x 35–50mm, elliptic, apex shortly, gradually acuminate, sub-acute; margin entire, sub-revolute; base broadly tapering, glabrescent above at maturity, laxly scaly beneath. **Scales** small, brown, irregularly lobed; centre slightly impressed. Mid-vein slightly but distinctly impressed above, very prominent beneath for the proximal ¾, less so distally, more densely scaly than the lamina; lateral veins 6–8 per side, distant from each other, diverging at an acute angle, straight below, obscurely curved-anastomosing near the edge, somewhat raised above (but impressed in the very middle), prominent beneath, reticulation obscure. **Petiole** 10–15 x 1–1.5mm, grooved above, sub-densely scaly.

Outer bracts to 25 x 8mm, ovate, inner ones spathulate, all hairy on both sides, otherwise not or very laxly scaly, long-ciliate. Bracteoles to 20mm, sub-filiform, glabrous below, narrowly spathulate, hairy distally. Inflorescence a *c.*8-flowered umbel. Pedicels 10–12mm, thick, densely sub-stellately scaly. Calyx *c.*2.5mm in diameter, oblique, irregularly shortly and obtusely 5-lobed, scaly. **Corolla** trumpet-shaped, white; tube *c.*45 x 3–4 x 4–5mm, straight or slightly curved, sub-densely sub-stellately scaly outside, densely, shortly and patently white hairy in the proximal ⅓, gradually less hairy distally inside; lobes 10–12 x 8–10mm, elliptic-obovate to obovate-spathulate, spreading, laxly scaly outside, glabrous inside. **Stamens** unequal, *c.*55mm, exserted; filaments linear and densely patently hairy proximally, less hairy and finally glabrous distally; anthers *c.*3 x 0.8mm, oblong, base obtuse. Disc sub-densely short-hairy. **Ovary** elongate-conical, densely covered with almost circular scales, *c.*8 x 1.5mm, tapering distally; style scaly at the very base, glabrous otherwise, equalling the corolla tube in length; stigma narrowly shortly obconical. **Fruit** 40–45 x *c.*4mm, elongate-cylindrical, curved, shortly tapering at both ends, laxly scaly.

Papua New Guinea, Sattelberg Region, Morobe District: Ogeramnang; Mt Saruwaged; Wau Salamoa track; Tukwabat village, S of Lae. In hill forest dominated by *Castanopsis* and in open grassland at 1770–2440m. *Fl.* March, Sept., Oct., *fr.* May.

The status of this species is not clear; it would appear to be relatively rare. A collection at Kew (Frodin 2824) agrees well with the description but it is from Telefomin, a very long way to the west of all other collections. It has never been cultivated.

163. **Rhododendron retrorsipilum** Sleumer
Blumea 1961. 11: 120.
Type: Henty NGF 11906, 16 Feb. 1960. New Guinea (NE), Morobe District, above Markham Point near Lae, 900m (L, LAE).
Derivation: Latin – *retro* – backwards; *pilus* – hair. Alluding to the backwardly pointing hairs in the corolla tube.

Shrub to 2m. Twigs slender, *c.*2mm in diameter, sub-densely scaly, early glabrescent; internodes 1–4cm. **Leaves** *c.*3 together in pseudowhorls. **Blade** 40–65 x 25–42mm, elliptic; apex broadly tapering to rounded; margin narrowly revolute; base broadly obtusely tapering to rounded, sub-densely scaly initially on both sides, early glabrescent above, more persistently scaly beneath, smooth to the touch. **Scales** sub-dendroid, each on top of a minute epidermal tubercle, small, marginal zone deeply stellate-incised; centre minute, deepened and elongated into a shorter or longer foot. Mid-vein above very narrowly impressed; beneath as wide as the petiole and strongly raised proximally, gradually narrowed and less prominent upwards, longitudinally striate; lateral veins

*c.*5 per side, spreading, straight, weakly or not impressed above, slightly raised beneath, without reticulation. **Petiole** 6–10 x 1–1.5mm.

Flower buds 23 x 8mm, elongate-ovoid. Outer bracts 4mm, inner ones gradually larger, up to 15mm, sub-densely covered with sessile scales in the upper outer part, fringed with scales. Bracteoles linear, to 10mm. Inflorescence *c.*6-flowered, glabrous in all outer parts. Pedicels 5–8mm, slender, finely short-hairy. Calyx *c.*2.5mm in diameter, oblique, disc-shaped, irregularly 5-lobed, lobes broadly triangular, sub-acute, fringed with long whitish hairs, becoming reflexed. **Corolla** trumpet-shaped, white; tube 20–23 x 3 x 3mm, sub-densely covered with retrorse white hairs almost to the mouth inside; lobes 8–10 x 3–4mm, narrow-spathulate, horizontally spreading. **Stamens** very unequal, up to 35mm, the shortest hardly exserted, the longest strongly exserted from the mouth; filaments filiform, densely covered with white retrorse hairs almost to the top; anthers narrowly oblong, *c.*3 x 0.7mm, cells sub-apiculate at base. Disc glabrous at the very base, hairy above. **Ovary** 5–6 x *c.*1.5mm, elongate-cylindric, densely covered with appressed, forwardly directed hairs and scales (which are almost hidden by the hairs), gradually narrowed distally; style slender, a little longer than the corolla tube, densely hairy proximally, more laxly so and more distinctly scaly upwards, finally glabrous; stigma globose, 5-lobed.

Papua New Guinea, Morobe District, range above Markham Point near Lae. Epiphytic shrub at 600–900m. *Fl.* Jan.–Feb.

Never cultivated. Michael Black (1966) commented that 'its small white tubular campanulate flowers were of little decorative value'. Now almost certainly extinct in the type locality, which has totally lost its forest to native gardens.

164. **Rhododendron oliganthum** Sleumer
Reinwardtia 1960. 5: 123.
Type: Carr *s.n.*, 15 Jan. 1936. New Guinea (SE), Central District, ascent to Mt Victoria, crest of the main range NW of 'The Gap', *c.*2895m (BM, SING, L, fragment).
Derivation: Greek – *oligos* – small; *anthos* – flower. The small-flowered rhododendron.

Shrub, *c.*1.2m. Twigs rounded, slender, tips densely reddish-brown-scaly; upper internodes 1.5–3cm. **Leaves** in tight pseudowhorls of 2–3 at the upper node only, sub-sessile. **Blade** 30–50 x 15–30mm, sub-ovate-elliptic; apex shortly acuminate, obtuse; margin recurved; base truncate to rounded or sub-cordate, glabrescent above at maturity, laxly scaly beneath. **Scales** thin, marginal zone irregularly dentate; centre slightly impressed. Mid-vein faintly impressed or nearly flat above, strongly raised beneath proximally, less so distally; lateral veins *c.*8 per side, straight, curved-anastomosing near the margin, prominent on both sides, lax reticulation, raised especially beneath. **Petiole** 1–2 x 1–1.5mm.

Flowers solitary or in twos, terminal. Pedicels 28–30mm, thick, obliquely thickened below the calyx, scaly and very shortly hairy. Calyx *c.*2.5mm in diameter, shortly 5-lobed and wavy. **Corolla** broadly trumpet-shaped, pink; tube 35–37 x *c.*4 x 5–6mm, cylindrical, straight, laxly scaly and very laxly short-hairy outside, sub-densely hairy inside in the proximal part, less so distally, glabrous at the mouth; lobes 10–12mm in diameter, spreading, broadly obovate to nearly circular, scaly outside at the base, otherwise glabrous. **Stamens** slightly exserted from the throat; filaments linear, sub-densely to laxly hairy in the proximal ⅔, glabrous distally; anthers *c.*2.6 x 1mm, oblong, base obtuse. Disc hairy especially at the upper margin. **Ovary** *c.*7 x 2mm, elongate-conical, densely hairy and scaly, with 5 longitudinal furrows, gradually tapering distally; style *c.*35mm, slightly exserted, laxly hairy and very laxly scaly to the middle, glabrous distally; stigma thickly conical-globose.

Papua New Guinea, Central District, Mt Victoria, NW of 'The Gap', in ridge forest, at 2895m. *Fl.* Jan.

Known only from the type collection and never cultivated.

---

165. Rhododendron pleianthum Sleumer
Reinwardtia 1960. 5: 122.
Type: Robins 362, 9 July 1957. New Guinea (C), Western Highlands, Mt Hagen, *c.*3050m (CANB, L, LAE).
Derivation: Greek – *pleio* – more than usual; *anthum* – flower. Alluding to the many-flowered inflorescence.

Shrub or tree to 6m. Twigs 5–7mm in diameter, rounded, tips laxly stellate-scaly; internodes 9–16cm. **Leaves** 5–7 together in tight pseudowhorls. **Blade** 65–140 x 40–90mm, elliptic or obovate-elliptic; apex rounded or obtuse; margin entire, flat; base slightly but distinctly cordate, glabrescent above at maturity, laxly scaly beneath. **Scales** stellate, the thin marginal zone quickly disappearing; centre small, slightly impressed, finally minutely impressed-spotted beneath. Mid-vein broad proximally, gradually narrowed upwards, impressed for the whole length above, thick and obtusely prominent beneath, 2–3mm wide at the base; lateral veins *c.*8 per

side, irregular, spreading, divided and anastomosing before the margin, impressed above, prominent beneath, veins and veinlets forming an impressed lax reticulation above, which is weakly raised or obscure beneath. **Petiole** 2–6 x 2–3mm, flattened, glabrous.

Outer bracts to 20 x 10mm, ovate, inner ones oblong-spathulate, obtuse, outside densely, coarsely hairy, inside more laxly hairy. Bracteoles *c.*20 x 2mm, linear-spathulate, densely short-hairy at the outside middle line. Inflorescence an 8–20-flowered open umbel, flowers horizontal to half-hanging. Pedicels *c.*20 x 1mm, densely scaly and very shortly hairy. Calyx *c.*4mm in diameter, disc-shaped, slightly oblique, sub-glabrous outside, shortly sub-acutely 5-lobed, or occasionally with irregular 2–9 x *c.*1mm long teeth, which are glabrous or very shortly hairy. **Corolla** 80–90 x 40–50mm, white, long-tubular below, expanded upwards, initially laxly scaly outside, the scales fragile and falling quickly, laxly hairy inside the tube, white or cream, suffused with pink distally or dark pink, scented; tube 55–70 x 4–5 x 7–9mm, straight; lobes *c.*20mm, obovate-spathulate. **Stamens** slightly longer than the corolla tube, unequal; filaments linear, in the lower ¾, sub-densely to more laxly hairy, distally glabrous; anthers 4.5–5 x 1–1.2mm, elongate-oblong, base obtuse, a little curved. Disc prominent, glabrous. **Ovary** *c.*8 x 2–2.5mm, elongate-cylindrical, gradually tapering distally, densely yellowish-hairy, laxly scaly although the scales are usually obscured by the hairs; style nearly as long as the corolla tube, for the proximal 10mm, sub-densely to laxly hairy and scaly (the scales clearly visible among the hairs), glabrous distally; stigma conical-globose. **Fruit** 50–80 x 7–8mm, elongate-fusiform, densely hairy and scaly.

Papua New Guinea, Western, Eastern and Southern Highlands; Mts Hagen, Kerigomna, Wilhelm, Otto, Wamtakin, Giluwe and Kubor. Terrestrial on margins of mossy forest-grassland, on ridge shrubberies and river banks, locally common, 2680–3260m. *Fl.* July–Oct.

Cultivated at Kew from material sent from New Guinea in 1968, it flowered in June 1986 and was figured in the *Botanical Magazine* (Halliday 1987). Michael Black (1966) wrote of a day climbing up to Kerigommna Sia through thick moss forest which opened out to islands of trees 'edged with a fine *Rhododendron* [*R. pleianthum*] growing up to 25 feet high [7.5m] and forming 25% of the shrubby vegetation. Its elegant pink and white flowers were scented rather like a daphne lying in trusses almost like loudspeakers. I was overwhelmed by the beauty of the plant'. It has certainly proved to be a wonderful horticultural plant, growing vigorously and flowering well even as a relatively small potted shrub.

166. Rhododendron tuba Sleumer

Reinwardtia 1960. 5: 125.

Type: Cruttwell 775, 23 June 1956. New Guinea (SE), Mt Daymen (Maneao Range), 2750m (K, E, L, LAE).

Derivation: Latin – *tuba* – a trumpet, alluding to the trumpet-shaped corolla.

Shrub to 5m. Twigs somewhat flattened, laxly scaly, often whitish when dry; internodes 3–10cm. **Leaves** 4–5 together in tight pseudowhorls. **Blade** 40–70 x 25–50mm, elliptic to broadly elliptic; apex obtuse, broadly acuminate or acute, rarely rounded; margin entire, flat to weakly and narrowly revolute; base broadly tapering, the extreme base sub-truncate or rounded, to sub-cordate, sub-densely scaly on both sides initially, glabrescent above, more persistently scaly beneath. **Scales** small, marginal zone thin, stellately lobed and quickly disappearing; centre minute and impressed, eventually leaving only fine blackish pits. Mid-vein impressed above, thick, broad and prominent in the proximal part beneath, narrowed upwards; lateral veins 6–8 per side, irregular, divided and anastomosing before the margin, slightly impressed above, a little though distinctly raised beneath, reticulation obscure above, distinct, sub-dense and prominent beneath. **Petiole** 2–4 x 1.5–2mm, weakly grooved, flattened, scaly.

Flower buds to 17 x 10mm, ellipsoid to obovoid, with the outermost tips reflexed, inner ones mucronate, slightly spreading. Outer bracts to 15 x 10mm, ovate; inner ones obovate, ending in a 1–3mm point, membranous, scaly at the tips outside at first, otherwise glabrous, or with some soft hairs outside, shining, scaly on the margins. Bracteoles to 15mm, filiform below, sub-spathulate distally, laxly scaly or glabrous. Inflorescence a 4–7-flowered, open one-sided umbel. Pedicels 12–20 x *c.*1mm, laxly stellately scaly, without hairs. Calyx *c.*4mm in diameter, very obliquely disc-shaped, membranous, sub-glabrous, with 5 irregular short teeth or longer lobes to 4mm. **Corolla** 65–80mm, trumpet-shaped, pink with white lobes; tube 55–65 x 5 x 8mm, weakly curved, laxly scaly outside, laxly hairy in the proximal ¾ inside; lobes 10–15 x 8–12mm, spreading, obovate. **Stamens** unequal, exserted to 10mm; filaments linear, laxly hairy in the proximal ¾, glabrous distally; anthers *c.*2.5 x 0.7mm, sub-obovate-oblong, base contracted to a very short apiculus. Disc slightly prominent, hairy on the upper side, glabrous below. **Ovary** *c.*8 x 2.5mm, cylindrical, gradually tapering distally; densely white hairy, minutely scaly (the small scales covered by the hairs); style slender, as long as the stamens, laxly covered with long white hairs and scales in the lower ½; stigma yellow, globose, shortly 5-lobed.

Papua New Guinea, N side of the summit of Mt Dayman. Terrestrial in margin of moss forest, at 2500–2750m. *Fl.* June–Aug.

Sleumer (1966) commented that '*R. tuba* is in many respects intermediate between *R. carringtoniae* and *R. rhodoleucum*, both also known from the Maneau Range, and possibly a local natural hybrid between them'. This has not been critically tested in the field. *Rhododendron tuba* was introduced into cultivation by R. Weeks and N. Cruttwell (ANRS 150) in 1974 to Australia and has been distributed widely. It grows vigorously, covering itself in the beautiful pink to white, scented bloom usually just once a year in the spring.

Rhododendron tuba.

Lynsey Muir

167. Rhododendron rhodoleucum Sleumer
Blumea 1961. 11: 119.
Type: Cruttwell 1084, 9 July 1959. New Guinea (SE), Milne Bay District, Maneau Range, Mt Aniata, *c.*2750m (L).
Derivation: Greek – *rhodo* – rose (red colour); *leuco* – indicating paleness. Alluding to the pale pink flowers.

Shrub to 4m. Twigs *c.*2mm in diameter, laxly scaly when young, internodes *c.*3–10cm. **Leaves** 4–6 together in tight pseudowhorls. **Blade** 30–70 x 20–60mm, broadly elliptic to broadly obovate-elliptic, sub-sessile; apex shortly and broadly tapering, obtuse, to almost rounded; margin flat; base deeply cordate, glabrescent with age above, laxly scaly beneath. **Scales** flat, small, marginal zone thin, wide, variously lobed; centre small, slightly impressed. Mid-vein narrowly impressed above, base as wide as the petiole, decreasing distally, grooved up to *c.*⅓ the length of the leaf, broadly prominent beneath in the proximal ½ but not strongly raised; lateral veins and reticulation smooth but distinct below, raised and very distinct above. **Petiole** 0–1 x 2–3mm, grooved, scaly.

Bracteoles almost filiform. Pedicels *c.*15mm, thick, sub-densely or laxly stellate-scaly, without hairs. Inflorescence an open 4–7-flowered umbel. Calyx 2.5–3mm in diameter, very obliquely disc-shaped, indistinctly 5-lobed, scaly outside. **Corolla** 93 x 50mm, trumpet-ventricose, usually a little curved, pink at the base of the tube, fading to the white lobes, scented; tube 60–82 x 4–6 x 9–10mm, (up to 13mm in the widest part just above the middle), laxly scaly outside, with dense patent or retrorse hairs proximally inside, becoming more laxly so distally; lobes 15–21 x 15–22mm, perpendicularly spreading, obovate to sub-circular, overlapping ⅓–½. **Stamens** exserted to 12mm, from the mouth, irregularly clustered on the lower side of the flower, dimorphic; filaments white, linear and sub-densely hairy proximally, narrower and more laxly sub-patently hairy distally, glabrous in the upper ¼; anthers 3.5–4 x *c.*1mm, white or cream, narrowly oblong, base obtuse. Disc hairy on the upper margin. **Ovary** 7–8 x *c.*2mm, sub-cylindrical, densely appressed-hairy and scaly, tapering distally; style lying on the lower side of the corolla, slender, densely or more laxly hairy and laxly scaly in the proximal ⅔, then exclusively sparsely scaly for 3–4mm and glabrous distally; stigma thick-rounded, shortly 5-lobed, green becoming exserted to 18mm. **Fruit** fusiform, *c.*35–50 x 5mm.

Papua New Guinea, Milne Bay District: Mt Aniata, Mt Donana. Also on Mt Dayman, (Maneau Range), Mt Suckling and Mt Paga. On the edge of stunted, mossy forest, sometimes on very steep banks, 2290–2750m, locally abundant. *Fl.* May–Oct.

Introduced into cultivation at Edinburgh by Paddy Woods in 1968 and again by Paul Kores in 1974. This species is very distinct with its sub-sessile, obtuse leaves with very distinctly raised reticulation. Its beautiful pink-flushed flowers give a magnificent display, at irregular intervals but often in October or November, in Edinburgh. The plants in cultivation are not so powerfully scented as some of the other species in this section but this is certainly well worth growing from a horticultural point of view. Sleumer (1961) suggested that *R. tuba* might be a natural hybrid between *R. rhodoleucum* and *R. carringtoniae*. This has not satisfactorily been resolved. *Rhododendron tuba* certainly shows strong similarities especially to *R. rhodoleucum*. The tapering leaf base and longer petiole will separate *R. tuba* from this species.

Rhododendron rhodoleucum.

168. Rhododendron loranthiflorum Sleumer
Notizbl. Berl.-Dahl. 1935. 12: 485.
Type: Kajewski 2045, 8 Aug. 1930. Solomon Is., Bougain-ville, Koniguru, Buin, 1000m (BRI, E, L, fragment).
Derivation: With flowers like a *Loranthus* (Loranthaceae).

Synonym: *R. subpacificum* Sleumer, Blumea 1963. 12: 105.

Ssp. **loranthiflorum**

Epiphytic, much-branched shrub. Twigs smooth, older rounded and often whitish, tips sub-angular or flattened and densely brown-scaly; internodes 1.5–12cm. **Leaves** 3–6 together in tight pseudowhorls. **Blade** 25–60 x 15–25mm, obovate; apex broadly obtuse or rounded; margin entire, very slightly revolute; base tapering, scaly on both sides initially, glabrescent above, sub-densely and persistently scaly beneath. **Scales** thin, irregularly and shallowly dentate or lobed at the margin; centre slightly impressed, sub-revolute. Mid-vein narrowly and shallowly impressed above in the proximal ⅔, broadly and shallowly prominent beneath in the proximal ½, distally smooth; lateral veins 3–5 per side, indistinct on both sides, reticulation obscure. **Petiole** 3–8 x 1–2mm, weakly to distinctly grooved above, scaly.

Flower buds to 10 x 6mm, ellipsoid to slightly obovoid, smooth in outline with all except the very basal bracts appressed, brownish-green, with a few scales outside. Bracts triangular at the base passing to broadly rounded, concave, the apex retuse often with a minute point, brown-scaly along the central line towards the apex, the margin entire but fringed with scales in the apical part. Bracteoles to 6mm, filiform, glabrous. Inflorescence with 3–7 flowers in a loose, open umbel, held semi-erect to half-hanging. **Flowers** white, faintly scented. Pedicels 10–22 x c.1.5mm, laxly brown-scaly, without hairs. Calyx 3–4mm in diameter, green, disc-shaped. **Corolla** 35–42 x 25–35mm, tubular-trumpet-shaped, white; tube 25–35 x 5–9 x 6–7mm, cylindrical, straight or very slightly curved, densely scaly outside, laxly papillose hairy in the proximal ½ inside; lobes 10–12 x 9–10mm, broadly elliptic, obovate or rounded, spreading to weakly reflexed, overlapping c.halfway, scaly outside, glabrous inside. **Stamens** at first exserted to 7mm in a group centrally, or slightly deflected to the lower side of the mouth, later the filaments curving and the anthers irregularly spreading back against the corolla lobes, weakly dimorphic; filaments filiform, shortly hairy in the lower ⅔; anthers c.1.5mm, oblong, base obtuse. Disc low, glabrous or densely hairy on the upper margin. **Ovary** c.6 x 1.5mm, sub-cylindrical, slightly 5-ribbed, densely scaly, the scales thick and sub-entire, also very shortly patently or with distally directed hairs, gradually tapering distally; style 35–40mm, scaly and

Rhododendron loranthiflorum ssp. *loranthiflorum*.

hairy in the proximal part, then hairy or scaly and finally glabrous distally; stigma c.2mm in diameter, at the mouth when the flower opens, becoming exserted to 7mm as the flower ages. **Fruit** 40–45 x c.3mm, cylindrical, slender, curved, tapering apically, 5-ribbed, densely brown-scaly and shortly hairy.

Papua New Guinea, New Britain: headwaters of Matabunu Creek. **Solomon Is.**: Bougainville, near Koniguru, Buin, New Georgia Group, Vangunu I. An epiphyte in high rain forest and in stunted forest on a crater rim, 180–1500m, locally common. *Fl.* Dec.

Introduced into cultivation in Australia from Lake Loloru, near Aropa, Bougainville Island, in 1964 by L.A. Craven, and to Edinburgh in 1983 from material from the same source, sent by Dr R. Withers. It is wonderfully floriferous and the plants cover themselves in masses of white flowers, often in late winter. This species appears to be vegetatively almost identical to *R. luraluense* which differs only in having a shorter, funnel-shaped tube and much larger lobes; it would be interesting to have more material from Bougainville Island.

Ssp. **lakekamuensis** W.N.Takeuchi
Edinb. J. Bot. 2000. 57(3): 333.
Type: Takeuchi & Julang 11503, 31 Oct. 1996. Papua New Guinea, Gulf Province, Lakekamu, east branch of the Avi Avi R., 175m (LAE, A, BRIT, E, K, L, NY).
Derivation: Named after Lakekamu, where it was found.

Distinguished from the type subspecies by the style exclusively scaly distally.

Papua New Guinea, Gulf Province, Lakekamu, E branch of the Avi Avi R., 175m. Epiphytic in lowland forest at the extraordinarily low altitude of 175m, this was, when described, a surprising extension of the range of the species to the New Guinea mainland. *Fl.* Oct.

Not in cultivation.

Subsection iv: *Malesia* H.F.Copel.

Phil. J. Sc. 1929. 40(2): 136, 151

Type: *R. bagobonum* H.F.Copel.
Series iii *Buxifolia* Sleumer, Reinwardtia 1960. 5: 145. Type: *R. buxifolium* Low *ex* Hook.*f.*
Subsection *Linearanthera* H.F.Copel., Phil. J. Sc. 1929. 40(2): 136, 152 (based on *R. vidalii* Rolfe).
Subsection *Astrovireya* Sleumer, Bot. Jahr. 1949. 74: 539 (based on *R. commonae* Foerster).
Section *Zygomorphanthe* Schltr., Bot. Jahr. 1918. 55: 145, *pro parte typo excluso*.

Leaves medium sized, the majority of well-developed leaves mostly 1–4cm long. Stomata on the abaxial (lower) leaf surface only.

Key to species from Vietnam, the Malay Peninsula, Sumatra and Java

1	Ovary hairy	2
+	Ovary scaly or glabrous	6
2	Filaments hairy at the base only	3
+	Filaments hairy well above halfway	5
3	Twigs scaly and minutely hairy, leaves up to 12mm wide	**171. pubigermen**
+	Twigs scaly only, leaves more than 15mm wide	4
4	Leaf apex acute to obtuse, pedicels 8–10mm, flowers pale yellow	**169. chevalieri**
+	Leaf apex obtuse to rounded, pedicels 10–18mm, flowers orange	**228. sumatranum**
5	Twigs scaly and hairy, anthers hairy, corolla tube glabrous inside	**170. pauciflorum**
+	Twigs scaly only, anthers without hairs, corolla tube hairy inside	**172. frey-wysslingii**
6	Stamens 5	**177. citrinum**
+	Stamens 10	7
7	Ovary glabrous	**173. multicolor**
+	Ovary scaly	8
8	Filaments glabrous	**174. pyrrhophorum**
+	Filaments hairy at the base	9
9	Leaves narrowly obovate-spathulate	**175. banghamiorum**
+	Leaves broadly elliptic to elliptic obovate	**176. ripleyi**

Key to species from Borneo

1	Leaves both hairy and scaly underneath	**178. meijeri**
+	Leaves scaly only, without simple hairs on the blade	2
2	Flowers hairy outside all over the tube	3
+	Flowers glabrous or scaly outside, sometimes with just a few hairs at the base	4
3	Leaves narrowly elliptic to linear, up to 6mm wide	**179. abietifolium**
+	Leaves obovate, more than 9mm wide	**180. burttii**
4	Flowers yellow, leaves distinctly rugose, especially when dry	**184. nieuwenhuisii**
+	Flowers pink, orange or red	5
5	Ovary predominantly scaly, with only a few sparse hairs, pedicels scaly	**182. buxifolium**
+	Ovary densely hairy, pedicels scaly and hairy	6

6 Leaves up to 15mm, thickly sub-succulent, corolla lobes more than 12mm ——————— **183. tuhanensis**
+ Leaves more than 15mm, leathery, corolla lobes less than 10mm ————————————— 7

7 Pedicels up to 6mm, style glabrous ——————————————————— **194. bagobonum**
+ Pedicels more than 12mm, style hairy at the base ——————————————— **181. sugaui**

Key to species from the Philippines

1 Leaves linear, up to 3mm wide —————————————————————— **185. taxifolium**
+ Leaves of other shapes, more than 5mm wide ——————————————————— 2

2 Corolla lobes up to 4mm, corolla tube contracted towards the mouth ————— **194. bagobonum**
+ Corolla lobes more than 10mm, corolla tube parallel or broadening distally —————————— 3

3 Ovary totally without hairs —————————————————————————— 4
+ Ovary with at least some hairs ———————————————————————— 5

4 Filaments and inside of corolla hairy, flowers orange and yellow ————————— **186. acrophilum**
+ Filaments and inside of corolla glabrous, flowers red ————————————— **187. wilkiei**

5 Corolla lobes more than 40mm ——————————————————— **256. mendumiae**
+ Corolla lobes less than 30mm ———————————————————————— 6

6 Corolla lobes more than 24mm, leaves dark green ————————————— **188. rousei**
+ Corolla lobes less than 18mm, leaves pale green ——————————————— 7

7 Stems with coarse hairs, flowers red ——————————————— **189. whiteheadii**
+ Stems with short, fine hairs, flowers white ——————————————— **190. vidalii**

Key to species from Sulawesi and Maluku

1 Ovary without hairs ————————————————————————————— 2
+ Ovary hairy ————————————————————————————————— 3

2 Petiole more than 4mm, leaf blade more than 30mm ——————————— **268. celebicum**
+ Petiole less than 3mm, leaf blade less than 30mm ——————————— **191. scarlatinum**

3 Filaments glabrous ————————————————————————————— 4
+ Filaments hairy at the base ————————————————————————— 5

4 Leaf base tapering, corolla tube less than 22mm ———————————— **192. leptomorphum**
+ Leaf base broadly tapering to rounded, corolla tube more than 25mm ————— **193. alternans**

5 Leaf base tapering, leaves broadest above the middle, corolla up to 10mm wide ———— **194. bagobonum**
+ Leaf base broadly tapering to rounded, leaves broadest in the middle, corolla more than 20mm wide ———
————————————————————————————————— **195. pseudobuxifolium**

Key to species from New Guinea

1 Ovary with hairs, with or without scales ————————————————————— 2
+ Ovary scaly only, without hairs ——————————————————————— 15

2 Largest petioles more than 5mm ——————————————————————— 3
+ Largest petioles less than 5mm ——————————————————————— 6

3 Flowers red, pedicels hairy and scaly —————————————————————— 4
+ Flowers pale green, pedicels scaly only —————————————————— **198. flavoviride**

4   Umbels 2–3-flowered, style hairy almost to the stigma _____ **197. vinkii**
+   Umbels more than 4-flowered, style hairy and scaly up to the basal ½ _____ 5

5   Leaf apex acute, bracts narrowly acute, filaments hairy at the base only _____ **196. nubicola**
+   Leaf apex obtuse to rounded, bracts obtuse to rounded, filaments hairy in the basal ½ _____ **295. culminicola**

6   Pedicels hairy and scaly _____ 7
+   Pedicels scaly only _____ 12

7   Corolla tube hairy outside _____ 8
+   Corolla tube scaly or glabrous outside _____ 9

8   Style hairy up to halfway, disc hairy on the upper side _____ **199. vitis-idaea**
+   Style hairy above halfway, disc glabrous _____ **201. hatamense**

9   Flowers solitary or paired, corolla glabrous outside and inside _____ **200. stevensianum**
+   Flowers mostly more than 3 in the umbel, corolla tube scaly outside or hairy inside _____ 10

10 Corolla tube scaly outside _____ 11
+   Corolla tube without scales outside, hairy inside _____ **201. hatamense**

11 Leaves entire, lateral veins 3–4 per side, style hairy to *c.*halfway _____ **202. cornu-bovis**
+   Leaves crenulate, lateral veins 4–6 per side, style with hairs at the base only _____ **203. commonae**

12 Pedicels up to 15mm _____ 13
+   Pedicels more than 20mm _____ 14

13 Corolla up to 30mm, glabrous inside _____ **204. rhodostomum**
+   Corolla more than 35mm, hairy inside _____ **205. takeuchii**

14 Filaments glabrous, style hairy for 2mm at base _____ **206. helodes**
+   Filaments hairy at the base, style hairy and scaly to more than 4mm _____ **207. psammogenes**

15 Corolla hairy inside _____ 16
+   Corolla glabrous inside _____ 17

16 Filaments papillose hairy, disc glabrous _____ **284. alticola**
+   Filaments long hairy, disc sparsely hairy on the upper margin _____ **285. sayeri**

17 Longest petioles more than 5mm _____ 18
+   Longest petioles less than 5mm _____ 21

18 Corolla glabrous outside _____ 19
+   Corolla scaly outside _____ 20

19 Corolla greenish-yellow, flushed with orange, more than 40mm _____ **208. brassii**
+   Corolla reddish-purple, less than 30mm _____ **209. porphyranthes**

20 Pedicels scaly and papillose, corolla lobes less than 6mm _____ **210. rubrobracteatum**
+   Pedicels scaly only, corolla lobes more than 10mm _____ **284. alticola**

21 Leaf blade up to 4mm wide _____ 22
+   Leaf blade more than 4mm wide _____ 23

22 Leaves less than 20mm, narrowly ovate-elliptic, style scaly at the base _____ **211. myrsinites**
+   Leaves more than 30mm, linear, style glabrous _____ **279. subulosum**

23 Largest petioles more than 4mm _____ 24
+   Largest petioles 3mm or less _____ 27

169. Rhododendron chevalieri Dop

Rév. de Bot. Appl. et d'Agric. Trop. 1929. 9(92): 256, *t*.10.
Type: Chevalier 38709, 1 Sept. 1928. S. Annan, forêt vierge du Honba (P).
Derivation: Named after the collector, Auguste Chevalier, who made many important collections in what is now Vietnam and Cambodia.

Shrub to 2m. Twigs 2–2.5mm in diameter, smooth, rounded and at first densely brown scaly; internodes 3–5mm. **Leaves** in moderately tight pseudowhorls, 4–5 together, apparently rigidly held semi-erect. **Blade** 40–50 x 13–24mm, elliptic to narrowly obovate, very shortly acuminate to a broadly acute or obtuse apex; margin entire, flat to slightly revolute distally distinctly revolute in the proximal ⅓, especially when dry; base tapering and decurrent, glabrescent above, densely scaly beneath. **Scales** rounded, with a moderately large centre but broad, paler flange, lightly impressed. Mid-vein narrowly impressed above in the proximal ½–⅔, then flat; narrowly raised beneath throughout its length, sometimes terminating in an indistinct terminal gland. **Petiole** 4–10 x *c*.2mm, weakly grooved above, densely brown-scaly, often flushed pink.

Bracts to 20 x 8mm, ovate, acute, with a few brown scales outside distally and along the margins, glabrous inside. Bracteoles 6 x 1mm, narrowly triangular, with a few teeth on the margin, glabrous. Inflorescence 1–4-flowered, the flowers held semi-erect. Pedicels 8–10 x 1–1.5mm, densely scaly, without simple hairs. **Corolla** 20–23 x 35–49mm, bright to pale yellow, without scent; tube 6–12 x 4–5 x 10–12mm, glabrous outside; lobes 15 x 12mm, half-spreading. **Stamens** spreading round the mouth of the flower, exserted to 7mm; filaments glabrous or with a few hairs at the base; anthers *c*.4 x 2mm. Disc glabrous. **Ovary** 5 x 25mm, with patent white hairs and brown scales; style 6 x 1mm, glabrous, bent to the lower side of the tube. **Fruit** 15–18 x 5–6mm, erect, prominently hairy and scaly.

Vietnam, (S) Prov. Khanh Hoa (Nhatrang) massif de Honba; Lam Dong, Lac Duong, Bi Doup peak area. Evergreen forest dominated by *Fokienia* and *Phyllostachys*. 1000–2100m.

Introduced into cultivation in 2001 by Mr Nguyen Duc To Luu; although flowering as a cutting in September, soon after introduction, it is still not sufficiently established to evaluate its potential.

170. Rhododendron pauciflorum King & Gamble
J. As. Soc. Beng. 1905. 74(2): 75.
Type: Wray 231, 1887. Malay Peninsula, Perak, G. Batu Puteh (CAL).
Derivation: Latin – *pauci* – few; *florum* – flowers. 'With few flowers', presumably alluding to the solitary or 2-flowered inflorescences.

Synonyms:
R. elegans Ridl., J. Linn. Soc. Bot. 1908. 38: 314.
R. calocodon Ridl., J. Fed. Mal. St. Mus. 1914. 5: 38.
R. pauciflorum var. *calocodon* (Ridl.) Sleumer, Reinwardtia 1960. 5: 156.

Shrub to 2m, with swollen roots and spreading branches. Twigs 1–2mm in diameter, laxly scaly and patently short hairy; internodes 1.5–3cm. **Leaves** 3–6 together in well-marked pseudowhorls at the upper 2–3 nodes. **Blade** 12–32 x 10–25mm, obovate to obovate-elliptic, broadly elliptic to almost circular; apex rounded, retuse, or broadly tapering, sometimes mucronate; margin entire, flat or a little recurved especially near the base, somewhat cartilaginous; base broadly tapering to the petiole, dark to medium green and a little shining above, paler and dull beneath, initially scaly on both sides, glabrescent above with age, more persistently and sub-densely scaly beneath. **Scales** circular or irregularly lobed, marginal zone relatively broad; centre impressed. Mid-vein impressed above in the proximal ⅔; broad and obtusely prominent proximally beneath, narrower and smooth or even a little impressed distally; lateral veins 3–4 per side, arising at 45° and curving upwards, smooth and mostly inconspicuous. **Petiole** 1–2 x 1–2mm, flat and grooved above, laxly short-hairy and scaly, sometimes hardly distinct from the blade.

Lynsey Muir

Rhododendron pauciflorum.

Flower buds to 9 x 5mm, ellipsoid to somewhat obovoid, pale brown and often flushed with pink or red. Bracts fully appressed, minutely appressed hairy outside and with a few scales near the apex, fringed with scales along the margins, outermost bracts minutely appressed hairy inside also, but the inner bracts glabrous inside. Outermost bracts triangular, passing through ovoid to the innermost which are spathulate with the marginal scales on long stalks. Bracteoles to 10mm, filiform, sparsely scaly. Inflorescence solitary or occasionally paired flowers, which are half-hanging to fully pendent. Pedicels 10–15 x *c*.1mm, pink, densely short-hairy and stellately scaly. Calyx *c*.2.5mm in diameter, obliquely cup-shaped, shortly obtusely 5-lobed, scaly and with a few simple white hairs. **Corolla** 20–22 x 15–19mm, broadly tubular or tubular campanulate, deep pink or red; tube 16–18 x 11–12 x 6–7mm, straight, pouched at the base and with some faint longitudinal lines, sparsely scaly and hairy outside, glabrous inside; lobes 4–5 x 8–9mm, broadly obovate, overlapping to ⅔, reflexed and becoming revolute. **Stamens** at first tightly clustered in the centre of the mouth, later spreading regularly around the perimeter; filaments pale pink, dimorphic alternately long and short, white-hairy throughout; anthers *c*.2 x 1mm, brown, hairy at the back. Disc low, glabrous. **Ovary** 3–4 x 2–2.5mm, ovoid-conical, silvery scaly and densely covered in semi-erect white hairs; style straight, 3–8mm, pale green or pink, glabrous or with a few hairs at the base; stigma green. **Fruit** 10–18 x *c*.4mm, sub-cylindrical, pink or green, hairy and scaly, shedding an outer layer and the valves then splitting and curving back, sometimes twisting, the placentae tending to break away distally in an irregular manner. Seeds 3.5mm, without tails *c*.1mm, the longest tail to 2mm.

Malaysia (Peninsula), Main Range from Mt Kerbau to Mt Batu Puteh and also on Mt Tahan. Epiphytic or terrestrial in mossy forest and on peaty soil, 1370–2135m, often common. *Fl.* Feb.–Nov.

This species has been in cultivation at least since 1968, when it was collected by Michael Black, Paddy Woods and Mohamid bin Sidek on Gunong Brinchang in the Cameron Highlands (Black 397). It has been repeatedly collected since. A specimen cultivated by Richard Cavender in Oregon, USA, trailed well over 1m from a hanging basket and was said to have never been without flowers over a seven-year period which rather contrasts with Sleumer's remark (1966) 'apparently rather common but rarely in flower'. In cultivation in Edinburgh it also flowers throughout the year and, although hardly covering itself in flowers, it is a small and very pretty species.

I am grateful to Dr Lakshminarasimhan Pakshirajan of the Calcutta Herbarium for examining the type and confirming that it does have hairs on the outside of the corolla tube. Because these are more or less transparent they are often difficult to see but all collections examined so far have them and thus the variety '*calocodon*' does not have any significance and has been reduced to synonymy.

Rhododendron pubigermen.

171. Rhododendron pubigermen J.J.Sm.

In Merr., Contr. Arn. Arb. 1934. 8: 122.

Type: Docters van Leeuwen 7747, 4 Feb. 1924. Indonesia, Sumatra, East Coast, Upper Petani Valley, Lan Debuk-dubuk marsh (BO, L).

Derivation: Latin – *pubens* – downy or hairy; *gemma* – a seed. Alluding to the tails on the seeds.

Shrub to 1.2m; branches slender, spreading. Twigs 1–2mm in diameter, rounded, densely sub-stellately scaly and sparsely patently hairy; internodes 1–6cm. **Leaves** 3–12 together in pseudowhorls at the upper 2–3 nodes. **Blade** 20–40 x 6–12mm, spathulate to broadly elliptic, usually broadest in the upper ½; apex obtuse to rounded sometimes minutely emarginate; margin slightly revolute when living, more so when dry; base gradually tapering, scaly on both sides initially, glabrous above at maturity, sub-densely and more persistently scaly beneath. **Scales** flat, pale-brown, with the marginal zone relatively narrow, irregularly and shallowly lobed; centres small, and impressed. Mid-vein impressed above, strongly prominent in the proximal ½ beneath; lateral veins not visible. **Petiole** 1–2.5 x 1–2mm, weakly grooved above, flattened, densely scaly, not clearly distinct from the leaf base.

Flower buds ovoid, to 8 x 6mm, the bracts completely appressed, shiny green when young, becoming purplish-red. Bracts to 7 x 5mm, sub-circular-ovate; outer ones obtuse, rough outside; inner ones sub-acuminate, glabrous and shiny outside; margins fringed with scales. Bracteoles *c.*8mm, linear-sub-spathulate, glabrous. Inflorescence of 1–4 flowers, horizontal to half-hanging. Pedicels 10–15 x *c.*1mm, densely scaly and minutely hairy. Calyx *c.*3mm in diameter, oblique, shortly cup-shaped, shortly 5-lobed. **Corolla** 13–16 x 16–27mm, open-campanulate, lobed to halfway or slightly more, fleshy, deep red, and sometimes with a musky scent; tube 7–10 x 5–8 x 10–12mm, laxly or sub-densely sub-stellately scaly outside, glabrous inside, straight; lobes 8–10 x 6–8mm, broadly obovate-sub-spathulate, half-spreading, not overlapping in the fully open state, scaly except near the margins. **Stamens** equally distributed regularly all round the mouth of the flower, sometimes with a small gap on the lower side, slightly alternately unequal, exserted to *c.*5mm; filaments linear, patently hairy proximally for 1–2mm, glabrous distally; anthers broadly oblong, 2mm. Disc prominent, glabrous. **Ovary** *c.*3.5 x 2.5mm, ovoid, densely covered with long, spreading, white, hairs which cover the scales, abruptly contracted distally; style 5–8mm, glabrous; stigma sub-globose, green. **Fruit** 15–20 x 6mm, narrowly elliptic, persistently sub-densely long-hairy, laxly scaly, the valves twisting after opening. Seeds 3.5–4.5mm, without tails 0.7–0.8mm, the longest tail *c.*2mm, irregularly crimped.

Indonesia, Sumatra, East and West Coast. Mostly epiphytic in rain forest, mossy forest or secondary forest, sometimes epiphytic in swampy habitats. 1200–2560m. *Fl.* Jan.–Dec., *fr.* June.

Introduced into cultivation in Edinburgh in 1988. This species is of small, compact stature and a neat ornamental. It flowers very freely, with its dark musk-smelling flowers produced in profusion several times a year.

172. Rhododendron frey-wysslingii J.J.Sm.

In Merr., Contr. Arn. Arb. 1934. 8: 123.

Type: Frey-Wyssling 25, 16 June 1930. Indonesia, Sumatra, Atjeh, Boer-ni-Telong (AA, L).

Derivation: Named after the Swiss botanist Albert Friedrich Frey-Wyssling, who collected this species.

Small, much-branched shrub, to 75cm. Twigs rounded, sparsely to sub-densely covered with sub-stellate low scales, older glabrescent parts at first a little rough with scale bases later becoming smooth; internodes 0.3–3.5cm. **Leaves** 5–8 together in dense pseudowhorls, obovate-elliptic or spathulate. **Blade** 18–35 x 4–8mm;

apex obtuse or rounded; margin slightly revolute; base tapering; glabrescent above, persistently scaly or slowly glabrescent beneath also. **Scales** small, flat, with a narrow marginal zone, sub-entire or irregularly shallowly lobed; centre relatively large and somewhat impressed. Mid-vein impressed above, obtusely raised beneath in the proximal ½, disappearing distally; lateral veins not visible. **Petiole** 1–2mm, scaly, flat.

Bracts to 6 x 2mm, narrowly ovate-acuminate, long subulate, membranous, sparsely scaly and papillose at the apex, glabrous proximally, the margins fringed with scales. **Flowers** solitary, half-hanging to hanging. Pedicels 10–13mm, thick, densely covered with stellate scales and with a few short hairs. Calyx *c*.3mm in diameter, small, disc-shaped, thin, shortly 5-lobed, scaly and often shortly hairy outside. **Corolla** 14–16 x 7–9mm, broadly tubular-campanulate, thin, red; tube 10–12 x 4–5 x 5–7mm, broadly cylindrical, densely covered with sub-entire, thick scales outside, laxly long-hairy in the proximal ½ inside; lobes *c*.3.5 x 3.5mm, ovate, obtusely pointed, scaly outside, erect to partly spreading. **Stamens** exserted to *c*.2mm, sub-equal; filaments linear, dilated at the base, densely patently hairy nearly to the top; anthers *c*.1.4mm, sub-quadrangular, truncate. Disc glabrous. **Ovary** *c*.4 x 2mm, ovoid-conical, densely scaly and long white-hairy, the hairs covering the scales, abruptly contracted distally; style 7–8mm, covered in the proximal ⅖ with white hairs; stigma globose. **Fruit** 13–15 x 4–5mm, sub-cylindrical, laxly hairy and scaly. Seeds 4mm, including the long tails.

Indonesia, N Sumatra, Gajo Lands: Bur ni Tèlong and Redelong Volcano, terrestrial on slopes, 1800–2000m. *Fl.* Jan., June, Sept.

Resembling *R. pubigermen* in the foliage but differing in the much more parallel-sided corolla tube with shorter corolla lobes which are held much more erect. Not known in cultivation.

173. Rhododendron multicolor Miq.

Fl. Ind. Bat. 1860. Suppl. 1: 251, 586.
Type: Teysmann 778. Sumatra, West Coast, Mt Singalang (U, lectotype, BO).
Derivation: Latin – *multi* – many; *color* – coloured. Alluding to the variation in the colour of the flowers.

Synonyms:
R. salicifolium (*non* Becc.) Blume, Fl. Jav. Pl. inéd. 1863–83. t.7 C, f.2.
R. multicolor var. *curtisii* Hort., Garden 1884. 26: 433.
R. curtisii T.Moore, Florist & Pomologist 1884. 113: t.615.

Azalea multicolor (Miq.) Kuntze, Rev. Gen. Pl. 1891. 2: 387.
R. javanicum (*non* (Blume) Benn.) Steen., Arch. Hydrobiol. 1932. Suppl. 11: 318.

Shrub to 1.5m. Twigs *c*.2mm in diameter, rounded, green or red, laxly to sub-densely scaly, older parts glabrescent; internodes 1.5–7cm. **Leaves** 3–6 together in tight or loose pseudowhorls. **Blade** 30–70 x 7–20mm, narrowly elliptic, often slightly broader in the distal ½; apex acute or shortly acuminate; margin entire and flat; base narrowly tapering, sometimes shortly obtuse, sub-densely scaly at first on both sides, glabrescent above, scaly for a longer time beneath. **Scales** small, irregularly lobed and with minute, dark centres, shallowly impressed. Mid-vein prominent proximally above, smooth proximally for a few millimetres and then narrowly impressed distally; lateral veins 6–8 per side, straight and ascending, indistinctly anastomosing before the margin, very slightly raised on both sides, often indistinct. **Petiole** 2–6 x 1–2mm, not grooved, flattened with a few scales.

Flower buds to 28 x 8mm, pale green, narrowly ovoid, acutely pointed, the bracts mostly appressed, the outermost sometimes slightly spreading, glabrous or with a few marginal scales. Bracts to 22 x 7–9mm, ovate to narrowly ovate, membranous, acute, glabrous and shining. Bracteoles to 15 x 1mm, linear, glabrous. Inflorescence an open umbel with 3–6 semi-erect to half-hanging flowers. Pedicels 15–25 x *c*.1.25mm, sparsely scaly or glabrous. Calyx *c*.4mm in diameter, oblique, rim-like, obtusely angled or very shortly lobed up to 1mm. **Corolla** 20–25 x 25–32mm, broadly funnel-shaped, sometimes sweetly scented, whitish cream to yellow, pink or red, lobed to halfway; tube 10–12 x 5–6 x 10–12mm, straight, glabrous outside, shortly hairy inside; lobes 13–15 x 11–13mm, spreading, overlapping up to halfway, sub-circular. **Stamens** irregularly spreading all round the mouth or loosely clustered on the lower side, exserted to 10mm; filaments linear, densely covered with long, spreading, white hairs in the proximal ¼–⅓, glabrous distally; anthers 1.5–2 x 1mm, broadly oblong to obovate. Disc prominent, glabrous. **Ovary** *c*.4 x 2mm, obovoid-cylindrical, glabrous, abruptly contracted distally; style glabrous, 7–10mm on the lower side of the tube but curving upwards; stigma *c*.1.5mm, obconical. **Fruit** 18–22 x *c*.5mm, sub-cylindrical.

Indonesia, Sumatra, widespread. Mostly terrestrial in open places, hillsides or pastures, also near volcanoes, sometimes epiphytic in mountain forest, 900–2100m, locally common. *Fl.* Jan.–Dec.

First cultivated by Veitch's 'Royal Exotic Nursery' from a collection made by Curtis in Sumatra and flowering for the first time in cultivation on 2 November 1883 when it was taken to Kew to be illustrated and described for *Curtis's Botanical Magazine* (Hooker 1884). This plant, with handsome red flowers, was used as the parent in many of the Veitch hybrids but the yellow form was introduced at the same time. This species has been grown at the Royal Botanic Garden Edinburgh since 1967 from material sent from Kew without collector or provenance. It is a pale yellow form with delicately orange-flushed margins to the lobes. A similar collection was made by R. Clough from near Lake Toba in 1973. The red form has not been in cultivation recently. When grown well this species can look very attractive and very similar to *R. salicifolium*, differing from this species in its glabrous ovary and the mid-vein on the leaves being raised on the upper side. The flower shape in *R. multicolor* is very reminiscent of *R. ripleyi* but the leaves are of a totally different shape and the ovary in *R. ripleyi* is densely scaly not glabrous.

174. Rhododendron pyrrhophorum Sleumer

Reinwardtia 1960. 5: 165.
Type: Steenis 9192, 23 Feb. 1937. Sumatra, Atjeh, from summit G. Lembuh to camp 'Halfweg', 1850m (BO, L).
Derivation: Greek – *pyrros* – flame coloured; *phorein* – to have. Alluding to the colour of the flowers which were described on the label as 'fire red'.

Slender shrub. Twigs *c*.1mm in diameter, rounded, laxly to sub-densely covered with flat appressed scales, without hairs, older parts glabrescent and smooth; internodes 2–6cm. **Leaves** 5–7 together in pseudowhorls. **Blade** 25–45 x 5–12mm, narrowly elliptic; apex rounded or obtuse; margin narrowly but distinctly revolute; base tapering and slightly decurrent, when young, sub-densely scaly on both sides; at maturity glabrescent and blackish punctate; minutely rugose above; sub-densely persistently scaly beneath. **Scales** irregularly crenate, lobed in the marginal brown zone; centre darker and slightly impressed. Mid-vein markedly impressed above, thick and very prominent beneath; lateral veins inconspicuous. **Petiole** 2–4 x *c*.1mm, flattened, densely scaly.

Bracts to 8 x 4mm, ovate-elliptic, membranous, glabrous outside, shiny, margin with fragile scales. Bracteoles *c*.6mm, linear-filiform, glabrous. **Flowers** solitary or in twos. Pedicels 10–15mm, slender, densely stellate-scaly, without hairs. Calyx *c*.2.5mm in diameter, disc-shaped, oblique, obscurely sub-acutely 5-lobed, densely scaly outside. **Corolla** 15–18mm, campanulate, thin, red, 5-lobed halfway; tube 6–9 x *c*.4 x 15–20mm, sub-densely to laxly

scaly outside, glabrous inside; lobes 6–8 x 6–8mm, broadly obovate-spathulate, slightly spreading. **Stamens** exserted to *c*.5mm, unequal; filaments linear, slightly dilated at the base, becoming filiform distally, glabrous; anthers *c*.1.8 x 1mm, ellipsoid. Disc prominent, glabrous. **Ovary** *c*.3 x 1.5mm, ovoid-conical, densely stellate-scaly, abruptly contracted distally; style *c*.8mm, slender, glabrous; stigma obconical, deeply 5-lobed.

Indonesia, N Sumatra, Gajo Lands, Mt Goh Lembuh. On a ridge in forest at 1850m. *Fl.* Feb.

Known only from the type collection. Never cultivated.

175. Rhododendron banghamiorum (J.J.Sm.) Sleumer

Reinwardtia 1960. 5: 163.
Type: Bangham 917, Dec. 1931–Feb. 1932. Sumatra, Atjeh, Redelong Volcano, *c*.1830m (A, K, SING).
Derivation: Named after the collector, W.N. Bangham, an American who collected in Sumatra with his wife for the Arnold Arboretum.

Synonym: *R. pubigermen* J.J.Sm. var. *banghamiorum* J.J.Sm. in Merr., Contr. Arn. Arb. 1934. 8: 123.

Shrub to 1.2m, slenderly branched. Twigs *c*.2mm in diameter, rounded, laxly scaly; internodes 2–5cm. **Leaves** 5–7 together in tight pseudowhorls. **Blade** 20–35 x 5–10mm, narrowly obovate; apex rounded, shortly retuse; margin slightly revolute, entire or sub-crenulate; base tapering, decurrent; initially sub-densely scaly on both sides, glabrescent above, persistently scaly beneath. **Scales** small, marginal zone irregularly stellately divided, quickly disintegrating; centre small, red brown, impressed. Mid-vein impressed above, obtusely prominent in the proximal ½ beneath, becoming flat distally; lateral veins and reticulation obscure. **Petiole** 1–2 x *c*.1mm, flattened.

Bracts to 6 x 4mm, ovate-sub-acuminate, glabrous and shining outside. Bracteoles *c*.8mm, filiform below, sub-spathulate distally, glabrous. Inflorescence 2–3-flowered, sometimes reduced to a solitary flower. Pedicels 12–15mm, slender, densely stellate-scaly, without hairs. Calyx *c*.3mm in diameter, shortly cup-shaped, mostly very oblique, densely scaly, with obtuse lobes to *c*.1mm. **Corolla** *c*.20mm, open campanulate, membranous, red, lobed to halfway; tube *c*.10 x 3–4 x *c*.10mm, laxly scaly outside, glabrous inside; lobes *c*.10 x 6–7mm, obovate-sub-spathulate. **Stamens** *c*.12mm, exserted to *c*.6mm, slightly unequal; filaments linear, sub-densely patently hairy proximally; anthers *c*.2 x 1.2mm, broadly oblong.

Disc glabrous. **Ovary** *c*.4 x 2mm, ovoid-conical, abruptly contracted distally, densely scaly; style 6–8mm, slender, glabrous; stigma rounded.

Indonesia, N Sumatra, Gajo Lands, Redelong Volcano, *c*.1830m.

Previously known only from the type collection, it was recently re-found and introduced into cultivation by Paul Smith from Mt Banda Hara in 2001. It is superficially similar to *R. pubigermen* but has much longer, more slender leaves as well as lacking hairs on the ovary. It has not been cultivated for long enough to know how it will perform as it only flowered for the first time in Edinburgh in 2005.

176. Rhododendron ripleyi Merr.

Notes Natl. Acad. Nat. Sci. Philad. 1940. 47: 4.
Type: Ripley & Ulmer 40, 17 April 1939. Sumatra, Atjeh, Mt Losir, 2500m (PH, A).
Derivation: Named after the first collector, S.D. Ripley, an American ornithologist who spent some time in SE Asia.

Key to the varieties

1 Style with a ring of short patent hairs at the very base —————————————— var. **basitrichum**
+ Style quite glabrous ———————————————— 2

2 Disc hairy at the upper margin, scales light coloured ————————————————————— var. **ripleyi**
+ Disc quite glabrous, scales dark chestnut brown ———— ———————————————— var. **cryptogonium**

Var. ripleyi

Shrub to 2.5m. Twigs 1–2mm in diameter, at first sub-densely covered with flat scales, later glabrescent; internodes 2–5cm. **Leaves** 4–8 together in loose pseudo-whorls, mostly with 1–2 leaves a little lower than the others. **Blade** 20–35 x 7–18mm, broadly elliptic to elliptic-obovate; apex obtuse, or apiculate with a protruding gland; margin finely crenulate with impressed scales and distinctly recurved; base broadly to narrowly tapering; densely scaly initially on both sides, glabrescent above with age, persistently (especially distally) scaly beneath. **Scales** small, of a light colour, the thin narrow marginal zone irregularly crenate or lobed; centre darker, strongly impressed, leaving a black pit in old leaves. Midvein slightly impressed above, somewhat prominent or smooth beneath; lateral veins 4–5 per side, spreading, impressed above, inconspicuous beneath, or inconspicuous on both sides. **Petiole** 2–5 x 1–2mm, flat, scaly.

Bracts to 10 x 5mm, ovate-elliptic, shortly acuminate, membranous, glabrous outside, shortly fringed with scales, often persistent at the base of the pedicels. Bracteoles to 10mm, linear, glabrous. Inflorescence 1–2-flowered, (rarely up to 4). Pedicels 10–20mm, densely appressed, sub-stellately scaly, without hairs. Calyx *c*.3.5mm in diameter, shortly cup-shaped, margin obtusely shallowly 5-lobed, scaly outside. **Corolla** 25–30mm, funnel-shaped-campanulate, red; tube *c*.15 x 4 x 10mm, laxly sub-stellately scaly outside, glabrous inside; lobes 8–13 x 6–10mm, spreading, spathulate-obovate to sub-circular. **Stamens** exserted to *c*.5mm, unequal; filaments linear, densely covered with long, white, sub-patent hairs for *c*.2mm proximally, glabrous distally; anthers *c*.2 x 1mm, broadly oblong, the base of each cell somewhat lobed. Disc prominent, shortly hairy on the upper margin only. **Ovary** *c*.3.5 x 2mm, ovoid-conical, abruptly contracted distally, densely stellate-scaly, without hairs; style 8–17mm, slender, quite glabrous; stigma globose, deeply 5-lobed.

Indonesia, N Sumatra, Gajo Lands, (Mt Losir). In mossy forest, 2500m. *Fl.* April.

Not recently recollected and never cultivated.

Var. basitrichum Sleumer

Reinwardtia 1960. 5: 164.
Type: Steenis 9570, 6 March 1937. Sumatra, Atjeh, G. Kemiri, E slope, 2800m (BO, L, fragment).
Derivation: Greek – *basi* – base; *trichum* – hair. Alluding to the hairs at the base of the style.

Leaves elliptic-obovate, 23–35 x 7–12mm, with a distinct apical gland. Corolla red.

Differing from the type as the style has a ring of short patent hairs at its very base.

Indonesia, N Sumatra, Gajo Lands, (Mt Kemiri). In ridge shrubbery at 2800m. *Fl.* March.

Sleumer in the original publication noted that this was possibly a hybrid of *R. ripleyi* with *R. pubigermen*. The matter has not been resolved.

Var. cryptogonium Sleumer

Reinwardtia 1960. 5: 164.
Type: Steenis 9167, 23 Feb. 1937. Sumatra, Atjeh, Gajo and Alas Lands, summit Mt Lembuh to camp 'Halfweg', 1850–3000m (BO, L).
Derivation: Greek – *crypto* – hidden; *gon* – generative organ. Somewhat obscure, the male and female organs are hidden within the flower.

Leaves as in var. *ripleyi* but up to 60 x 23mm. Flowers red. Differs in its glabrous disc, sparsely to very sparsely hairy filaments and darker scales.

Indonesia, N Sumatra, Gajo Lands, 1850–3000m, in ridge shrubbery, locally common. *Fl.* Jan., Feb.

Sleumer in his original description says: 'The dark chestnut scales suggest a hybrid of *R. ripleyi* with *R. malayanum*; they are very dense in the youngest, not yet fully developed leaves, touching each other as in *R. malayanum*'. A recent collection from Mt Kaba matches the description of this variety and was growing with *R. malayanum* but it is still not certain that this is a hybrid.

177. **Rhododendron citrinum** (Hassk.) Hassk.

Cat. Hort. Bog. 1844. 161.
Type: Hasskarl *s.n.* Indonesia, Java, Mt Gedeh Tjibureum, not preserved. Lectotype: Docters van Leeuwen 8245, the same locality (BO).
Derivation: Latin – *citrinus* – lemon yellow, alluding to the colour of the flowers.

Synonyms:
Azalea citrina Hassk., Flora 1842. 25(2): 30.
R. zippelii Blume, Fl. Jav. Pl. inéd. 1863–83. *t.*4.
R. jasminiflorum (*non* Hook.) Koord., Junghuhn Gedenkb. 1910. 184.

Var. **citrinum**

Small, spreading shrub, to 2m. Twigs 1–2mm in diameter, rounded, densely covered with flat pale-brown scales at first, glabrescent with age; internodes 1–5cm.

Leaves 4–5 together in pseudowhorls, very unequal. **Blade** 20–60 x 10–30mm, elliptic, broadly-elliptic, rarely obovate-elliptic; apex broadly acute, obtuse to rounded, sometimes with a very small terminal gland; margin narrowly revolute in dry specimens, flat when fresh; base tapering; densely to sparsely scaly, quickly glabrescent above, more persistently scaly beneath. **Scales** flat, small, variously obtusely angled or more deeply indented in the marginal area which often decays leaving the small, dark, slightly impressed centres. Mid-vein slightly impressed above, prominent beneath, often conspicuously purplish-red for most of its length; lateral veins 5–8 per side, widely spreading, anastomosing, faintly raised beneath, often inconspicuous. **Petiole** 5–12 x *c.*1mm, scaly, slender, distinctly grooved above when fresh.

Flower buds ovoid, to 10 x 5mm, smooth, green with a strong reddish-purple flush, often with a few spreading to recurved bracts around the base. Outer bracts triangular to ovate-acuminate, with pale brown scales at the tips outside and also minutely and densely, shortly hairy; inner ones ovate to spathulate, minutely and densely shortly hairy outside, fringed along the margin with scales, these inner ones with a highly irregular margin. Bracteoles to 8mm, filiform, almost glabrous. Inflorescence 1–4-flowered, the flowers half-hanging to hanging vertically downwards, without scent or sometimes reported as a little fragrant. Pedicels 15–20mm, red, slender, shortly hairy and sparsely scaly below, more densely so distally. Calyx 3–4mm in diameter, oblique, disc-shaped, or shortly and obtusely 5-lobed sometimes with one lobe a little longer than the others, scaly outside. **Corolla** 15–19 x 10–14mm, campanulate, pale-yellow to yellowish-white, lobed nearly

Rhododendron citrinum var. *citrinum* with petaloid calyx.

halfway; tube 10–12 x 4–5 x 8–9mm, laxly scaly to almost glabrous outside in the Javanese, but more densely scaly in the Balinese specimens; glabrous inside; lobes *c*.9 x 10mm, semi-erect, obovate-spathulate, apex rounded or very slightly retuse, overlapping to ¾. **Stamens** 5, loosely clustered on the lower side of the flower, the anthers exserted to *c*.5mm; filaments 12–15mm, linear, glabrous, pale yellow, red or orange; anthers 2.2–2.6 x *c*.1mm, oblong, deeply emarginate at both ends, yellow or orange. Disc prominent, glabrous. **Ovary** 3–4 x *c*.1.5mm, green, obliquely oblong-ellipsoid, somewhat 5-angled, papillose-scaly mostly at the base, occasionally all over, abruptly contracted distally; style 6–8mm, red or orange, glabrous, slightly expanded upwards; stigma rounded-sub-globose, on the lower side of the mouth. **Fruit** 15–27 x *c*.4mm, obliquely cylindrical, shortly tapering at both ends, slightly curved, red, deeply 5-grooved, glabrous, on opening the valves reflexing and often twisting, the placentae breaking away from the base and weakly spreading. Seeds 5.5–6mm, without tails *c*.1.2mm, the longest tail to 2.6mm, the tails crimped, sometimes strongly so.

Indonesia, W Java, Mt Salak, Mt Gedeh, Mt Galunggung, Mt Patuha, Mt Gegerbintang, Mt Masigit, Mt Pangrango and Mt Malabar. Also reported for C Java and possibly growing on Mt Diëng but no specimens have been preserved. Bali, Mt Abang. In very humid primary forest, sub-alpine forest or forest margins, 1000–2900m. *Fl.* Sept.–March.

Collected in Java by Mr Henshall for Rollisons Nursery and flowering in May 1854 from which material it was figured in *Curtis's Botanical Magazine* (*t*.4797). Reintroduced into cultivation to Edinburgh from Mt Gedeh, Java in 1984, probably also before that but not known to have survived from previous introductions. It is a delicate species with its charming pale yellow bell-shaped flowers which appear several times a year. It also sometimes produces petaloid calyces, giving the flowers a semi-double appearance.

Var. **discoloratum** Sleumer
Reinwardtia 1960. 5: 145.
Type: Meijer 4871. Sumatra, Mt Sago near Pajakumbuh, summit region, 1800–2000m (L, BM, SING).
Derivation: Latin – *discolor* – of another colour, alluding to the usually red or orange flowers of this variety.

Synonyms:
R. magniflorum Forbes, Wand. 1885. 208 *nom. nud.*
R. citrinum (*non* Hassk. *s.str.*) Miq., Fl. Ind. Bat. 1860. Suppl. 1: 251, 586.
R. multicolor (*non* Miq.) Moore, J. Bot. 1925. 63: 57.

Corolla mostly orange, bright red, rarely pale yellow. Ovary completely or almost entirely covered in scales.

Indonesia, Sumatra, Atjeh, West Coast, Palembang and Lampong. In mossy forest, on ridges, 1220–2500m.

The fact that pale yellow flowers are recorded from Sumatra makes this variety of doubtful significance as some Javan specimens have the ovaries entirely covered with scales.

178. **Rhododendron meijeri** Argent, A.Lamb & Phillipps
Notes RBG Edinb. 1984. 42(1): 116.
Type: Meijer SAN 34640, July 1961. Malaysia, Sabah, G. Tambuyukon, 2450m (SAN).
Derivation: Named after Dr Willem Meijer, Dutch botanist and outspoken conservationist, who found this species on the first known ascent of Mt Tambuyukon.

Shrub to 1m. Twigs green, rounded, rough with hairs and scales; internodes 1–3cm. **Leaves** in dense pseudowhorls of 8–12. **Blade** 12–27 x 12–18mm, broadly elliptic, oblong or obovate; apex broadly pointed, or rounded occasionally slightly retuse; margin entire, slightly recurved, often red; base rounded to tapering; covered with simple white hairs and sub-densely scaly. **Scales** irregularly lobed with a broad marginal flange and small impressed centre. Mid-vein slightly impressed above and broadly but shallowly raised beneath for most of its length; lateral veins obscure or 3–5 per side, slightly raised below and spreading at *c*.45°. **Petiole** 1.5–3 x 2.2–2.6mm, green, hairy and scaly, broadly but shallowly grooved on the upper side.

Flower buds (see p.327) 18 x 10mm, ovoid, purplish red, surrounded by a collar of green, narrowly triangular, to subulate cataphylls; outer bracts narrowly ovate with subulate protruding tips; inner bracts broadly ovate with mucronate appressed apices, densely silvery white hairy distally on the outer sides, less densely so on the inner side. Inflorescence of 7–8 white or pale purplish-pink semi-erect to horizontal flowers in an open umbel, without scent. Pedicels *c*.10 x 1.25mm, densely white-hairy and with some brown scales. Calyx a low, densely white-hairy ring. **Corolla** occurring in two size classes: large, *c*.26 x 45mm with the tube *c*.17 x 15 x 7mm and lobes 22 x 24mm; and small, *c*.25 x 31mm x 29mm, tube 12 x 5 x 10mm and lobes *c*.16 x 15mm, with scattered brown scales outside and some simple hairs inside on the tube; lobes semi-erect to spreading, overlapping from ⅔ to most of their length and with some brown scales outside. **Stamens** clustered below the mouth of the flower;

Debbie White

Rhododendron meijeri.

filaments 9mm, broadening and hairy in the proximal ⅓; anthers 3 x 1mm, brown, incurved to completely obscure the stigma when young, later straightening. **Ovary** 3 x 3mm, densely white hairy with semi-erect hairs; style 3mm, rough, hairy at the base otherwise glabrous; stigma 1.5–2.5mm in diameter. **Fruit** 16 x 8mm, the valves stiffly spreading, only slightly curving. Seeds 2mm, without tails 1.1mm, the longest tail 0.5mm.

Malaysia (Borneo), Sabah. It is only known growing terrestrially around the summit of Mt Tambuyukon at 2400–2500m in open shrubby vegetation amongst ultramafic rocks where it was flowering in July.

A very distinct species with its small, elliptic to obovate, very hairy leaves and short, pale pink to white flowers. Professor Sleumer knew of this species from a colour slide taken by Willem Meijer but he got only sterile specimens at Leiden and would not describe it from these fragments. Introduced into cultivation by Paul Smith in 1995, it grows slowly but has most attractive delicately purplish-pink flowers, usually just once a year but the timing is highly irregular: it has flowered in December, March and April. It occasionally hybridises in the wild with *R. baconii*; the hybrid has been cultivated and produces exquisite delicately pink flowers on attractive dark green foliage.

179. Rhododendron abietifolium Sleumer
Blumea 1961. 11: 122.
Type: Collenette 602, 12 Dec. 1960. North Borneo, Mt Kinabalu, new route (E ridge), *c.*3200m (L, K).
Derivation: Latin – *Abies* – genus of coniferous trees; *folium* – leaf. The distinctive narrow leaves superficially looking like those of an *Abies*.

Shrub or small tree to 3m. Twigs rounded, green, finely covered in small brown scales, quickly glabrescent; internodes 1–4cm. **Leaves** in loose pseudowhorls 10–20 together. **Blade** 18–32 x 4–6mm, narrowly elliptic to linear, often slightly broader in the distal ½; apex broadly pointed; margin entire, strongly recurved, often completely rolled when dry; base tapering; sparsely scaly and quickly glabrescent above, sparsely but more persistently scaly below. **Scales** sub-circular or shallowly lobed, often with large centres. Mid-vein deeply impressed above, thickly prominent between the revolute parts of the lamina beneath; lateral veins obscure. **Petiole** 3–8 x 1–1.5mm, grooved above, laxly scaly.

Flower buds to 10 x 7mm, ovoid-conical, with the erect subulate points of the bracts standing out, dark-red. Outer bracts keeled, apiculate, inner ones ovate with subulate acumen, the margins densely scaly, minutely

199

Rhododendron abietifolium.

hairy or glabrous outside. Bracteoles *c.*10 x 0.5mm, linear, glabrous, irregularly incised distally. Inflorescence of 2–4-flowered open umbels. **Flowers** half-hanging to hanging, pink with a violet tinge, without scent. Pedicels 16–20 x *c.*1mm, densely patently long-hairy, laxly scaly with fragile scales. Calyx *c.*3mm in diameter, disc-like, weakly angled, sometimes becoming reflexed, patently hairy outside and with a few scales. **Corolla** 20–25 x 30–34mm, broadly tubular below, sub-campanulate, dilated towards the mouth; tube 18–20 x 6–8 x 9–10mm, sub-densely covered with soft, white, patent hairs and almost without scales, although often with small clusters of scales at the lobe junctions; lobes 13–15 x 8–10mm, broadly obovate-spathulate, hairy outside, glabrous inside, not, or overlapping to *c.*½. **Stamens** at first clustered on the lower side of the mouth, becoming irregularly spreading, exserted to *c.*7mm; filaments linear, patently hairy for the lower ¼–⅓, glabrous distally; anthers 2–2.5 x *c.*1mm, broadly oblong, each cell with a small basal apiculus. Disc prominent, glabrous or with hairs on the upper margin. **Ovary** *c.*5 x 3mm, ovoid, densely patently white-hairy, and with scattered brown scales, abruptly contracted distally; style with a few hairs at the base otherwise glabrous, *c.*12mm, expanding to *c.*20mm, lying on the lower side of the tube; stigma rounded, bright red, becoming exserted to *c.*8mm. **Fruit** 12 x 6mm, obovoid-cylindric, dark purple, densely short-hairy and laxly scaly. Seeds 1.8mm, without tails 0.8mm, the longest tail 0.6mm.

Malaysia (Borneo), Sabah, Mt Kinabalu, E ridge above the Mesilau R. Terrestrial in summit shrubberies at 3160–3650m, locally common. *Fl.* July–Dec., *fr.* Aug.

This species has an extraordinarily restricted distribution, having been found only in the vicinity of the type locality. It was introduced into cultivation to Edinburgh in 1980. It grows slowly and flowers sparingly and irregularly, but has a most attractive 'bonsai-like' habit with its small, dark green, revolute leaves, and the flowers are a delightful, glowing pink. Commonly hybridises in the wild with *R. buxifolium* to give *R.* x *sheliae* Sleumer.

---

180. Rhododendron burttii P.Woods
Notes RBG Edinb. 1978. 37(1): 57.
Type: Burtt & Martin B.5549, 16 Oct. 1967, (cultivated specimen April 1970). Sarawak, 5th Div., G. Murud (E, L, SAR).
Derivation: Named after B.L. Burtt, botanist at Edinburgh, who made a series of expeditions to Sarawak and who first collected this species with Adam Martin on Gunong Murud.

Shrub to 80cm. Twigs smooth, green or reddish, very finely hairy and laxly scaly. **Leaves** 5–8 in tight pseudo-whorls, with a variable number of smaller reduced scale leaves. **Blade** 18–28 x 9–12mm, obovate; apex broadly pointed to rounded; margin entire, slightly recurved; base tapering; laxly scaly above and with a few simple hairs but quickly glabrescent; below laxly and more persistently scaly but without hairs. **Scales** stellate, flat, with a broad marginal flange and small slightly impressed centre. Mid-vein impressed above, raised below; lateral veins 2–3 per side, faint or obscure. **Petiole** 4–5 x 1–2mm, hairy and scaly, weakly grooved at the junction with the lamina, green.

Flower buds to 8 x 4mm, ellipsoidal, green, tips of the bracts stiffly erect, hairy outside and with marginal brown scales. Inflorescences often lateral as well as terminal, of 1–2 occasionally up to 4 flowers, hanging vertically. Pedicels 17 x 1mm, red, with long, white, spreading hairs. Calyx a low green disc with a hairy margin. **Corolla** 23 x 26mm, bright-red, without scent; tube *c.*17 x 8 x 6mm, swollen just above the base and then narrowed slightly, becoming parallel sided and straight, long-hairy and with a few scales outside, hairy only near the base inside; lobes 10 x 6mm, wide-spreading, not overlapping. **Stamens** spreading all round the mouth of the flower; filaments 18mm, white, passing to pink distally, broadened and hairy in the proximal 4mm; anthers 1.4 x 0.8mm, brown. **Ovary** *c.*4 x 3mm, shortly cylindrical, densely hairy, with white semi-appressed hairs and brown scales covered by the hairs; style 5 x 0.5mm, green with a few hairs near the base only; stigma green, 1mm in diameter. **Fruit** 16 x 5mm, cylindrical, white-hairy and with brown scales, the valves spreading widely after opening. Seeds 3.3mm, without tails 1mm, the longest tail 1.2mm.

Malaysia (Borneo), Sarawak, Mt Murud, Mt Lawi. Sabah, Mt Lotung, Crocker Range and in the area of the River Rekong Waterfall near Long Pasia. Erroneously reported from Kinabalu although it could easily be on that mountain. Epiphytic in mossy sub-montane forest at 1500–1600m. *Fl.* Jan.–Dec.

This delightful plant is easily known amongst Bornean species by its usually solitary or paired, hairy, red, hanging flowers and its small (10mm wide) leaves with only sparse, small, scales. It superficially most closely resembles *R.*

borneense ssp. *villosum* which has similar hairy, red flowers and small leaves but *R. burttii* has much longer pedicels, the flowers hanging freely vertically downwards and it has quite different scales to *R. borneense*. *Rhododendron burttii* has been cultivated in the Royal Botanic Garden Edinburgh since 1967 when it was first collected by Burtt and Martin from Mt Murud in Sarawak; later collections from Sabah are also in cultivation with a slightly different, more erect habit. It is a most attractive though somewhat sprawling small plant. It flowers freely but irregularly and may flower as many as eight times in a year.

181. Rhododendron sugaui Argent *sp. nov.*
Type: Sugau et al. SAN 138836, 11 April 1994. Malaysia, Sabah, Telupid District, Mt Tawai, *c.*1250m (SAN).
Derivation: Named after John Sugau, senior botanist working with the Forest Department, Sandakan, who found this plant.

R. burttii affinis sed ramulis glabris et corolla extus glabra differt.

Shrub to 1m. Twigs 1–2mm in diameter, rounded, laxly scaly, without simple hairs; internodes 1–5cm. **Leaves** in tight pseudowhorls 4–6 together, sometimes with one or two much smaller ones. **Blade** 20–35 x 8–12mm, elliptic or occasionally spathulate; apex rounded or minutely retuse; margin entire, strongly but narrowly revolute; base tapering; laxly silvery scaly above but quickly glabrescent; below densely scaly. **Scales** sub-stellate, with a broad, thin, silvery, margin and small, darker and slightly impressed

Rhododendron burttii.

centre. Mid-vein impressed into a groove throughout its length above, strongly raised for the whole length beneath; lateral veins not visible. **Petiole** 2–4 x *c*.1mm, laxly scaly initially.

Inflorescence up to 5-flowered, the flowers hanging. Pedicels 15–18 x *c*.0.6mm, densely hairy, apparently without scales. Calyx *c*.4mm in diameter, distinctly lobed and sometimes with one or two much longer lobes, hairy outside. **Corolla** *c*.25 x 12mm, bright pink, narrowly funnel-shaped; tube *c*.13 x 3 x 7mm, glabrous outside, hairy inside in the proximal ½; lobes *c*.9 x 6mm, broadly elliptic. Disc hairy on the upper side. **Stamens** *c*.18mm, exserted to *c*.4mm; filaments densely hairy in the proximal ⅓, glabrous distally; anthers *c*.2mm. **Ovary** *c*.4.5 x 2mm, densely hairy; style *c*.15mm, hairy for *c*.2mm proximally, glabrous distally; stigma *c*.1.5mm in diameter, rounded.

> **Malaysia** (Borneo), Sabah, Telupid District, Mt Tawai, *c*.1250m.

Very similar to *R. burttii* but with non-hairy twigs and no hairs on the outside of the corolla. Mt Tawai is an isolated mountain and this species is very likely to be endemic. Known only from the type collection.

182. Rhododendron buxifolium Low *ex* Hook.*f*.
In Hook., Ic. Pl. 1852. *t*.890.
Type: Low *s.n.*, March 1851. North Borneo, Mt Kinabalu, 2745–4096m, top (K, CGE, L).
Derivation: Latin – *Buxus* – *Buxus sempervirens* – 'the European box'; *folium* – leaf. An allusion to the similarity of the leaves to that of this shrub.

Synonym: *R. buxifolium* var. *robustum* Sleumer, Reinwardtia 1960. 5: 173.

Shrub or tree to 5m. Twigs *c*.3mm in diameter, initially laxly covered with scales and sometimes with very fine papillose hairs, later glabrescent but with thick raised leaf

Rhododendron buxifolium.

Rhododendron buxifolium.

scars; internodes 1–4cm. **Leaves** 5–8 in dense pseudo-whorls. **Blade** 10–35 x 6–25mm, broadly elliptic, ovate- or obovate-elliptic or sub-circular; apex obtuse, often rounded-obtuse, sometimes slightly emarginate, with an inconspicuous apical gland; margin slightly recurved, distinctly crenulate; base rounded, cordate, or broadly tapering, sub-densely to laxly scaly on both sides initially, early glabrescent with minute pits above; more persistently scaly beneath. **Scales** irregularly crenate or lobed with a narrow marginal zone; centre often large, swollen and persistent, deeply impressed. Mid-vein narrow and slightly impressed above, broad and obtusely prominent beneath; lateral veins 5–6 per side, somewhat irregular, spreading, slightly impressed above in old leaves, inconspicuous beneath, reticulation lax and faintly impressed above, obscure beneath. **Petiole** 1.5–3 x 1–3mm, grooved above, flattened, rugose.

Flower buds (see p.327) to 17 x 11mm, ovoid, green, with the points of the bracts standing erect away from the bud. Outer bracts ovate-acuminate, the dorsal mid-vein tapering to a short subulate acumen, hairy and laxly scaly outside, hairy inside, margins ciliate near the apex only; inner ones ovate-obtuse to spathulate. Bracteoles to 20 x 1mm, linear below, sub-spathulate distally. Inflorescence of 5–10 flowers in open umbels. **Flowers** semi-erect to half-hanging. Pedicels 12–24 x 1–2mm, sub-stellately scaly. Calyx 3–4mm in diameter, a low scaly disc, often revolute. **Corolla** 26 x 37mm, broadly funnel-shaped or sub-campanulate, pink to deep red, strongly honey-scented; tube 15–18 x 4–5 x 12–15mm, sub-densely scaly outside, glabrous inside, straight, the base pouched; lobes 15–18 x 13–15mm, spreading, slightly reflexed, overlapping *c*.½, obovate-spathulate. **Stamens** sub-equal, at the mouth of the tube; filaments *c*.13mm, linear, glabrous, pink; anthers *c*.3mm, oblong, pale-brown, cells obtuse or narrowed into a short distinct basal apiculus. Disc prominent, glabrous. **Ovary** *c*.4–4.5 x 2–3mm, sub-ovoid-conical, apex obtuse, abruptly contracted distally, densely scaly and occasionally with some very sparse hairs; style 9 x 1mm, glabrous, or scaly at the base for *c*.1mm, red, as long as the stamens; stigma *c*.2mm in diameter, red, rounded. **Fruit** 14–18 x 7–8mm, ovoid-fusiform, brown-scaly. Seeds 1.7mm, without tails *c*.1mm, the longest tail 0.4mm.

Malaysia (Borneo), Sabah, Mt Kinabalu. In forest above 3100m, but more frequent in shrubberies and in open places amongst the granite rocks, up to 3900m. *Fl.* Jan.–Dec. but with a major flowering in Feb./March.

The variety *robustum* recognised by Sleumer (1960) has little significance, except to indicate the effects of exposure: the type specimen is from the upper end of the range from an exposed site and thus has small leaves compared with the plants lower down. It is one of the most magnificent botanical sights on Mt Kinabalu when in full flower on a fine sunny day. It was introduced into cultivation in Edinburgh by Ian Sinclair in 1982 but grows slowly: the plants are only *c*.80cm high after more than 20 years but they now flower irregularly usually in late spring. The taxonomic position of this species is anomalous. It has the scale type of *Discovireya* and has just a few hairs on the margins of the bracts, but the flower shape is much more typical of *Euvireya* where it was placed by Sleumer (1960).

---

183. Rhododendron tuhanensis Argent & Barkman
The New Plantsman 2000. 7(4): 214–219.
Type: Barkman & Beaman 59, 20 Jan. 1995. Sabah, Ranau District, Kinabalu Lipson, 2800–2900m (SNP).
Derivation: Named from the Dusen word 'Tuhan' which means landslide, as the plant is known only from steep landslides in the ultramafic area of Mt Kinabalu.

Shrub to 40cm. Twigs rounded, red or green with brown scales on top of white, slender, stalks which appear as short hairs when the scale is removed. **Leaves**

in tight pseudowhorls of *c*.6 full-sized leaves and one or two smaller ones with some slender fragile scale leaves along the internodes. **Blade** 8–15 x 7–13mm, sub-circular to elliptic; apex obtuse, rounded or retuse; margin entire when fresh, crenulate after drying; base rounded or broadly tapering, flat or slightly concave, sub-succulent; sub-densely scaly above at first but quickly glabrescent; persistently sub-densely scaly below. **Scales** highly variable, mostly with a broad irregular margin and small centre but occasionally with a large domed centre and smaller marginal zone, brown, leaving a small dark spot at the point of attachment when they have gone. Midvein impressed above mostly for the whole leaf length but sometimes disappearing just below the apex; below, smooth when fresh, broadly raised for the whole length after drying; lateral veins mostly not visible but occasionally one or two spreading at about 45° from near the base. **Petiole** 1–3 x 1–2mm, green or red, scaly, grooved in the distal ½ on the upper side.

Flower buds 13–15 x 6–10mm, ovoid, dark shining red in the upper ⅓, red below, the outermost bracts rigidly standing out away from the bud, ovate or triangular with broad bases and long, narrow, subulate points; inner bracts broadly ovate, narrowing to mucronate apices. Bracteoles *c*.8 x 0.5mm, broadening distally to *c*.1mm, glabrous but irregularly toothed distally. Inflorescence an open umbel of 2–4 flowers, sometimes solitary, the flowers half-hanging. Pedicels 13–15 x *c*.1mm, densely hairy and with scattered inconspicuous scales. Calyx a low scaly ring with a few hairs near the attachment to the pedicel. **Corolla** red, 20–28 x *c*.20mm; tube 8–16 x 5–6 x 10–14mm, with a few scales outside and some scattered hairs near the base both inside and out; lobes 12–16 x 10–16mm, not overlapping or overlapping to ¾. **Stamens** arranged regularly or irregularly just below the mouth of the flower, slightly dimorphic, 7 and 8mm; filaments laxly hairy near the base especially on the inner side, glabrous

Todd Barkman

Rhododendron tuhanensis.

distally; anthers *c*.3 x 1mm, brown, curving inwards. **Ovary** *c*.3 x 3mm, densely white-hairy and with inconspicuous brown scales, abruptly contracting distally; style 5mm, hairy at the base, (up to 1mm), otherwise glabrous. **Fruit** 7–11 x 5–6mm, broadly cylindrical, the outer layer peeling back before the valves split open. Seeds *c*.1.5mm, without tails *c*.1mm, the longest tail 0.3mm, the tails often hook-like.

Malaysia (Borneo), Sabah, Mt Kinabalu. Discovered by Todd Barkman in July 1994 within less than 300m of the main summit trail. At present known from one landslide area on the ultra-mafic 'apron' of this mountain, where it was first collected. There are several other similar, but much less accessible, sites where it could occur but it is at present known only from about a dozen plants in three groups on this one landslip. The plants are mostly completely exposed and suffer severely in drought years but have not been killed. It has been collected in flower in Jan. and July but the site has not really been sufficiently monitored to indicate any definitive flowering pattern.

This species is similar to *R. buxifolium* but differs most significantly in the much smaller habit, the hairy ovary and hairy pedicels. It also has nearly glabrous bracts without any white hairs along the margins or outside as in *R. buxifolium* and should clearly be placed in section *Euvireya*. It would pass on leaf size as series *Linnaeopsis*

but that series has hitherto been recorded only in New Guinea, and the erect habit with its thick sub-succulent leaves is unlike any of the species in that group. For the present it is placed in series *Buxifolia*; its true relationships may be with *R. baconii* or *R. rugosum*. Introduced into cultivation in Edinburgh by Paul Smith in 1995, it grows very slowly, producing its relatively large pink flower irregularly throughout the year.

184. Rhododendron nieuwenhuisii J.J.Sm.

Ic. Bog. 1910. 4: 75. *t*.323.

Type: Amdjah 122, 28 Oct. 1898. Central Borneo, Sg. Buleng (SING, lectotype A, BO, L).

Derivation: Named in honour of A.W. Nieuwenhuis, Professor of Ethnology at Leiden University in the Netherlands, who made several expeditions to Borneo in the 1890s.

Slender shrub to 60cm. Twigs 1–3mm in diameter, rounded, green but distinctly brown-scaly; internodes 2–7cm. **Leaves** 3–7 together in tight pseudowhorls, together with conspicuous, subulate, cataphylls. **Blade** 25–80 x 6–30mm, narrowly elliptic or very narrowly ovate; apex long-acuminate and often somewhat curved, acute; margin slightly recurved; base tapering to rounded or

Rhododendron nieuwenhuisii.

weakly cordate, rugose, especially when dry, moderately densely scaly on both sides initially, becoming glabrescent above, more persistently scaly beneath. **Scales** brown, sessile, highly variable, the largest deeply, stellately lobed, or sub-dendroid; centre small and not impressed. Mid-vein distinctly impressed above and very thick and prominent beneath; lateral veins 7–13 per side, widely spreading, slightly to strongly raised above and impressed beneath (especially when dry) so as to make the surface rugose, reticulation obscure. **Petiole** 2–4 x *c*.2mm, distinctly grooved above, densely brown-scaly.

Flower buds to 20 x 7mm, narrowly ovoid, acute, pale green although prominently brown-scaly. Outer bracts subulate with the tips slightly spreading, inner ones larger, ovate-acuminate, acute, the points mostly appressed, stellate-scaly outside, and with scales along the margins, often persistently clasping the flower after it has opened. **Flowers** solitary or in twos, horizontal or half-hanging. Pedicels 3–5 x *c*.2mm, densely stellately scaly. Calyx *c*.2.5mm in diameter, oblique, shortly 5-lobed, scaly outside. **Corolla** 35–45 x 55–65mm, deep, bright yellow, saucer-shaped; tube 12–15 x 8–9 x 16–20mm, but contracted in the middle to *c*.7mm, white with scattered brown scales outside and deeply sulcate in the proximal ½, distally, yellow, smooth and glabrous, except for small clusters of scales at the junctions with the lobes, glabrous inside; lobes 20–30 x 17–25mm, spreading almost horizontally and overlapping ½–⅔, broadly obovate with rounded or emarginate apices. **Stamens** *c*.18mm; filaments slender, bent through a right angle, glabrous at the base, hairy above the angle and then glabrous distally; anthers linear-oblong, 4–5 x 1–1.5mm. Disc prominent, hairy at the upper margin. **Ovary** *c*.8 x 4mm, sub-cylindrical, with long, white, sub-patent hairs which cover scales, abruptly contracted distally; style 10–15mm, glabrous, yellow, at first deflexed downwards or to one side; stigma club-shaped, becoming deeply 5-lobed. **Fruit** 35–43 x 5–6mm, fusiform-cylindric, densely hairy with a persistent style up to 13mm; valves reflexing and twisting after opening. Seeds 7.5–9.5mm, without tails 0.6–0.7mm, the longest tail 4–5mm.

Indonesia, Kalimantan. **Brunei. Malaysia** (Borneo), Sabah and Sarawak. Widespread throughout Borneo. Mostly epiphytic in dense humid forest, along rivers particularly near waterfalls, also recorded from 'heath-forest', 100–800m. Its flowering time is not well known and is probably quite variable and intermittent throughout the year. In cultivation it flowers several times a year. Pollinators are not known but might be expected to be large bees or other large insects as the flower is broadly accessible and yellow.

This very distinctive species is unlikely to be confused with any other. With its rugose leaves and broad 'saucer-shaped', mostly solitary yellow flowers it is unlike any other.

A delightful species, it was introduced into cultivation in the Royal Botanic Garden Edinburgh in 1978 from Sarawak and has been grown for some years in the University Botanic Garden in Leiden in the Netherlands. It flowers regularly but to thrive requires much warmer, moister conditions than most of the other vireyas, reflecting its moist lowland ecology in the wild. It is one of the few vireyas which will thrive under 'stove' conditions. Hybrids with other species have not been recorded.

185. Rhododendron taxifolium Merr.
Phil. J. Sc. 1926. 30: 419.
Type: Ramos & Edaño B.S. 44880, 27 Feb. 1925. Philippines, Luzon, Benguet, Mt Pulog, *c*.2700m (PNH†, A, BM, E, K, L, P).
Derivation: Like a *Taxus* – a small genus of gymnosperms with similar narrow leaves.

Shrub to 1m. Twigs 1–2mm in diameter, rounded, laxly brown scaly and minutely hairy; internodes 1–3cm. **Leaves** crowded into moderately dense pseudowhorls of 12–25 at the upper 3–4 nodes. **Blade** 25–43 x 1.5–3mm, linear, sub-sessile; apex acute to obtuse; margin flat, minutely serrulate with impressed scales when young; base tapering, glabrescent above at maturity, laxly and irregularly scaly beneath. **Scales** flat, sub-circular or weakly lobed; centre small, impressed. Mid-vein in a groove above, smooth below; lateral veins not visible. **Petiole** 1.5–2.5 x 0.75–1mm, not clearly distinct from the lamina, not grooved above, scaly.

Flower buds at first conical, later ovate, acutely pointed, to 12 x 7mm, green, the bracts appressed or slightly spreading at the apex. Bracts broadly ovate, abruptly subulate at the apex, glabrous outside, or with a few scales near the apices, margin densely brown scaly, to 12 x 6mm. Bracteoles linear, laxly hairy and scaly, *c*.6mm. **Flowers** occasionally solitary, mostly 3–5 flowers in an open umbel, half-hanging although occasionally caught up in the new leaves and held semi-erect. Pedicels slender, hairy and laxly scaly, *c*.10mm. Calyx disc-shaped, scaly and shortly hairy outside, obtusely and shortly 5-lobed, 3–4mm in diameter. **Corolla** 16–20 x 20–25mm, tubular-sub-campanulate, white, without scent; tube 10 x 4 x 7–8mm, laxly sub-stellately-scaly outside, hairy within; lobes *c*.10 x 8mm, broadly obovate, scaly centrally near the base, apex rounded. **Stamens** spread evenly all round at the mouth

Debbie White

Rhododendron taxifolium.

of the corolla, not exserted, distinctly dimorphic; filaments white, linear, sub-densely to laxly patently hairy nearly to the top; anthers *c.*2mm, brown, oblong. Disc glabrous. **Ovary** *c.*3 x 1.5mm, sub-cylindrical, densely, patently, white-hairy, with a few scales between the hairs; style columnar, hairy below, glabrous distally, *c.*5mm; stigma sub-globose, green at first lying on the lower side of the tube, centrally placed in old flowers. **Fruit** 9–14 x 4–5mm, pale yellowish-green. Seeds 1.8–2.2mm, without tails 0.9–1mm, the longest tail 0.7mm.

Philippines, Luzon, Mt Pulag (Pulog), epiphytic on trees in mossy montane forest at *c.*2600–2700m. *Fl.* Feb.–March.

Rhododendron taxifolium must be considered a threatened species in the wild as it is restricted to the montane forest. This vegetation, despite being in a national park, is dwindling in extent due to illegal incursions of farmers from below and fires in the summit grasslands above. The mountains viewed in all directions are devoid of montane forest. This makes it unlikely to be found elsewhere.

It was introduced into cultivation in 1992 to Edinburgh, from where it was distributed with permission from the National Museum, Manila in the interests of conservation. It is now in many collections throughout the world. It grows easily and flowers profusely, always causing comment with its bizarre appearance. Sleumer (1966) placed this species in his series *Stenophylla* on account of its narrow linear leaves but it is unlikely to be related to

R. stenophyllum or to the other two species in that series which are from New Guinea. It seems much more likely to be related to, and possibly just an extreme form of, *R. vidalii*, a relationship which Copeland (1929) had suggested.

186. Rhododendron acrophilum Merr. & Quisumb.
Phil. J. Sc. 1953. 82: 333.
Type: Edaño PNH 34, 13 May 1947. Philippines, Palawan, Mt Mantalingahan, Brooke's Point, at *c.*1725m (A, BM, K, L, PNH).
Derivation: Greek – *acro* – summit; *philus* – loving. A summit-loving plant but not apt – see below.

Shrub to 1m. Twigs 1–2mm in diameter, rounded, at first covered with flat stellate scales, quickly glabrescent; internodes 1.5–4cm. **Leaves** 4–6 in tight to somewhat loose pseudowhorls. **Blade** 25–50 x 10–20mm, elliptic or slightly obovate; apex broadly acute, obtuse to rounded; margin entire, flat, narrowly cartilaginous, often red; base broadly tapering; sub-densely scaly on both sides, glabrescent and shiny above, more persistently scaly below. **Scales** irregularly stellately lobed with a broad marginal flange and small slightly darker brown centre, not or only slightly impressed. Mid-vein slightly impressed into a narrow groove above, broad and slightly raised for the proximal 6–8mm beneath, otherwise smooth; lateral veins 6–8 per side curving upwards at *c.*45°, very slightly raised above, smooth or obscure beneath. **Petiole** 3–4 x 1.5–2mm, not or only weakly grooved above, flattened, scaly, and often minutely hairy.

Flower buds to 27 x 12mm, ellipsoid or narrowly ovoid, acutely pointed, the tips of the bracts slightly spreading, white with conspicuous waxy deposits. Bracts to 15 x 8mm, ovate, apiculate, translucent, often flecked with brown, almost totally glabrous but with a few scales near the midline, lacking marginal scales. Inflorescence of 3–5 flowers in an open umbel, mostly horizontal but sometimes semi-erect to half-hanging, usually bicoloured with a yellow tube and orange lobes, sometimes pure yellow and occasionally almost completely orange. Pedicels 13–18 x *c.*1.5mm, red, sub-densely scaly, without hairs. Calyx obliquely thickened, disc-shaped, obscurely lobed, *c.*3mm in diameter. **Corolla** 15–30 x 40–55mm, shortly tubular-funnel-shaped; tube 10–15 x 6–7 x 12–17mm, sparsely stellately scaly outside, densely white-hairy inside; lobes 15–27 x 15–24mm, obovate, spreading horizontally or a little reflexed, overlapping to *c.*½ on upper side of the flower, not overlapping or only to ⅓ on the lower side. **Stamens** unequal, irregularly spreading, mostly on

Eve Bennett

Rhododendron acrophilum.

the lower side of the mouth, sometimes in two groups on each side, exserted to *c.*6mm but reflexing back against the corolla with age; filaments linear, white, densely white-hairy in the proximal 5–6mm, glabrous and filiform distally; anthers 2.7–3 x 1.25mm, narrowly oblong, shortly apiculate basally. Disc deeply lobed, minutely hairy on the upper side, otherwise glabrous. **Ovary** 5–6.5 x 2–3mm, cylindrical, abruptly contracted distally, densely stellate-scaly, without hairs; style 10–14mm, at first depressed to the lower side of the mouth, later becoming central in position, completely glabrous or with some scales at the base; stigma *c.*3mm in diameter, circular, yellow. **Fruit** 26–35 x 5–6mm, spindle-shaped, with pronounced longitudinal grooves, scaly.

Philippines, Palawan, Mt Mantalingahan, Brooke's Point, an epiphyte in dense montane rain forest at *c.*1725m. Known only from this single location. *Fl.* May.

Introduced into cultivation in 1992 and flowering for the first time in 1993 as small 15cm plants. It has proved to be a really good horticultural plant, with its compact habit, bright green leaves and freely produced, usually bicoloured, orange and yellow flowers. It flowers irregularly at least twice, at different times of the year, new buds being encouraged by prompt dead-heading. Winter flowers when the plants are in poor light can be pure yellow, the same plants in the summer producing bicoloured flowers with deep orange lobes; plants growing in climates with really strong light can be completely orange. The original collection was described with white flowers and occurring at the top of Mt Mantalingahan.

This is almost certainly an error (see Argent & Madulid 1995).

187. Rhododendron wilkiei Argent
Gardens Bull. Sing. 2004. 56(1&2): 88, *f.*4.
Type: Argent et al. 48. Philippines, Palawan, Thumb Peak, Original collection 30 Jan. 1998, 1200m; Acc. No. 19981810: 11 July 2003 (PNH, E).
Derivation: Named after Peter Wilkie, botanist and explorer in SE Asia, who nearly died of a malarial attack helping to collect this species.

Weak shrub to *c.*30cm. Stems pale green, rounded, *c.*1.5mm in diameter, moderately densely covered in brown stellate scales. **Leaves** in pseudowhorls 1–2cm apart, consisting of 3–4 larger and 2–3 smaller leaves, mostly only possessing leaves at the terminal node. **Blade** 25–40 x 10–15mm, elliptic; apex broadly acute to obtuse, sometimes with an obscure, white, non-protruding, gland-like structure at the point; margin entire, flat; base broadly tapering; with some sparse silvery, stellate scales at first but quickly glabrescent above; below moderately brown scaly. **Scales** rounded, or sub-stellately lobed, impressed into small pits; centres small and indistinct; distributed 2–4 diameters apart in the mature leaves. Mid-vein narrowly impressed above; below, slightly prominent just beyond the petiole but then somewhat impressed distally, translucent green especially towards the base; lateral veins 2–4 per side, smooth, broadly spreading, but disappearing before the margin, distinct above but obscure below.

207

Petiole 2–3 x *c*.1.5mm, not distinctly grooved above but with a central line, pale green with brown stellate scales.

Flower buds green, to 18 x 8mm, narrowly conical but contracted near the base, sharply pointed with the basal bracts spreading, the upper (inner) bracts mostly appressed. Bracts glabrous or with a few small, scattered scales outside and with scales along the margins. Inflorescence terminal, of solitary or paired flowers, held half-hanging. Pedicels 10–15 x 1–2mm, moderately scaly but without simple hairs. **Flowers** narrowly funnel-shaped. Calyx a low scaly disc or with two irregular longer lobes up to 2mm long. **Corolla** *c*.27 x 44mm, red, without scent; tube *c*.15 x 4 x 10mm, glabrous both inside and out; lobes *c*.19 x 21mm, spreading horizontally, overlapping to about ½–⅔, emarginate. **Stamens** regularly arranged around the mouth of the flower; filaments pale pink, glabrous; anthers 2–2.5 x *c*.1.25mm, dark purple. Disc green, glabrous. **Ovary** *c*.6 x 2.5mm, ellipsoid, sparsely brown-scaly, without simple hairs; style *c*.20mm, pink, at first lying on the lower side of the corolla tube, rising to a central position as the flower ages, glabrous; stigma *c*.1.25mm in diameter, purplish-red, hardly expanded from the style. **Fruit** 33 x 5mm, fusiform but slightly wider in the distal ½. Seeds 4.5–5mm, without tails 0.8mm, the longest tail 2mm.

Philippines, Palawan, Thumb Peak, low mossy sub-montane forest, *c*.1200m.

Known only from the type locality. This species is similar to *R. acrophilum*, which is from the same island, but differs in the flower colour, which is usually bicoloured with a yellow tube and orange lobes in that species. The filaments and inside of the corolla are glabrous in *R. wilkiei*, not hairy as in *R. acrophilum*, and it lacks the white waxy substance associated with the flower buds which that species possesses. It is also much less vigorous in its growth habit. Introduced into cultivation in 1998, it first flowered in July 2003 and has flowered in June and July subsequently. It is an attractive species but so far has grown very slowly.

---

188. **Rhododendron rousei** Argent & Madulid
The New Plantsman 1998. 5(1): 25.
Type: Argent 19902332, Aug. 1989. Philippines, Sibuyan Is., Mt Giting Giting, Camp 3 above Magdiwang, on ridge leading to Mayos Peak, 1300m (PNH, E).
Derivation: Named after Dr John Rouse, of Melbourne, for his outstanding contribution to our knowledge of vireya rhododendrons.

Shrub to *c*.1m. Twigs at first laxly covered with brown scales but these quickly falling to leave the surface minutely warty and often longitudinally grooved, without simple hairs. **Leaves** crowded into tight pseudo-whorls of 3–7 full-sized leaves and several much smaller ones. **Blade** 25–50 x 15–30mm, elliptic to obovate; apex broadly obtuse to rounded, sometimes slightly retuse; margin recurved, strongly so when dry, often cartilaginous although this is obscured by the curved edges; base tapering, slightly decurrent; dark shining green above, much paler green beneath; laxly to sub-densely scaly on both sides when young, glabrescent above, persistently scaly beneath. **Scales** round to irregularly shallowly lobed, small, flat, dark brown. Mid-vein impressed above, raised below; lateral veins 3–5 per side, distinctly impressed above, smooth below, becoming slightly raised after drying. **Petiole** 5–12 x 2–2.5mm, grooved above, scaly.

Flower buds to 18 x 10mm, green and shiny, sometimes flushed with red, with pale brown reflexed tips to the bracts. Outermost bracts subulate from a broad triangular to ovate base, becoming larger inwards and concave-ovate with acutely pointed and channelled tips, finally broadly spathulate; membranous, glabrous outside except for a few scales near the tips and a fringe of scales along the margins; minutely hairy inside. Bracteoles to 22 x 2mm, filiform, broadening slightly upwards and often with a forked tip, glabrous or occasionally with a few hairs. Inflorescence an open umbel of 2–6 flowers, held horizontally to semi-erect. Pedicels 16–21 x *c*.2mm, green,

Rhododendron wilkiei.

Rhododendron rousei.

moderately to densely scaly with pale brown scales, without simple hairs. Calyx 4mm in diameter, irregularly lobed, up to 1.5mm. **Corolla** 22–28 x 45–57mm, white, without scent; tube 11–13 x 6–7 x 10–13mm, funnel-shaped, minutely brown scaly outside and with a few white hairs near the base especially in the shallow grooves, with irregular white hairs inside; lobes 24–28 x 22–25mm, minutely and obscurely brown scaly proximally to about halfway up the lobe outside, lobes overlapping ⅓–⅔, widely spreading to almost 90°. **Stamens** arranged in a regular cluster in the mouth of the flower, weakly dimorphic with only the anthers exceeding the corolla tube, expanding slightly back against the corolla as the flower ages; filaments 12–13mm, white, patent hairy in the proximal ⅓–½; anthers *c.*2.5 x 1mm, brown. Disc green, 10-lobed, with erect hairs on the upper side and on the outer rim of the lobes. **Ovary** *c.*4 x 3mm, green, densely silvery scaly and moderately white hairy; style green at the base, white above, patently white-hairy for up to 1.5mm proximally, otherwise completely glabrous; stigma *c.*2mm in diameter, pale yellow, slightly lobed. **Fruit** 8–12 x 5–7mm, shortly cylindrical, deep purplish red, densely hairy and covered in dark brown scales, the valves gaping to *c.*45°, not twisting. Seeds 1.5–2.2mm; without tails 0.5–0.8mm, the longest tail 0.6–0.7mm.

Philippines, Romblon Province, Sibuyan Island, Mt Giting Giting, Camp 3 above Magdiwang, on ridge leading to Mayos Peak. Growing amongst ultramafic boulders in open sub-montane forest at 1300m.

Introduced into cultivation in Edinburgh in 1989. This species is related to *R. vidalii* but is distinct in that the young stems lack simple hairs and are warty with scale

stalks when the scales have gone. It also has larger, darker green leaves and much larger flowers, with the corolla lobes 24–27mm (up to 13mm in *R. vidalii*).

This species has a good, freely branching habit and the glossy dark green foliage is a very attractive feature. The flowers are a beautiful pure white and have a good strong texture that makes them last well compared with many other species. It has been much admired, particularly as it is almost always in flower, with individual plants repeatedly flowering throughout the year. It tends to flower best in November or December in Edinburgh, which makes it a truly worthwhile plant to cultivate.

189. Rhododendron whiteheadii Rendle
J. Bot. 1896. 34: 356.
Type: Whitehead *s.n.* Philippines, Luzon, Mountain Province, Ifugao subprovince, Mt Polis, 1830m (PNH†, BM).
Derivation: Named after John Whitehead, an ornithologist who collected plants.

Synonym: *R. curranii* Merr., Phil. J. Sc. 1908. 3: 255, 381.

Shrub to 2.5m. Twigs 2–4mm in diameter, densely hairy and scaly; internodes 2–5cm. **Leaves** 3–7 together in tight pseudowhorls. **Blade** 25–40 x 15–35mm, elliptic, obovate, or ovate; apex rounded, sometimes minutely emarginate, and sometimes with a minutely protruding terminal gland; margin entire or slightly irregular, flat or narrowly and weakly revolute; base tapering, slightly decurrent; laxly to sub-densely scaly on both sides at first, quickly glabrescent above, more persistently scaly beneath. **Scales** variable in size, the largest irregularly lobed, with

209

small dark brown centres, smaller ones, circular dark brown, all impressed in shallow pits. Mid-vein impressed above, smooth, shallowly impressed or weakly prominent beneath (distinctly raised when dry); lateral veins 4–6 per side, emerging at *c.*45°, often only faintly visible above, smooth and faintly visible beneath, reticulation inconspicuous. **Petiole** 4–5 x 1–1.5mm, grooved above, flattened, brown-scaly and sometimes minutely hairy.

Bracts 9–13 x 6–8mm, ovate, obtuse, laxly hairy outside, fringed with dark brown scales. Inflorescence 2–4-flowered, in an open umbel, flowers half-hanging. Pedicels *c.*13mm, scaly and long-hairy, or sometimes entirely without hairs. Calyx *c.*3mm in diameter, small, disc-shaped, obscurely lobed, shortly hairy outside. **Corolla** 22–30 x 23–27mm, funnel-shaped, red, without scent; tube 10–15 x 4–4.5 x 5–8mm, straight, grooved, laxly hairy and scaly outside, glabrous or laxly hairy inside; lobes *c.*12 x 12mm, obovate-spathulate, spreading almost to the horizontal, not overlapping, laxly scaly and sometimes with a few hairs proximally outside. **Stamens** exserted 17–20mm; filaments linear and densely sub-patently hairy in the lower ½, filiform and glabrous distally; anthers narrowly oblong, *c.*3 x 1mm. Disc prominent, glabrous below, shortly hairy on the upper margin. **Ovary** *c.*5 x 1mm, cylindrical, densely hairy with appressed hairs which cover small scales, abruptly tapering distally; style *c.*10mm, patently hairy in its lower ⅓–⅔, glabrous distally; stigma round. **Fruit** *c.*25 x 5–6mm.

Philippines, Luzon, Mountain Province, Ifugao subprovince, Mt Polis; Mt Tabayoc; Benguet subprovince, Mt Pulag; Zambales Province, Mt Tapulao. Epiphytic or terrestrial in shrubberies, banks or open mossy forest, considered to be rare, 1800–2400m. *Fl.* Feb.

Not known in cultivation. Sleumer (1966) sank this species into *R. vidalii* on the grounds that only flower colour separated the two species but later (Sleumer 1973) asserted the distinctness due to the large fruit of a specimen collected on Mt Pulag which meant fruit size could be used as well. Hybrids between these two species with pink flowers appear to exist, and the status of *R. whiteheadii* is far from satisfactorily established. The type specimen in the Natural History Museum, London has larger leaves than is usual for *R. vidalii* and the hairs on the stems are much longer and coarser.

---

190. Rhododendron vidalii Rolfe
J. Bot. 1886. 24: 348.
Type: Vidal 1529. Philippines, Luzon, Mt Polis, Bontoc, 1000–1200m (K, Fl, L).
Derivation: Named after Sebastian Vidal y Soler, Spanish botanist who worked and collected in the Philippines, who 'was the first of the local botanists … to recognize the necessity of a local botanical library and herbarium' (Steenis-Kruseman 1950).

Synonyms:
R. verticillatum (*non* Low *ex* Lindl.) S.Vidal, Rev. Pl. Vasc. Filip. 1886. 171.
R. lussoniense Rendle, J. Bot. 1896. 34: 356.
R. curranii Merr., Phil. J. Sc. 1908. 3: 255, 381.

Ssp. **vidalii**

Shrub to 3m. Twigs 1–2mm in diameter, minutely hairy, sometimes very sparsely so, and often laxly scaly;

Rhododendron vidalii ssp. *vidalii.*

internodes 1.5–5cm. **Leaves** 3–5 together in tight pseudo-whorls. **Blade** 15–40 x 10–20mm, elliptic, narrowly ovate or narrowly obovate; apex rounded, sometimes minutely emarginate, and sometimes with a minutely protruding terminal gland; margin entire or slightly irregular, flat or narrowly and weakly revolute, distinctly so when dry; base tapering, slightly decurrent, pale green, laxly to sub-densely scaly on both sides at first, quickly glabrescent above, more persistently scaly beneath. **Scales** very variable in size, the largest irregularly lobed, with small dark brown centres, smaller ones, circular dark brown, all impressed in shallow pits. Mid-vein impressed above, smooth, shallowly impressed or weakly prominent beneath (distinctly raised when dry); lateral veins 4–6 per side, emerging at *c.*45°, often only faintly visible above, smooth and faintly visible beneath, reticulation inconspicuous. **Petiole** 3–8 x 1–1.5mm, grooved above, flattened, brown-scaly and sometimes minutely hairy.

Flower buds to 10 x 4mm, narrow-ovoid, or ellipsoid, imbricate, green but with distinctly brown scaly margins, terminal but sometimes with lateral flower buds around the terminal. Bracts membranous, glabrous or sub-densely to laxly hairy outside, fringed with dark brown scales, outer ones broadly ovate, acuminate to subulate, inner ones larger, to 10 x 6mm, ovate to spathulate, often mucronate. Bracteoles to 10mm, filiform, laxly hairy. Inflorescence 2–4-flowered, (sometimes appearing more when several lateral buds are flowering together), an open umbel. **Flowers** half-hanging. Pedicels 12–25 x *c.*1mm, scaly and long-hairy, or sometimes entirely without hairs. Calyx *c.*3mm in diameter, small, disc-shaped, obscurely lobed, shortly hairy outside. **Corolla** 22–30 x 20–25mm, funnel-shaped, white, with or without scent; tube 10–15 x 4–4.5 x 5–8mm, straight, grooved, laxly hairy and scaly outside, glabrous or laxly hairy inside; lobes 10–16 x 10–13mm, obovate-spathulate, spreading almost to the horizontal, not overlapping, laxly scaly and sometimes with a few hairs proximally outside. **Stamens** exserted 8–12mm, spreading all round the mouth or weakly disposed in two groups on either side; filaments linear and more or less densely sub-patently hairy in the lower ½, filiform and glabrous distally; anthers narrowly oblong-oid, *c.*2 x 1mm. Disc prominent, glabrous below, shortly hairy on the upper margin. **Ovary** *c.*5 x 1mm, cylindrical, densely hairy with appressed hairs which cover small scales, abruptly tapering distally; style patently hairy in its lower ⅓–⅔, glabrous distally, green, lying on the lower side of the tube; stigma round, green, centrally placed when receptive. **Fruit** 15–30 x 4–5mm, sub-cylindrical-fusiform, often curved, becoming erect, when immature green but distinctly white-hairy, on opening the valves becoming recurved and twisted. Seeds *c.*3mm including the long tails at both ends.

Philippines, Luzon, Mountain Province, Mt Polis, Mt Caua, Mt Data. Benguet Province, Loö, Bandschan. Isabella, Bayabat. Cagayan, Cagua Volcano. Bataan, Mt Mariveles. Laguna, Mt Maquiling, Lukban Cone. Batangas Province, Mt Malarayat. Zambales Province, Mt Tapulao. Penicuason Province, Mt Isarog. Mindoro, Mt Halcon. Mostly epiphytic in mossy forest, but also terrestrial on banks in barren places, shrubberies or grassland and on exposed ridges, locally common, 1000–2100m. *Fl.* Jan.–Dec.

This species has been in cultivation since 1997 from Mt Halcon and Mt Isarog when it was collected by an Edinburgh/National Museum Manila expedition. The earlier collection from Sibuyan Island which was distributed under the name *R. vidalii* is now considered to be *R. rousei*. It is a pleasant, easily grown species but suffers in comparison with *R. rousei* which has both better foliage and better flowers.

Ssp. **brachystemon** Argent
Folia Malaysiana 2003. 4(2): 119, pl.7b.
Type: Argent et al. HAL 20, 26 Oct. 1999. Philippines, Mindoro Oriental Province, Mt Halcon. Mossy ridge at *c.*1200m (PNH, A, E, L).
Derivation: Greek – *brachy* – short; *stemon* – stamen. Alluding to the characteristic short stamens clustered below the mouth of the corolla tube.

Differing from the type subspecies in that the stamens are shorter, clustered in the mouth of the flower

Rhododendron vidalii ssp. *brachystemon*.

not exserted and the ovary is shorter, *c.*3mm, and gradually tapering distally.

At present known only from the type locality. It has been in cultivation since 1997 and grows and flowers easily, usually in late spring in Edinburgh. It looks attractive when grown well but similarly to ssp. *vidalii* it suffers in comparison with *R. rousei* which is in all respects a superior horticultural plant.

191. Rhododendron scarlatinum Sleumer

Reinwardtia 1960. 5: 168.
Type: Eyma 782, 19 June 1937. Celebes (C), Enrekang, Rante Mario, W slope, 2950m (BO, L).
Derivation: Latin – *scarlatinus* – scarlet or red, alluding to the flowers.

Small and slender shrub. Twigs 1–1.5mm in diameter, rounded, laxly scaly and often whitish, lower parts glabrescent and smooth; internodes 2.5–5cm. **Leaves** spirally arranged or in loose pseudowhorls. **Blade** 20–30 x 10–18mm, elliptic, apex rounded, often very shortly apiculate; margin sub-cartilaginous, undulate, crenulate or almost entire; base nearly rounded or broadly tapering; laxly scaly initially, glabrescent and a little rugose with age above, laxly and persistently scaly beneath. **Scales** flat, sub-circular, the brown marginal zone angular or irregularly lobed; centre minute, darker, weakly impressed. Midvein narrowly impressed above, broader, flattened and weakly, or not, prominent beneath; lateral veins inconspicuous. **Petiole** 2–3 x 1–2mm, somewhat flattened.

Bracteoles *c.*13mm, filiform, glabrous. Inflorescence a 3–6-flowered open umbel. Pedicels 15–30 x 0.5mm, subdensely covered with stellate scales and short patent hairs. Calyx *c.*3mm in diameter, disc-shaped, irregularly and shortly 5-lobed, scaly and hairy outside. **Corolla** *c.*35mm, tubular, red; tube *c.*25 x 5–6 x 7–8mm, straight, cylindrical, the base pouched, glabrous inside and out; lobes *c.*10 x 7–8mm, spreading, broadly obovate-spathulate, slightly retuse. **Stamens** unequal, 27–33mm; filaments linear, glabrous; anthers *c.*3 x 1.5mm, oblongoid-obovoid; cells tapering towards the base, apiculate at the very base. Disc prominent, glabrous. **Ovary** 28–32mm, sub-ovoid-cylindrical, densely sub-stellately scaly, without hairs, abruptly contracted distally; style 28–32mm, slender, glabrous; stigma obconical. **Fruit** (immature) 15 x 4mm, sub-cylindrical.

Indonesia, Sulawesi, Latimodjong Range, W slope of Mt Rantemario, in forest, 2950m. *Fl.* June.

Known only from the type collection. Never cultivated.

192. Rhododendron leptomorphum Sleumer

Reinwardtia 1960. 5: 160.
Type: Eyma 3617, 5 Sept. 1938. Celebes (E), Menado, O. a Poso, Mt Loemoet, pilaar-top en W. bijtop (summit), *c.*2280m (BO, L, fragment).
Derivation: Greek – *lepto* – thin; *morphe* – form. Both the plant and the flowers are described as slender on the collecting label.

Shrub to 2m. Twigs 5mm in diameter, densely stellate-scaly at first, glabrescent and smooth later. **Leaves** *c.*4 together in pseudowhorls. **Blade** 20–30 x 7–10mm, narrowly elliptic or elliptic; apex shortly acuminate, subacute; margin cartilaginous, slightly revolute, wavy and sub-crenulate; base tapering; glabrescent and rugulose above at maturity, brown and sub-densely scaly beneath. **Scales** flat, irregularly crenate or sub-stellately lobed in the marginal zone; centre large and impressed. Mid-vein very narrowly impressed proximally on the upper surface, prominent beneath; lateral veins darker coloured, inconspicuous. **Petiole** 3–5 x *c.*0.8mm, nearly rounded, scaly.

Flowers solitary. Pedicels 15–20 x *c.*0.6mm, densely stellate-scaly, less densely shortly hairy. Calyx *c.*4mm in diameter, disc-shaped, membranous, reflexed and obscurely lobed. **Corolla** 30mm, tubular, scarlet, slightly oblique; tube 19–22 x *c.*6 x *c.*10mm, almost straight, lobed at the base, glabrous or with a few stellate scales at the base outside, glabrous inside; lobes 8–10 x 7–9mm, broadly obovate-spathulate to sub-circular. **Stamens** exserted to *c.*5mm, unequal; filaments linear below, filiform distally, glabrous; anthers *c.*2.5 x 1.2mm, broadly oblong. Disc prominent, glabrous. **Ovary** *c.*4 x 1.8mm, sub-cylindrical, densely shortly yellowish hairy, no scales visible, gradually tapering distally; style *c.*23mm, thick, glabrous, slightly exceeding the stamens; stigma rounded.

Indonesia, Sulawesi, Poso area, Mt Lumut, terrestrial shrub on the summit at *c.*2280m.

Known only from the type collection. Never cultivated.

193. Rhododendron alternans Sleumer

Reinwardtia 1960. 5: 159.
Type: Eyma 1363, 28 July 1937. Celebes (C), Masamba, top of Mt Kambuno, 2860m (L, A, BO, K).
Derivation: Latin – *alternans* – alternating, presumably referring to the leaves which were originally described as partly opposite.

Shrub to 3m. Twigs 2–3mm in diameter, rounded, laxly stellate-scaly, early glabrescent and smooth; internodes

4–8cm. **Leaves** in loose pseudowhorls in the upper ½ of the internodes. **Blade** 25–40 x 12–20mm, elliptic or ovate-elliptic, more rarely sub-obovate; apex shortly and broadly sub-acuminate, or almost rounded, with a faint apical gland; margin pale, cartilaginous, entire or weakly crenulate with impressed scales; base broadly tapering or rounded, sometimes sub-truncate or sub-cordate, sub-densely scaly above but quickly glabrescent, sub-densely and persistently scaly below. **Scales** sub-stellate or obtusely lobed, marginal zone wide; centre minute, slightly impressed. Mid-vein broad proximally, impressed above, prominent in the lower ½ beneath, becoming hardly visible towards the apex of the blade; lateral veins *c*.5 per side, spreading, slightly conspicuous above only. **Petiole** 1.5–3 x 1–1.5mm.

Outer bracts to 18 x 7mm, ovate, sub-acuminate or obtuse, inner ones ovate-oblong to sub-spathulate, all hairy outside and fringed with scales. Bracteoles to 15mm, linear, laxly hairy. Inflorescence a 3–4-flowered open umbel. **Flowers** hanging. Pedicels 15–20 x 1mm, slender, densely covered with reddish-brown sub-stellate scales and very short white hairs. Calyx *c*.2.5mm in diameter, oblique, disc-shaped, margin obscurely lobed, scaly and very shortly hairy. **Corolla** 25–32 x 15–20mm, tubular, red, glabrous outside and in; tube 20–25 x *c*.4 x 6–7mm, cylindrical, straight, the base 5-pouched; lobes 7–9 x 7–9mm, spreading, obovate-spathulate or nearly circular. **Stamens** unequal, the longest nearly as long as the corolla; filaments linear, glabrous; anthers 2.7 x 1mm, oblongoid; bases sometimes shortly appendaged. Disc prominent, glabrous. **Ovary** *c*.4 x 2.5mm, thick, sub-ovoid to conical, densely covered with short, sub-patent white hairs and with scales between the hairs, abruptly contracted distally; style slender, glabrous, as long as the stamens; stigma sub-globose. **Fruit** 20–28 x *c*.5mm, sub-cylindrical, tapering at both ends, sub-densely hairy and laxly scaly.

Indonesia, C Sulawesi, summit of Mt Kambuno, terrestrial in shrubbery, or epiphytic in low forest, *c*.3000m, common. *Fl.* July.

Not recollected and never cultivated.

194. Rhododendron bagobonum H.F.Copel.
Phil. J. Sc. 1929. 40: 151, *t*.4, *f*.1–2.
Type: Clemens *s.n.* Philippines, Mindanao, Davao, Mt Apo (UC).
Derivation: Named after the 'Bagobones' – an ethnic group in the southern Philippines.

Synonyms:
R. cuneifolium Stapf var. *subspathulatum* Ridl., J. Str. Br. R. As. Soc. 1900. 33: 23.
R. galioides J.J.Sm., Bull. Jard. Bot. Buit. III, 1935. 13: 445.

Shrub to 1m. Twigs 1–1.5mm, slender, rounded, tips laxly scaly and sometimes shortly patently hairy; internodes 1–5cm. **Leaves** 6–15 together in loose pseudowhorls. **Blade** 15–27 x 5–12mm, spathulate-elliptic to obovate; apex broadly acute to obtuse or broadly acute; margin flat or slightly revolute when dry, minutely crenulate; base long-tapering; glabrous and shiny above; laxly to sub-densely and persistently scaly beneath. **Scales** with the marginal zone irregularly lobed; centre small, impressed. Mid-vein narrowly impressed above, flat or slightly raised in the proximal ½ beneath; lateral veins obscure. **Petiole** 0.5–2.5 x 1mm, weakly to distinctly grooved above, laxly scaly.

Flower buds to 16 x 6mm, ovoid with an acute, subulate point, glossy green flushed with red. Bracts to 14 x 3mm, narrowly ovate-acuminate or elliptic, shortly subulate, membranous, glabrous. Bracteoles *c*.5mm, linear-spathulate. **Flowers** solitary, occasionally paired, stiffly held, horizontal to half-hanging. Pedicels 4–6 x *c*.2mm,

Rhododendron bagobonum.

Rhododendron bagobonum.

Sheila Collenette

densely, shortly, patently hairy and scaly. Calyx *c.*2.5mm in diameter, disc-shaped, obscurely obtusely 5-lobed, sparsely scaly and hairy. **Corolla** 12–16 x 8–9mm, tubular, red or orange; tube 7–15 x 4–6 x 4–5mm, straight, laxly scaly outside, laxly hairy in the proximal ½ inside; lobes 3–4 x 3–4mm, sub-erect, ovate to sub-circular. **Stamens** slightly dimorphic, as long as the corolla tube, arranged regularly in the mouth of the corolla; filaments flat, linear, laxly patently hairy in the proximal ½; anthers 1mm, obovoid. Disc low, glabrous. **Ovary** 4–5 x *c.*2.5mm, sub-ovoid-cylindrical, densely hairy and scaly (the scales covered by the hairs), abruptly contracted distally; style *c.*4mm, columnar, glabrous, central or lying on the lower side of the mouth. **Fruit** 20–25 x 3.5–4.5mm, fusiform, with a short sub-persistent style, laxly hairy and scaly. Seeds narrow-fusiform, *c.*3mm including the long tails.

Philippines, Mindanao, Mt Apo, Camiguin Is., Mt Hibok-hibok; Palawan, Mt Mantalingajan. **Malaysia** (Borneo), Sarawak, Mt Penrissen, Mt Mulu, Kelabit Highlands (4th Div.), Baru Laga Plateau (7th Div.). Sabah, Mt Kinabalu, Mt Alab, Mt Lotung. **Indonesia**, Sulawesi, Mt Sojol; Maluku, Mt Binaia. Mostly epiphytic in primary montane forest on mountain ridges, also in heath-forest, and colonising roadsides and landslips, locally common, 900–2135m. *Fl.* Jan.–Dec.

Introduced into cultivation in Edinburgh in 1980 from Sabah and with many subsequent introductions from different locations. It is a small species which tends to sprawl, which is unlike its usually stiffly erect habit in the wild. The flowers are very freely produced at any time of the year and it habitually self-pollinates so that fruit are usually automatically set. It is one of the few species which have no scales on the upper surface of the leaves, these surfaces being truly glabrous, and the bracts are also glabrous. On flower bud characteristics it would appear closely related to *R. exuberans* and *R. nervulosum*. It hybridises in the wild with *R. crassifolium* to give *R.* x *planecostatum* and has been used to produce hybrids in cultivation such as the delightful 'Lucy Sorenson'. It superficially resembles, and has been confused with, species in section *Discovireya*; the scale type and bract margin indumentum will always distinguish them. In Borneo at least, the style is always shorter than the ovary in *R. bagobonum* whereas in members of *Discovireya* such as *R. borneense* and *R. cuneifolium* the style is very much longer than the ovary. The glabrous upper surface of the leaf gives it a shiny appearance which also contrasts with the dull, initially scaly surface of members of *Discovireya*.

195. Rhododendron pseudobuxifolium Sleumer
Reinwardtia 1960. 5: 154.

Type: Eyma 866, 20 June 1937. Indonesia, Sulawesi, Enrekang, Rantmario, 3300m (BO, L).

Derivation: Latin – *pseudo* – false; *buxifolium* – a rhododendron from Kinabalu in E Malaysia, alluding to the similarity in form.

Low erect shrub to 60cm. Twigs short, stiff, 1.5–2mm in diameter, densely short-hairy and caducously scaly; internodes 2–4cm. **Leaves** crowded in the distal part of the upper 1–2 internodes, or in loose pseudowhorls of 4–9 leaves. **Blade** 10–25 x 7–14mm, elliptic to broadly elliptic; apex obtuse, often minutely apiculate; margin distinctly cartilaginous and minutely crenulate; base broadly tapering to rounded, above moderately densely and sub-persistently scaly, beneath laxly and persistently scaly. **Scales** brown, flat, angular or sub-stellately lobed; centre small and impressed. Mid-vein narrow, flat above, slightly prominent and purplish beneath; lateral veins 5–7 per side, the lower 2–3 pairs from or from somewhat above the base, the other higher from the mid-vein, all straight below, curved distally sometimes obscure and obscurely anastomosing, faintly impressed above, a little raised beneath, reticulation obscure. **Petiole** 2–4 x 1–1.5mm, grooved above, purplish-red, slightly flattened.

Flower buds 13–24 x 6–10mm, green. Bracts ovate-oblong to broadly-oblong-sub-spathulate, apiculate or mucronate, rigidly membranous, purplish and shiny when dry, glabrous outside, margin caducously scaly. Inflorescence a 3–4-flowered open umbel. **Flowers** half-hanging, without scent. Pedicels densely sub-stellately scaly and shortly hairy, 15–20mm x *c.*1.5mm, elongating up to 35mm in fruit. Calyx *c.*3mm in diameter, membranous, disc-shaped, margin wavy and reflexed, very shortly obtusely 5-lobed. **Corolla** 28–35 x 20–34mm, deep pink; tube 21–26 x 6–9 x 10–11mm, straight, cylindrical but

Rhododendron pseudobuxifolium.

flaring in the upper 3–4mm, completely glabrous out-side, sparsely hairy in the basal ½ inside; lobes 10–14 x 10–14mm, obovate, reflexed to the perpendicular, over-lapping *c*.halfway. **Stamens** clustered centrally just inside the mouth; filaments linear, sparsely hairy in the basal ⅓, glabrous distally; anthers *c*.2 x 1mm, broadly oblong-elliptic. Disc glabrous. **Ovary** ovoid-conical, densely covered with distally directed white hairs which cover scales, abruptly contracted distally; style 8–10mm, slen-der, glabrous, except for some hairs at the base; stigma globose, deeply 5-lobed. **Fruit** 10–12 x *c*.6mm, erect, pur-ple where exposed and with persistent white hairs. Seeds 1.6–1.8mm, without tails 0.5mm, the longest tail 0.7mm.

Indonesia, C Sulawesi, Latimodjong Range on Mt Rante-mario at 3300m. *Fl.* March, June. Growing amongst moss in open areas near the summit and hybridising with possibly *R. celebicum* although that species occurred much lower on the mountain in the forest. The hybrids were characterised by having longer leaves which lack the crenulations on the margin and longer flowers.

Introduced to cultivation in Edinburgh by Paul Smith and Louise Galloway in 2000, flowering for the first time in June 2003. A pretty species but too early to say how it will perform in cultivation.

---

196. **Rhododendron nubicola** Wernham

Trans. Linn. Soc. London, II, Bot. 1916. 9: 98.
Type: Kloss *s.n.* New Guinea (W), Mt Carstensz, 2500–3200m (BM).
Derivation: Latin – *nubes* – cloud; *cola* – dwelling. Alluding to the cloudy habitat.

Synonyms:
R. acrocline Sleumer, Reinwardtia 1960. 5: 158.
R. hatamense (*non* Becc.) Sleumer, Reinwardtia 1960. 5: 153, *pro parte*.

Shrub to 2m. Twigs 2–5mm in diameter, scaly but early glabrescent; internodes 2–10cm. **Leaves** 3–5 together in tight pseudowhorls. **Blade** 20–40 x 15–35mm, elliptic to broadly elliptic; apex acute; margin entire, narrowly revolute; base broadly tapering, slightly decurrent; at first densely covered on both sides with flattish, pale scales, glabrescent above at maturity, laxly to sub-densely scaly beneath. **Scales** flat, rounded to irregularly lobed, with a broad flange and small slightly impressed centre. Mid-vein narrowly impressed above, distinctly raised beneath throughout its length; lateral veins 4–10 per side, wide-spreading, straight before curving near the margin, indis-tinctly anastomosing, slightly impressed above and raised

beneath, reticulation obscure. **Petiole** 8–13 x 1–1.5mm, grooved above, scaly.

Flower buds to 25 x 8mm, narrowly ovoid, the bracts standing vertically or spreading, not appressed. Outer bracts ovate with a long subulate point, inner ones ellip-tic, narrowly acute, scaly along the central line outside and along the margins, glabrous inside. Bracteoles to 20 x 3mm, filiform to linear, glabrous. Inflorescence of 4–8 flowers in an open umbel, curving downwards. Pedi-cels 6–8 x *c*.1mm, laxly scaly, and hairy. Calyx obliquely disc-shaped, wavy, obtusely and shortly lobed, *c*.4mm in diameter, densely scaly outside. **Corolla** 30–40 x 12–25mm, obliquely tubular, red or pink; tube 25–35 x 4–6 x 8–15mm, distinctly curved, laxly to sub-densely scaly out-side, glabrous inside; lobes 8–12 x 8–14mm, broadly obo-vate to sub-circular, sub-erect or spreading, overlapping ⅓–⅔. **Stamens** tightly clustered on the upper side of the mouth, not or only weakly exserted; filaments linear, very laxly hairy in the lower ½, glabrous distally, red; anthers 2–3.5 x 1–1.5mm, obovate to broadly oblong, purple. Disc prominent, shortly hairy at the upper margin. **Ovary** 4–5 x *c*.2mm, sub-cylindrical, densely white-hairy, and densely (but obscurely) scaly, gradually tapering distally; style slender, with some sparse hairs and scales at the base, becoming exserted; stigma to *c*.1.5mm in diameter.

Indonesia, New Guinea (W), Wissel Lakes, Mt Carstensz and Oranje Mts. Open places in the sub-alpine forest or in open alpine vegetation, 2500–3000m.

Differs from *R. culminicola* by the narrowly subulate to acute bracts and the almost glabrous filaments. It also grows at lower altitude and tends to have more acutely pointed leaves. Not known to have been cultivated.

---

197. **Rhododendron vinkii** Sleumer

Blumea 1963. 12: 91.
Type: W. Vink BW 12177, 26 Feb. 1962. New Guinea (W), Fak-fak, hinterland, bivouac Hambar, 840m (L, A, CANB, K, LAE, UC).
Derivation: Named after W. Vink, forest botanist at Manokwari (later on the staff at Leiden), who collected this plant with Professor Sleumer.

Shrub. Twigs 1.5–3mm in diameter, rounded, densely covered at the ends with sub-circular, sessile or sub-sessile scales; internodes 2–5cm. **Leaves** 3–5 together in pseudowhorls at the upper 2–3 nodes. **Blade** 35–60 x 15–22mm, elliptic to slightly obovate; apex broadly taper-ing, obtuse, rarely slightly retuse; margin slightly revo-lute especially proximally; base tapering into the petiole;

densely scaly on both sides initially, glabrescent above with age, persistently scaly beneath. **Scales** circular or almost so, thick, impressed, distant (for 2–3 times their diameter). Mid-vein slightly impressed above, prominent proximally beneath but gradually narrowed and less prominent distally; lateral veins 6–8 per side, impressed above, obscure beneath, reticulation faintly impressed above, or almost inconspicuous. **Petiole** 5–8 x *c*.1mm, grooved above, densely scaly.

Outer bracts to 10mm, ovate, inner ones obovate to spathulate, glabrous outside, but with a scaly margin. Bracteoles filiform. Inflorescence 2–3-flowered. Pedicels 12–18mm, slender, densely patently hairy and scaly. Calyx *c*.2.5mm in diameter, obliquely rounded, indistinctly obtusely 5-lobed. **Corolla** *c*.25mm, sub-obliquely tubular, light red, sub-densely covered with thick sub-circular scales outside, laxly hairy inside; tube *c*.20 x 3–4 x *c*.6mm, lobes *c*.5 x 6–7mm, spathulate-obovate. **Stamens** slightly exserted from the throat; filaments linear and shortly hairy below, glabrescent in the upper ¼; anthers broadly oblong, *c*.2mm. Disc densely erect-hairy. **Ovary** *c*.4 x 2mm, cylindrical, yellowish hairy, the hairs covering scales, abruptly contracted distally; style 12–16mm, thick, densely patently hairy proximally, less so distally, glabrous for *c*.2mm below the globose stigma.

Indonesia, New Guinea (W), hinterland of Fak-Fak, 840m, in primary *Agathis* forest on clayey soil. Once found. *Fl*. Feb.

Not yet recollected and never cultivated. This species was anomalous amongst the New Guinea discovireyas in having such large leaves; the bud scales on the type specimen clearly are fringed with stalked scales and although many of the scales have large centres they are very variable and it is better placed in subsection *Malesia*. It is tempting to regard it as a hybrid but only observations in the field will provide the answer to this.

---

198. Rhododendron flavoviride J.J.Sm.

Med. Rijksherb. 1915. 25: 4.

Type: Pulle (Versteeg) 2455, 9 Feb. 1913. New Guinea (W), Kajan Mts, 3200m (BO, K, L, U).

Derivation: Latin – *flavus* – pale yellow; *viridi* – green. Alluding to the flower colour.

Erect shrub or tree to 10m. Twigs 2–4mm in diameter, rounded, green, densely pale brown or translucently scaly, becoming glabrescent; internodes 2.5–8cm. **Leaves** 3–6 together in tight pseudowhorls at the upper 1–3 nodes. **Blade** 30–70 x 20–33mm, broadly-elliptic or ovate-elliptic sometimes obovate-elliptic; apex obtuse or rounded;

margin narrowly to broadly revolute; base rounded, or broadly tapering; initially scaly on both sides, glabrescent above, the scales leaving dense, minute, black pits, more persistently and sub-densely scaly beneath. **Scales** flat, or concave, marginal zone wide, transparent, shortly sub-stellately-lobed; centre minute, impressed becoming dark. Mid-vein narrow and slightly impressed above, grooved proximally for a few millimetres, beneath strongly raised to within *c*.1cm of the apex; lateral veins 4–8 per side, spreading at a wide angle, irregular, anastomosing, slightly depressed above and raised beneath in dried leaves, reticulation dense, slightly impressed above, faintly to markedly raised beneath. **Petiole** 3–11 x 2–3mm, grooved above, densely scaly.

Flower buds to 30 x 16mm, narrowly ovoid, acutely to broadly and bluntly pointed, smooth, green, but with just the basal bracts with the tips becoming revolute. Bracts broadly spathulate, glabrous except for a fringe of brown scales along the edges, hooded and emarginate at the apex, green along a broad median stripe, translucent towards the edges. A few of the shortest bracts with brown scales outside. Bracteoles to 20mm, linear to linear-spathulate, glabrous or with a few scales on the margins apically. Inflorescence a 3–6-flowered open umbel. Pedicels 10–30 x *c*.1.5mm, densely covered with pale brown appressed, sub-stellate scales, without hairs. Calyx 4–5mm in diameter, obliquely disc-shaped, shortly and obtusely 5-lobed. **Corolla** 45–50 x 33–42mm, on opening almost horizontal, becoming vertically hanging, pale-green, fragrant or without scent; tube 35–38 x 6–8 x 12–15mm, sub-cylindrical, distinctly curved, laxly but obscurely, sub-stellate-scaly outside, shortly hairy inside; lobes 16 x 18mm, sub-circular, spreading horizontally or sometimes a little reflexed, overlapping to about ½ their length, with a few very small scales near the base outside. **Stamens** exserted to 9mm, clustered around the style on the lower side of the mouth; filaments green, filiform, sub-densely to laxly patently hairy in the proximal ½; anthers 2.5–3 x 1mm, cream to pale brown, oblongoid curved, the base obtuse. Disc glabrous or hairy at the upper margin. **Ovary** *c*.5 x 2mm, sub-cylindrical-conical, base and apex tapering, yellowish or silvery, densely sub-patently hairy, the hairs covering small scales; style at first with the stigma just below the anthers in the mouth of the flower, later exserted to 15mm, hairy and scaly in the proximal ¼–⅓, scaly and sometimes very laxly hairy up to the middle, glabrous above; stigma globose.

Indonesia, New Guinea (W), Oranje Mts, Kajan Mts and near Lake Habbema. In open, swampy localities, or on the edge of sub-montane forest, *c*.3200m. *Fl*. Feb., Aug.

Rhododendron flavoviride.

Flowering for the first time in cultivation at the Royal Botanic Garden Edinburgh in 1999 from plants raised from seed collected by Paul Smith by climbing a 10m tree near Lake Habbema. It has since flowered regularly in spring and summer and is always cause for comment by visitors when in bloom with its unusual pale green hanging flowers. Despite herbarium notes recording the flowers as scented the plants at present in cultivation are completely without scent.

199. Rhododendron vitis-idaea Sleumer

Reinwardtia 1960. 5: 156.
Type: Carr 15098, 15 Jan. 1936. New Guinea (SE), Owen Stanley Range, NW of 'The Gap', *c.*2895m (BM, A, K, L, fragment, NY, SING).
Derivation: Latin – *vitis* – vine; *ida* – from Mt Ida (Greece) (Smid 1990), but this is indirect and an allusion to the similarity of the leaves to those of *Vaccinium vitis-idaea*, the cowberry of Europe.
Synonym: *R. vandeursenii* Sleumer, Blumea 1961. 11: 123.

Slender shrub to 2m. Twigs 1–2mm in diameter, at first densely covered with stalked stellate scales, glabrescent and densely warty later, without hairs; internodes 2.5–6cm. **Leaves** 3–5 together in tight pseudowhorls. **Blade** 8–50 x 5–25mm, obovate-elliptic or obovate; apex obtuse to rounded, not apiculate; margin cartilaginous, distinctly revolute; base tapering; sub-densely or laxly scaly on both sides initially, glabrescent and shining above with age, persistently scaly beneath. **Scales** flat, marginal zone irregularly stellately lobed; centre impressed, eventually glabrescent beneath leaving only impressed black points. Mid-vein impressed above, obtusely prominent beneath; lateral veins *c.*3 per side, obscure above, somewhat raised and curved-anastomosing beneath, reticulation obscure. **Petiole** 2–3 x 0.8–1mm, almost rounded in section, scaly.

Flower buds to 12 x 7mm, ovate, smooth. Bracts to 10 x 5mm, the outermost subulate with a few scales outside, then ovate, often with a mucronate point, membranous, minutely hairy outside but without scales except along the margins. **Flowers** solitary or paired, hanging vertically. Pedicels 8–20mm, slender, densely covered with reddish-brown, stellate scales and short spreading hairs. Calyx *c.*2.5mm in diameter, obliquely disc-shaped, shortly obtusely 5-lobed, scaly outside. **Corolla** 15–55mm, tubular, bright red, sometimes with a darker purplish margin to the lobes; tube 8–45 x 3–4 x 12–15mm, laxly stellate-scaly and minutely hairy outside, glabrous inside, somewhat curved; lobes 8–10 x 6–8mm, half-spreading, broadly obovate or sub-circular. **Stamens** exserted to *c.*5mm; filaments linear, glabrous; anthers 1.8–2 x *c.*1mm, obovate-oblong. Disc prominent, glabrous below, hairy on the upper margin. **Ovary** *c.*4 x 1.5mm, sub-cylindrical, slightly tapering at the base, densely shortly patent-hairy and sub-densely scaly; style slender, as long as the stamens, patently hairy in the lower ⅓–½; stigma sub-globose. **Fruit** *c.*40 x 6mm, cylindrical, laxly hairy and scaly.

Papua New Guinea, Owen Stanley Range; Morobe District, Rawlinson Range, Mt Bangeta, Porget, Merimanta, Mt Wilhelm area, Porul road, Owen Stanley Mts near 'The Gap', Mt Ganeve, above Bakaia. Epiphytic or terrestrial, forest or open hillside, common in sub-alpine shrubberies, 2195–2590m. *Fl.* Jan.–Nov.

Kores & van Royen (1982) synonymised *R. vandeursenii* with *R. vitis-idaea* as a result of field work showing that the corolla length difference that had been used to separate these species was unworkable. This extends the range of the species considerably.

200. Rhododendron stevensianum Sleumer

Blumea 1973. 21(2): 371.
Type: Stevens & Searle LAE 58178, 22 March 1973. Papua New Guinea, Eastern Highlands District, Kundiawa sub-district, Loop road no. 2, Dpom Sina Sina (L, LAE).
Derivation: Named after Peter Stevens, botanist who worked in New Guinea and made a considerable contribution to vireya research with collections and observations and was one of the collectors of the type specimen.

Shrub to 60cm. Twigs rounded, *c.*1.5–2mm in diameter, densely brown scaly, the scales on slender stalks which leave the surface appearing shortly hairy after the scales have fallen off; internodes 1–2cm. **Leaves** in tight pseudowhorls, with 2–3 full-sized leaves and sometimes one or two smaller ones. **Blade** 15–35 x 10–25mm, ovate, occasionally broadly elliptic; apex obtuse to rounded,

Rhododendron stevensianum.

sometimes minutely emarginate; margin entire or minutely crenulate, slightly cartilaginous, flat; base cordate, green and sparsely scaly above, quickly becoming glabrescent, sometimes weakly sulcate; below sparsely but more persistently brown scaly. **Scales** rounded to somewhat lobed and slightly impressed. Mid-vein narrow and slightly impressed in the proximal ½, otherwise smooth above, distinctly raised below, at least in the larger leaves; lateral veins 4–6 per side, wide-spreading, slightly raised above, obscure below. **Petiole** 2–3 x 1–1.75mm, weakly grooved above, scaly, semi-erect so that the leaves appear almost sessile.

Flower buds *c.*11 x 3mm, smooth, imbricate, green or lightly flushed with purple, narrowly ellipsoid to ovoid, surrounded by one or two cataphylls which are densely scaly and hairy on both sides. Outer bracts broadly ovate brown scaly outside and fringed with scales, glabrous inside, inner bracts ovate, glabrous or with a small group of scales near the apex and a fringe of very fragile scales which leave short hairs when they have fallen off. Inflorescence of solitary, hanging flowers, rarely in twos. Pedicels 8–12 x *c.*1.25mm, pink, densely covered with short patent hairs. Calyx green, densely patently hairy. **Corolla** 28–33 x 22–28mm, dull purple; tube 20–25 x 6 x 9–10mm, strongly curved, glabrous outside and inside; lobes *c.*10–12 x 9–11mm, spreading horizontally or a little reflexed, overlapping to *c.*¼. **Stamens** tightly clustered on the upper

side of the mouth, sometimes exserted to 4mm; filaments purplish-red, glabrous; anthers *c.*1.8 x 1mm, brown. Disc green, sub-glabrous to densely hairy on the upper margin. **Ovary** 4 x 2.5mm, green, conical, covered in silvery scales and distally pointed white hairs; style 7–10mm, (elongating to 20mm in fruit), green or red, glabrous, or with a few patent hairs near the base, held on the upper side of the tube. **Fruit** 16–21 x *c.*5mm, horizontal to semi-erect, green and weakly longitudinally grooved with a persistent purple style, the valves curling back beyond the horizontal and becoming slightly twisted, the placentae remaining adherent to the central column. Seeds 4–5mm, without tails *c.*1mm, the longest tail *c.*2mm, tails often somewhat crimped.

Papua New Guinea, known from the Eastern Highlands, Kundiawa subdistrict, Sina Sina, Mt Giluwe, Southern Highlands and Enga Province between 2000 and 2300m altitude, recorded as both an epiphyte and terrestrial but mostly epiphytic and probably under-recorded due to its rather inconspicuous flowers.

Cultivated since 1990, the plant grows easily and is of small, compact, busy habit. The flowers are dull purple, not very conspicuous but very dainty and are produced over a long period mostly towards the end of the northern summer.

201. Rhododendron hatamense Becc.

Malesia 1878. I: 202.
Type: Beccari 5811. New Guinea (W), Arfak, Hatam, 1525–2135m (Fl).
Derivation: Named after the place from which it was first collected.

Synonyms:
R. coenenii J.J.Sm., Nova Guinea 1914. 12(2): 132, *t.*30a.
R. gibbsiae J.J.Sm. in Gibbs, Phyto. Fl. Arfak Mts 1917. 169.

Low shrub, to 50cm, branches spreading. Twigs slender, laxly scaly; internodes 0.8–6cm. **Leaves** 3–6 together in pseudowhorls. **Blade** 20–60 x 9–30mm, ovate-elliptic to elliptic; apex shortly acuminate or broadly tapering, obtuse, sometimes rounded, or apiculate; margin cartilaginous, distinctly revolute; base broadly tapering; glabrescent above with age, persistently sub-densely scaly beneath. **Scales** small, flat, sub-stellate, faintly impressed, eventually glabrescent beneath with only blackish pits remaining. Mid-vein impressed above, prominent beneath; lateral veins 4–6 per side, straight below, looping near the margin, impressed above, distinctly raised beneath, or sub-obscure. **Petiole** 2–4mm, flat.

Bracts to 10 x 5mm, ovate-acuminate, shortly subulate, membranous, glabrous, except for the marginal scales. Bracteoles to 10mm, filiform. Inflorescence 2–6-flowered. Pedicels 10–24mm, slender, densely scaly and patently hairy. Calyx *c.*3mm in diameter, disc-shaped, often reflexed, obscurely 5-lobed, scaly and hairy outside. **Corolla** *c.*25mm, tubular-funnel-shaped, sub-oblique, bright to dark red, waxy and glossy; tube 15 x 4–5 x 5–6mm, sub-cylindrical, laxly hairy, mainly in the proximal ½ outside, or sometimes glabrous, always without scales, laxly patently hairy in the proximal ½ inside; lobes 8 x 12mm, spreading, broadly obovate-spathulate. **Stamens** exserted to *c.*5mm; filaments linear, laxly patently hairy above the base to the proximal ¼, glabrous distally; anthers *c.*2mm, dark purple to almost black, oblong-obovate. Disc glabrous. **Ovary** *c.*5 x 3mm, sub-ovoid, densely, shortly covered with spreading hairs, the hairs covering the scales, tapering distally; style equalling the stamens, hairy nearly to the top; stigma sub-globose.

Indonesia, New Guinea (W), Vogelkop Peninsula, Arfak, Tamrau and Nettoti Mts. Epiphytic in mossy *Nothofagus* forest, 1550–1900m, apparently very scattered or rare. *Fl.* Oct.–March.

Sleumer (1960) noted a Clemens collection (12327), from Papua New Guinea, Morobe District, A-mieng, on Yaneng R. (a tributary of the R. Buso), was similar but with smaller flowers and less hairy pedicels. This material has not been examined but would be a very surprising extension to the range of this species.

---

202. Rhododendron cornu-bovis Sleumer
Reinwardtia 1960. 5: 152.
Type: Cheesman 1192, 17 June 1938. New Guinea, Weigeo I., top of Mt Nok (Buffelhoorn), E shore of Majalibit Bay, *c.*860m (BM).
Derivation: Latin – *cornu* – horn; *bovis* – an ox. After the Dutch name of Mt Nok where it was collected.

Small straggling shrub to 2m. Twigs *c.*1mm in diameter, rounded, tips flattened and densely covered with reddish-brown, sub-stellate scales; internodes 2–4cm. **Leaves** 4–6 together in pseudowhorls. **Blade** 25–40 x 8–14mm, obovate-elliptic to obovate; apex broadly tapering, obtuse or rounded; margin slightly recurved; base tapering, scaly on both sides at first, quickly glabrescent above, persistently sub-densely scaly beneath. **Scales** large, flat, irregularly stellately divided in the marginal zone; centre slightly impressed. Mid-vein grooved above, prominent beneath; lateral veins 3–4 per side, inconspicuous, often obscure beneath. **Petiole** 2–4mm, scaly.

Bracts to 8 x 5mm, broadly ovate to ovate-elliptic, obtuse, glabrous outside, except for the marginal scales. Bracteoles *c.*5mm, filiform, laxly scaly. Inflorescence 2–3-flowered. Pedicels 10–14 x 0.5–0.7mm, slender, sub-densely stellately scaly and sparsely, shortly patently hairy. Calyx *c.*2.5mm in diameter, disc-shaped, oblique, scaly and shortly hairy outside, indistinctly 5-lobed. **Corolla** *c.*25 x 20mm, obliquely tubular-funnel-shaped, pink to red; tube 12–14 x 4–5 x 6–8mm, sub-densely to laxly covered with reddish-brown sub-stellate scales outside, laxly hairy inside, slightly curved; lobes 9–10 x 6–7mm, spreading, obovate-spathulate. **Stamens** exserted to *c.*5mm, sub-equal; filaments filiform, laxly patently hairy for the proximal ⅔, glabrous distally; anthers *c.*1.6mm, broadly oblong. Disc prominent, glabrous. **Ovary** *c.*5 x 2mm, sub-cylindrical, densely short-hairy and scaly, the scales covered by the hairs, tapering distally; style oblique, laxly patently hairy in the proximal ½, without scales, glabrous distally, nearly equalling the corolla in length; stigma sub-globose. **Fruit** (sub-mature) 22 x 4mm, sub-fusiform-cylindric, curved, densely hairy and scaly.

Indonesia, New Guinea (W), Waigeou I., (W of Vogelkop), top of Mt Nok (Buffelhoorn), reported to be common there in mossy forest and shrubberies at 860m. *Fl.* June.

Never cultivated.

---

203. Rhododendron commonae Foerster
Fedde Rep. 1914. 13: 223.
Type: Keysser *s.n.* Papua New Guinea, Morobe District, Mt Saruwaged, ('Bolan') (B†, BM).
Derivation: Said to be named after the author's wife!

Synonyms:
R. stonori Sleumer, Reinwardtia 1960. 5: 155.
R. nitens Sleumer, Reinwardtia 1960. 5: 162, *non* Hutchinson, 1936.
R. pseudonitens Sleumer, Blumea 1961. 11: 124.

Compact, stiff, often flat-topped shrub, to 6m. Sometimes forming a thick woody basal burl from which numerous epicormic shoots arise. Twigs *c.*3mm in diameter, rounded or angular, green or red, stellate-scaly and minutely short-hairy; internodes 1.5–4.5cm. **Leaves** spirally arranged, or in very loose pseudowhorls, clustered more densely in the upper part of the internodes. **Blade** 10–43 x 8–22mm, elliptic to obovate-elliptic, narrowly obovate or in the high altitude forms almost circular; apex obtuse to rounded with a conspicuous apical gland which is sometimes extended into a down-turned point;

margin flat or slightly revolute, cartilaginous and distinctly crenulate; base broadly tapering; shiny green and glabrescent above although the scales often leaving blackish pits; beneath, paler-green sub-densely brown scaly. **Scales** rounded to lobed, with small centres, impressed into the leaf surface and leaving distinct pits where they have fallen off. Mid-vein impressed above, broad and obtusely prominent in the lower ½ beneath, less so distally; lateral veins 4–6 per side, irregular, curved ascending, slightly impressed above in fully mature leaves, faintly raised or hardly visible beneath, reticulation inconspicuous. **Petiole** 2–4 x 1–2mm, grooved above and slightly flattened, scaly and obscurely shortly hairy.

Flower buds to 15 x 12mm, green, the bract apices standing out as short points. Bracts to 15 x 11mm, the outer ones subulate, intermediate ovate-acuminate, abruptly subulate in the upper ¼–½, innermost ones obovate-spathulate, shining, glabrous or scaly along the dorsal midline and at the apex (never hairy!), fringed with scales. Bracteoles to 12 x 1mm, linear. Inflorescence of 4–6-flowered open umbels. **Flowers** half-hanging to semi-erect. Pedicels 8–18 x *c.*1.5mm, laxly to densely brown-stellate-scaly, without hairs or with minute papillose hairs between the scales and sometimes some longer hairs just under the calyx. Calyx *c.*4mm in diameter, oblique, scaly at the base, deeply 5-lobed, lobes narrowly triangular or sometimes linear-subulate up to 10mm, glabrous, or occasionally long-hairy at the apex, irregular in both shape and length, sub-persistent. **Corolla** 20–35 x 27mm, tubular, oblique and curved, (rarely straight), deep red to purplish, pink, pale yellow or white; tube 25–30 x 6–7 x 10–12mm, laxly to sub-densely stellately scaly outside, glabrous or shortly hairy inside, swollen at the base and conspicuously grooved in the proximal ½; lobes 10–11 x 9–10mm, sub-spathulate-circular, spreading to reflexed and overlapping to *c.*⅓. **Stamens** exserted to 10mm, loosely arranged in the upper ½ of the flower;

Rhododendron commonae.

filaments linear, purplish-pink, glabrous or laxly shortly papillose-hairy; anthers obovate-oblong, 2–2.3 x 1mm. Disc prominent, glabrous. **Ovary** 4–5 x 2–3mm, conical to sub-cylindrical, densely covered with short slightly distally directed, silvery hairs which cover small scales; style glabrous or with some hairs for the basal 5mm, ultimately as long as the stamens, on the upper side of the tube, moving to a central position as the stigma becomes receptive; stigma obliquely globose. **Fruit** 10–20 x 6–8mm, ellipsoid, standing erect, sub-densely short-hairy and scaly. Seeds *c.*3mm, the tails included.

Indonesia, New Guinea (W), Mt Jaya. **Papua New Guinea**, Star Mts, Yobobos, Mt Sugarloaf, Sirunki, Yogonda, Mt Hagen area, Tomba, Kubor Mts, Mt Wilhelm lakes area, Mt Michael, Finisterre Mts, Sarawaket Mts. Terrestrial in grassland at the edge of *Papuacedrus* forest, in open semi-swampy places, also on crests of high ridges, stony ground, 1800–4000m, becoming very small-leafed at high altitudes, flowering freely in fully exposed positions, locally plentiful. The plant's ability to grow from dormant buds on the thick woody basal burl gives this species some ability to regenerate after the upper stems have been destroyed by fire or frost. *Fl. fr.* throughout the year.

Van Royen & Kores (1982) reduced *R. pseudonitens* to this species on the basis of field work which showed the size difference between them was untenable. They also recorded wild hybrids with *R. culminicola* and *R. womersleyi* in the Finisterre Mts and with *R. macgregoriae* in the Tari Gap.

Introduced into cultivation repeatedly, possibly the earliest was seed collected by Sleumer and cultivated at Kew where it flowered in February 1965 with dark red flowers. It grows easily, forming nice rounded clumps, and flowers freely and irregularly several times a year. At least three colour forms are in cultivation: bright red, pink and a very pale yellow.

204. Rhododendron rhodostomum Sleumer
Reinwardtia 1960. 5: 157.
Type: Clemens 9922, 28 Feb. 1939. New Guinea (NE), Morobe District, Mt Saruwaged, upper Camp, 2745–3265m (A, L).
Derivation: Greek – *rhodo* – rose or rosy-red; *stoma* – mouth. The flowers originally described as white with a pink mouth.

Shrub to 60cm; branches spreading. Twigs 1–1.5mm in diameter, rounded, densely covered with sub-stellate, shortly stalked scales at first, becoming glabrescent and distinctly warty and rough to the touch; internodes 2–6cm. **Leaves** 4–5 together in pseudowhorls. **Blade**

20–35 x 10–21mm, elliptic or obovate-elliptic, rarely broadly obovate; apex broadly tapering, or rarely almost rounded, the extreme tip apiculate with a short, thickened gland; margin slightly revolute; base tapering; scaly on both sides, at first, becoming glabrescent above, persistently, sub-densely scaly beneath. **Scales** angular or obtusely lobed in the narrow marginal zone; centre large, thick, impressed, becoming blackish. Mid-vein slightly impressed above in its proximal part, raised beneath; lateral veins sub-inconspicuous. **Petiole** 1–5mm, flattened, scaly.

Bracts to 12 x 5mm, ovate-acuminate, apiculate subulate, membranous, scaly at the tips outside, glabrous elsewhere, margin with fragile scales. Bracteoles *c*.8mm, filiform, glabrous. **Flowers** solitary. Pedicels *c*.10mm, slender, very densely reddish-brown-stellate-scaly, not hairy at all. Calyx *c*.2.5mm in diameter, oblique, disc-shaped, scaly outside, very shortly obtusely 5-lobed. **Corolla** 23–27mm, tubular, fleshy, white with a pink mouth; tube *c*.20 x 6–7 x 7–9mm, cylindrical, slightly curved, sub-densely sub-stellate-scaly outside, glabrous inside; lobes 6–7 x 6–7mm, broadly obovate or sub-circular, glabrous. **Stamens** reaching just below the mouth; filaments flattened and linear, glabrous; anthers 2.5 x 1mm, sub-obovate-oblong, cells often contracted at the base into a short apiculus. Disc prominent, shortly hairy at the upper margin, glabrous elsewhere. **Ovary** *c*.5 x 2mm, sub-cylindrical, densely, very shortly greyish hairy and sub-stellately scaly, gradually tapering distally; style slender, patently hairy in the proximal ½, glabrous distally, equalling the corolla in length; stigma club-shaped. **Fruit** (immature) 20 x 3mm, fusiform, densely shortly hairy and laxly scaly.

Papua New Guinea, Mt Saruwaged and Rawlinson Range. Epiphytic in mossy forest and forest margins, 1525–3655m. *Fl.* Feb.–March, June.

Never cultivated.

205. Rhododendron takeuchii Argent

Folia Malaysiana 2003. 4(2): 117, pl.6a & b.
Type: Takeuchi & Wiakabu 9528, 26 Jan. 1994. Papua New Guinea, New Ireland, Hans Meyer Range, ridge adjacent to the Weitin River, *c*.1175m (A, LAE, L).
Derivation: Named after Dr Wayne Takeuchi, the senior collector of the type of this species and an experienced botanist in New Guinea.

Shrub to 80cm. Twigs *c*.2mm in diameter, sub-densely scaly with flat appressed scales but without simple hairs; internodes 2.5–10cm. **Leaves** in tight pseudowhorls of 3–8 together. **Blade** 25–40 x 12–22mm, elliptic to obovate; apex obtuse to rounded; margin entire, narrowly revolute; base broadly tapering, then decurrent with very narrow flanges on each side of the petiole; upper leaf surface glabrescent; lower surface sparsely and more persistently scaly. **Scales** disc-shaped with broad, silvery, lobed margins and dark centres, slightly impressed. Mid-vein narrowly impressed above, raised beneath for most of its length; lateral veins 2–5 slender, straight veins arising at an acute angle on each side, and disappearing before the margin or obscure, reticulation obscure. **Petiole** 2–3 x 1–1.5mm, grooved above, somewhat flattened, smooth, densely scaly when young and with narrow lateral wings.

Flower buds to *c*.7 x 4mm. The outer bracts subulate, the inner ovate, somewhat scaly in the central area outside and with a fringe of scales along the margins, without simple hairs. Bracteoles filiform, glabrous. Inflorescence *c*.4-flowered umbels. Pedicels 10–14 x 0.6mm, sub-densely scaly but without simple hairs. **Flowers** narrowly funnel-shaped, pink or red. Calyx a low disc, only weakly lobed, densely scaly outside, glabrous within. **Corolla** 35–43 x *c*.30mm; tube *c*.20 x 4 x 8mm, slightly curved, moderately to densely scaly outside, densely patently hairy inside; lobes *c*.20–24 x 12mm, laxly scaly outside. **Stamens** exserted to *c*.10mm; filaments patently hairy in the proximal ⅔, glabrous distally; anthers 1.8 x 0.7mm, with rounded bases to the cells and oblique pores. Disc prominent, densely hairy along the upper margin. **Ovary** *c*.4 x 1.8mm, sub-ovoid, densely covered in sub-appressed silvery hairs which partially cover an underlayer of brown scales, tapering abruptly distally; style *c*.20mm, sparsely patently hairy in the proximal ⅓, glabrous distally and entirely without scales along its whole length; stigma *c*.2.5mm in diameter, a broad irregular disc. **Fruit** *c*.17 x 4mm, with the hairs persisting and becoming patent, the outer layer peeling irregularly and the valves spreading and twisting on dehiscence.

Papua New Guinea, New Ireland, Hans Meyer Range, ridge adjacent to the Weitin River and Mt Angil. Epiphytic in mossy montane forest and a ridge dominated by *Syzygium* and *Podocarpus*, 1175–1800m. *Fl.* Jan., Feb.

Very similar to small-leafed forms of *R. culminicola* from the New Guinea mainland but these are all from very much higher altitude (above 3000m) than the present species. The base of the leaf blade in *R. takeuchii* is decurrent, with narrow wings which extend for virtually the entire length of the petiole, whereas in *R. culminicola* the base although sometimes narrowly tapering clearly stops at the petiole. The petioles themselves are quite different: those of *R. culminicola* are much more robust, being at least 2mm wide and rugose, while in *R. takeuchii* they are less than 1.5mm wide and quite smooth in comparable dried specimens. The flower measurements given by Sleumer (1966) for *R. culminicola* are so wide as to encompass those of *R. takeuchii* but if the ratio of corolla lobes to corolla tube length is used there is a clear distinction between them: *R. culminicola* has lobes ¼–⅓ the length of the tube whereas *R. takeuchii* has lobes well over ½ the length of the tube. *Rhododendron takeuchii* superficially resembles *R. neobritannicum* which would seem a more likely geographical alliance as this species comes from the adjacent island of New Britain; however, *R. neobritannicum* has totally different scales, being in section *Phaeovireya*, a glabrous corolla and filaments and an ovary lacking simple hairs. Not known in cultivation.

206. Rhododendron helodes Sleumer

Reinwardtia 1960. 5: 161.
Type: Brass 9316, Aug. 1938. W New Guinea, Lake Habema camp (A, L).
Derivation: Greek – *helodes* – growing in marshy places.

Shrub, with strong, spreading branches, to 50cm. Twigs *c.*3mm in diameter, rounded, densely covered with appressed sub-stellate scales becoming glabrescent; internodes 3.5–8cm. **Leaves** 4–6 together in pseudowhorls at the upper 2–3 nodes. **Blade** 20–40 x 8–15mm, elliptic, broadly elliptic or rarely sub-obovate; apex shortly broadly acuminate, sub-acute or blunt, apiculate with a protruding gland; margin narrowly cartilaginous, irregularly crenulate with impressed scales or sub-entire; base broadly tapering and decurrent; laxly impressed-scaly or glabrescent above, more distinctly and persistently scaly beneath, but eventually glabrescent, leaving impressed, dark points, laxly scaly distally, dense and touching proximally, and on the petiole. **Scales** with a fragile, marginal transparent zone, large and variously lobed; centre more persistent, small and impressed. Mid-vein impressed in the proximal ⅔ above, dilated and obtusely prominent beneath, gradually disappearing distally; lateral veins 2 per side just above the base, high-ascending and with 2–3 other less conspicuous veins arising further from the base. **Petiole** 3–5 x 2–3mm, flat.

Outer bracts few, short, ovate-subulate, inner ones to 18 x 7mm, more numerous, broadly obovate-spathulate, shortly acuminate, sub-acute, at first densely reddish-scaly, early glabrescent. Inflorescence 1–4-flowered. Pedicels 20–30 x *c.*1mm, very densely covered with red or orange, stellate scales, but without hairs. Calyx *c.*5mm in diameter, disc-shaped, scaly outside, the membranous margin reflexed and irregularly lobed, lobes up to 1mm and appressed to the corolla. **Corolla** 30–35mm, tubular, red or yellowish red; tube 20–25 x 6–7 x 10–12mm, slightly narrowed distally before becoming gradually dilated again to the mouth, sub-densely stellately scaly outside, glabrous inside; lobes 9–11 x 7–9mm, erect or spreading, broadly spathulate or sub-circular, very slightly emarginate, sub-densely scaly except near the margins. **Stamens** unequal, the longest as long as the corolla tube; filaments linear, glabrous; anthers *c.*2mm, obovate. Disc prominent, glabrous. **Ovary** *c.*8 x 3mm, sub-cylindrical, abruptly contracted distally, densely covered with white or yellowish hairs, which are directed forwards and cover numerous scales; style *c.*20mm, slender, exceeding the stamens in length, shortly hairy for 2mm proximally, glabrous distally; stigma globose.

Indonesia, New Guinea (W), Lake Habbema region. Terrestrial in low shrubberies, grassy marshes and open boggy slopes, locally frequent, at 3225m. *Fl.* Aug.

A poorly known species which has not been recollected recently. Never cultivated.

207. Rhododendron psammogenes Sleumer

Reinwardtia 1960. 5: 150.
Type: Brass 11759, Dec. 1938. New Guinea (NW), Balim R., 2100m (A, L, fragment).
Derivation: Greek – *psammos* – sand; *genos* – child. Alluding to the sandy habitat.

Erect shrub to 1m. Twigs rounded, at first, laxly covered with minute pale scales, later glabrescent; internodes 3–10cm. **Leaves** in well-marked pseudowhorls. **Blade** 25–55 x 14–28mm, elliptic; apex broadly tapering, then often almost rounded and very shortly apiculate; margin entire, narrowly revolute; base broadly tapering or rounded, initially scaly on both sides, gradually glabrescent above, sub-densely scaly beneath. **Scales** pale reddish-brown, minute, marginal zone variously lobed; centre impressed. Mid-vein impressed above, thick and prominent beneath proximally, less prominent distally; lateral veins 5–6 per side, irregular, straight proximally, obscurely anastomosing, slightly impressed above, slightly or not raised beneath. **Petiole** 2–4mm, thick, flat.

Bracts to 10 x 5mm, ovate to ovate-elliptic or sub-spathulate, membranous, scaly outside, or quickly glabrescent, margin fringed with scales or very shortly irregularly toothed. Bracteoles to 10mm, linear, laxly scaly.

Inflorescence a 7–9-flowered open umbel. Pedicels 25–30 x *c*.1.5mm, densely covered with thick, lobed scales. Calyx *c*.3mm in diameter, oblique, irregularly 5-toothed to 1mm, but sometimes up to 3mm, elongate-triangular and acute. **Corolla** 30–33mm, funnel-shaped, sub-oblique, white or pale yellow, thin; tube 18–20 x 3–4 x 4–5mm, cylindrical, densely covered with thick, sub-circular, lobed scales outside, with white spreading hairs in the lower ½ of the corolla tube inside; lobes 10–12 x 7–8mm, spreading, obovate-spathulate, shallowly retuse. **Stamens** exserted to *c*.5mm, unequal; filaments linear and densely patently hairy proximally, more slender and glabrous distally; anthers *c*.2.5mm, oblong. Disc glabrous below, shortly yellowish hairy on the upper margin. **Ovary** *c*.5 x 2mm, sub-cylindrical, densely covered with scales and white, forwardly directed hairs, gradually tapering distally; style slender, laxly patently hairy and scaly in the lower ⅓–½, glabrous distally, as long as or slightly longer than the stamens; stigma thick, rounded.

Indonesia, New Guinea (W), Balim R. Valley, at 2100m, terrestrial amongst bracken in unfertile sandy soil. *Fl.* Dec.

Known only from the type collection although a similar collection, differing in the more scaly style although similarly hairy, was found in the Lake Habbema region, on sandy soil in a forest opening. Never cultivated.

---

208. Rhododendron brassii Sleumer
Reinwardtia 1960. 5: 170.
Type: Brass 9139, Aug. 1938. New Guinea (W), Lake Habbema, 3225m camp (A, BO, L).
Derivation: Named in honour of Leonard Brass, famous for his botanical collecting expeditions in New Guinea.

Erect shrub to 2.5m. Twigs rounded, reddish and often whitish, when dry, smooth, tips laxly to densely covered with small, flat, sub-stellate scales; internodes 5–16cm, often with conspicuous broad hemispherical to rounded buds in the leaf axils. **Leaves** spiral, equally spaced along the branches. **Blade** 30–50 x 15–25mm, elliptic, broadly elliptic or sub-obovate; apex broadly obtuse or rounded, apiculate with a thick prominent gland; margin flat or weakly revolute, entire or minutely irregular to denticulate-crenulate and narrowly cartilaginous; base broadly tapering and somewhat decurrent, more rarely almost rounded, laxly scaly above but quickly glabrescent, the scales leaving minute pits, more persistently brown-scaly beneath. **Scales** small, sub-circular, variously sub-stellately lobed; centre small, slightly impressed. Mid-vein impressed above especially at the base and obtusely

prominent beneath; lateral veins 6–8 per side, ascending at an angle of *c*.45°, slightly impressed above, raised or inconspicuous beneath, reticulation visible only beneath. **Petiole** 3–6 x 1.5–2mm, grooved above, flattened, scaly.

Flower buds to 30 x 14mm, ovoid, smooth with the bracts fully appressed, green or flushed with purplish red. Bracts 20–30 x *c*.15mm, membranous, glabrous except for the fringe of scales on the margins, outer, ovate, obtuse or emarginate. Bracteoles *c*.20 x 1–1.5mm, linear, glabrous. Inflorescence 3–6-flowered, in an open or one-sided umbel, the flowers hanging vertically or sometimes half-hanging. Pedicels 20–25 x *c*.1.5mm, laxly sub-stellately scaly below, more densely so distally, without hairs. Calyx 4–5mm in diameter, very obliquely disc-shaped, shortly, obtusely, 5-lobed, scaly outside. **Corolla** 45–50 x 25–30mm, dull yellow or greenish-yellow with a strong red flush on the proximal ½ of the tube, without scent, narrowly funnel-shaped, fleshy, glabrous both in and outside; tube 30–38 x 6–7 x 10–15mm, almost straight; lobes 12–15 x 14–18mm, broadly rounded to ovate, spreading horizontally, overlapping to *c*.halfway. **Stamens** very unequal, loosely clustered on the lower side of the mouth, exserted to *c*.10mm; filaments linear, glabrous, pale yellow; anthers 2.5–3 x 1.3–1.5mm; cells obovoid and basally apiculate. Disc green, prominent, glabrous. **Ovary** *c*.5 x 2.5mm, sub-ovoid-cylindrical, very densely covered with silvery sub-circular or angled, flat scales, gradually tapering distally; style slender, laxly scaly proximally for up to 10mm, glabrous distally, exserted up to 15mm from the corolla; stigma thick-capitate, green. **Fruit** 15 x 6mm, obliquely fusiform-cylindrical.

Indonesia, New Guinea (W), near Lake Habbema and the Wamena R. on N slope of Mt Wilhelmina (Trichora). Shrubby forest, or grassy margins of *Podocarpus* forest, or open shrubberies on ridges, locally plentiful, 3200–3225m. *Fl.* Aug.–Sept.

Rhododendron brassii.

Cultivated since 1990 when it was introduced to Edinburgh. It makes a leggy shrub, flowering irregularly throughout the year. Sleumer (1973) notes under *R. ultimum* that it may not be specifically different from that species. In fact, in the field, the differences are very obvious: *R. brassii* grows at a lower altitude and is a tall, erect shrub with green or silvery-green leaves, whereas *R. ultimum* is at higher altitude and is a low, spreading shrub with purplish leaves. Both have been grown side by side in cultivation and retain their distinctive habits. A hybrid with *R. versteegii* (*R.* x *nebulicolum*) has been described from the wild by Danet (2005).

209. Rhododendron porphyranthes Sleumer
Blumea 1963. 12: 108.
Type: Sleumer & Vink 4452, 26 Jan. 1962. W New Guinea, Arfak Mts, Mt Saru-mot, near Iray, Anggi Gigi Lake (L, A).
Derivation: Greek – *porphyra* – the purple dye obtained from a marine gastropod; *anthes* – flowers. Alluding to the flower colour.

Weak, erect, 1- to few-stemmed shrub to 50cm. Twigs 1–2mm in diameter, young ones purplish, laxly scaly; internodes 3–9cm. **Leaves** 4–6 together in loose pseudo-whorls. **Blade** 30–50 x 15–23mm, obovate to elongate-obovate; apex rounded, to obtuse, sometimes a little emarginate; margin slightly revolute and sub-crenulate with impressed scales; base tapering; immature ones sub-densely or laxly scaly on both sides, mature ones shining, early glabrescent above, more slowly so beneath. **Scales** small, flat, marginal zone angular or stellately lobed; centre small and impressed. Mid-vein slightly grooved proximally, flat distally above, as thick as the petiole at the base, gradually decreasing distally beneath; lateral veins 3–4 per side, obscure, without visible reticulation. **Petiole** 6–10 x *c.*1mm, winged in the upper part by the decurrent blade, nearly rounded below.

Flower buds *c.*20 x 8mm, oblong. Bracts to 12 x 7mm, ovate, distinctly keeled; inner ones obovate to spathulate, all shining and laxly scaly outside, fringed with deciduous scales. Inflorescence 2-flowered. Pedicels *c.*10mm, slender, sub-densely sub-stellately scaly. Calyx *c.*2mm in diameter, oblique, wavy. **Corolla** *c.*23mm, sub-campanulate-tubular, zygomorphic, hanging, waxy, reddish-purple, shiny, glabrous; tube 15–18 x *c.*3 x *c.*6mm, straight, distinctly 5-pouched near the base; lobes 6–8 x 6–8mm, erect, broadly obovate-spathulate. **Stamens** exserted to *c.*4mm; filaments linear, glabrous; anthers *c.*2 x 1.5mm, sub-obovate-elliptic, the base obtuse. Disc prominent,

glabrous. **Ovary** 2.5 x 1.2mm, sub-cylindrical, tapering distally; style 7–8mm, slender, glabrous; stigma club-shaped.

Indonesia, New Guinea (W), Arfak Mts: Mt Sarumont near Iray, Anggi Gigi Lake, and near Lake Habbema. Known only from the type collection and one other. Terrestrial in *Nothofagus* forest at 2320m, and *Libocedrus* forest at 3500m. *Fl.* Jan., Oct.

Not cultivated.

210. Rhododendron rubrobracteatum Sleumer
Reinwardtia 1960. 5: 175.
Type: Brass 9278, Aug. 1938. New Guinea (NW), Lake Habbema, 3345m (A, L, fragment).
Derivation: Latin – *rubro* – red; *bractea* – bract. Alluding to the red colour of the bracts on the flower bud.

Shrub to 70cm. Twigs 1.5–2mm in diameter, laxly sub-stellately scaly when young, glabrescent and smooth later, or possibly warty; internodes 2–7cm. **Leaves** 3–5 together in pseudowhorls, with one or two inserted lower than the rest. **Blade** 20–38 x 10–16mm, elliptic to elliptic-oblong; apex shortly acuminate, sub-acute or obtuse, often apiculate with a protruding terminal gland; margin narrowly cartilaginous, entire, wavy or sub-crenulate, not or very weakly revolute; base broadly to narrowly tapering, sometimes truncate or rounded, minutely rugose above in old dry leaves, with scale remains or glabrescent, laxly and more persistently scaly beneath. **Scales** with the thin marginal zone irregularly sub-stellately lobed; centre slightly impressed. Mid-vein impressed above, obtusely prominent beneath; lateral veins inconspicuous. **Petiole** 3–7 x 1–1.5mm, a little flattened, scaly.

Flower buds to 20 x 14mm, the bracts standing erect away from the bud. Bracts 10–22 x 4–9mm, ovate-acuminate, tapering to a short acumen or subulate, red, membranous, glossy, glabrous, initially with scales along the margin. Bracteoles *c.*6mm, filiform. Inflorescence of 2–5 flowers in an open umbel, the flowers hanging vertically. Pedicels 13–20 x *c.*1mm, densely reddish-stellate-scaly and densely papillose. Calyx *c.*3mm in diameter, obliquely disc-shaped, obscurely and bluntly 5-lobed, scaly outside. **Corolla** 20–26mm, tubular, sub-oblique, red or pale orange-pink, thin; tube 16–20 x *c.*5 x 7–8mm, straight or slightly curved, pouched at the base, laxly to sub-densely stellately scaly outside, glabrous inside; lobes 5–6 x 5–6mm, half-spreading, broadly obovate or sub-circular, slightly retuse. **Stamens** exserted to *c.*4mm, unequal; filaments linear, glabrous; anthers *c.*2mm, broadly oblong, base obtuse. Disc glabrous. **Ovary** *c.*4 x 1.5mm, sub-cylindrical, densely stellately scaly, gradually narrowed distally; style slender, glabrous, nearly equal-ling the stamens in length; stigma rounded. **Fruit** *c.*22 x 3.5mm, fusiform.

Indonesia, New Guinea (W), Lake Habbema and vicinity; Mt Jaya; Valentin Mts. Epiphytic or terrestrial, in open shrubberies on ridges and epiphytic on high trees in mossy forest, 1900–3345m. *Fl.* Aug., Oct.

Similar to *R. calosanthes*; for differences see under that species. Also very similar to and possibly to be united with *R. subcrenulatum* (see under that species). Never cul-tivated.

211. Rhododendron myrsinites Sleumer

Reinwardtia 1960. 5: 142.
Type: Brass 12630, Feb. 1939. 18km SW of Bernard Camp, Idenberg R., 2150m (A, L, fragment).
Derivation: With a resemblance to *Myrsine* (Myrsinaceae), a cultivated ornamental.

Shrub to 50cm. Twigs *c.*1mm in diameter, sub-densely sub-stellately scaly; internodes 2–5cm. **Leaves** 3–5 together in pseudowhorls, or spirally arranged, close together in the upper ⅓ of the internodes. **Blade** 14–20 x 3–4mm, very narrowly ovate-elliptic; apex shortly acu-minate, minutely apiculate; margin sub-crenulate with impressed scales, sub-revolute; base broadly tapering; laxly scaly on both sides initially, becoming glabrescent above, persistently scaly beneath. **Scales** with the marginal zone variously sub-stellately lobed; centre minute and slightly impressed. Mid-vein slightly impressed above, prominent beneath; lateral veins obscure. **Petiole** *c.*2mm, slender, scaly.

Bracts to 20 x 6mm, glabrous, membranous, red-brown, shining, ovate; the upper with a 5–6mm subulate point. Inflorescence of solitary or paired flowers. Pedicels *c.*18mm, slender, densely stellate-scaly. Calyx *c.*2mm in diameter, oblique, disc-shaped, obscurely lobed. **Corolla** *c.*35mm, fleshy, red; tube *c.*25 x 4 x 8mm, cylindrical, slightly curved, glabrous inside and out, base lobed; lobes 8–9 x 5–6mm, erecto-patent, broadly obovate. **Stamens** unequal, exserted to *c.*2mm; filaments linear, glabrous; anthers obovate, 1–1.3mm. Disc glabrous. **Ovary** cylindri-cal-fusiform, very densely scaly, without hairs, *c.*6 x 2mm, gradually tapering distally; style *c.*14mm, slender, scaly at the base only, glabrous distally; stigma globose.

Indonesia, New Guinea (W), Idenburg R., Bernhard Camp. Epiphytic on tall trees in mossy forest, at 2150m. *Fl.* Feb.

Known only from the type collection. Never cultivated.

212. Rhododendron purpureiflorum J.J.Sm.

Med. Rijksherb. 1915. 25: 3.
Type: Pulle 563, 5 Dec. 1912. New Guinea (W), Perameles Mts, 1100m (BO, L).
Derivation: Latin – *purpureo* – purple; *florum* – flower. Alluding to the flower colour.

Shrub to 50cm. Twigs 1–1.5mm in diameter, sub-densely covered with orange-brown stellate scales; inter-nodes 1.8–5.5cm. **Leaves** 3–6 together in pseudowhorls with several subulate cataphylls along the internodes. **Blade** 27–60 x 4–7(sometimes up to 11)mm, linear-elliptic; apex obtuse or broadly acute; margin flat; base taper-ing; scaly on both sides when young, glabrescent above with age, laxly persistently scaly beneath. **Scales** with the marginal zone irregularly, often obtusely, lobed, flat, pale; centre weakly or not impressed. Mid-vein impressed above, strongly obtusely prominent beneath; lateral veins obscure. **Petiole** 2–5mm, scaly.

Inflorescence 2–4-flowered. Pedicels 12–15mm, slen-der, sub-densely orange-brown, stellately scaly. Calyx *c.*2.5mm in diameter, disc-shaped, oblique, scaly, very shortly obtusely 5-lobed. **Corolla** 27–32mm, tubular, somewhat zygomorphic, reddish-purple or pale pink, laxly sub-stellately scaly or glabrous outside, glabrous inside;

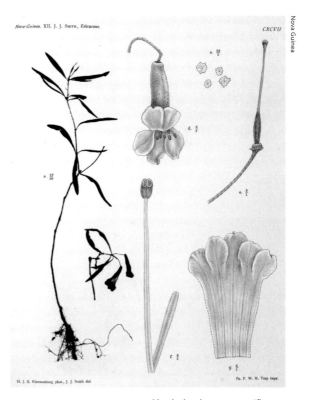

Rhododendron purpureiflorum.

tube 17–22 x *c.*4 x 6–7mm, sub-cylindrical, base pouched; lobes 7–9 x 5–6mm, half-spreading, broadly-obovate. **Stamens** unequal, the longest exserted to *c.*3mm; filaments linear, glabrous; anthers *c.*1.5mm, obovoid. Disc prominent, glabrous. **Ovary** *c.*4 x 1.6mm, fusiform, tapering both proximally and distally, densely scaly; style slender, glabrous, as long as the stamens; stigma sub-oblique, globose, purple.

Indonesia, New Guinea (W), Perameles and Schrader Mts, and Idenberg R., near Bernhard Camp. Epiphytic on tall trees in mossy forest, 1100–2150m. *Fl.* Dec., Feb., May–June.

Never cultivated.

213. **Rhododendron ultimum** Wernham
Trans. Linn. Soc. London, II, Bot. 1916. 9: 99.
Type: Kloss *s.n.*, 31 Jan. 1913. New Guinea (SW), Mt Carstensz, 3200–3810m (BM, L, fragment).
Derivation: Latin – *ultimum* – the last, probably referring to the fact that it is the highest *Rhododendron* on Mt Carstensz.

Prostrate shrub to 10cm. Twigs *c.*2mm in diameter, often pale and sub-densely covered with sub-stellate scales when young, later, glabrescent but with numerous thick cushions of leaf bases remaining; internodes 2.5–6cm. **Leaves** densely spirally arranged, of a distinctive purple-colour. **Blade** 18–27 x 10–19mm, broadly elliptic to elliptic-obovate; apex rounded, with a small protruding apical gland; margin minutely crenulate and weakly revolute; base broadly tapering; laxly to sub-densely scaly initially on both sides, early glabrescent above, persistently scaly beneath. **Scales** small, flat, sub-circular, marginal zone large, thin, variously angled, sub-stellate or crenate; centre small, dark, faintly impressed. Mid-vein slightly impressed above, broad and obtusely prominent beneath in the proximal part; lateral veins inconspicuous. **Petiole** 2–4 x 1–2mm, rounded or somewhat flattened.

Outer bracts 10–15mm, ovate, inner ones to 20–25 x 8–15mm, obovate to spathulate, apex shortly acuminate, or obtuse, membranous, entirely glabrous. Bracteoles to 18 x 1mm, linear, glabrous. Inflorescence 2–4-flowered, flowers half-hanging. Pedicels 12–15 x 0.8mm, densely sub-stellately scaly, without hairs. Calyx *c.*3mm in diameter, obliquely disc-shaped, obscurely lobed, scaly outside. **Corolla** 35–45mm, funnel-shaped, bright orange, fleshy; tube 20–30 x *c.*5 x 9–10mm, straight, glabrous on both sides; lobes 14–17 x 12–15mm, broadly obovate to subcircular, semi-erect. **Stamens** exserted to *c.*6mm, unequal; filaments linear, glabrous; anthers *c.*2.8–3 x 1.3–1.5mm, obovate-oblong, each cell ending in a short basal apiculus. Disc prominent, glabrous. **Ovary** *c.*6 x 2.5mm, sub-cylindrical, densely sub-stellately scaly, tapering distally; style scaly at the base, glabrous distally, slightly longer than the stamens; stigma shortly obconical.

Indonesia, New Guinea (W), Mt Jaya (Carstensz), 3200–4100m. Growing on the open valley floor in dark peaty soil with limestone fragments.

Introduced into cultivation in 2000, it is not growing happily: the leaves have become much smaller and it has not produced its wonderful large, brightly coloured flowers. It is typical of the very high altitude species that they are the most difficult to cultivate.

Rhododendron ultimum.   *Rhododendron ultimum* in high valley, Mt Jaya.

214. Rhododendron atropurpureum Sleumer

Reinwardtia 1960. 5: 172.

Type: Womersley NGF 8870, 1 Aug. 1956. Papua New Guinea, Mt Wilhelm, Lake Piunde vicinity, 3620m (L, BM, BRI, CANB, K, LAE, SING).

Derivation: Latin – *atro* – blackish or very dark; *purpureus* – purple. The plant with dark blackish-purple flowers, but not apt (see below).

Erect shrub to 3m. Twigs *c.*2.4mm in diameter, densely covered with sub-stellate, shortly stalked brownish scales and very short papillose hairs at the upper internodes, older parts glabrescent and minutely warty; internodes 3.5–9cm often with prominent sub-spherical lateral buds in the upper leaf axils. **Leaves** spirally arranged in the upper ⅔ of the internodes. **Blade** 17–38 x 12–25mm, broadly elliptic or ovate-elliptic, sometimes sub-obovate-elliptic; apex broadly tapering, sub-acuminate or obtuse to rounded, the thick apical gland prominent; margin indistinctly cartilaginous and distinctly crenulate, flat; base rounded or slightly cordate, fully mature leaves with the remains of the scales persisting, a little rough, finally glabrescent above, sub-densely scaly beneath. **Scales** small, membranous, marginal zone irregularly crenate or denticulate, quickly disappearing to leave persistent large, blackish-red, impressed, circular centres. Mid-vein reddish-brown and more densely and persistently scaly than the rest of the upper surface, slightly impressed above, robust and obtusely prominent beneath; lateral veins 3–5 per side, spreading, faintly impressed above, slightly raised beneath, often inconspicuous above or rarely so on both sides. **Petiole** 4–5 x 1–1.5mm, flattened, densely scaly.

Bracts 10–15 x 8–12mm, outer bracts ovate, bluntly pointed, the inner ones obovate, glabrous, but scaly on the margins. Inflorescence an open umbel of 2–3 flowers, half-hanging to hanging. Pedicels 10–15 x *c.*1mm, densely covered with dark, reddish, stellate, shortly stalked scales, but without hairs. Calyx 3–4mm in diameter, a low disc, shortly obtusely 5-lobed, densely scaly outside. **Corolla** 35–45 x 25–30mm, bright red when fresh, becoming dark purple in the drying process, without scent; tube 25–35 x 6–8 x 10–15mm, straight or distinctly curved, with 5 small pouches at the base, densely covered with thick sub-stellate scales outside, glabrous inside; lobes 10–15 x 10–13mm, spreading, broadly obovate or sub-circular, slightly retuse, scaly outside except towards the margins. **Stamens** exserted to 10–15mm, clustered on the upper side of the flower; filaments linear, 1.5mm wide at the base, glabrous; anthers 3.5–4 x *c.*1.5mm, broadly ellipsoid, each cell bearing a short basal apiculus. Disc prominent, glabrous. **Ovary** 5–6 x *c.*3mm, ovoid-conical, gradually

Rhododendron atropurpureum.

tapering distally, densely sub-stellately scaly but without simple hairs; style nearly equalling the stamens in length, sub-densely to sparsely scaly in the proximal ⅓, glabrous distally; stigma rounded. **Fruit** 20–25 x 6mm, fusiform-cylindrical, shortly tapering at the base, more gradually so towards the apex, a little oblique, remaining densely scaly. Seeds 20–25mm, without tails *c.*10mm, the longest tail to 8mm, often with a broad tail at one end and a much more slender finely pointed one at the other.

Papua New Guinea, Eastern Highlands, Mt Wilhelm; Western Highlands, Mt Kinkain, common here in edge of sub-alpine forest or alpine shrubbery, at 3590–3840m. Main flowering appears to be June to Sept. but it has also been collected in flower in April and Dec. and is probably to be found with some flowers throughout the year.

A hybrid with *R. commonae* has been recorded from Mt Wilhelm and hybrids with *R. womersleyi* are also found, having smaller leaves and hairs at the base of the style.

Introduced into cultivation by K.L. Wade from Mt Wilhelm in 1966 and on subsequent occasions. Doubtfully still in cultivation as it is considered difficult to grow. The description of the colour of the flowers on the type specimen was made after the flowers had been dried without the benefit of a true recollection of the colour when fresh, which is a bright rich red.

215. Rhododendron subuliferum Sleumer

Reinwardtia 1960. 5: 171.

Type: Brass 10830, Oct. 1938. New Guinea (W), Bele Valley, 25km NE of Lake Habbema (A, BO, L).

Derivation: Latin – *subulifer* – awl-bearing, alluding to the distinctive subulate bracts.

Shrub to 2m. Twigs 1–1.5mm in diameter, rounded, densely sub-stellate with shortly stalked scales, quickly glabrescent, leaving the surface warty with low scale bases; internodes 3–9cm. **Leaves** 3–6 together in tight pseudowhorls. **Blade** 25–45 x 10–23mm, obovate, more rarely elliptic; apex rounded or obtuse, sometimes minutely emarginate; margin entire or minutely crenulate, distinctly revolute in the proximal ½, hardly or not revolute distally; base tapering; glabrescent and densely rugulose above, densely scaly beneath. **Scales** with the thin marginal zone angular or obtusely sub-stellately lobed; centre persistent, thickened, reddish brown and slightly impressed. Mid-vein narrowly impressed above, prominent beneath but tapering gradually distally; lateral veins 1–3 per side, inconspicuous or obscure. **Petiole** 3–4 x 1–1.5mm, scaly, flattened.

Flower buds to 10 x 4mm, with the outermost bract tips spreading, the inner ones erect. Bracts 10–15 x 5–6mm, ovate but with long subulate points, glabrous outside or with minute, almost papillose hairs and fragile scales along the margins, glabrous inside. Bracteoles *c.*10mm, filiform. **Flowers** in pairs or solitary, hanging vertically. Pedicels 10–18 x 0.75mm, densely covered with stellate, stalked scales and short hairs. Calyx *c.*3mm in diameter, oblique, very shortly irregularly 5-lobed, revolute, scaly and hairy outside, ciliate on the margin. **Corolla** 30–50 x 20–25mm, tubular, slightly expanded distally, dark-red, without scent; tube 30–35 x 4–5 x 8–13mm, weakly curved, laxly scaly or glabrous outside, glabrous inside; lobes 6–12 x 6–10mm, erect, or half-spreading, spathulate-obovate or sub-circular. **Stamens** unequal, exserted to 10mm; filaments linear, 1mm wide at the base, glabrous; anthers *c.*3 x 1mm, broadly oblong, cells obtuse or provided with an indistinct basal apiculus, very dark almost black. Disc prominent, glabrous or with hairs on the upper margin. **Ovary** 6–8 x *c.*2mm, sub-cylindrical, densely stellately scaly, gradually tapering distally; style glabrous, or with a few hairs at the base, as long as or slightly longer than the corolla; stigma rounded.

Indonesia, New Guinea (W), Bele R. Valley, NE of Lake Habbema; Sibil valley, Snow Mts. High epiphyte, frequent in mid-mountain mossy forest, or common terrestrially on white sand in clearings, at 1550–2600m. *Fl.* Oct.–Nov.

Not known to have been cultivated.

216. Rhododendron inconspicuum J.J.Sm.

Med. Rijksherb. 1915. 25: 1.
Type: Pulle 1000, 2 Feb. 1913. New Guinea (W), Wichmann Mts, 1000m (BO, K, L, U).
Derivation: Latin – *inconspicuus* – inconspicuous. Named from a herbarium specimen that had been prepared with

Rhododendron inconspicuum.

formaldehyde and was totally brown. Not inappropriate as the flowers of this species are in any case very small.

Synonyms:
R. invasiorum Sleumer, Reinwardtia 1960. 5: 60.
R. luteosquamatum Sleumer, Reinwardtia 1960. 5: 166.

Erect shrub or tree to 5m, or occasionally up to 10m. Twigs 1.5–2mm in diameter, rounded, at first densely covered with sub-stellate, stalked scales, becoming glabrescent, warty and rough to the touch; internodes 1.5–4cm. **Leaves** in loose pseudowhorls at the upper ends of the internodes or spirally arranged in the upper ½ of the internode. **Blade** 10–35 x 6–20mm, elliptic, ovate-elliptic or ovate; apex broadly tapering, obtuse or rounded; margin not or slightly cartilaginous, distinctly crenulate, slightly or not revolute; base tapering to rounded, rarely sub-cordate, dark green above, much paler and often yellowish green or brownish beneath, densely scaly initially on both sides, early glabrescent but densely marked with blackish minute pits above, more persistently and densely scaly beneath. **Scales** round to angular, distant, or only partly touching each other, the thin, marginal zone irregularly crenate or shortly sub-stellately lobed; centre relatively large, dark yellow, thick and a little impressed. Mid-vein narrowly impressed above, prominent beneath proximally, less so distally; lateral veins 4–7 per side, spreading, faintly impressed above and raised beneath in fully mature leaves, often inconspicuous. **Petiole** 1–3 x 1.5–5mm, grooved above, densely scaly.

Flower buds to 11 x 6mm, pale greenish-brown, ovoid, acutely pointed, smooth, densely scaly outside, often with lateral flower buds around the terminal bud. Bracts to 10 x 4mm, ovate; outer acute or apiculate; inner obtuse, thin and membranous, with scales along a broad outside middle line, or quite glabrous and shining; margin irregular with a few brown scales. Bracteoles to 10mm, linear proximally, sub-spathulate distally, sparsely scaly. Inflorescence 3–7-flowered in an open umbel, half-hanging to hanging. Pedicels 8–14mm, slender, densely covered with shortly stalked scales. Calyx 2.5–3.5mm in diameter, disc-shaped, irregularly, very shortly and obtusely 5-lobed, densely scaly outside. **Corolla** 11–16mm, shortly tubular, pink to red, densely covered with thick, sub-stellate, yellow scales outside, glabrous inside; tube 7–12 x 4 x 6mm, straight; lobes 3–4.5 x 3–4.5mm, erect or only slightly spreading, sub-circular. **Stamens** exserted to *c.*3mm, unequal; filaments filiform, glabrous; anthers *c.*1mm, obovoid. Disc low, glabrous. **Ovary** 3–4 x 1.5–2mm, ovoid-conical, very densely covered with thick sub-circular scales, abruptly tapering distally; style thick, quite glabrous, as long as the ovary; stigma rounded to deeply 5-lobed. **Fruit** 12–17 x 4–5mm, fusiform-cylindrical, longitudinally 5-ribbed, somewhat curved, densely scaly, with a sub-persistent style. Seeds *c.*3mm including the tails.

Indonesia and **Papua New Guinea**. Widespread in New Guinea, from the Vogelkop Peninsula, Arfak Mts, in the west along the Main Range to Mt Dayman in the Milne Bay District in the east. In mossy forest or forest openings, *Vaccinium*-shrubbery, commonly on old landslides, the edges of deep gullies or steep mountainsides with grassy slopes in full sun, often on infertile sandy soil, sometimes on limestone ridges, locally common, 1800–3400m. *Fl. fr.* Jan.–Dec.

This species is easily confused with *R. yelliotii* (section *Albovireya*) and superficially looks very similar. The main differences between the two species are as follows. In *R. inconspicuum* the scales on the undersurface of the mature leaves are dense, but usually with gaps between them, only occasionally touching; the bracts are sometimes scaly along the middle line outside, and not hairy at all, often shining. In *R. yelliotii* the scales are much denser, generally all of them touching each other; the bracts are scaly and shortly hairy outside, the margins distinctly ciliate. These two species are however reported to hybridise (Kores & van Royen 1982) which then blurs the distinctions. Sleumer (1973) reduced *R. invasiorum* to synonymy with *R. inconspicuum* and Kores & van Royen (1982) confirmed this collecting intermediate specimens from the Murray Pass and Mt Suckling areas. Sleumer (1966) also commented that '*R. luteosquamatum*, [which] is perhaps only a variety of *R. inconspicuum*'. The differences are insignificant: *R. inconspicuum* often has the distinctive yellow scales of *R. luteosquamatum* and the longer petiole length is insufficient to warrant even varietal distinction.

First introduced into cultivation in 1961 by seed distributed by Professor Sleumer, plants from this accession are still in cultivation. It has had several subsequent introductions. The flowers are very small, not at all showy, and it is grown more for curiosity as a species than for its beauty.

217. Rhododendron lamii J.J.Sm.
Nova Guinea 1936. 18: 96, *t.*20, 1.
Type: Lam 1620, 17 Oct. 1920. New Guinea (N), Doorman-top, 3280m (BO, L).
Derivation: Named after the collector, H.J. Lam, former director of the Rijksherbarium and professor at Leiden University, previously posted in Indonesia and collecting extensively between 1919 and 1933.

Shrub to 2m. Twigs 5–6mm in diameter, rounded, laxly scaly at first; internodes 0.8–1.7cm. **Leaves** 6–7 together in tight to loose pseudowhorls with persistent large cataphylls between the foliage leaves. **Blade** 18–33 x 8–18mm, broadly elliptic-obovate; apex broadly sub-acuminate or obtuse to rounded, with a thick and somewhat protruding gland; margin distinctly crenulate, flat or a little recurved; base broadly tapering and decurrent, sub-sessile, initially sub-densely scaly on both sides, early glabrescent above, less so beneath. **Scales** small, marginal zone narrow, irregularly sub-stellately lobed or crenate; centre slightly or not impressed. Mid-vein faintly impressed above, flat beneath; lateral veins 4–6 per side, erecto-patent, obscure on both sides, reticulation inconspicuous. **Petiole** 1–2 x 3–4mm, flattened.

Outer bracts to 10 x 8mm, membranous, glabrous outside, ovate, apiculate; middle bracts to 20–35 x *c.*15mm, ovate-elliptic, innermost bracts to 50 x 20mm, elliptic-obovate to spathulate, not fringed. Bracteoles to 20 x 1mm, linear, glabrous. Inflorescence 3–4-flowered. Pedicels *c.*10 x 1mm, densely scaly, without hairs. Calyx *c.*4mm in diameter, oblique, disc-shaped, shortly sub-acutely 5-lobed. **Corolla** 30 x 45mm, funnel-shaped, dark red, fleshy, glabrous both in and outside, 5-lobed to nearly halfway; tube *c.*15 x 4 x 10mm; lobes 12–15 x 12–15mm, obovate to sub-circular. **Stamens** unequal, slightly exserted; filaments linear, dilated above the base, glabrous; anthers *c.*3.5 x 1.8mm, obovate, base sub-acutely tapering into 2 appendages which are very close together. Disc prominent, glabrous. **Ovary** 6 x 2.5–3mm, sub-cylindrical, densely scaly, tapering distally; style thick, glabrous, exceeding the stamens in length; stigma obconical, distinctly lobed. **Fruit** *c.*25 x 7mm, thick-fusiform, on pedicels to 30 x 2mm. Seeds 3mm, without tails *c.*1mm, the longest tail 1mm, with a very broad tail at one end.

Indonesia, New Guinea (W), Mt Doorman, on an open slope with rocks, 3280m. *Fl. fr.* Oct.

Not recently recollected and never cultivated.

218. Rhododendron simulans Sleumer
Reinwardtia 1960. 5: 168.
Type: Lam 1622, 17 Oct. 1920. New Guinea (N), Doorman-top, 3300m (BO, L).
Derivation: Latin – *simulans* – imitating or resembling, presumably due to the resemblance to *R. wrightianum*.

Synonyms:
R. simulans J.J.Sm. *ex* Lam, Nat. Tijd. N.I. 1929. 89: 95, 99, 133, 134 *nom. nud.*
R. wrightianum Koord. var. *ovalifolium* J.J.Sm., Nova Guinea 1936. 18: 94, *pro parte.*

Shrub to 70cm. Twigs 1.5–2mm in diameter, rounded, tips densely covered with stalked scales, older parts glabrescent, densely warty and rough; internodes 2–6cm. **Leaves** crowded at the tips or 3–5 together in pseudo-whorls. **Blade** 15–20 x 6–10mm, narrowly elliptic to elliptic or sub-obovate-elliptic; apex shortly acuminate, broadly acute, with a very small terminal gland; margin cartilaginous, distinctly revolute, especially proximally; base tapering and decurrent, the extreme base often sub-truncate; glabrescent above when mature; sub-densely scaly beneath. **Scales** angular or lobed, flat; centre small, slightly elevated on small protrusions. Mid-vein impressed above; thick and strong proximally beneath, gradually narrowed distally; lateral veins inconspicuous. **Petiole** 2–3 x *c.*1mm, nearly rounded.

Flower buds to 18 x 8mm, narrowly ovate, narrowly acute, the subulate points to the bracts standing slightly out. Bracts to 20 x 6mm, membranous, outer ones subu-late, inner ones ovate-acuminate, apex subulate, glabrous and glossy. Inflorescence 2–4-flowered. Pedicels *c.*15mm, thick, densely covered with reddish stellate scales, with-out hairs. Calyx *c.*3mm in diameter, obliquely disc-shaped, red, shortly irregularly 5-lobed, scaly outside. **Corolla** *c.*25mm, tubular below, funnel-shaped distally, fleshy, red, with a few scales, or glabrous outside, glabrous inside; tube 16–20 x *c.*5 x 7–10mm, straight, base lobed; lobes 7–10 x 7–10mm, spreading, broadly obovate or sub-circular. **Stamens** sub-equal, 22–24mm long; filaments linear, gla-brous; anthers 2–2.5 x 1mm, ellipsoid. Disc very promi-nent, glabrous. **Ovary** *c.*5 x 2.5mm, sub-ovoid-cylindrical,

densely reddish-brown-stellate-scaly, gradually tapering distally; style *c.*17mm, glabrous; stigma thick-obconical, distinctly 5-lobed. **Fruit** 20–23 x 6mm, sub-cylindrical, the thin valves twisted.

Indonesia, New Guinea (W), Mt Doorman, on steep open slopes with rocks, 3300–3500m. *Fl.* Oct.

Not recently recollected and never cultivated.

219. Rhododendron papuanum Becc.
Malesia 1878. I: 201.
Type: Beccari 5793A, July 1875. New Guinea (W), Vogelkop peninsula, Mt Arfak, Hatam, 1525–2135m (Fl, L, fragment).
Derivation: Of Papua – geographical area where 'Papuans' or Melanesians were found, in this case the island of New Guinea.

Much-branched shrub to 50cm, with fleshy roots. Twigs 1–2mm in diameter, the upper 1–2 internodes sub-densely covered with minute brown stalked scales, gla-brescent and minutely warty, or a little rough to the touch after the scales have gone; internodes 2–7cm. **Leaves** 4–6 together in tight pseudowhorls. **Blade** 10–18 x 6–12mm, obovate, broadly elliptic to circular; apex rounded, some-times slightly retuse; margin slightly revolute; base broadly tapering, more rarely rounded, glabrescent above when mature, sub-densely scaly beneath. **Scales** small, vari-ously angled or sub-stellately lobed at the margin; centre dark, small and distinctly impressed. Mid-vein impressed above, obtusely prominent in the proximal ½–¾ beneath, disappearing distally; lateral veins obscure. **Petiole** *c.*2 x 0.6–1mm, somewhat flattened, scaly.

Flower buds to 10 x 4mm, cylindrical-conical, imbri-cate, smooth. Bracts to 6 x 3mm, membranous, ovate to ovate-oblong, obtuse, glabrous outside, or minutely sub-papillose-hairy, fringed with scales initially. Bracteoles filiform, glabrous, to 6mm. Inflorescence 1–3-flowered. Pedicels 15mm, (up to 25mm in fruit), slender, erect, densely covered with shortly stalked, brown, stellate scales, almost without hairs. Calyx *c.*2.5mm in diameter, brown-scaly, irregularly 5-lobed, the lobes 1–1.5mm (one or two, up to 2.5mm), sub-acute, spreading or reflexed. **Corolla** 13–15mm, tubular, deep pink to purplish red; tube 8–10 x *c.*3 x *c.*4mm, straight, glossy, sub-densely scaly outside, glabrous inside; lobes 4–5 x 4–5mm, sub-circular, spreading. **Stamens** *c.*12mm; filaments linear, glabrous; anthers 1mm, obovoid. Disc low, glabrous. **Ovary** 4.5 x 1.5mm, sub-cylindrical, densely stellate-scaly, completely without hairs, with 5 deep longitudinal furrows, abruptly contracted distally; style 6–7mm, slender, scaly at the base, laxly patently hairy for the following 2mm, glabrous distally; stigma dilated, obliquely shortly obconical. **Fruit** (sub-mature) 18–23 x 4mm, fusiform, densely scaly, with a persistent style.

Indonesia, New Guinea (W), Vogelkop Peninsula, Arfak, Nettoti and Tamrau Mts, possibly also in the Oranje Mts. Terrestrial in open places on moss-cushions, or epiphytic in mossy forest, 1525–2550m. *Fl.* July–Dec.

A delicate species with small flowers. Not known in cultivation.

220. Rhododendron wrightianum Koord.

Nova Guinea 1912. 8: 880.
Type: Römer 1059. New Guinea (SW), Oranje Mts, Erica top, *c.*1460m (BO).
Derivation: Named after C.H. Wright, formerly assistant keeper of the Kew Herbarium.

Key to the varieties

1 Bracts with silky hairs and scaly outside, at least in the distal part ——————————————— 2

+ Bracts laxly scaly outside, not hairy at all. Pedicels scaly, with or without hairs ————— var. **insulare**

2 Pedicels scaly, with or without papillae ————— ——————————————— var. **wrightianum**

+ Pedicels scaly and densely shortly hairy ————— ——————————————— var. **cyclopense**

Var. **wrightianum**

Shrub to 1m. Twigs 1–2mm in diameter, rounded, densely covered with shortly stalked, stellate scales, not hairy, becoming glabrescent and then warty with the persistent scale stalks; internodes 1–6cm. **Leaves** 3–5 together in tight pseudowhorls. **Blade** 10–20 x 5–10mm, obovate-elliptic to obovate; apex obtuse or rounded; margin sub-crenulate with impressed scales or entire, minutely cartilaginous and slightly recurved; base tapering or broadly tapering; laxly silvery scaly above at first, quickly glabrescent; beneath laxly brown-scaly but these very fragile and falling early. **Scales** with the narrow marginal zone irregularly crenulate or sub-stellately lobed; centre dark, proportionally large and somewhat impressed. Mid-vein narrowly slightly or not impressed above, distinctly but only weakly prominent beneath; lateral veins 1–3 per side, or obscure, reticulation obscure. **Petiole** 1–2 x 0.5–1mm.

Bracts to 8 x 4mm; outer bracts ovate, sub-acuminate or obtuse, inner ones elliptic, all distinctly hairy and laxly scaly outside at least in the distal ½, and fringed with scales, often still persistent at flowering time. Bracteoles to 7mm, filiform. Inflorescence 1–4-flowered in an open umbel, the flowers hanging vertically. Pedicels 5–15mm, slender, densely covered with stellate and shortly stalked scales, and often with short papillose hairs. Calyx *c.*2.5mm in diameter, shortly cup-shaped, oblique, with irregular lobes, densely scaly outside. **Corolla** 22–30 x 10–15mm, tubular, slightly dilated upwards, red, pink or rarely white; tube 20 x 4–5 x 8–10mm, laxly to sub-densely stellate-scaly outside, glabrous inside, straight or slightly curved; lobes *c.*7 x 7mm, half-spreading, sub-circular. **Stamens**

Rhododendron wrightianum var. *wrightianum*.

Ken Grant

exserted to *c.*4mm, unequal; filaments linear, glabrous; anthers *c.*2 x 1mm, broadly ellipsoid, the base of each cell sub-apiculate. Disc glabrous. **Ovary** 4–5 x 1.5–2mm, sub-cylindrical, densely scaly, gradually tapering distally; style 17–20mm, scaly in the proximal ⅕–⅓; stigma club-shaped. **Fruit** 30–35 x *c.*3.5mm, fusiform; valves reflexing and twisting, the placentae at first remaining attached to the central column, eventually irregularly breaking away from the base. Seeds *c.*6mm, without tails to 1mm, the longest tail 3.2mm.

Indonesia, New Guinea (W), Oranje and Nassau Mts. **Papua New Guinea**, Milne Bay District, Mt Garatun. Epiphytic in mossy forest, or terrestrial in openings, on sandy or peaty soil, 1370–3250m. *Fl.* Oct.–March.

Var. **cyclopense** J.J.Sm.
Nova Guinea 1914. 12: 130.
Type: Gjellerup 542, 20 June 1911. New Guinea (W), Mt Cyclops (BO, L).
Derivation: Named after Mt Cyclops, the mountain on which it was collected.

Leaves 13–40 x 7–17mm. Pedicels scaly and densely, shortly hairy. Bracts as in var. *wrightianum*.

Indonesia, New Guinea (W), Mt Cyclops. Epiphytic or on moss-covered soil, in open *Nothofagus–Rapanea* ridge forest, 1480–1800m. *Fl.* June–Oct.

Cultivated in Edinburgh since 1967 from material from Mt Cyclops supplied by Professor Sleumer, who also

Rhododendron wrightianum var. *cyclopense*.

distributed the material to the Strybing Arboretum, USA and probably to Boskoop in the Netherlands.

Var. **insulare** Sleumer
Reinwardtia 1960. 5: 174.
Type: Brass 25637, 5 Jan. 1956. New Guinea (SE), Milne Bay District, Mt Pabiname, 820m (L, A).
Derivation: Latin – *insularis* – pertaining to islands, alluding to the islands from which it is recorded.

Leaves 10–20 x 6–15mm. Bracts laxly scaly outside, not hairy, up to 8mm in length. Pedicels scaly and sometimes laxly and very shortly hairy.

Papua New Guinea, Milne Bay District, Normanby and Goodenough Is. Common high epiphyte in tall mossy forest, 820–1600m. *Fl.* Jan., Oct.

Not known to have been cultivated.

221. **Rhododendron subcrenulatum** Sleumer
Reinwardtia 1960. 5: 174.
Type: Brass 9274, Oct. 1938. New Guinea (NW), Lake Habbema, 3225m camp (A, L).
Derivation: Latin – *sub* – somewhat; *crenulatus* – having small rounded teeth. Alluding to the leaf margin.

Erect shrub to 50cm. Twigs *c.*2mm in diameter, at first densely covered with sub-stellate and distinctly stalked scales, quickly glabrescent leaving them minutely warty and rough to the touch; internodes 2.5–5cm. **Leaves** 3–5 together in tight pseudowhorls. **Blade** 20–30 x 8–14mm, narrowly elliptic or sub-ovate or sub-obovate; apex shortly acuminate, obtuse at the extreme point with a thick gland; margin narrowly cartilaginous, slightly or not revolute, sub-crenulate or entire; base broadly tapering or sub-truncate; sub-densely scaly on both sides, early glabrescent above, persistently scaly beneath. **Scales** small, marginal zone thin, lobed or irregularly crenate; centre thick, raised on low protuberances. Mid-vein distinctly and narrowly impressed above, thick and obtusely prominent in the proximal part beneath; lateral veins inconspicuous. **Petiole** 2–3 x 1.5–2mm, densely scaly, a little flattened.

Bracts to 15 x 8mm; outer bracts ovate, with a 4–5mm long, subulate, acumen, inner bracts ovate-elliptic, with a 10mm point, innermost bracts sub-spathulate, obtuse; scaly outside in the distal part or quite glabrous; margin initially fringed with scales. Bracteoles *c.*10mm, linear. Inflorescence 1–4-flowered, the flowers hanging vertically. Pedicels 15–20 x *c.*1mm, densely covered with reddish, stellate scales but without hairs. Calyx 3–4mm in diameter, sub-obliquely disc-shaped, shortly obtusely 5-lobed, densely stellate-scaly outside. **Corolla** 25–30mm, tubular, sub-oblique, dark red; tube 20–23 x *c*.4 x 8–10mm, straight or only slightly curved, sub-densely stellate-scaly outside, glabrous inside; lobes 5–7 x 5–7mm, half-spreading, sub-circular. **Stamens** unequal, the longest almost as long as the corolla; filaments linear, glabrous; anthers 2.5 x 1mm, broadly oblong, rounded at the base. Disc glabrous, or shortly hairy at the upper margin only. **Ovary** 6–7 x *c*.2.5mm, sub-cylindrical, densely stellate-scaly, gradually tapering distally; style equalling the stamens, scaly proximally to ⅕–⅓, glabrous distally; stigma rounded.

Indonesia, New Guinea (W), Lake Habbema, 3225–3345m, terrestrial, common at the edges of mossy forest, or in open mossy shrubberies and in an open shrubbery on a dry ridge. *Fl.* Aug.

Never cultivated. Differing from *R. rubrobracteatum* in that the pedicels are scaly but not papillose, the style is scaly ⅕–⅓ and not glabrous. The difference that Sleumer (1966) uses in his key to separate them – twigs warty vs. twigs smooth – does not separate them according to the Kores & van Royen (1982) descriptions which describe both species with warty twigs, although they use this difference like Sleumer in their key. Further work will probably unite these two species.

222. Rhododendron calosanthes Sleumer
Blumea 1961. 11: 125.
Type: Kalkman 454227, July 1959. New Guinea (C), Star Mts, Mt Antares, 3000–3200m (L).
Derivation: Greek – *kalos* – beautiful; *anthos* – flowers. The rhododendron with beautiful flowers.

Shrub, *c*.40cm. Twigs slender, at first laxly sub-stellate, the older parts glabrescent, smooth, 1–2mm in diameter; internodes 1.5–2.5cm. **Leaves** 4–6 in loose pseudowhorls. **Blade** 20–25 x 5–9mm, narrowly elliptic; apex sub-acutely tapering or sub-acuminate; margin sub-crenulate with impressed scales at first in the crenulations or sub-entire; base tapering, initially laxly scaly on both sides, slowly glabrescent above, sub-persistently scaly beneath. **Scales** with the thin marginal zone sub-stellate; centre small, impressed. Mid-vein hardly impressed above or flat, thick and obtusely prominent beneath; lateral veins inconspicuous. **Petiole** 2–3 x 0.7–1mm.

Bracts to 20 x 10mm, membranous, red, glabrous and shining outside, ovate; outer ones acuminate-apiculate, inner ones obtuse. Inflorescence of solitary or paired, hanging, flowers. Pedicels 15–20mm, slender, densely stellately scaly. Calyx *c*.2.5mm in diameter, obliquely disc-shaped, often covered by the basal lobed part of the corolla tube, hardly lobed, scaly outside. **Corolla** 30–35mm, weakly zygomorphic, red, thin; tube 20–25 x 5–6 x 8–10mm, straight, laxly sub-stellately scaly outside, otherwise glabrous; lobes *c*.10 x 5–8mm, half-spreading, broadly obovate-oblong. **Stamens** very unequal, the longest reaching the mouth, hardly exserted; filaments linear, glabrous; anthers 1.5–1.8 x 1mm, obovate-oblong, base obtuse. Disc prominent, glabrous. **Ovary** 4 x 1.5mm, sub-obliquely cylindrical, densely covered with sub-stellate, brown scales but without hairs, tapering distally; style slender with some scales at the base, glabrous distally; stigma rounded, shortly 5-lobed.

Indonesia, New Guinea (W), Star Mts, Mt Antares. In alpine or semi-alpine shrubby vegetation, 3000–3200m, rare. *Fl.* July.

Never cultivated. Sleumer (1961) commented that it was related to *R. rubrobracteatum* but differed in having smaller leaves and a larger corolla.

Rhododendron x sarcodes Argent & Madulid
The New Plantsman 1995. 2(3): 156.
Type: Argent, Madulid & Gaerlan, A11. Philippines, Mindanao, Mt Apo, *c*.1800m (E, PNH).
Derivation: Greek – *sarco* – fleshy; with fleshy flowers.

Small shrub to 80cm. Twigs scaly. **Leaves** in loose pseudowhorls or spirally arranged. **Blade** 30–50 x 11–18mm, elliptic, shiny and glabrescent above, laxly scaly below. **Petiole** 5–7 x 1.5–2mm, not grooved above, scaly.

Flowers 1–4 in an open umbel, horizontal to half-hanging, glossy red. **Corolla** *c*.30 x 32mm; tube 26 x 9 x 13mm, glabrous outside, hairy inside; lobes 12 x 11mm, not overlapping. **Stamens** with the filaments hairy in the proximal ½; anthers 2mm. Disc hairy on the upper side. **Ovary** densely scaly in the proximal ½, laxly so distally; style glabrous.

Philippines, Mindanao, Ilomavis District, Mt Apo. 1800m. In open montane forest. Known only from the type locality.

Almost certainly the hybrid between *R. bagobonum* and *R. javanicum* ssp. *schadenbergii*. Cultivated since 1992, very similar to *R.* x *planecostatum* but lacking the hairs on the ovary of that hybrid.

Subsection v: *Euvireya* H.F.Copel.

Phil. J. Sc. 1929. 40(2): 137, 159 *s.str.*

Type: *R. javanicum* (Blume) Benn.
Series iv *Javanica* Sleumer, Reinwardtia 1960. 5: 176. Type: *R. javanicum* (Blume) Benn.
Section *Schistanthe* Schltr., Bot. Jahr. 1917. 55: 140, *pro parte* (lectotype *R. hansemanni* Warb.).
Section *Hapalanthe* Schltr., Bot. Jahr. 1918. 55: 155 (lectotype *R. zoelleri* Warb.). Section *Zygomorphanthe* Schltr., Bot. Jahr. 1918. 55: 145, *pro parte* (based on *R. keysseri* Foerster).
Subsection *Leiovireya* H.F.Copel., Phil. J. Sc. 40(2): 137, 167 (based on *R. crassifolium* Stapf).
Subsection *Schizovireya* Sleumer, Bot. Jahr. 1949. 74: 538 (based on *R. macgregoriae* F.Muell.).

Leaves large, the majority of well-developed leaves more than 4cm long. Stomata on the abaxial (lower) leaf surface only. Medium to large shrubs or small trees.

Key to species from Mainland Asia, Peninsular Malaysia, Sumatra, Java and the Lesser Sunda Islands

1	Ovary hairy all over	2
+	Ovary scaly or glabrous sometimes with a few hairs at the base	6
2	Pedicels scaly and laxly to densely hairy	3
+	Pedicels scaly only	4
3	Petiole less than 2mm wide, grooved above	**224. longiflorum**
+	Petiole more than 4mm wide, not grooved above	**227. javanicum** ssp. **teysmannii**
4	Leaves more than 50mm wide, petioles more than 18mm	**223. triumphans**
+	Leaves less than 40mm wide, petioles less than 10mm	5
5	Flowers bicoloured yellow and orange, corolla tube more than 15mm, anthers not exserted	**233. renschianum**
+	Flowers orange to red, corolla tube less than 15mm, anthers exserted to 6mm	**228. sumatranum**
6	Petiole less than 4mm, as long as broad	7
+	Petiole more than 4mm, distinctly longer than broad	10
7	Leaves narrowly elliptic, less than 20mm wide	**173. multicolor**
+	Leaves elliptic to ovate-elliptic, more than 25mm wide	8
8	Style less than 6mm, as long as the ovary	**229. perplexum**
+	Style more than 7mm, distinctly longer than the ovary	9
9	Corolla less than 50mm, fruit less than 40mm	**230. sessilifolium**
+	Corolla more than 50mm, fruit more than 40mm	**231. beccarii**
10	Leaves less than 20mm wide	**173. multicolor**
+	Leaves more than 20mm wide	11
11	Filaments glabrous	12
+	Filaments hairy at least near the base	13
12	Largest leaves less than 90mm, petioles not grooved above, corolla more than 30mm	**225. robinsonii**
+	Largest leaves more than 100mm, petioles grooved above, corolla less than 25mm	**226. rarilepidotum**
13	Corolla lobes less than 15mm, flower buds often lateral	**232. loerzingii**
+	Corolla lobes more than 25mm, flower buds never lateral	**227. javanicum**

Key to species from Borneo

1 Leaves linear, less than 6mm wide _____ **234. stenophyllum**
+ Leaves of other shapes, more than 6mm wide _____ 2

2 Petiole minutely, shortly hairy all over _____ **235. verticillatum**
+ Petiole scaly only, without short simple hairs _____ 3

3 Ovary glabrous or scaly _____ 4
+ Ovary hairy _____ 7

4 Lateral veins more than 10 per side, corolla tube constricted in the middle part __ **227. javanicum** ssp. **cockburnii**
+ Lateral veins fewer than 10 per side, corolla tube broadening regularly distally _____ 5

5 Mid-vein strongly raised above to more than halfway _____ **236. crassifolium**
+ Mid-vein not raised above or not raised beyond to less than halfway _____ 6

6 Leaves spirally arranged, inflorescence more than 15-flowered, style glabrous _____ **237. jiewhoei**
+ Leaves in pseudowhorls, inflorescence less than 15-flowered, style scaly in the proximal ½ _____ **238. kemulense**

7 Twigs minutely hairy _____ 8
+ Twigs with scales only _____ 10

8 Leaf base tapering _____ **227. javanicum** ssp. **cladotrichum**
+ Leaf base rounded to cordate _____ 9

9 Corolla tube up to 12mm wide at the mouth, leaf apex broadly acute _____ **239. monkoboense**
+ Corolla tube more than 16mm wide at the mouth, leaf apex obtuse to rounded _____ **240. apiense**

10 Largest leaves less than 30mm wide _____ 11
+ Largest leaves more than 30mm wide _____ 23

11 Leaves distinctly rugose, scales dendroid _____ 12
+ Leaves smooth or weakly rugose, scales stellate, flat _____ 13

12 Flowers red or pink, corolla tube longer than the lobes _____ **241. rugosum**
+ Flowers yellow, corolla lobes longer than the tube _____ **184. nieuwenhuisii**

13 Leaf blade narrowly elliptic, leaves mostly less than 25mm wide _____ 14
+ Leaf blade elliptic or narrowly ovate, leaves mostly more than 25mm wide _____ 16

14 Petiole less than 2mm, flowers orange, flower buds red _____ **242. nervulosum**
+ Petiole more than 3mm, flowers mostly yellow, flower buds green _____ 15

15 Largest leaves less than 16mm wide _____ **243. salicifolium**
+ Largest leaves more than 20mm wide _____ **227. javanicum** ssp. **gracile**

16 Leaf apex rounded or retuse _____ 17
+ Leaf apex obtuse to acute _____ 20

17 Flowers dark red, shortly hairy on the corolla tube outside _____ **244. yongii**
+ Flowers pink, scaly or glabrous on the corolla tube outside _____ 18

18 Corolla tube more than 35mm _____ 19
+ Corolla tube less than 25mm _____ **245. baconii**

19 Leaves up to 70mm, corolla lobes much shorter than the tube _____ **246. praetervisum**
+ Leaves more than 90mm, corolla lobes almost as long as the tube _____ **227. javanicum** ssp. **kinabaluense**

20 Petiole up to 5mm, less than 2x as long as broad _____ 21
+ Petiole mostly more than 5mm, at least 2x as long as broad _____ 22

21 Flowers white, minutely but conspicuously densely brown scaly outside _____ **248. lanceolatum**
\+ Flowers orange to red, inconspicuously and sparsely scaly outside _____ **249. exuberans**

22 Pedicels scaly, without hairs, leaf blade mostly more than 100mm _____ **250. commutatum**
\+ Pedicels scaly and hairy, leaf blade mostly less than 80mm _____ **224. longiflorum**

23 Corolla tube shortly hairy outside _____ 24
\+ Corolla tube scaly or glabrous outside _____ 25

24 Flowers dark red, stamens on upper side of corolla, scales stellate, leaves smooth _____ **244. yongii**
\+ Flowers pink, stamens on lower side of corolla or irregular, scales dendroid, leaves rugose _____ **241. rugosum**

25 Petiole as broad as long or broader _____ 26
\+ Petiole longer than broad _____ 28

26 Leaves sub-circular, hardly longer than broad _____ **247. orbiculatum**
\+ Leaves distinctly longer than broad _____ 27

27 Flowers white, leaves strongly wrinkled near the base _____ **248. lanceolatum**
\+ Flowers pink, leaves smooth _____ **245. baconii**

28 Pedicels with simple hairs _____ 29
\+ Pedicels with scales only _____ 35

29 Leaves very deeply sulcate, more than 80mm wide _____ **251. intranervatum**
\+ Leaves smooth or nearly so, less than 50mm wide _____ 30

30 Style glabrous _____ 31
\+ Style hairy in the proximal ⅓–½ _____ 33

31 Corolla lobes longer than the tube, powerfully scented _____ **252. maxwellii**
\+ Corolla lobes as long as or shorter than the tube, without scent _____ 32

32 Flowers pink, corolla tube more than 30mm, flowers hanging _____ **246. praetervisum**
\+ Flowers orange to red, corolla tube less than 25mm, flowers semi-erect _____ **249. exuberans**

33 Filaments glabrous or with hairs at the base only _____ **249. exuberans**
\+ Filaments hairy to at least ⅓ _____ 34

34 Corolla lobes distinctly longer than the tube, scented _____ **252. maxwellii**
\+ Corolla lobes shorter than the tube, without scent _____ **224. longiflorum**

35 Leaf base broadly to narrowly tapering _____ 36
\+ Leaf base rounded to cordate _____ 39

36 Leaf apex rounded or retuse _____ **252. maxwellii**
\+ Leaf apex obtuse to acute _____ 37

37 Flowers yellow, very young leaves expanding revolute _____ **253. retivenium**
\+ Flowers orange to red, very young leaves expanding flat _____ 38

38 Corolla lobes less than 5mm, style glabrous _____ **249. exuberans**
\+ Corolla lobes more than 10mm, style hairy nearly to the top _____ **250. commutatum**

39 Scales dendroid, corolla tube less than 25mm _____ **254. polyanthemum**
\+ Scales flat, stellate, corolla tube more than 30mm _____ 40

40 Leaves spirally arranged, less than 3x as long as broad, above 2700m altitude _____ **255. lowii**
\+ Leaves in distinct pseudowhorls, more than 3x as long as broad, below 2000m altitude _____
_____ **227. javanicum** ssp. **brookeanum**

Key to species from the Philippines

1	Ovary hairy and often scaly	2
+	Ovary without simple hairs, scaly or glabrous	9
2	Flowers white	3
+	Flowers coloured yellow or orange	6
3	Pedicels hairy and scaly	**265. madulidii**
+	Pedicels scaly only	4
4	Flower buds with bract tips reflexed, corolla lobes more than 35mm	**256. mendumiae**
+	Flower buds with bract tips appressed, corolla lobes less than 25mm	5
5	Flower buds spherical, leaf blade acute	**257. kochii**
+	Flower buds acutely pointed, leaf blade obtuse to rounded	**259. mindanaense**
6	Flowers more than 80mm, bicoloured with yellow tube and orange lobes	**227. javanicum** ssp. **palawanense**
+	Flowers less than 40mm, yellow or orange	7
7	Flowers yellow, foliage leaves abruptly changing to bracts	8
+	Flowers orange, foliage leaves gradually changing to bracts the transitional forms with translucent decurrent margins	**260. reynosoi**
8	Ovary and style *c.*½ the length of the stamens	**261. brachygynum**
+	Ovary and style as long as the stamens	**262. leytense**
9	Corolla more than 80mm	**227. javanicum** ssp. **palawanense**
+	Corolla less than 50mm	10
10	Flowers white	**258. williamsii**
+	Flowers yellow or red	11
11	Filaments glabrous	**263. loboense**
+	Filaments hairy at the base	12
12	Flowers yellow, ovary scaly	**264. xanthopetalum**
+	Flowers red or pink, ovary glabrous or with only a few scattered scales	**227. javanicum** ssp. **schadenbergii**

Key to species from Sulawesi and Maluku

1	Ovary scaly or glabrous, without simple hairs	2
+	Ovary with simple white hairs, with or without scales	4
2	Filaments hairy	**266. impressopunctatum**
+	Filaments glabrous	3
3	Corolla broadly funnel-shaped, tube more than 15mm wide at the mouth	**267. seranicum**
+	Corolla cylindrical, tube less than 12mm wide at the mouth	**268. celebicum**
4	Corolla tube more than 35mm	5
+	Corolla tube less than 35mm	7
5	Leaves sub-circular, not or hardly longer than broad	**247. orbiculatum**
+	Leaves distinctly longer than broad	6
6	Leaves long acuminate, anthers less than 5mm	**269. rhodopus**
+	Leaves shortly acuminate, anthers more than 6mm	**270. bloembergenii**

7	Leaf base acutely tapering	8
+	Leaf base broadly tapering, rounded or cordate	9
8	Corolla tube less than 25mm, corolla lobes more than 16mm	**271. poromense**
+	Corolla tube more than 30mm, corolla lobes less than 16mm	**272. leptobrachion**
9	Flowers orange or dark red	10
+	Flowers white or pale pink	12
10	Scales sub-dendroid, very fragile, flowers orange to yellow	**273. vanvuurenii**
+	Scales stellate, sub-persistent, flowers pink to red	11
11	Petiole *c.*2mm wide, pedicels up to 30mm, scaly and with minute hairs	**274. stresemannii**
+	Petiole *c.*4mm wide, pedicels up to 50mm, scaly only	**275. impositum**
12	Pedicels scaly and hairy	**276. buruense**
+	Pedicels scaly only	13
13	Leaves spirally arranged	**275. impositum**
+	Leaves in pseudowhorls	14
14	Style hairy and/or scaly up to ⅓ (Buru)	**277. toxopei**
+	Style hairy and/or scaly up to ⅔ (Sulawesi)	**278. lompohense**

Key to species from New Guinea

1	Ovary scaly only without simple hairs	2
+	Ovary scaly and hairy	8
2	Filaments glabrous	3
+	Filaments hairy at least at the base	5
3	Leaves linear, up to 3mm wide	**279. subulosum**
+	Leaves not linear, more than 20mm wide	4
4	Petiole more than 8mm, inflorescence more than 9-flowered	**280. glabriflorum**
+	Petiole less than 6mm, inflorescence less than 9-flowered	**281. pachycarpon**
5	Pedicels hairy and scaly, corolla more than 70mm, orange with white lobes	**282. pachystigma**
+	Pedicels scaly only, corolla less than 70mm, red	6
6	Leaf blade more than 100mm, leaf base obtuse, rounded or cordate	**283. angulatum**
+	Leaf blade less than 90mm, leaf base tapering	7
7	Filaments papillose hairy, style scaly at the base only	**284. alticola**
+	Filaments laxly long hairy, style scaly in the proximal ⅓	**285. sayeri**
8	Corolla tube hairy outside at least to halfway	9
+	Corolla tube glabrous or scaly outside or with a few hairs near the base only	14
9	Corolla tube straight	10
+	Corolla tube distinctly curved	11
10	Bracts scaly on both sides at the apex (E New Guinea)	**286. aurigeranum** ssp. **hirsutum**
+	Bracts with appressed hairs outside, glabrous inside (W New Guinea)	**287. laetum**
11	Petiole hardly longer than broad	**288. christi**
+	Petiole distinctly longer than broad	12
12	Flowers yellow or green, leaves more than 40mm wide	13
+	Flowers red, leaves less than 40mm wide	**289. villosulum**

13 Flowers yellow, leaves ovate, the bases rounded   **290. curviflorum**
+ Flowers green, leaves elliptic, the bases tapering   **291. milleri**

14 Largest leaves less than 100mm   15
+ Largest leaves more than 100mm   24

15 Corolla tube as long as or shorter than the lobes   **292. macgregoriae**
+ Corolla tube much longer than the lobes   16

16 Pedicels hairy and scaly   17
+ Pedicels scaly only, without simple hairs   20

17 Corolla yellow to orange, tube straight   **293. christianae**
+ Corolla red or pink, tube mostly curved   18

18 Filaments glabrous   **294. rosendahlii**
+ Filaments hairy at least at the base   19

19 Corolla tube scaly outside   **295. culminicola**
+ Corolla tube glabrous outside   **296. arfakianum**

20 Leaf base auriculate, petiole as broad as long   **297. blackii**
+ Leaf base tapering, petiole distinctly longer than broad   21

21 Corolla red   **298. hirtolepidotum**
+ Corolla white or pale green   22

22 Corolla tube curved, pale green   **198. flavoviride**
+ Corolla tube straight, white   23

23 Corolla lobes more than 15mm, petiole more than 10mm   **299. comparabile**
+ Corolla lobes less than 15mm, petiole less than 5mm   **300. luraluense**

24 Corolla tube less than 15mm   25
+ Corolla tube more than 20mm   27

25 Corolla tube curved, lobes orange with distinct yellow triangular marks on the upper three lobes   **301. wentianum**
+ Corolla tube straight, without distinctive markings on the upper lobes   26

26 Petiole less than 5mm, filaments glabrous or with a few hairs near the base   **302. glabrifilum**
+ Petiole more than 5mm, filaments densely hairy in the proximal ½   **292. macgregoriae**

27 Corolla glabrous inside   **294. rosendahlii**
+ Corolla hairy inside   28

28 Flowers pale pink to white   29
+ Flowers red, yellow or orange   30

29 Corolla lobes 5, leaves in loose pseudowhorls or spiral   **303. schlechteri**
+ Corolla lobes 7, leaves in tight pseudowhorls   **304. leucogigas**

30 Petiole less than 2mm, broader than long   **305. brevipes**
+ Petiole more than 3mm, longer than broad   31

31 Corolla tube less than 30mm   32
+ Corolla tube more than 30mm   35

32 Pedicels more than 60mm   **306. englerianum**
+ Pedicels less than 60mm   33

33 Flowers red _____ **298. hirtolepidotum**
+   Flowers orange, sometimes tinged with red _____ 34

34 Inflorescence 3-flowered, corolla more than 60mm _____ **307. mollianum**
+   Inflorescence more than 9-flowered, corolla less than 45mm _____ **308. cuspidellum**

35 Flowers red, tube curved _____ **310. scabridibracteum**
+   Flowers yellow or orange, at least on the tube which is straight _____ 36

36 Petiole 3–4mm, almost as wide as long _____ **309. baenitzianum**
+   Petiole more than 7mm, distinctly more than 2x as long as broad _____ 37

37 Flower buds smooth, the bract tips appressed, glabrous inside, with small appressed hairs outside __ **311. zoelleri**
+   Flower buds with reflexed bract tips, which are scaly on both sides _____ **286. aurigeranum**

Key to species from Australia

1 Corolla tube straight, filaments hairy, anthers irregularly distributed around the mouth or on the lower side _____
_____ **313. viriosum**
+   Corolla tube curved, filaments glabrous, anthers clustered on the upper side of the mouth _____ **312. lochiae**

---

223. Rhododendron triumphans Yersin & A.Chev.
Rév. de Bot. Appl. et d'Agric. Trop. 1929. 9(92): 256, *t*.11.
Type: Chevalier 38601, 15 Sept. 1918. Sud Annnam, Massif du Honba (P, L, fragment).
Derivation: Latin – *triumphans* – winning honours. Named by the authors for the beauty of the flowers and the date when it was seen flowering on which they received good news about the Great War in Europe.

Shrub to 2m. Twigs 4–5mm in diameter, rounded, laxly scaly but quickly glabrescent. **Leaves** spirally arranged. **Blade** 140–190 x 55–80mm, elliptic; apex acute to obtuse, sometimes shortly acuminate; margin entire, flat; base tapering, broadly tapering to rounded; sparsely scaly and quickly glabrescent above, densely or sub-densely scaly beneath. **Scales** sub-stellate with a broad thin marginal zone and small slightly impressed centre. Mid-vein broadly raised above in the proximal ⅓ becoming impressed distally; strongly raised beneath throughout although becoming more slender distally; lateral veins 10–14 per side, very slightly raised on both sides when dry. **Petiole** 18–26 x 2–3mm, not grooved above, laxly scaly.

Inflorescence 5–9 flowers in an umbel, red, without scent. Pedicels 38–42 x *c*.1mm, scaly without hairs. Calyx *c*.4–5mm in diameter, a low disc, glabrous. **Corolla** 70–80 x 60–80mm, funnel-shaped; tube 30–40 x 5–7 x 20–27mm, glabrous outside and inside; lobes 40–45 x 32–38mm, obovate, glabrous. **Stamens** *c*.40mm; filaments red; anthers up to 5mm, purple, oblong. **Ovary** *c*.10 x 4mm, cylindrical or slightly angled, hairy; style to 30mm, slender, glabrous, pink; stigma disc-shaped. **Fruit** fusiform, angled.

Vietnam, Khanh Hoa, Massif du Honba. Epiphytic on trees or on peat on blocks of granite.

Reported by the collector to be a 'magnificent ornamental plant, remarkable for the beauty of its flowers'. Not known to be in general cultivation although reportedly seen being sold in a market in Vietnam. Commonly confused with the old Veitch hybrid 'Triumphans' (spelt with a capital letter), which is superficially similar but not of wild origin and still cultivated in various collections worldwide. Professor Sleumer (1958) considered it 'practically identical to *R. brookeanum* [*R. javanicum* ssp. *brookeanum*]' but found 'a striking difference however, between these species in the petiole'. We still have no recent observations on this species which should most likely be included in the *R. javanicum* complex.

---

224. Rhododendron longiflorum Lindl.
J. Hort. Soc. Lond. 1848. 3: *f*.89.
Type: J. Hort. Soc. Lond. 1848. 3: *f*.89.
Derivation: Latin – *longus* – long; *florum* – flower. The long-flowered rhododendron.

Synonyms:
R. tubiflorum Low *ex* Lindl., J. Hort. Soc. Lond. 1848. 3: 88.
R. lobbii Veitch, Cat. 1870. 22.
R. javanicum (Blume) Benn. var. *tubiflorum* Hook., Bot. Mag. 1885. *t*.6850.
R. orion Ridl. var. *aurantiacum* Ridl., Fl. Mal. Pen. 1923. 2: 217.

Key to the varieties

1   Corolla tube straight, lobes not pouched at the
     apex ———————————————— 2
+   Corolla tube curved, lobes usually pouched at the
     apex ——————————— var. **longiflorum**

2   Corolla lobes less than 25mm ————— 3
+   Corolla lobes more than 30mm — var. **longipetalum**

3   Corolla more than 40mm ——— var. **subcordatum**
+   Corolla less than 30mm ———— var. **bancanum**

Var. **longiflorum**

Shrub to 3m. Twigs rounded, initially laxly brown-scaly, quickly glabrescent; internodes 2–12cm. **Leaves** 4–5 together in tight pseudowhorls at the upper 1–3 nodes. **Blade** 40–90 x 20–40mm, narrowly obovate, obovate-elliptic, or elliptic; apex shortly and bluntly tapering or sub-acuminate; margin flat or very slightly revolute, often slightly convex; base tapering to rounded, rarely sub-cordate, at first densely scaly on both sides, later glabrescent above, laxly and more persistently scaly beneath. **Scales** small, marginal zone irregularly sub-stellately lobed; centre deeply impressed. Mid-vein slightly impressed above, prominent in its proximal part beneath; lateral veins 5–6 per side, faintly impressed above, smooth beneath, often obscure. **Petiole** 3–25 x 1.5–2mm, flattened, grooved above, brown-scaly.

Flower buds to 12 x 8mm, conical, brown, smooth. Outer bracts ovate to sub-circular, inner ones broadly spathulate, all laxly scaly and sometimes also minutely hairy outside. Bracteoles to 15mm, filiform to linear-spathulate. Umbels open, 5–10-flowered, the flowers horizontal to semi-erect. Pedicels 10–30 x *c*.2mm, mostly laxly, rarely densely hairy and laxly scaly. Calyx a thin oblique, very short rim. **Corolla** 40–60 x 30mm, orange, pink or red often with a yellow throat; tube 30–40 x 3–5 x 7–12mm, scaly outside, hairy inside in the proximal ½, curved upwards; lobes 13–21 x 7–12mm, obovate to sub-circular, not or only shortly overlapping, spreading and becoming reflexed, mostly hooded at the apex. **Stamens** spreading irregularly around the mouth, exserted for 10–15mm, reflexing back in old flowers; filaments to 55mm, linear and sub-densely to laxly hairy in the proximal ⅓, glabrous and nearly filiform distally; anthers 2.8–3 x 1mm, oblong. **Ovary** 6 x 2mm, elongate-conical, densely covered with sub-appressed hairs which cover scales; style to *c*.50mm, exserted, densely hairy in the proximal ½; stigma lobed, *c*.3mm in diameter. **Fruit** 30–40 x 5–6mm, cylindrical, with longitudinal grooves. Seeds 3.5mm, without tails 1mm, the longest tail 1.5mm.

Rhododendron longiflorum var. *longiflorum*.

Thailand, Yala Province, Betong District. **Malaysia**, Peninsula; Sabah, Sarawak (Borneo). **Brunei. Indonesia**, Sumatra, Karimata Arch., Mentawei Is.; Kalimantan (Borneo). Terrestrial or epiphytic, often on tall trees in primary or secondary forest, along rivers and in mangrove, quartzite rocks, sandstone pavement, limestone hills or sandy clay; in heath-forest (kerangas); from sea level up to 1500m. *Fl.* Jan.–Dec.

Hybridising with *R. jasminiflorum* ssp. *heusseri* in the Samosir Peninsula, Sumatra (see under that subspecies). Specimens from West Malaysia, especially from Mt Tahan, are distinct in having short, thick petioles and large flowers. They may warrant description as a distinct form.

This species was first introduced into cultivation about 1860 and it appeared in Veitch's catalogue in 1870 as *R. lobbii*. It contributed parentage to many of the Veitch hybrids produced in the late 1800s such as 'Duchess of Edinburgh'. This species was also grown by Professor Holttum in Singapore as one of his main parents in a breeding programme which was to produce rhododendrons for lowland tropical gardens. This work never came to fruition due to the invasion of Singapore in 1942. This species undoubtedly requires more heat than most vireyas to grow well. It has most attractive flowers and will bloom repeatedly throughout the year if conditions are right. It would be good to see it fulfil its potential as a horticultural plant in tropical gardens.

Var. **longipetalum** Argent, A.Lamb & Phillipps
Notes RBG Edinb. 1984. 42(1): 114.
Type: Phillipps & Ampal 1337, 21 Feb. 1980. Sabah, Sinsuron Rd. (E).
Derivation: Latin – *longus* – long; *petalum* – petal. Referring to the very long petal lobes.

Leaves as in var. *longiflorum*. Corolla *c*.52 x 70mm, tube 40 x 8 x 15mm, straight; lobes 35 x 20mm.

Malaysia (Borneo), Sabah, Crocker Range, Sinsuron Road; Mt Madalon, 760–1060m. Epiphyte in lowland forest.

This variety was first collected along the Sinsuron Road where the forest has been very much reduced, and it is likely to be extinct here. It is an area where *R. javanicum* ssp. *brookeanum* is common and it is possible that this variety is a hybrid between this species and *R. longiflorum*; however, the leaves are typical of *R. longiflorum* var. *longiflorum*.

Var. **bancanum** Sleumer
Reinwardtia 1960. 5: 210.
Type: de Leeuw 2, 22 Sept. 1928. Bangka, Top of G. Maras, 600–700m (L, A, BO).
Derivation: Named after the island from which it was described.

Leaves elliptic or broadly elliptic. **Petiole** 9–20 x 1.5–2mm. Bracts densely hairy outside. **Corolla** 20–25mm, tube straight, base 2.5–3mm in diameter, widened to 3.5–4.5mm distally, lobes 15–16 x 8–10mm, obovate-spathulate. **Stamens** *c.*35mm, anthers 2.5 x 1mm. **Ovary** *c.*4 x 2mm; style 23mm.

Differs from var. *longiflorum* mainly by smaller flowers and longer petioles.

Indonesia, Bangka Is., top of Mt Maras, Menumbing, and R. Liat, 425–700m.

Var. **subcordatum** (Becc.) Argent
Rhododendrons of Sabah, Sabah Parks Publ. 1988. 8: 32.
Type: Beccari P.B. 3231. Borneo, Sarawak, Batang Lupar, Tian Laju, *c.*1000m (Fl, K).
Derivation: Latin – *sub* – somewhat; *cordatus* – heart-shaped. Referring to the rounded lobes of the leaf base.

Synonym: *R. subcordatum* Becc., Malesia 1878. I: 203.

Rhododendron longiflorum var. *subcordatum*.

Vegetatively as in the type variety. Corolla tube straight, not curved, lobes spreading not becoming reflexed, overlapping at the base and rarely hooded at the apex.

Malaysia (Borneo), Sarawak, Batang Lupar, Tian Laju. Sabah, near Nabawan, 700–1000m. Terrestrial and epiphytic in heath-forest.

225. Rhododendron robinsonii Ridl.
J. Fed. Mal. St. Mus. 1909. 4: 44.
Type: Ridley 13588, Dec. 1900. Malay Peninsula, G. Berumbun, 1035–1535m (SING, BM, K).
Derivation: Named after Herbert C. Robinson, one time director of the Malay States Museums.

Shrub to 2.5m. Twigs 4–6mm in diameter, round, green, laxly scaly; internodes 4–10cm. **Leaves** 3–5 together in loose pseudowhorls. **Blade** 80–160 x 35–60mm, elliptic; apex shortly acuminate, narrowly to broadly acute, rarely obtuse; margin entire, flat or weakly revolute; base narrowly tapering, sometimes a little decurrent; minutely silvery scaly above at first, the scales leaving small impressed pits, laxly to sub-densely and more persistently scaly beneath. **Scales** irregularly lobed in the marginal zone; centre dark, shallowly impressed. Mid-vein strongly raised above proximally, gradually tapering distally becoming smooth or even slightly impressed in the distal ½, beneath broadly and shallowly raised; lateral veins 8–10 per side, curved-spreading and obscurely interarching at some distance from the margin, slightly prominent on both sides or obscure, reticulation obscure, or faintly visible beneath only. **Petiole** 10–25 x 3–4mm, without a groove, laxly, minutely scaly.

Flower buds to 35 x 20mm, ovoid, acuminate. Bracts to 25 x 13mm, outer bracts ovate-acuminate, sub-acute, initially laxly scaly outside, but quickly glabrescent, inner ones ovate-elliptic, obtuse, glabrous. Bracteoles to 20 x 2mm, linear proximally, sub-spathulate distally, glabrous. Inflorescence 5–12-flowered, a complete or slightly open umbel. Pedicels 20–45 x *c.*1mm, laxly scaly, glabrescent. Calyx 3–4mm in diameter, oblique, disc-shaped or rim-like, obscurely lobed or wavy, with a few scales outside. **Corolla** 30–35 x 30–35mm, funnel-shaped, yellow often flushed with orange or red; tube *c.*15 x 5–6 x 10–15mm, pouched at the base, glabrous inside and out; lobes 13–18 x 10–15mm, spreading, broadly elliptic-obovate. **Stamens** 20–25mm, exserted to *c.*10mm, unequal, irregularly arranged around the flower; filaments linear, glabrous; anthers 3–3.5 x 1–1.3mm, oblong, a little curved, base obtuse. Disc prominent, glabrous. **Ovary** 5–6 x 2–2.5mm, ovoid-conical, initially with some fragile sub-stellate scales, or glabrous, often minutely warty, abruptly contracted distally; style 10–15mm, slender, glabrous; stigma 2–3mm in diameter, knob-like, thickly 5-lobed. **Fruit** *c.*30 x 6mm, fusiform, somewhat oblique and curved, glabrous.

Malaysia (Peninsula), Main Range from Perak to Selangor, and in the Taiping Hills. Epiphytic on tall trees, especially those overhanging rivers, also terrestrial on rocks by streams, occasionally on wooded hillsides or swamps, locally common, 1035–1830m. *Fl. fr.* Jan.–Dec.

First introduced into cultivation in Edinburgh in 1973 by Mrs Elizabeth Stevens of Guildford. It grows as a lanky plant and flowers irregularly, usually in the Scottish spring. It is superficially similar to *R. javanicum*, differing only in the completely glabrous filaments. Sleumer comments on its similarity to *R. rarilepidotum*, considering it different mostly on flower colour. This difference does not work as *R. rarilepidotum* often has yellow flowers. In cultivation *R. rarilepidotum* has much smaller, more conspicuously scaly leaves, and the petioles are usually at least weakly grooved above. *Rhododendron robinsonii* never has grooved petioles in the fresh state.

226. Rhododendron rarilepidotum J.J.Sm.

In Merr., Contr. Arn. Arb. 1934. 8: 126.
Type: Lörzing 8166, 19 Jan. 1921. Sumatra, east coast, G. Sinmabung, 2000–2470m (BO, A, K, L).
Derivation: Latin – *rari* – rare or seldom; Greek – *lepidotum* – covered with small scales. Presumably because the scales easily fall off so that the leaves are glabrescent. Not especially apt.

Shrub to 4m. Twigs 4–5mm in diameter, rounded, internodes laxly to densely scaly, becoming glabrescent, smooth; internodes 4–11cm. **Leaves** 3–7 in loose pseudo-whorls. **Blade** 50–90 x 20–35mm, elliptic, rarely slightly obovate-elliptic; apex shortly acuminate, acute or broadly acute; margin entire, flat or weakly and narrowly revolute; base narrowly to broadly tapering; densely scaly on both sides at first, glabrescent above when mature but minutely blackish punctate where the scales have been, laxly to sub-densely and persistently scaly beneath. **Scales** small, marginal zone irregularly sub-stellately lobed, disintegrating with age; centres dark, large, minutely but visibly impressed. Mid-vein slightly raised above in the proximal ½, often grooved in this part also, smooth or a little impressed distally; beneath shallowly raised in the proximal ½–¾, smooth distally; lateral veins 6–10 per

side, wide-spreading, smooth or very slightly raised above, smooth and often obscure beneath, reticulation obscure. **Petiole** 7–18 x 3–4mm, smooth or grooved distally, scaly.

Bracts to 25 x 12mm, membranous, glabrous, outer ones ovate, sub-obtuse, inner ones ovate-elliptic, slightly keeled. Bracteoles *c.*20 x 1.5mm, linear below, sub-spathulate distally, glabrous. Inflorescence a full or semi-open umbel of 6–12 flowers held semi-erect to horizontal. Pedicels 15–20 x *c.*1mm, laxly to sub-densely scaly. Calyx *c.*4mm in diameter, oblique, rim-like, wavy. **Corolla** 20–25 x 35–40mm, broadly funnel-shaped, orange, often darker at the base of the tube, or yellow, sometimes scented; tube 12–20 x 8–9 x 16–18mm, base slightly 5-lobed, laxly scaly or glabrous outside, glabrous inside; lobes 13–19 x 12–17mm, obovate-sub-circular, reflexing to the perpendicular, overlapping *c.*halfway. **Stamens** exserted to *c.*10mm, spreading all round the flower, unequal; filaments linear, glabrous; anthers 2–3 x 1.3mm, obtuse at the base. Disc prominent, glabrous. **Ovary** 4–6 x 2–2.5mm, sub-cylindric-conical, mostly glabrous from the beginning, rarely laxly scaly at first, becoming glabrous during the flowering, abruptly contracted distally; style 12–18mm, slender; stigma 2–3mm in diameter, lobes distinct. **Fruit** 25–30 x 5–7mm, fusiform, often slightly curved, glabrous.

Indonesia, Sumatra, Gajo Lands; East Coast; West Coast, Mt Kaba. In sub-alpine shrubberies, and open volcanic areas, mostly terrestrial, rarely epiphytic, 1000–2500m. *Fl.* Jan.–Dec.

Sleumer (1966) noted that '*R. rarilepidotum* is closely related to *R. robinsonii* from the Malay Peninsula and mainly differs by its smaller, generally red to dark red corollas'. Recent field work has established that yellow corollas often occur and in some populations, such as those on Mt Kaba, they may predominate. For differences with *R. robinsonii* see under that species. *Rhododendron rarilepidotum* was first introduced into cultivation by John

Rhododendron rarilepidotum (yellow form).

Rhododendron rarilepidotum (orange form).

Dransfield in 1975 and it flowered at Kew in November 1983. It has been in cultivation in Edinburgh since 1981; the original collections have dark reddish-orange flowers and are scented, the flowers often have 6 petals and one clone has long petaloid calyx lobes. A later collection by David Binney is yellow-flowered. As a species it grows vigorously as a compact, medium-sized shrub, flowering irregularly but very freely usually in spring or autumn, and is a very worthwhile horticultural subject.

Rhododendron x **ootrichum** Sleumer (*R. rarilepidotum* x *R. sumatranum*)
Reinwardtia 1960. 5: 191.
Type: Heusser 6. Sumatra, East Coast, Mt Sibayak, summit (L, A, BO, SING).
Derivation: Greek – *oo* – a female organ; *trichum* – hair. Alluding to the ovary being covered in hairs.

Synonym: *R. rarilepidotum* var. *ootrichum* Sleumer, Reinwardtia 1960. 5: 191.

Differs by the white-hairy ovary, broader and more shortly acuminate leaves, more densely scaly pedicels and slightly smaller bracts. Corolla red, very laxly hairy inside. Fruit 20–25 x 6mm.

Indonesia, Sumatra, East Coast, Mt Sibayak and Mt Pinto, 1750–2100m.

227. Rhododendron javanicum (Blume) Benn.
In Benn. & Br., Pl. Jav. Rar. 1838. 85 (excluding *t*.19).
Type: Blume *s.n.* (coll. Zippel?). Java, G. Salak, 800–2215m (L, U).
Derivation: Named after Java, the island on which it was first collected.

Synonyms:
Vireya javanica Blume, Bijdr. 1826. 854.
Azalea javanica (Blume) Kuntze, Rev. Gen. 1891. 2: 386.

This species is presently treated in a broad sense including *R. brookeanum* and *R. moultonii*. This complex of mainly low altitude forest epiphytes is characterised by large, elliptic, acutely pointed leaves and large, funnel-shaped flowers in a range of colours. As conceived here, it is widespread, occurring through Sumatra, Peninsular Malaysia, the Philippines, Borneo, Java and Bali to Sulawesi. It is highly variable in its leaf arrangement and ovary indumentum, even within some populations, and is difficult to deal with satisfactorily although various populations are distinct.

Key to the subspecies

1   Largest leaves to 30mm wide _____ ssp. **gracile**
+   Largest leaves more than 30mm wide _____ 2

2   Twigs shortly, minutely hairy when young _____
    _____ ssp. **cladotrichum**
+   Twigs scaly or glabrous when young _____ 3

3   Ovary scaly or glabrous _____ 4
+   Ovary densely hairy _____ 8

4   Flowers red _____ 5
+   Flowers yellow and/or orange _____ 6

5   Corolla tube clearly contracted in the middle, broader at both base and apex _____ ssp. **cockburnii**
+   Corolla tube parallel sided or expanded continuously distally _____ ssp. **schadenbergii**

6   Leaves spirally arranged, flowers more than 70mm __
    _____ ssp. **palawanense**
+   Leaves in pseudowhorls, flowers less than 70mm __ 7

7   Lateral veins more than 16 per side, straight, spreading at *c*.90° _____ ssp. **moultonii**
+   Lateral veins fewer than 12 per side, spreading at *c*.45° _____ ssp. **javanicum**

8   Pedicels hairy _____ ssp. **teysmannii**
+   Pedicels with scales only _____ 9

9   Leaves in tight to loose pseudowhorls, flowers mostly uniformly coloured _____ ssp. **brookeanum**

+ Leaves spirally arranged, flowers strongly bicoloured with a yellow tube and orange lobes _____ 10

10 Ovary densely hairy all over _____ ssp. **kinabaluense**
+ Ovary glabrous or hairy only in the basal ½ _____
_____ ssp. **palawanense**

Ssp. **javanicum**

Shrub or tree to 5m, trunk up to 8cm in diameter. Twigs 3–6mm in diameter, young shoots rounded and laxly sub-stellately scaly, becoming glabrescent and smooth; internodes 3–15cm. **Leaves** 4–8 together in tight, or occasionally loose, pseudowhorls. **Blade** 80–150 x 25–50mm, narrowly-elliptic, elliptic to elliptic-ovate; apex shortly acuminate, acute; margin entire, flat; base acutely tapering; initially laxly scaly on both sides, early glabrescent above, laxly and more persistently scaly beneath, eventually spotted with brown after the scales have gone. **Scales** small, flat, with a variously lobed marginal zone; centre dark, not impressed. Mid-vein strong, broad and obtusely prominent proximally on both sides, narrowly impressed distally above, prominent throughout beneath; lateral veins 7–10 per side, at *c*.45°, minutely channelled above and smooth below when fresh, slightly prominent on both sides when dry, indistinctly anastomosing before the margin, reticulation a lax network, faintly raised or often obscure on both sides. **Petiole** 6–23 x 2–4mm, without a groove, compressed dorsally, often brown or red, scaly.

Flower buds 30–40 x 15–20mm, ovoid, with an acute point, the bract tips standing out at *c*.45°. Bracts to 35 x 22mm; outer bracts broadly ovate, shortly subulate-mucronate, inner ones ovate-elliptic to elliptic, obtuse, all membranous, glabrous except for fragile marginal scales. Bracteoles to 30 x 1.5mm, linear, glabrous. Inflorescence of 4–12 flowers in a complete umbel. Pedicels 20–40 x 2.5mm, laxly stellately scaly especially distally, without hairs. Calyx *c*.4mm in diameter, oblique, disc-shaped, obtusely 5-angular, glabrous or laxly scaly. **Corolla** 30–50 x 70–80mm, funnel-shaped, orange with red or violet markings at the mouth, or occasionally yellow; tube often red inside, without scent, lobed to *c*.halfway; tube 17–28 x 8–10 x 20–25mm, lobed at the base and obtusely 5-angled, glabrous or nearly so, with just the occasional scale outside, shortly hairy or occasionally glabrous inside; lobes 30–35 x 25–30mm, slightly unequal, spreading, slightly reflexing, overlapping up to ⅓, obovate to sub-spathulate. **Stamens** slightly dimorphic, exserted to *c*.15mm, loosely arranged mostly on the lower ⅔ of the

mouth, often with one or two stamens on the upper side; filaments purple, linear, densely hairy in the proximal ⅓, filiform and glabrous distally; anthers 2.5–4 x *c*.1.3mm, oblong, purple, strongly turned inwards. Disc prominent, shortly hairy on the upper margin. **Ovary** 7–9 x *c*.3mm, obliquely conical-cylindrical, 5-angled, glabrous or very sparsely scaly, tapering distally; style glabrous, as long as the shorter stamens, lying on the lower side of the tube, the tip curving upwards; stigma 3–5mm in diameter, dark purple, rounded. **Fruit** 30–50 x 7–9mm, fusiform, 5-angled, glabrous. Seeds 6–7mm including the tails.

Indonesia, Sumatra, Natuna I., Lingga Arch., Java, Bali. Mostly epiphytic and in primary and secondary forest, but also terrestrial near craters, on narrow ridges, between rocks and on steep slopes, 800–2550m, locally common. *Fl. fr.* Jan.–Dec., with preference for the dry season.

Possibly first introduced into cultivation by a man named Rollison, of which we have only an indirect reference. The first well-documented introduction was by Thomas Lobb, the collector in SE Asia for Veitch's nurseries, who collected living plants probably about 1845 – the plant was figured in *Curtis's Botanical Magazine* in 1847 where it was described as 'certainly one of the finest things ever introduced to our gardens'. The orange flowers were novel at the time in *Rhododendron* and caused a sensation. This typical form of the species may well have been in cultivation ever since. It grows and flowers well, having a better habit than many of the other subspecies, and can cover itself in the bright orange blossoms usually in the winter months. There is a yellow form which has been growing in the Botanic Garden in Cibodas, Java for several years. This has made a compact plant about 1.5m high and is said to cover itself in flowers in the dry season.

Ssp. **brookeanum** (Low *ex* Lindl.) Argent, A.Lamb & Phillipps Notes RBG Edinb. 1984. 42(1): 113.
Type: Low *s.n.* Borneo, Sarawak, Upper Limbang R. (CGE, BM, K).
Derivation: Named after Sir James Brooke (Rajah Brooke), an Englishman who became governor of Sarawak in 1841 after helping the Sultan of Brunei to suppress a revolt.

Synonym: *R. brookeanum* Low *ex* Lindl., J. Hort. Soc. Lond. 1848. 3: 82, 83.

Shrub to 4m. Roots large and fleshy. Twigs obtusely angular to rounded, laxly covered with appressed sub-stellate scales at first, quickly glabrescent; internodes 2–15cm. **Leaves** 3–5 together in distinct pseudowhorls. **Blade** 120–250 x 35–80mm, elliptic to narrowly

Anthony Lamb

Rhododendron javanicum ssp. *brookeanum*.

ovate-elliptic, sometimes sub-sessile; apex gradually and shortly acuminate, acute; margin entire, flat; base tapering, or sometimes sub-truncate, or even rounded at the very base; glabrescent above, the scales leaving dense, minute, dark pits after they have fallen, laxly to very laxly scaly for some time beneath, eventually completely glabrescent. **Scales** small, marginal zone variously sub-stellately lobed; centre minute, shallowly impressed. Midvein broad, slightly raised above in the proximal ½ then smooth, strongly raised below; lateral veins 14–24 per side, spreading, inarching to the margin, slightly raised on both sides, reticulation coarse and inconspicuous, sometimes dense and more visible raised especially beneath. **Petiole** 7–15 x 4–6mm, without a groove, laxly scaly.

Flower buds to 50 x 30mm, smooth, green. Bracts to 40 x 20mm, thin, outer ones ovate-sub-acuminate, inner ones elliptic to spathulate, glabrous. Pedicels 20–50 x 1–2mm, sparsely scaly or glabrous. Inflorescence a complete umbel of 5–14 flowers. Calyx 4–5mm in diameter, shortly disc-shaped or rim-like, obscurely angled or lobed, glabrous. **Corolla** 50–80 x 50–80mm, funnel-shaped, orange-pink with white or cream centre, or yellow, throat then mostly yellow, often with a delicate lemon-like fragrance; tube 30–35 x 6–8 x 20–25mm, straight, angular, pouched at the base, glabrous outside, laxly hairy proximally inside; lobes 25–45 x 25–35mm, sub-circular, slightly retuse or delicately wavy at the margin. **Stamens** exserted to

*c.*20mm, sub-equal, arranged all round the mouth or in two irregular groups on either side; filaments linear, densely sub-patently hairy in the proximal ⅓, glabrous distally; anthers 4–6 x 1–1.3mm, oblong, curved, base obtuse. Disc prominent, shortly hairy on the upper margin. **Ovary** sub-cylindrical, densely long hairy and scaly, abruptly contracted distally; style 8–10 x 2–3mm, at first shorter than, later equalling the stamens, glabrous; stigma deeply lobed. **Fruit** 35–50 x 7–8mm, fusiform-cylindric, scaly and shortly hairy with some elliptic minute warts.

Widespread in Borneo. **Brunei**. **Malaysia**, Sarawak and Sabah. **Indonesia**, Kalimantan. Epiphytic on mangrove or rocks at sea level, ascending to 1525m in the mossy forest, with preference for trees along rivers at the lower altitudes. *Fl.* Jan.–Dec.

First introduced into cultivation by Thomas Lobb about 1850 for the nurserymen Veitch and Sons who exhibited a plant in flower in London in 1855. It was used in the parentage of the famous Veitch hybrids but subsequently lost to cultivation. Sleumer (1966) reports that this was introduced to the lowlands of the Malay Peninsula and flowers freely there. A collection made by Mr and Mrs E.F. Allen in 1966 was named 'Raja'. This had lemon-scented golden yellow flowers and received an RHS First Class Certificate in 1972. Various other introductions have been made subsequently and some of these are still being cultivated. It can be a spectacular plant with large flowers in a variety of shades but it is usually of somewhat sprawling habit.

Ssp. **gracile** (Lindl.) Argent, A.Lamb & Phillipps
Notes RBG Edinb. 1984. 42(1): 114.
Type: Low *s.n.* Borneo, Sarawak, 'Sirul' rocks, mouth of Sarawak R. (CGE).
Derivation: Latin – *gracilis* – thin or slender, the leaves being more slender than the type.

Synonym: *R. gracile* Lindl., J. Hort. Soc. Lond. 1848. 3: 84.

Twigs with scales only. Leaves in tight to loose pseudo-whorls, smooth, not puckered, up to 30mm wide. Petiole 3–10mm, grooved above or smooth, scaly. Flowers mostly yellow, sometimes orange. Anthers *c.*4mm. The ovary covered in simple hairs.

Widespread in Borneo. **Brunei**. **Malaysia**, Sabah and Sarawak. **Indonesia**, Kalimantan. Sea level to 1500m. *Fl.* Jan.–Dec.

This subspecies includes all the slender-leafed forms of *R. javanicum*, some of which may merely be impoverished forms of ssp. *brookeanum* but they usually have grooved petioles and retain their narrow leaves in cultivation. It is recorded on Mt Kinabalu in the vicinity of the

Rhododendron javanicum ssp. *gracile*.

Park Headquarters and surrounding hills. On the southern slopes of Mt Lotung this subspecies grows terrestrially in low pole forest at about 1000m altitude where it is quite strikingly distinct in appearance. This population shows strong similarities to *R. salicifolium* Becc. from southern Sarawak, although it is larger than that species without the tendency to curvature of the leaves. A pink-flowered form of this subspecies from Sarawak was cultivated for some years in the Royal Botanic Garden Edinburgh and maintained its distinctive appearance. It is possible that this plant and many similar forms from Sarawak are the result of hybridisation with *R. longiflorum*.

Ssp. **cladotrichum** (Sleumer) Argent *comb. nov.*
Basionym: *R. brookeanum* var. *cladotrichum* Sleumer, Rein-wardtia 1960. 5: 224.
Type: Endert 4000, 2 Sept. 1925. Borneo, W Kutei, Long Suh, 300m (L, A, BO).
Derivation: Greek – *clad* or *clados* – branch or shoot; *trichome* – hair. Referring to the hairs on the stem.
Synonym: *R. javanicum* ssp. *javanicum* [*non* (Blume) Benn.], Rhododendrons of Sabah, Sabah Parks Publ. 1988. 8: 20.

Shrub to *c*.1.5m, twigs minutely hairy, leaves in pseudo-whorls, smooth, not rugose, minutely hairy along the mid-vein. Flowers orange with a pink throat.

Indonesia (Borneo), Kalimantan, Central East, W Kutei.
Malaysia (Borneo), Sabah, Mt Silam near Lahad Datu, 300–500m.

Distinctive in the finely very shortly hairy stems but otherwise similar to Javan forms of *R. javanicum* with smooth leaves and orange flowers. Cultivated since 1995 it has attractive flowers but is not particularly vigorous.

Ssp. **cockburnii** Argent, A.Lamb & Phillipps
Notes RBG Edinb. 1984. 42(1): 113.
Type: Cockburn SAN 83123, 15 May 1976. Sabah, Lamag Dist., SE of Inarat, ridge to Mt Lotung (SAN).
Derivation: Named after P.F. Cockburn, former forest botan-ist at Sandakan who collected this plant on G. Lotung.

Shrub with scaly stems, leaves in loose pseudowhorls. **Blade** 100–180 x 30–55mm, narrowly elliptic, apex acute, margin flat, base tapering, strongly rugose with 9–18 lat-eral veins per side spreading at almost 90°. **Petiole** 12–20 x *c*.3mm.
Inflorescence of 2–5 flowers, semi-erect to half-hang-ing. **Corolla** bright red; tube constricted at the proximal ⅓, expanded both towards the base and distally.

Malaysia (Borneo), Sabah, Mt Lotung and Long Pa Sia area at *c*.1000m. *Fl.* May.

Most similar to ssp. *schadenbergii* but that subspecies has many fewer lateral veins and smoother leaves and lacks the distinctive corolla shape. It approaches *R. trium-phans* Yersin & A.Chev. from Vietnam in respect of flower size and colour and the long slender petioles but that spe-cies has simple hairs on the ovary and smoother leaves.

Ssp. **schadenbergii** (Warb.) Argent *comb. nov.*
Basionym: *R. schadenbergii* Warb. in Perkins, Frag. Fl. Philip. 1905. 172.
Type: Schadenberg *s.n.* Philippines, Luzon, Abra Province, 1300m (B†).

Rhododendron javanicum ssp. *cockburnii*.

Rhododendron javanicum ssp. *schadenbergii.*

Derivation: Named after Dr Alexander Schadenberg, German ethnologist who also collected plants in the Philippines.

Synonyms:
R. sarasinorum Warb. in Sarasin, Reisen in Celebes 1905. 2: 386.
R. clementis Merr., Phil. J. Sc. Bot. 1908. 3: 160, 381.
R. spectabile Merr., Publ. Gov. Lab. Philip. 1929. 29: 42.
R. javanicum var. *schadenbergii* (Warb.) Sleumer, Reinwardtia 1960. 5: 195.

Twigs scaly. **Leaves** spirally arranged. **Blade** 80–110 x 25–60mm, apex acute, margin flat, base tapering. Lateral veins 6–12 per side. **Petiole** 15–20 x 3–4mm. Pedicels 20–30mm, glabrous or scaly. Calyx *c.*5mm in diameter. **Corolla** 20–45mm, red or pink. **Stamens** with the filaments hairy at the base; anthers 5–7mm. **Ovary** glabrous or with a few scattered scales.

Philippines, Luzon; Camiguin de Misamis; Jolo; Mindanao. **Indonesia**, Sulawesi (NE), Menado. The records from Palawan in the Philippines are all likely to be ssp. *palawanense*. The record from Menado is doubtful and has not been checked; it is more likely to be *R. seranicum.*

Rhododendron javanicum ssp. *schadenbergii* has been in cultivation in Edinburgh since 1992 from material collected in Mindanao. These plants had spectacular red flowers in the wild but have been disappointing in cultivation. They flower sparingly and do not have the vibrant colour that they did in the wild. It would be interesting to see how they performed in a climate with stronger light.

The status of *R. clementis* is not clear. I have followed Sleumer (1966) in treating it as a synonym of this subspecies but the variations in the Philippines are still far from well understood.

Ssp. **palawanense** Argent
Gardens Bull. Sing. 2004. 56: 90.
Type: Argent & Romero Acc. 19922770. Cultivated specimen collected 16 Jan. 1998. Philippines, Palawan, Mt Mantalingajan (PNH, E).
Derivation: Named from the island of Palawan from which it was collected.

Shrub to 1.5m. **Leaves** spirally arranged, smooth. Flower buds green, narrowly ovoid with an acute apex and appressed bracts. Pedicels glabrous or sparsely scaly. **Flowers** *c.*100 x 90mm, bicoloured, with a yellow tube, hairy inside near the base and forming a yellow 'star' in the mouth, lobes *c.*50 x 25mm, orange. **Stamens** with hairs in the basal ¼ of the filaments; anthers *c.*5mm with grey pollen. **Ovary** glabrous or variably hairy and scaly.

Philippines, Palawan, Mt Mantalingajan; Cleopatra Needle; Thumb Peak. A vegetative specimen from Victoria Peak is probably the same subspecies.

This subspecies is very similar to ssp. *kinabaluense* from Mt Kinabalu. These two subspecies are both high altitude forms (for this species). They both have large, conspicuously bicoloured flowers, flower buds with appressed bracts and leaves arranged in regular spirals. Subspecies *palawanense* differs from ssp. *kinabaluense* in having smooth leaves, more slender flower buds with acutely pointed bracts which are never emarginate and longer flowers, with longer and narrower lobes to the corolla.

Ssp. **kinabaluense** (Argent, A.Lamb & Phillipps) Argent *stat. nov.*
Basionym: *R. javanicum* ssp. *brookeanum* var. *kinabaluense* Argent, A.Lamb & Phillipps, Notes RBG Edinb. 1984. 42(1): 113.
Type: Collenette 39/79, Sept. 1979. Sabah, Sinsuron Road, W of G. Alab, 1400m (E).
Derivation: Latin – coming from Kinabalu.

Shrub to 2.5m. Twigs 8–12mm in diameter, round, scaly only. **Leaves** spirally arranged. **Blade** 100–200 x 35–70mm, narrowly elliptic; apex acute; margin flat and entire; base tapering; deeply and regularly sulcate. **Petiole** 10–18 x 4–7mm, scaly, not grooved.

Inflorescence a complete umbel of 12–25 erect to horizontal flowers. **Flowers** bicoloured with orange lobes and a yellow tube. **Stamens** hairy in the proximal ½. **Ovary** hairy all over.

Malaysia (Borneo), Sabah, Mt Kinabalu and the Crocker Range. It grows from 1000 to 1800m, which is higher than the

Debbie White

Rhododendron javanicum ssp. *palawanense*.

altitudes at which ssp. *brookeanum* grows, and is distinctly sub-montane in its ecology, growing as an epiphyte in forest or on the ground in openings such as road cuttings and landslips. *Fl.* Jan.–Dec.

This subspecies has extremely handsome large orange flowers with yellow centres which are similar to the previous subspecies (for differences see there). It has been in cultivation since 1966 when it was collected by Mr and Mrs E.F. Allen on Mt Kinabalu. One of the clones collected was named 'Mandarin' and this received a first class certificate of merit from the Royal Horticultural Society of Great Britain in 1970 (J. Roy. Hort. Soc. Lond. 1970. 95: 229). It grows and flowers easily and what makes it especially attractive as a temperate greenhouse plant is that spectacular flowers are produced mostly in the gloom of winter, in December or January. It is however a large and somewhat leggy plant which needs a good deal of space to reach its potential.

Ssp. **moultonii** (Ridl.) Argent
J. Linn. Soc. Bot. 1982. 85: 16.
Type: Moulton 3. Borneo, Sarawak, Upper Limbang R., B. Labeng Barian (Mt Derian), 1220–1525m (SAR).
Derivation: Named after J.C. Moulton, Englishman, naturalist, curator of the Sarawak Museum and founder

of the *Sarawak Museum Journal*, who first collected this rhododendron from the Upper Limbang River, Sarawak.

Synonym: *R. moultonii* Ridl., J. Str. Br. R. As. Soc. 1912. 63: 61.

Similar to ssp. *brookeanum* but with the ovary completely glabrous. Flowers yellow or orange.

Malaysia (Borneo), Sarawak, Upper Limbang R., Mt Derian; Mt Dulit; Upper Baram R., Mt Muler. Sabah, Long Pa Sia area; Sugut/Paitan area and around G. Alab on the Crocker Range.

Intermediates with ssp. *brookeanum* with only very sparsely hairy ovaries do occur.

Ssp. **teysmannii** (Miq.) Argent *stat. nov.*
Basionym: *R. teysmannii* Miq., Fl. Ind. Bat. Suppl. 1860. 1: 251, 585.
Type: Teysmann H.B. 777. Sumatra W coast, Mt Singalang (U, BO, CAL, K).

Synonyms:
Azalea teysmannii (Miq.) Kuntze, Rev. Gen. Pl. 1891. 2: 387.
R. javanicum var. *teysmannii* (Miq.) King & Gamble, J. As. Soc. Beng. 1905. 74(2): 75.
R. basirotundatum J.J.Sm., *pro parte* in Merr., Contr. Arn. Arb. 1934. 8: 124.

Differing from ssp. *javanicum* by the ± densely hairy ovary and from ssp. *brookeanum* by the hairy pedicels.

Malaysia (W). **Indonesia**, Sumatra, Java, Bali. Montane forests, 800–2000m.

Sleumer (1966) noted specimens collected in North Sumatra that had capsules 5.8–8cm long, thus distinctly longer than stated above for *R. javanicum s.lat.* In these long capsules they agree with *R. beccarii*, also from Sumatra (East Coast), which, however, has a practically glabrous (or certainly not hairy) ovary. Sleumer stated: 'It is possible that these North Sumatran specimens correspond with *R. basirotundatum* described from Atjeh (Burni Telong) without fruits and might represent a fourth variety. Material at hand is not sufficient to decide this question'.

Introduced into cultivation by Thomas Lobb sometime before 1860 if the Fitch painting preserved at Kew is to be believed, but this may be ssp. *brookeanum*. Also collected by Curtis for Veitch's nurseries around 1880. Both collections have been lost to cultivation and it has only recently been reintroduced. It grows and flowers well but is hardly distinct from ssp. *brookeanum*, differing only in the hairy pedicels. DNA work may yet unite these subspecies. The editors comment in Sleumer (1966): '*R. teysmannii* was figured by Blume & Miquel as having yellow flowers. This I presume, is an error by an omission of the draughtsman, similarly as was made for *R. album*; there is no difference in colour with *R. javanicum*'. There is no reason to doubt the flower colour as both colour forms occur.

---

228. Rhododendron sumatranum Merr.
Pap. Mich. Ac. Sc. 1933. 19: 182.
Type: Bartlett 7998, 18 May 1927. Sumatra, East Coast, Tapanuli, Habinsaran, summit of Dolok Surungan (MICH, L).
Derivation: Named after the island of Sumatra, on which it was discovered.

Much-branched shrub to 3m. Twigs 1.5–3mm in diameter, rounded, often red, at first sub-densely covered with flat, sub-stellate scales, becoming glabrescent; internodes 2–8.5cm. **Leaves** 5–7 together in pseudowhorls, unequal. **Blade** 25–80 x 15–40mm, obovate or obovate-elliptic; apex obtuse or rounded, often emarginate; margin flat, or weakly and narrowly recurved, base tapering and a little decurrent, glabrescent above at maturity, sub-densely and persistently scaly beneath. **Scales** small, marginal zone irregularly lobed; centre dark and impressed.

Mid-vein narrowly impressed above, obtusely prominent proximally beneath; lateral veins 4–6 per side, spreading, distinctly impressed above and raised beneath, often inconspicuous on both sides, reticulation obscure. **Petiole** 4–10 x *c*.1.5mm, red, somewhat flattened, grooved above, densely scaly.

Flower buds to 8 x 5mm, ovoid; outer bracts sub-circular, inner ones ovate to oblong-ovate, obtuse to acute, white or grey appressed hairy in the upper, outer part, with both scales and hairs along the margins. Inflorescence a 1–4-flowered open umbel, the flowers hanging vertically. Pedicels 10–18mm, slender, densely sub-stellate-scaly, without hairs. Calyx 4–5mm in diameter, obliquely disc-shaped, very shortly obtusely lobed. **Corolla** 25–30 x 34mm, campanulate or broadly funnel-shaped, bright orange-red, without scent; tube 10–12 x 8–9 x 15–16mm, straight, laxly sub-stellately scaly outside, glabrous inside; lobes 15–18 x 14–16mm, curving outwards and overlapping to ¾, slightly emarginate. **Stamens** regularly to irregularly arranged in the centre of the flower, exserted to *c*.6mm; anthers 2–2.5 x *c*.1mm, obovate-oblong, base sub-obtuse, pale brown, strongly curving inwards; filaments orange, linear, dilated and patently hairy for 2–4mm at the base, glabrous and filiform distally. Disc glabrous, not very prominent. **Ovary**

Rhododendron sumatranum.

4.5 x 3–3.5mm, ovoid-conical, patently long hairy, abruptly contracted distally; style 8–10mm, depressed to the lower side of the flower, glabrous; stigma green, thick-obconical. **Fruit** 18–30 x 7–9mm, ellipsoid, densely patently hairy and scaly, green often flushed with red, the valves spreading and twisting on opening, the placentae remaining coherent. Seeds 4.5–6mm, without tails 0.8–1mm, the longest tail 3.2mm.

Indonesia, N Sumatra, Atjeh, Tapanuli, East Coast. Mostly terrestrial, occasionally epiphytic, in open forests, summit vegetation, sub-alpine shrubberies or grassland, locally common, 1800–2700m. *Fl.* Jan.–Dec. in the wild.

Commonly hybridising with *R. retusum*, the resulting plants having narrower flowers than the pure species. Also hybridising with *R. rarilepidotum* to give a range of forms. A probable hybrid with *R. adinophyllum* was collected on Mt Kemiri by David Binney (982482). A rare yellow-flowered form was noted by the de Wilde's on Mt Bandahara. This species could be confused with *R. ripleyi* but that species has a scaly ovary without hairs or with just a few at the apex and usually has more pointed leaves. *Rhododendron sumatranum* was introduced into cultivation at an unknown date probably in the 1960s and several times recently. It grows and flowers well, forming bushy, bright green plants, that produce beautiful bright orange, bell-shaped flowers in profusion, usually in March to May in Edinburgh but often producing a few out of season flowers.

---

229. Rhododendron perplexum Sleumer

Reinwardtia 1960. 5: 197.
Type: Ultée 108, no date. Sumatra, W coast, Kerintji, *c*.1000m (BO).
Derivation: Latin – *perplexus* – confused, intricate or obscure, alluding to the uncertain nature of this species.

Shrub. Twigs *c*.4mm in diameter, rounded, red-brown, glabrous; the one known (upper) internode 10cm. **Leaves** 4 in a pseudowhorl. **Blade** 85–135 x 40–55mm, ovate to elliptic-ovate, gradually acuminate towards the sub-acute apex; margin a little revolute; base rounded to slightly cordate, or unequal, glabrescent above; sub-densely scaly beneath. **Scales** minute, irregularly sub-stellately lobed in the marginal zone; centre darker, slightly impressed. Midvein thick, striate lengthwise, a continuation of the thick petiole, obtusely and very prominent in the proximal part above, broad and flat beneath; lateral veins 12–15 per side, at an angle of nearly 90°, parallel, obscurely inarching before the margin, slightly impressed above, hardly raised

beneath, reticulation lax, obscure on both sides. **Petiole** 4–6 x *c*.3mm, slightly flattened and grooved above, initially scaly.

Inflorescence 9-flowered. Pedicels 20–27mm, strong, laxly or very laxly scaly, more densely so just below the calyx, not hairy. Calyx 4–5mm in diameter, disc-shaped, obscurely lobed or crenate, thick, glabrous. **Corolla** 25–27mm, funnel-shaped; tube 10–13 x *c*.5 x *c*.10mm, glabrous outside, densely shortly grey-hairy for the proximal ⅔ inside; lobes 13–15 x 10–13mm, elliptic-obovate. **Stamens** sub-equal, nearly as long as the corolla; filaments linear and densely sub-patently white-hairy in the proximal ½, filiform and glabrous distally; anthers 3.5 x 1.3mm, broad-oblong. Disc prominent, glabrous. **Ovary** 5–6 x *c*.2mm, sub-cylindrical, glabrous, tapering distally; style columnar, glabrous, *c*.6mm; stigma knob-like.

Indonesia, Sumatra, West Coast, Kerintji, probably epiphytic at *c*.1000m. Known only from the type collection.

Similar to the Bornean *R. crassifolium* differing chiefly in the petiole length which is not the good distinction implied by Sleumer (1966), since subsequent field work in Borneo has shown *R. crassifolium* can have a petiole almost as short. Further collections are needed to clarify the position of this species which could possibly be a hybrid with *R. sessilifolium* as one of the parents. Never cultivated.

---

230. Rhododendron sessilifolium J.J.Sm.

In Merr., Contr. Arn. Arb. 1934. 8: 125.
Type: Heusser 1, 17 Dec. 1930. Sumatra, Near Prapat, Road to Pangulubao (Pengkulu Bao), 1600m (BO).
Derivation: Latin – *sessili* – sessile; *folium* – leaf. The rhododendron with the sessile or stalk-less leaves.

Shrub to 3m. Twigs rounded, green, 2–3mm in diameter, sparsely to sub-densely covered with flat, pale brown scales; internodes 4–10cm. **Leaves** 4–6 together in tight pseudowhorls, sessile or sub-sessile. **Blade** 80–175 x 24–50mm, elliptic; apex gradually or abruptly acuminate, acute or broadly acute; margin entire, flat, often red; base broadly tapering to rounded or sub-truncate, occasionally slightly cordate, often with conspicuous 'ear-like' folds at the base; sparsely scaly and quickly glabrescent above, persistently and more densely scaly beneath. **Scales** small, irregularly shallowly lobed with dark centres, slightly impressed, remaining brownish punctate after the scales have gone. Mid-vein wide, as thick as the petiole at the base, raised above for the proximal ½–¾, impressed

Rhododendron sessilifolium.

in a broad shallow groove beneath; lateral veins 10–13 per side, spreading at an acute to a wide angle, straight below, curved distally, indistinctly anastomosing, very slightly raised above, smooth and often obscure beneath, reticulation mostly obscure. **Petiole** 2–4 x 2–4mm, without a groove, densely scaly.

Flower buds (see p.327) ovoid, to 35 x 18mm, pale green or sometimes flushed with pink, outer bracts standing out away from the bud, the larger ones with deeply channelled sub-subulate points. Bracts almost totally glabrous outside, with a minute fringe of fragile marginal scales, glabrous inside, ovate to ovate-long-acuminate. Bracteoles to 15 x 2mm, sub-filiform, glabrous. Inflorescence an open to full umbel of 5–10 semi-erect to horizontal, pale yellow, scentless flowers. Pedicels 25–30 x 1–1.5mm, laxly-scaly, without hairs. Calyx *c.*4mm in diameter, oblique, rim-like, obscurely lobed. **Corolla** 25–50 x 41–50mm, broadly funnel-shaped; tube 20–22 x 8–9 x 17–18mm, glabrous outside and laxly hairy inside, base deeply sulcate; lobes 20–30 x 15–22mm, reflexed to the perpendicular or beyond, overlapping ⅓–½, obovate. **Stamens** exserted to *c.*15mm, irregularly arranged around or mostly on the lower side of the mouth, sub-equal; filaments linear and densely sub-patently hairy in the proximal ¼, glabrous distally; anthers *c.*4 x 1.3mm, broadly oblong, cream coloured. Disc prominent, deeply lobed, glabrous. **Ovary** 5–7 x 2.5–3mm, cylindrical, narrowed towards the base, sub-glabrous, with just a few scattered scales and sometimes with a few hairs near the base, abruptly contracted distally; style 12–28mm, glabrous,

lying on the lower side of the tube, curving upwards distally as the stigma becomes receptive; stigma 3–4mm in diameter, rounded. **Fruit** 35–40 x 8–10mm, sub-cylindrical.

Indonesia, Sumatra, Tapanuli, East Coast, West Coast. Terrestrial, or rarely epiphytic, in open primary or secondary forest, roadsides and crater sides, 1100–1980m, locally common. *Fl.* Jan.–Dec.

Introduced into cultivation before 1974 when plants came to Edinburgh from Sydney University in Australia; there have been many introductions since. Sleumer (1966) mentions plants with light orange or possibly also red flowers. These have not been evident in extensive field work in Sumatra recently but may occur and may indicate hybrids (see *R. beccarii* and *R. perplexum*). David Binney in New Zealand grows two distinct forms: a large-flowered and a small-flowered. They differ mainly in the size of the corolla lobes, which are 30 x 22mm vs. 20 x 15mm, but the overall flower size and tube length are also slightly different. This species is easy to grow and has good clear pale yellow flowers, mostly in April–May, in Edinburgh, but it can flower at any time and usually flowers more than once a year. It occurs at relatively low altitude and although plants in Edinburgh have not displayed symptoms of cold in the winter it might be expected to be a relatively heat tolerant species in cultivation.

231. Rhododendron beccarii Sleumer

Reinwardtia 1960. 5: 192.

Type: Beccari P.S. 218, Giugno-Luglio 1878. Sumatra, West Coast, Mt Singalang, *c*.1700m (FI, BM, K, L, MEL).

Derivation: Named after the famous Italian collector and early explorer Odoardo Beccari.

Apparently small shrub. Twigs 4–8mm in diameter, rounded, with lax sub-stellate, appressed scales when young, becoming glabrescent, smooth, and pale; internodes 5–17cm. **Leaves** 5–8 together in pseudowhorls, sub-sessile. **Blade** 100–160 x 40–60mm, elliptic to ovate-elliptic, apex gradually long-acuminate (2–3cm), acute, or nearly so; margin slightly revolute; base broadly tapering, extreme base sub-truncate, glabrescent at maturity, but remaining blackish punctate above; laxly and more persistently scaly beneath but eventually glabrescent and punctate beneath too. **Scales** small, marginal zone irregularly sub-stellately lobed; centre minutely impressed. Mid-vein 2–4mm wide, obtusely prominent on both sides proximally; lateral veins 10–12 per side, obliquely ascending, faintly interarching before the margin, little raised on both sides, sometimes hardly visible, reticulation obscure. **Petiole** 0–2 x 2–4mm, flattened.

Flower buds 30–35 x 10–15mm, ovoid-acuminate. Bracts to 30 x 10mm; outer bracts ovate, acuminate, inner ones oblong-ovate, all sub-acute, glabrous outside, margin initially scaly. Bracteoles to 25 x 0.5mm, filiform, glabrous. Inflorescence 4–6-flowered. Pedicels 20–30mm, laxly scaly. Calyx *c*.4mm in diameter, oblique, disc-shaped, obscurely lobed, sub-glabrous. **Corolla** 50–65mm, funnel-shaped, red or orange; tube 30–35 x 5–6 x 15–20mm, lobed at the base, sub-cylindrical near the base, gradually widened distally, glabrous outside, densely shortly white-hairy in the proximal ½ inside; lobes 20–30 x 15–20mm, obovate spathulate. **Stamens** unequal, the longest nearly as long as the corolla; filaments linear and densely sub-patently white-hairy proximally, filiform and glabrous distally; anthers *c*.4 x 1mm, oblong, base obtuse. Disc prominent, glabrous. **Ovary** *c*.10 x 2.5mm, sub-cylindrical, glabrous or very laxly scaly, tapering distally; style nearly as long as the corolla tube, glabrous; stigma rounded. **Fruit** 40–60 x 6–7mm, sub-fusiform, red, slightly curved, glabrous.

Indonesia, Sumatra, West Coast: Mt Singgalang, Mt Sago. Epiphytic in montane mossy forests, 1400–2450m. *Fl.* Jan.–Aug., *fr.* June–Aug.

Apparently rare, not recently recollected and never cultivated. The status of this species is still very uncertain. The differences between this species and *R. sessilifolium* remain matters of degree. The orange or red flower colour suggests that this might be a hybrid between *R. sessilifolium* and perhaps *R. rarilepidotum*.

232. Rhododendron loerzingii J.J.Sm.

In Koorders & Valeton, Bijdr. 1914. 13: 105, 107.

Type: Loerzing 594, 10 Aug. 1912. Java, Central, Kedu, G. Tlerep, NE slope, Blintjung ridge, 1800m (BO, L).

Derivation: Named after the collector, a German who collected extensively in the Dutch East Indies.

Erect shrub to 2.5m. Twigs spreading, rounded, tips sub-densely covered with flat sub-stellate scales, lower down glabrescent and smooth; internodes 2–10cm. **Leaves** in loose pseudowhorls, 3–5 together. **Blade** 60–120 x 23–44mm, narrowly elliptic to elliptic; apex shortly acuminate, sub-acute, rarely obtuse; margin narrow, cartilaginous and revolute; base broadly acutely tapering; initially scaly on both sides, glabrescent above, more persistently scaly beneath. **Scales** sub-dense, small, reddish-brown, the narrow marginal zone variously lobed or sub-stellate; centre dark, distinctly impressed, leaving black pits when the scales have gone. Mid-vein narrow and slightly impressed above, thick and obtusely prominent beneath; lateral veins 8–10 per side, spreading, anastomosing before the margin, faintly impressed above, slightly raised beneath, reticulation inconspicuous. **Petiole** 4–10 x 1.5–2mm, compressed and grooved above.

Flower buds 18 x 8mm, ovoid, smooth, often lateral at the base of older inflorescences. Bracts to 17 x 11mm, ovate, inner ones obovate, obtuse or mostly apiculate, glabrous except for scales on the upper part of the outside and fragile marginal scales. Bracteoles 7–10 x 0.5–1mm, linear below, spathulate at the apex, glabrous. Inflorescence 3–9-flowered. Pedicels 20–25mm, slender, densely stellate-scaly, without hairs. Calyx *c*.3mm in diameter, obliquely round or cup-shaped, scaly outside, with unequal triangular teeth up to 3mm. **Corolla** 22–30mm, tubular, expanded at the lobes, scarlet; tube 15–22 x 4–5 x 7–8mm, sparsely scaly outside, hairy in the proximal ½ inside; lobes 9–13 x 6–10mm, obovate, sub-equal. **Stamens** as long as the corolla tube; filaments linear, sub-densely covered with long, patent hairs in the proximal 3–5mm, glabrous distally; anthers 1–1.5mm, obovate, apex truncate, base sub-acute. Disc prominent, glabrous. **Ovary** 5–7 x *c*.3mm, sub-cylindrical-conical, abruptly contracted distally, densely scaly, and with just a few scattered hairs, especially proximally between the scales; style thick, glabrous, nearly as long as the stamens; stigma rounded, with thick lobes. **Fruit** 20–23 x *c*.5mm, cylindrical, 5-angular, densely scaly. Seeds *c*.6mm including the tails.

Indonesia, C Java, Kedu: Mts Tlerep and Sumbing. In grassland or shrubberies on dry but fertile soil, very rich in humus, apparently rare, 1800–2000m. *Fl.* March–Nov., *fr.* Aug.–Nov.

The lateral flower buds on such a large-leafed species are very curious and it would be interesting to have more material of this species. Not recently recollected and never cultivated.

233. Rhododendron renschianum Sleumer

Bot. Jahr. 1940. 71: 146.

Type: Rensch 1495, (1498), 16 July 1927. Flores, Mt Geli Mutu, 1500–1700m (B†, BO, L, fragment).

Derivation: Named after Mrs Ilse Rensch-Maier who collected the original specimen.

Synonym: *R. renkkchianum* Sleumer, Reinwardtia 1960. 5: 220 (orthographic error).

Shrub, *c*.50cm. Twigs 1.5–3mm in diameter, scaly at first, older parts glabrescent; internodes 3–4cm. **Leaves** 4–6 spirally arranged in the upper ⅓ of the upper internodes, 2 or 3 of these leaves closer together in a loose pseudowhorl. **Blade** 35–70 x 15–35mm, elliptic or mostly elliptic- or obovate; apex shortly acuminate, sub-acute or obtuse, sometimes rounded; margin entire, slightly revolute; base tapering; quickly glabrescent above, sub-persistently and sub-densely scaly beneath. **Scales** small, marginal zone irregularly lobed; centre distinctly impressed, blackish with age. Mid-vein impressed above, strongly raised beneath; lateral veins 4–5 per side, spreading, obscurely anastomosing, slightly impressed above, mostly obscure beneath, reticulation obscure. **Petiole** 4–8 x 1–2.5mm, grooved above, semi-rounded, scaly.

Flower buds to 14 x 6mm, ellipsoid to ovoid, acutely pointed, slightly flattened, smooth, glabrous except for the marginal fringing scales and some scales on one or two of the smallest outer bracts outside. Bracts to 10 x 6mm, membranous, outer ones ovate-apiculate or subulate, inner ones ovate or obovate and obtuse, glabrous outside, margin with fragile scales. Bracteoles to 12mm, linear, sub-spathulate apically. Inflorescence 3–8-flowered in an open umbel, the flowers hanging or half-hanging, bicoloured yellow and orange, without scent. Pedicels *c*.20 x 1mm, laxly to sub-densely sub-stellately scaly. Calyx *c*.3mm in diameter, obliquely disc-shaped, very shortly lobed, scaly outside. **Corolla** 30–40 x 25–39mm, narrowly funnel-shaped, laxly scaly outside, glabrous or practically so inside; tube 17–27 x 4–9mm x 6–15mm, cylindrical,

Rhododendron renschianum.

straight, base somewhat pouched, mostly yellow but variably flushed with orange in the distal ½; lobes 10–17 x 8–16mm, semi-erect to spreading, obovate, not, or only very slightly, overlapping near the base, orange with a distinctive, translucent line from the throat to near the apex. **Stamens** as long as the corolla tube, not exserted, dimorphic, irregularly grouped on the upper or lower sides of the mouth; filaments linear, hairy for 2 or 3mm proximally, glabrous distally; anthers oblong, *c*.2mm. Disc prominent, glabrous. **Ovary** 5–9 x *c*.2mm, sub-cylindrical, densely covered with very short, sub-patent grey hairs and some fragile scales; style with some hairs at the base, as long as the stamens, lying on the upper or lower side of the corolla tube when young; stigma circular. **Fruit** 12–20 x 5–6mm, cylindrical, sub-densely short-hairy, without scales.

Indonesia, Lesser Sunda Is., Flores: Mts Geli Mutu (Kelimutu), Mandaswai and Mt Desu. Epiphytic in *Casuarina* forest and summit vegetation, terrestrial on stony ground, on the slopes and crater edge, 1500–2300m. *Fl.* May–Nov.

Introduced into cultivation by David Mitchell to the Royal Botanic Garden Edinburgh in 1994, and by Hansjörg and Margot Brentel to Austria in 2002. It grows well and has beautiful bold bicoloured yellow and orange flowers produced in great abundance. It has so far flowered in December, February, March and April in Edinburgh and occasionally throws out of season flowers.

234. Rhododendron stenophyllum Hook.*f. ex* Stapf
Trans. Linn. Soc. London, II, Bot. 1894. 4(2): 196.
Type: H. Low *s.n.*, 1867. North Borneo, Mt Kinabalu (K).
Derivation: Greek – *stenos* – narrow; *phyllum* – leaf. The narrow-leafed rhododendron.

Key to the subspecies

1   Leaves 2.5–6mm wide, less than 25 times as long as wide, occurring between 2700 and 2800m altitude _____ ssp. **stenophyllum**

+   Leaves 1.4–2.2mm wide, 30 or more times as long as wide, occurring between 1500 and 2400m altitude _ _____ ssp. **angustifolium**

Ssp. **stenophyllum**

Shrub to 3m. Twigs smooth, shiny-green and very finely scaly. **Leaves** in pseudowhorls, 10–15 together, gradually passing to scale leaves on the elongate parts of the stem and these soon falling off. Vigorously growing shoots may have very loose pseudowhorls or the leaves in a loose spiral. **Blade** 40–70 x 2.5–5mm, linear; apex acute; margin entire and flat; base narrowly tapering; glabrescent above, sparsely scaly beneath. **Scales** small, brown, stellately lobed or sub-circular with small centres. Mid-vein slightly impressed above, otherwise smooth; lateral veins obscure or up to 7 pairs issuing at an acute angle; stiff. **Petiole** *c.*3 x 2mm, not clearly distinct from the blade, green with a shallow groove on the upper side, sparsely scaly.

Flower buds 30–35 x 10–14mm, slenderly conical, acute, purplish or orange-red, with the bract tips free, erect and slightly spreading. Bracts to 24 x 6mm, glabrous or with a very few small scales along the margins, acutely long pointed. Bracteoles filiform, glabrous, *c.*10mm. Inflorescence 1–3-flowered, the flowers held stiffly horizontally or slightly angled downwards. Pedicels 8–10 x *c.*1.5mm, red, scaly, occasionally also with simple hairs. Calyx a low scaly disc. **Corolla** 32 x 45mm, bell-shaped, bright waxy orange to red, without scent; tube 22 x 13 x 16mm; lobes 20 x 22mm, strongly overlapping for *c.*¾ of their length. **Stamens** arranged all round the mouth of the flower, slightly dimorphic; filaments 12–15mm, orange or red, hairy at the base; anthers 5mm, cream. **Ovary** 4.5 x 2.5mm, densely white-hairy; style glabrous, 6.5mm, (elongating in fruit to 13mm); stigma cream, slightly lobed, 2.5mm in diameter. **Fruit** 18 x 5mm, sub-cylindrical, hairy.

Malaysia (Borneo), Sabah, Mt Kinabalu. Mossy sub-montane forest, mainly terrestrial in light, open situations, 2700–2800m. *Fl.* Jan.–Dec., most abundant Feb.–June.

This subspecies is very easy to recognise with its very narrow, linear, dark-green, sparsely scaly leaves and waxy orange to red flowers. The type sheet at Kew has both subspecies represented. The top left has been selected as the type as this most closely conforms to the species as described by Stapf and Burbidge. Hybrids with this subspecies have not been recorded.

It was first collected by Sir Hugh Low in 1867 on his epic climb of Mt Kinabalu and was named by J.D. Hooker at the Kew Herbarium but he did not publish the name. It was collected again in 1878 by F.W. Burbidge who was plant hunting for the London nurserymen James Veitch and Sons, but there is no record of it having been successfully transported alive. Burbidge was obviously impressed with the plant as he illustrated it in the book of his travels (Burbidge 1880) and gave the first if rather unorthodox description: 'another species growing on mossy trunks, bore waxy, bell-shaped flowers of a clear orange-scarlet colour. The dark glossy green foliage of this last reminded one of that of a *Sciadopitys* (umbrella pine) in form being linear and arranged in whorls'. It remained for Stapf (1894) to properly describe this species and legitimise the name. The first known record of its cultivation was from a collection made by Sheila Collenette in 1979, who introduced living plants to Edinburgh. These grow and flower well.

Rhododendron stenophyllum ssp. *stenophyllum*.

Rhododendron stenophyllum ssp. *angustifolium*.

Ssp. **angustifolium** (J.J.Sm.) Argent, A.Lamb & Phillipps
Notes RBG Edinb. 1984. 42(1): 115.
Lectotype: Endert 3990, 13 Oct. 1925, Borneo, Central East,
W Kutei, Mt Kemul, summit, 1850m (BO, A, K, L, SING).
Derivation: Latin – *angustatus* – narrow; *folium* – leaf. The
narrow-leafed rhododendron.

Synonym: *R. stenophyllum* var. *angustifolium* J.J.Sm., Bull.
Jard. Bot. Buit. III, 1935. 13: 452.

Differing from ssp. *stenophyllum* in the longer, narrower leaves, 60–120 x 1.4–2.2mm. Pedicels always softly
hairy besides being scaly, 8–18mm. Seeds 6mm, without
tails 0.8mm, the longest tail 3mm. Always grows at much
lower altitude than the type subspecies.

Malaysia (Borneo), Sabah, Mt Kinabalu, Mt Trus Madi, Mt
Alab, Mt Lumarku and the Long Pa Sia region. Sarawak, Mt Murud
and Mt Mulu. **Brunei**, Mt Pagon. **Indonesia**, Kalimantan, Batu
Tiban and Mt Kemul. Mossy sub-montane forest, 1500–2400m.

Flowering appears to be less abundant than in ssp.
stenophyllum, and large areas are often occupied by this
subspecies as a common undershrub which are totally
without flowers. It has however been recorded in flower
from September to April. Hybrids with this species appear
to be common and fairly easily identified as the narrow
leaves are characteristic in the progeny. *Rhododendron* x
liewianum has been described from Mt Kinabalu (Argent
et al. 1988) as it is quite prominent with its pink flowers
and narrow leaves, *R. fallacinum* x *R. stenophyllum* has

been reported from G. Alab, and there is some evidence
that at least some plants referred to *R. nervulosum* may be
R. crassifolium x *R. stenophyllum* in origin.

This subspecies is widely cultivated in collections
in America, Australia and Europe where it is prized for
its bizarre appearance and very handsome flowers. It
has been grown in the Royal Botanic Garden Edinburgh
since 1967, from an introduction by Burtt and Martin; the
original plant is now nearly 2m across and produces over
150 umbels of flowers, usually in the spring. This refutes
reports that it does not survive long on its own roots
although this may well be the case in areas with high
summer temperatures.

235. Rhododendron verticillatum Low *ex* Lindl.
J. Hort. Soc. Lond. 1848. 3: 86, 87.
Type: Low *s.n.* Borneo, Sarawak, G. Penrissen, *c.*1430m
(CGE, K).
Derivation: Latin – *verticillatus* – whorled, alluding to the
tight pseudowhorls of leaves.

Synonyms:
R. velutinum Becc., Malesia 1878. I: 204.
R. verticillatum f. *velutinum* (Becc.) Sleumer, Reinwardtia
1960. 5: 185.

Generally epiphytic shrub to 2m, the roots reported
to be long and fleshy. Twigs 3–5mm in diameter, densely
shortly patent white hairy and sparsely scaly with small
dark brown scales; internodes 5–10cm. **Leaves** 4–7
together in tight pseudowhorls usually with 1–3 much
smaller leaves. **Blade** 6–10 x 2–4mm, broadly elliptic, elliptic to narrowly ovate; apex acute to rounded, with very
short hairs particularly on the underside near the petiole; margin entire, flat or weakly revolute; base broadly
tapering to rounded or sub-cordate, scaly initially on both
sides, glabrescent above except for the mid-vein where
the scales tend to persist, beneath, remaining laxly scaly
for a long time. **Scales** very small, dark brown, rounded
to stellately lobed; centre small, slightly impressed. Mid-
vein broad and raised above for up to 10mm but rapidly
tapering and becoming narrowly grooved distally; below
bright red, raised throughout most of its length and
tapering gradually; lateral veins 7–10 per side, curved-
ascending, somewhat impressed above, indistinctly raised
beneath, often obscure on both sides. **Petiole** 10–25 x
2–3.5mm, smooth, rounded, without a groove, scaly and
very shortly hairy.

Flower buds to 20 x 15mm, dark purple, the tips of
the bracts reflexed outwards. Bracts broadly elliptic,

Rhododendron verticillatum.

broadly ovate to broadly obovate, with a broad spreading to reflexed apiculus, appressed hairy all over outside and with a patch of scales about the centre line distally, inside glabrous except for the apiculus which is both scaly and hairy inside and out, fringed with small dark brown scales; inner bracts narrowly spathulate, glabrous except for the fringe of scales. Bracteoles to 25mm, filiform, with just a few scales distally. Inflorescence a full umbel with 8–15 flowers, which are erect to horizontal. Pedicels 30–40 x 2–3mm, densely covered with long patent hairs and laxly with small scales. Calyx oblique, *c.*4mm in diameter, sub-circular, irregularly and shortly 5-lobed with one lobe occasionally up to 2mm long, shortly hairy and scaly outside. **Corolla** 50–60 x 40–50mm, narrowly funnel-shaped, red to reddish-orange; tube 30–36 x 5–10 x 11–15mm, deeply grooved in the proximal part, densely to laxly scaly and with some scattered hairs outside, sub-densely hairy inside; lobes 20–30 x 13–22mm, semi-erect to spreading horizontally, broadly elliptic. **Stamens** exserted to *c.*10mm, irregularly grouped around the mouth, or in two fairly coherent groups on either side; filaments 35–45 x *c.*1mm, filiform, laxly hairy in the proximal ⅓, glabrous distally; anthers *c.*2.5 x 0.7mm, oblong, curved, the cells sometimes with a small basal apiculus. Disc densely white-hairy at its upper margin, glabrous below. **Ovary** 5–8 x 3–4mm, sub-cylindric-conical, abruptly contracted distally, densely to sparsely covered with hairs, and very small scales; style held on the lower side of the tube, at first at the mouth, later exserted up to 15mm, hairy and scaly for the lower ⅗–⅘, glabrous distally; stigma rounded. **Fruit** 33 x 6mm, cylindrical, reddish-purple, patently hairy and scaly. Seeds 3–3.3mm, with crimped tails, without tails *c.*1mm, the longest tail 1.2mm.

Malaysia (Borneo), Sarawak, Mt Penrissen, Mt Santubong, Lundu, top of Mt Gading, Bongo Mts, Batang Lupar, Merurong Plateau (Bintulu), Hose Mts, Batu Laga, Kapit. **Indonesia** (Borneo), Kalimantan (W), Mt Kenepai. Epiphytic in moss forest, and occasionally on the ground, 700–1500m. An old record from near Kuching reports it from 'swampy jungle' implying it was growing at near sea level. *Fl.* Jan., Feb.

The type specimen in Cambridge has hairy petioles and leaves so that *R. velutinum* cannot be maintained even as a forma. It is doubtful if forms exist without the short hairs on the leaves except by erosion in old stems. Introduced into cultivation in Edinburgh by Ian Sinclair in 1982. It grows easily as a lanky shrub, flowering irregularly with fine trusses of beautiful red flowers.

It is similar to *R. polyanthemum* but has a much longer corolla tube than that species, different scales and quite different flower bud morphology.

236. Rhododendron crassifolium Stapf

Trans. Linn. Soc. London, II, Bot. 1894. 4: 195.

Type: Low *s.n.* North Borneo, Mt Kinabalu, 1525–2745m (K).

Derivation: Latin – *crassus* – thick; *folium* – leaf. Alluding to the thick leaves.

Synonyms:

R. crassinervium Ridl., J. Str. Br. R. As. Soc. 1912. 63: 61.

R. brevitubum J.J.Sm., Ic. Bog. 1914. 4: 253, *t.*381.

R. murudense Merr., Sarawak Mus. J. 1928. 3: 542.

Var. **crassifolium**

Shrub to 2.5m. Twigs 3–5mm in diameter, sparsely scaly, quickly glabrescent; internodes 1.5–15cm. **Leaves** spirally arranged or in lax pseudowhorls of 3–4 together. **Blade** 80–140 x 40–80mm, elliptic, or broadly elliptic, occasionally obovate-elliptic; apex obtuse or rounded, sometimes shortly obtusely acuminate; margin entire, flat; base broadly tapering, rounded or truncate, sometimes slightly cordate; initially scaly on both sides, glabrescent and blackish punctate above when mature, scaly for longer beneath. **Scales** lax, small, flat, irregularly lobed; centre minute, faintly or not impressed. Mid-vein very strongly raised above for the proximal ½–⅔, smooth near the apex, only weakly raised beneath or completely smooth; lateral veins 8–12 per side, sub-parallel, broadly spreading to almost a right angle, anastomosing before the margin, slightly raised above and smooth below when fresh, raised on both sides when dry, the surface smooth or distinctly rugosely puckered above, reticulation dense. **Petiole** 7–15 x 5–8mm, somewhat flattened, not grooved, sparsely scaly.

Flower buds to 45 x 25mm, ovate, acute to obtuse, pale translucent pink or whitish, with the outer bracts standing vertically away from the buds or appressed. Bracts ovate-acuminate, glabrous, to 25 x 10mm. Bracteoles to 20mm, linear, glabrous. Inflorescence 8–20-flowered in a complete umbel, semi- erect to half-hanging. Pedicels 20–60 x *c*.2mm, sparsely scaly. Calyx 3–4mm in diameter, a fleshy ring, glabrous. **Corolla** 25–30 x 25–45mm, shortly funnel-shaped, pink, red or more rarely orange or white; tube 12–15 x 6–10 x 12–15mm, glabrous outside, sparsely hairy inside, distinctly 5-pouched at the base; lobes 12–22 x 13–19mm, obovate-elliptic, not, or overlapping up to ½, often with the lateral margins revolute. **Stamens** dimorphic, 12–20mm, regularly arranged around the mouth, only the longest slightly exserted up to 2mm; filaments linear,

densely sub-patently hairy in the proximal ¼–⅓, filiform and glabrous distally; anthers 2.5–3 x 1.3mm, sub-elliptic. Disc prominent, glabrous. **Ovary** 5–6 x 2.5–3mm, glabrous, or with some minute scales depressed into pits in the surface, abruptly contracted distally; style 3–4mm, centrally placed, glabrous; stigma 2–3mm in diameter, dark red, 5-lobed. **Fruit** 18–25 x 5–6mm. Seeds 4–5mm, without tails 0.8mm, the longest tail 2.8mm.

Malaysia (Borneo), Sabah, Kinabalu, Crocker Range, Mt Trus Madi. Sarawak, Mt Mulu, Mt Murud, Mt Dulit, Upper Limbang R., Mt Derian. **Indonesia**, Kalimantan (Borneo), C Mt Liang Gagang, Mt Mili. Epiphytic in deep shade of mossy forest but also terrestrial on open landslides, locally common and widespread, 1200–2200m. *Fl.* Jan.–Dec.

Rhododendron crassifolium is a variable but nevertheless very distinct species. Hybrids with *R. stenophyllum* have been recorded and are very similar to *R. nervulosum*. *Rhododendron* x *planecostatum* is the hybrid with *R. bagobonum*. *Rhododendron brevitubum* was reduced to synonymy by Argent *et al.* (1988). It differed by the hairs inside the corolla tube being in 5 distinct vertical stripes. The hairs inside the corolla of *R. crassifolium* are commonly in 5 indistinct stripes and in other ways the plants are very similar: at best *R. brevitubum* could be considered as a local variant.

Introduced into cultivation in 1967 when it was collected by Bill Burtt and Adam Martin. It has not been a particularly popular plant due to a sprawling habit when in a pot; however, if given space in a bed it will grow into a broad bush and it can look very attractive, flowering profusely at least once a year, usually in the northern spring but often at other times. There is considerable variation

Rhododendron crassifolium var. *crassifolium*.

in the flower colour and the degree to which the corolla lobes are reflexed along their sides, and several good forms are in cultivation.

Var. **pseudomurudense** (Sleumer) Argent *comb. nov.*
Basionym: *R. murudense* (*non* Merr.) J.J.Sm., Bull. Jard. Bot. Buit. III, 1935. 13: 449.
Type: Endert 4323, 18 Oct. 1925. Borneo, Central East, W Kutei, Mt Kemul (BO, L).
Derivation: Latin – *pseudo* – false; *murudense* – of Mt Murud. The original Smith collection having been from Mt Murud.

Differing only in the glabrous filaments.

Indonesia, Central East Borneo, Mt Kemul. **Malaysia** (Borneo), Sarawak, Mt Murud, 1600–1850m, (summit), common epiphyte in primary forest. *Fl.* Oct.

Never cultivated.

237. **Rhododendron jiewhoei** Argent *sp. nov.*
Type: Dauni, Soinin & Patrick SAN 146491, 5 July 2005. Sabah, Mt Magdalena, Tawau Hills Park, 1310m (SAN).
Derivation: Named in honour of Tan Jiew Hoe, plant enthusiast, explorer and collector who has supported many natural history projects.

R. crassifolio affinis sed floribus multo minoribus et costa inferne valde elevata haud plana differt.

Shrub to *c.*50cm. Twigs 4–5mm in diameter, rounded, sparsely scaly and quickly glabrescent. **Leaves** arranged in a loose spiral. **Blade** 95–150 x 22–40mm, elliptic to sub-spathulate; apex rounded; margin entire, revolute when dry; base narrowly tapering; glabrescent above, sub-densely and more persistently scaly below. **Scales** lobed, with a thin, broad marginal flange, and small slightly impressed centre. Mid-vein raised above in the proximal ¼–½; strongly raised below to within 10mm of the apex; lateral veins 6–10 per side, emerging at a wide angle, slender, often somewhat obscure. **Petiole** 14–18 x *c.*3mm, not grooved above, laxly scaly initially.

Inflorescence of *c.*20 flowers in a slightly open umbel, the flowers half-hanging. Pedicels 22–30 x *c.*0.8mm, glabrous, orange. Calyx *c.*3.5mm in diameter, a low glabrous disc. **Corolla** *c.*25 x 20mm, funnel-shaped, dull red outside, pale orange inside, without scent; tube 10 x 3 x 6mm, glabrous outside, densely hairy in the proximal ½

inside; lobes *c.*11 x 6mm, broadly elliptic to oblong, erect, not overlapping. **Stamens** to 14mm, exserted to *c.*4mm, arranged regularly all round the flower, dimorphic; filaments hairy in the proximal ⅓, glabrous distally; anthers *c.*2mm. Disc 10-lobed, glabrous. **Ovary** 28 x 13mm, glabrous; style *c.*30mm, glabrous; stigma *c.*1.6mm in diameter, rounded, only weakly lobed.

Malaysia (Borneo), Sabah, Tawau Hills Park, Summit area of Mt Magdalena, 1310m, lower montane forest.

This interesting species looks in many respects like a miniature version of *R. crassifolium* but the flowers are less than ½ the size and the mid-vein is strongly raised underneath, not smooth as in that species. It is tempting to think that the ultramafic environment is causing the miniaturisation of the flowers but the difference in leaf structure is significant and the environment would be doubtful to account for this difference. Cultivation alongside *R. crassifolium* would demonstrate how much of the difference between these species is genetic and how much environmental.

238. **Rhododendron kemulense** J.J.Sm.
Bull. Jard. Bot. Buit. III, 1935. 13: 448.
Type: Endert 4255, 17 Oct. 1925. Borneo (C, E), W Kutei, Mt Kemul, 1800m (BO, BM, L, SING).
Derivation: Named after the mountain on which it was collected.

Tree, trunk *c.*35cm in diameter. Twigs 3–4mm in diameter, rounded, red brown, with lax, small sub-stellate, flat scales, early glabrescent; internodes 2–8.5cm. **Leaves** 5–7 together in pseudowhorls. **Blade** 70–120 x 20–45mm, elliptic to narrowly ovate-elliptic; apex gradually tapering or shortly acuminate, sub-acute or obtuse; margin weakly recurved; base acutely narrowed; densely minutely scaly on both sides when very young, glabrescent and shining above when mature, more persistently scaly beneath. **Scales** minute, marginal zone irregularly lobed, fragile and disappearing early; centre dark, shallowly impressed, finally glabrescent beneath too, but remaining conspicuously punctate. Mid-vein narrow and impressed above, as broad as the petiole and obtusely prominent proximally beneath; lateral veins 7–10 per side, irregular, ascending, obscurely anastomosing, very slightly impressed above, slightly prominent or inconspicuous beneath, reticulation obscure. **Petiole** 4–15 x 2–2.5mm, semi-rounded, rugose, grooved above, minutely scaly.

Bracteoles 20–30 x 0.5–1mm, linear, laxly hairy. Inflorescence a 7–12-flowered umbel. Pedicels 20–

25 x *c*.1mm, laxly scaly at both ends, laxly shortly hairy, often glabrescent. Calyx 4–5mm in diameter, sub-oblique, disc-shaped, obscurely 5-angular, minutely scaly. **Corolla** 50–70 x 30–40mm, narrowly funnel-shaped, orange-pink; tube 30–40 x 3–5 x *c*.10mm, straight, sparsely minutely scaly outside, shortly hairy in the proximal ½ inside; lobes 20–30 x 15–25mm, broadly elliptic-obovate. **Stamens** 40–50mm, sub-equal; filaments linear and densely patently short-hairy in the proximal ⅓, narrower, filiform and glabrous distally; anthers 3–4 x *c*.1mm, oblong, base obtuse. Disc shortly hairy on the upper margin, otherwise glabrous. **Ovary** *c*.6 x 2.5mm, sub-cylindrical, scaly especially at the base and apex, early glabrescent, tapering distally; style nearly as long as the stamens, sub-densely scaly proximally, more laxly so to the middle, glabrous distally; stigma knob-like.

Indonesia (Borneo), Kalimantan, Mt Kemul. **Malaysia** (Borneo), Sarawak, Mt Mulu. In primary forest, said to be common locally, 1800–1850m. *Fl.* Oct.

This species is somewhat intermediate between *R. polyanthemum* and *R. verticillatum*. A plant from Mt Mulu is in cultivation but has yet to be evaluated.

---

239. Rhododendron monkoboense Argent

Folia Malaysiana 2003. 4(2): 113.
Type: Aban SAN 95214, 15 March 1982. E Malaysia, Sabah, Beluran District, Bt Monkobo, 1829m (SAN, K, KEP, L).
Derivation: Named after G. Monkobo, the mountain from which it was collected.

Shrub or small tree to 2m. Twigs finely scaly and minutely but densely patently hairy but quickly glabrescent; internodes 1–2cm. **Leaves** arranged in pseudo-whorls of 2 or 3 together, or on young vigorous growth, spirally arranged. **Blade** 90–180 x 50–95mm, sub-ovate to broadly elliptic; apex broadly acute; margin flat and entire; base rounded to slightly cordate; upper leaf surface smooth to slightly rugose, glabrescent, lower surface laxly scaly. **Scales** small, with a small centre and lobed, silvery, thin flange. Mid-vein weakly raised above in the proximal ⅔, then becoming impressed, very strongly and broadly raised beneath throughout its length and finely striate when dry; lateral veins 7–16 per side, spreading almost at a right angle to the mid-vein, slender and hardly tapering until near the edge of the leaf, forking towards the margin, curving and anastomosing to form a weak but distinct, looping intramarginal vein and with a conspicuously raised reticulation viewed from above; beneath smooth with the lateral veins less conspicuous but still distinctly reticulate. **Petiole** 5–9 x 4–5mm, minutely patently hairy and scaly, almost rounded in section, somewhat flattened but not grooved above.

Inflorescence an umbel of *c*.4 flowers. Pedicels 16–20 x 1.5mm, with a sparse to moderate covering of scales but no simple hairs. **Flowers** 75 x 72mm, yellow with a reddish flush; tube *c*.33 x 6 x 12mm, with a few sparse scales near the base outside otherwise glabrous, irregularly but densely short-hairy inside (but the hairs not in lines); lobes 45 x 35mm, slightly retuse at the apex. **Stamens** irregularly arranged; filaments *c*.34mm, densely hairy in the basal ⅓ becoming glabrous distally; anthers *c*.5 x 1.75mm. Disc apparently glabrous. **Ovary** 5–6 x *c*.2mm, sparsely scaly and covered with very short patent white hairs; style *c*.35 x 1mm, with a few scales in the basal 5mm, glabrous distally; stigma *c*.4mm in diameter. **Fruit** (immature) 30 x 5mm, fusiform, minutely hairy.

Malaysia (Borneo), Sabah, known only from a few collections all from Mt Monkobo in the Beluran District. Probably terrestrial in mossy forest on the summit area (1829m). *Fl.* March. Given the very restricted area of the summit of Mt Monkobo this species must be regarded as a very rare point endemic with no other very obvious places for it to occur.

Most similar to *R. lowii*, with which this species has been confused, but differing in the indumentum of the ovary which is of much shorter, patent hairs than in that species; flower shape is also different with a much broader tube in *R. lowii*. The leaf venation is also very different, especially the mid-vein which is very strongly raised both above and below in *R. lowii* but strongly raised only below in *R. monkoboense*. The ovary indumentum is very similar to that of *R. retivenium* but the leaf shape is quite different, being much broader with rounded to cordate lamina bases. It shares with *R. retivenium* flower shape and size, and a similar (but not identical) pattern of venation – there is a much stronger development of a looping intramarginal vein in this species and the reticulation is much more pronounced. It differs from both *R. retivenium* and *R. lowii* in the very fine indumentum of patent simple hairs in addition to the scales on the young twigs and the lower altitude from which it is recorded. Never cultivated.

240. Rhododendron apiense Argent

Folia Malaysiana 2003. 4(2): 102, pl.1.

Type: Argent RBGE 19781745, 22 May 2001. Sarawak, 4th Division, G. Api (SAR, E).

Derivation: Named after Mt Api, the mountain where it was found, which in the Malaysian language means 'mountain of fire'. This is the only known locality of this species, which in addition has fiery-coloured flowers.

Shrub to 1m. Twigs *c*.4mm in diameter, green, rounded, laxly to sub-densely, pale-brown scaly and minutely, sparsely shortly patently hairy; internodes 2–12cm. **Leaves** loosely spirally arranged along the stem. **Blade** 50–100 x 43–60mm, broadly ovate or ovate-elliptic, occasionally broadly elliptic; apex obtuse, rarely rounded and mucronate but without an obvious apical gland; margin entire, flat, with a thin (*c*.0.5mm), reddish-purple edge; base distinctly cordate, occasionally broadly tapering and then with translucent auricles at the base of the lamina; glabrescent above, laxly and more persistently scaly beneath. **Scales** stellate, pale-brown, marginal zone appressed to the leaf surface; centres small and impressed. Mid-vein strongly raised above for about ¾ of the length of the leaf, slightly raised beneath or shallowly impressed in the proximal ½; lateral veins 7–10 per side, spreading almost perpendicularly, strongly raised above, the leaf surface deeply sulcate between the veins, disappearing before the margin, reticulation weak or obscure. **Petiole** 10–23 x 4–5mm, reddish-purple, rounded above, without a groove, sparsely to sub-densely scaly.

Flower buds ovoid, 20–35 x 15–22mm, bracts firmly appressed except for a very short point. Outer bracts translucent, truncate to emarginate, almost glabrous, with just a few small scales outside but without any on the margins. Inflorescence a 5–8-flowered open umbel, the flowers held horizontally. Pedicels 34–38 x *c*.3mm, shortly, white, patent-hairy and with a few papillae towards the distal end but without scales. Calyx green, glabrous or with a few low, irregular papillae. **Corolla** 55–65 x 50–60mm, bright golden yellow, often flushed with orange on the tube and around the edges of the lobes, without scent; tube *c*.30 x 12 x 22mm, funnel-shaped, glabrous outside but densely shortly white, patent-hairy in the proximal ½ inside, conspicuously 5-lobed at the base; lobes 35 x 27mm, spreading almost at a right angle and overlapping to over halfway, glabrous. **Stamens** irregularly spreading around the mouth of the flower, occasionally in two groups, slightly dimorphic; filaments white, densely white hairy proximally, the hairs thinning distally and becoming glabrous for the uppermost ⅔; anthers *c*.4 x 1mm, arching inwards, tapering towards the base

which is distinctly apiculate. Disc purplish-brown, lobed, shortly white hairy on the upper side. **Ovary** 10 x 5mm, green, sparsely patently white hairy and with a few rounded silvery scales, abruptly tapering distally; style 20 x 1.5mm, glabrous, green, slightly broadened to the pink, circular but 5-lobed stigma. **Fruit** 20–30 x 8–10mm, green or flushed red, often flecked with white, fusiform. Seeds *c*.3mm, without tails 0.8mm, the longest tail 1.5mm.

Malaysia (Borneo), Sarawak, 4th Division, Mulu National Park, Mt Api. Common in the sub-alpine shrubbery of the summit ridge, growing on deep peat which overlies limestone. *c*.1600m. *Fl.* Jan.

Rhododendron apiense is a peculiar species somewhat reminiscent of *R. intranervatum* Sleumer (from southern Sarawak) in having broad, sulcate leaves but it has sub-densely scaly (and minutely hairy), not laxly scaly young twigs, the ovary is only sparsely patently hairy, compared with the densely appressed hairy ovary of *R. intranervatum*, and it is much less sulcate. The mid-vein is only slightly raised beneath in this species, being level with the surface from about the midpoint of the leaf, often from the base, whereas in *R. intranervatum* it is strongly raised underneath to the apex. It differs from *R. javanicum* ssp. *brookeanum*, to which it is probably most closely related, in that the leaves are less than twice as long as wide with most leaves having a cordate base. It has distinctly basally apiculate anthers and a broader ovary with a shorter broader fruit. Apart from the distinctive leaf shape, the flowers differ from *R. javanicum* ssp. *brookeanum* in having larger, much more overlapping lobes and it grows at higher altitude than most forms of this species. Introduced into cultivation in Edinburgh in 1978, it is a lanky shrub which did not flower well until it was quite large and even then it has not produced the truly magnificent flowers which it did in the wild. It is still an attractive species and it is possible that it may perform better in climates with stronger light.

241. Rhododendron rugosum Low *ex* Hook.*f.*

Ic. Pl. 1852. *t*.885.

Type: Low *s.n.*, 1858. Borneo, North Borneo, Mt Kinabalu, 2135–3350m (K, CGE).

Derivation: Latin – *ruga* – a wrinkle or fold, referring to the rugose leaves.

Var. **rugosum**

Shrub or small tree to 8m. Twigs rounded, 3–4mm in diameter, densely covered with brown, deeply stellate-incised, stalked, fragile scales and so early glabrescent;

Rhododendron rugosum var. *rugosum*.

Rhododendron rugosum var. *rugosum*.

internodes 2–8cm. **Leaves** 3–6 together in tight pseudo-whorls. **Blade** 60–120 x 25–55mm, elliptic, broadly ovate-elliptic or narrowly elliptic, often variable in shape and size in the same pseudowhorl; apex shortly acuminate, broadly acute, the extreme point deflexed downwards; margin entire or weakly crenulate, broadly revolute, the leaves sometimes with strongly rolled margins; base broadly tapering; with a dense orange-brown, scaly indumentum on both sides initially, quickly glabrescent above, and only slightly less so beneath. **Scales** fragile, dendroid, with a small centre deepened in the middle and extended into a shorter or longer foot, which stands within a minute epidermal depression, marginal zone narrowly, irregularly, stellate-incised, nearly to the centre, very variable in size. Mid-vein with a cushion-like, triangular, grooved, raised area proximally then distally narrowly and deeply impressed above; extremely prominent throughout its length beneath and usually deep red in colour; lateral veins 5–9 per side, spreading and anastomosing before the edge, deeply impressed above, very prominent beneath; the surface uneven with deep folds, sub-densely reticulate, slightly impressed and prominent above, but often obscure beneath. **Petiole** 7–25 x 2–4mm, dark red, grooved above, densely brown, stellate-scaly initially.

Flower buds to 18 x 10mm, sub-spherical with the outer bracts abruptly contracted to subulate, keeled points which stand vertically. Outer bracts ovate-acuminate, apex short-apiculate or sub-mucronate, laxly to sub-densely scaly and often hairy in the upper ½ outside, margin with

scales at first. Bracteoles filiform, laxly hairy and scaly, to 20mm. Inflorescence an 8–14-flowered open umbel, the flowers half-hanging to hanging. Pedicels 10–30 x *c.*1mm, densely hairy and scaly. Calyx thick, disc-shaped, margin wavy and obtusely shortly 5-lobed, hairy and scaly outside, *c.*4mm in diameter. **Corolla** 25–30 x *c.*25mm, pink or purplish-pink, without scent; tube 15–20 x 5–6 x 7–10mm, cylindrical, straight or slightly curved, densely short-hairy and laxly scaly outside, hairy in the proximal ½ of the tube inside; lobes 12–14 x 10–14mm, obovate to sub-spathulate, sometimes slightly retuse at the apex, curving outwards and overlapping to *c.*½. **Stamens** irregularly arranged around the flower but predominantly on the lower side, exserted to *c.*6mm; filaments *c.*20mm, white, hairy in the proximal ⅓, glabrous distally; anthers 2–3 x *c.*1mm, obovate-oblong, base of each cell protracted into a short apiculus. Disc hairy at the upper margin, glabrous elsewhere. **Ovary** 4–5 x 2–2.5mm, sub-cylindrical, grey-green, hairy, the hairs covering small scales, abruptly contracted distally; style *c.*20 x 1mm, becoming exserted to *c.*6mm, with some patent hairs at the base or up to the lower ⅓, glabrous distally or completely glabrous; stigma 2.5mm in diameter, indistinctly lobed. **Fruit** 15–20 x 5–6mm, densely hairy and scaly, cylindrical, shortly tapering at apex and base, deeply 5-furrowed, purple, erect, the valves curving back on opening. Seeds *c.*2.5mm, without tails *c.*1mm, the longest tail 0.8mm.

Malaysia (Borneo), Sabah, Mt Kinabalu, Mt Trus Madi and Mt Alab. Possibly also from Mt Murud in Sarawak but at least some of the records of *R. rugosum* from this mountain are referable to *R. yongii*. Epiphytic or terrestrial in low mossy forest and open exposed ridges, in widely different habitats from dense shade to full sun, locally abundant, and with a very broad altitudinal range, 2000–3500m on Mt Kinabalu at least, where it is almost always to be found in flower, although it flowers at different elevations at different times. Miss Gibbs, following her visit to Kinabalu in 1910 (Gibbs 1914), commented that 'the lovely heads of waxy pink flowers formed one of the most vivid impressions in the ascent'. *Fl. fr.* Jan.–Dec.

Often confused with *R. acuminatum* due to the superficial similarity of the leaves. A close examination of the scales will easily distinguish these species but the flower colour is also different, *R. acuminatum* being reddish orange not the purplish-pink of this species. *Rhododendron acuminatum* also lacks the small hairs on the outside of the flowers. Natural hybrids with various species have been recorded: *R.* x *coriifolium*, *R.* x *keditii* and *R.* x *liewianum* have been named but the hybrids with *R. maxwellii* and *R. fallacinum* have also been recorded.

Probably first introduced into cultivation to Kew in 1964 by J. Comber from where, when it flowered in 1980, it was figured in the *Botanical Magazine* (Hunt 1981a). There have been many introductions subsequently. It grows slowly and usually flowers just once a year in the spring, although when this happens it can be spectacular covered in attractive luminescent pink corollas. The new foliage, covered in bright orange-brown scales, can also be most attractive.

Var. **kinabaluense** (Merr.) Argent *comb. nov.*
Basionym: *R. kinabaluense* Merr., J. Str. Br. R. As. Soc. 1917. 76: 108.
Type: Clemens 10892. North Borneo, Mt Kinabalu (A, BM).
Derivation: Named after the mountain on which it was collected.

Synonym: *R. rugosum* var. *laeve* Argent, A.Lamb & Phillipps, Rhododendrons of Sabah, Sabah Parks Publ. 1988. 8: 63.

Differing from the type variety in the larger, (largest leaves over 60mm wide), smooth, not wrinkled leaves.

Rhododendron x coriifolium (Sleumer) Sleumer
(*R. buxifolium* x *R. rugosum*)
Blumea 1963. 12: 340.
Type: Corner & Stainton 1137, 5 July 1961. Sabah, Mt Kinabalu, E slope, camp 4, 3200m (L, K).

Synonyms:
R. coriifolium Sleumer, Blumea 1963. 12: 107.
R. rugosum var. *coriifolium* Sleumer, Flora Malesiana 1966. I, 6(4): 612.

Leaves 20–50 x 15–25mm, stiff, more distinctly crenulate than in *R. rugosum*, apex and base obtuse. **Petiole** 3–5 x 2–3mm. Inflorescence 5–12-flowered. **Corolla** of a deeper red than found in *R. rugosum* but more pink than in *R. buxifolium*.

Malaysia (Borneo), Sabah, E slope of Mt Kinabalu, in open low forest and sub-alpine shrubberies, 3050–3200m. *Fl.* Feb., March, July, Aug.

This hybrid is very common in the sub-alpine shrubberies above the forest in the zone of overlap between the two parent species. It virtually replaces pure *R. rugosum* above 3000m and forms hybrid swarms with great variability and back crossing to at least *R. rugosum*.

Introduced into cultivation to Edinburgh in 1971 from material collected by A. Bacon. It is an attractive dark-green bushy plant which grows better than both its putative parents, flowering with a brilliant display of bright pinkish-purple flowers.

242. Rhododendron nervulosum Sleumer
Bot. Jahr. 1940. 71: 146.
Type: Clemens 33186, 19 May 1933. Borneo, North Borneo, Mt Kinabalu, 2440–3050m (BM, A, BO, E, L, NY).
Derivation: Latin – *nervus* – a nerve or vein; *ulus* – the diminutive; *osum* – abundant or marked. Alluding to the abundant development of small veins in the leaves.

Shrub to 1.5m. Twigs 1.5–2.5mm in diameter, sparsely scaly to almost glabrous; internodes 2–10cm. **Leaves** 3–5 together in tight pseudowhorls. **Blade** 56–80 x 7–14mm, narrowly elliptic to almost linear; apex acute; margin entire, slightly revolute in the proximal ½; base narrowly tapering; glabrescent above, laxly scaly beneath. **Scales** small, deeply, irregularly and broadly lobed in the marginal zone; centre minute, slightly or not impressed. Mid-vein slightly impressed above in the proximal ½, very slightly raised below throughout its length; lateral veins 4–6 per side, diverging at an acute angle, the whole leaf smooth with obscure reticulation when fresh, becoming more prominent when dry. **Petiole** 1–2 x *c*.2.5mm, indistinctly grooved above and with a few pale brown scales.

Flower buds *c*.25 x 15mm, narrowly ovoid, acute. Bracts to 28 x 10mm, translucent red or pink, ovate, long-acuminate, the apex tapering to a 2–3mm long acute point, glabrous outside. Bracteoles to 15mm, subulate, glabrous. Inflorescence an irregular open umbel of 2–5 flowers which are semi-erect to half-hanging. Pedicels 10–13 x 1.5–1.6mm, laxly scaly and sparsely covered in

Rhododendron nervulosum.

spreading white hairs. Calyx a low ring, with sparse scales. **Corolla** 30–35 x 25mm, funnel-shaped, lobed to half-way, glossy orange or red; tube 16–17 x 6–8 x 11–14mm, straight, glabrous inside and out; lobes 12–15 x 10–12mm, sub-erect, strongly overlapping for most of their length, obovate-sub-spathulate. **Stamens** *c.*20mm, arranged regularly all round the mouth, not exserted; filaments linear, dilated and laxly hairy in the lower ¼, glabrous and narrower distally; anthers 4.5 x 1.25mm, elongate-oblong, each cell shortly pointed at the base. Disc prominent, glabrous. **Ovary** 7 x 3mm, conical, densely white-hairy and with some small brown scales; style 8mm, glabrous; stigma 1.5mm in diameter. **Fruit** 10 x 6mm, ovoid-cylindrical, densely hairy and scaly.

Malaysia (Borneo), Sabah, Mt Kinabalu (Kinataki R., Mesilau R., Marai Parai Spur); Mt Lotung. The record from Bt Raja in Kalimantan (Indonesian Borneo) (Sleumer 1966) is now referable to *R. exuberans.* Mostly terrestrial, rarely epiphytic, in mossy forest or open, sunny landslides, not common, 1900–3050m. *Fl.* March–Aug., Dec.

It is very similar to hybrids that occur on Mt Kinabalu between *R. crassifolium* and *R. stenophyllum* but these occur at lower altitude and have longer, rounded, swollen petioles without a groove on the upper side. Introduced into cultivation in 1980 it is of lanky growth and intermediate in appearance between *R. stenophyllum* and *R. exuberans* (it still might be a hybrid between these two species) and does not have the charm of either of them.

243. Rhododendron salicifolium Becc.

Malesia 1878. I: 202.

Type: Beccari P.B. 2929, 1865–68. Malaysia, Sarawak, Mt Mattan (G. Serapi) (Fl, K, L, P).

Derivation: Named from the resemblance of the leaves to those of the genus *Salix* (Salicaceae).

Shrub to 2m. Twigs rounded, 2–3mm in diameter, laxly scaly; internodes 3–8cm. **Leaves** 4–10 together in well-marked pseudowhorls sometimes with one or two much smaller leaves. **Blade** 50–100 x 6–16mm, narrowly elliptic to sub-linear, often slightly curved; apex acute; margin entire or irregularly sinuate, weakly revolute; base narrowly tapering, glabrescent above when mature, sparsely scaly beneath. **Scales** flat, circular or irregularly disc-shaped, marginal zone entire or variously, often obtusely and shallowly lobed; centre minute, weakly impressed. Mid-vein narrow, impressed above, prominent beneath in the proximal ½–¾; lateral veins 5–10 per side, ascending and joining towards the margin, slightly raised above, faintly so or not visible beneath, sub-densely reticulate and very slightly raised above only when dry. **Petiole** 4–6 x 1–1.5mm, grooved above, laxly scaly.

Flower buds to 25 x 8mm, very narrowly conical, acute, the bract tips erect, slightly gaping, green or flushed with pink. Bracts to 24 x 5mm, very narrowly ovate, with acute channelled points, glabrous. Bracteoles subulate, glabrous, to 10mm. Inflorescence 1–5-flowered in an open umbel, the flowers horizontal to half-hanging. Pedicels scaly at base and apex, almost glabrous between, 12–17 x *c.*1.25mm. Calyx disc-shaped, obtusely and very shortly 5-lobed, laxly scaly outside, 3–4mm in diameter.

Rhododendron salicifolium.

Corolla 25–35 x 30–50mm, funnel-shaped, tubular below, pale yellow or suffused with orange around the edges of the lobes, without scent; tube 15–20 x 5–6 x 10–12mm, straight, constricted about the middle and often fluted in the proximal ½, glabrous outside, hairy inside; lobes 22–26 x 13–26mm, spreading, obovate-spathulate, overlapping up to ½. **Stamens** irregularly spreading, exserted to *c*.10mm; filaments linear and densely hairy in the lowest 3–4mm, glabrous and more filiform distally; anthers obovate-oblong, *c*.2.5 x 0.8mm, base obtuse. Disc prominent, green, hairy on the upper margin. **Ovary** 6–8 x 2–2.5mm, densely hairy and scaly; style lying on the lower side of the tube, curving upwards to present the stigma in a central position when receptive, hairy at the base for 1–2mm, otherwise glabrous; stigma globose, becoming disc-shaped and deeply 5-lobed. **Fruit** 20–30 x 4–5mm, fusiform-cylindric. Seeds *c*.6mm, without tails 0.8mm, the longest tail *c*.3mm.

Malaysia (Borneo), Sarawak, Mt Serapi (Mattang or Mattan) and Mt Santubong. Terrestrial on summit rocks and amongst moss along the ridges in open sub-montane forest, 900–1000m. *Fl.* Jan., Sept.

There is a flowering specimen at Kew communicated by the nurseryman Veitch in 1897 (Curtis 92) but there is no indication that this had been cultivated; in all probability it was preserved in the wild and living materials had not survived the journey. Introduced into cultivation in 1982 by Ian Sinclair from the type locality where it had not been collected since H.N. Ridley collected specimens in 1915. It had been found by Betty Molesworth-Allen in 1956 but remained unrecognised until after its 1982

rediscovery (Argent 1988). It is a dainty plant in cultivation, flowering about twice a year in Edinburgh in summer and autumn. It is grown in the cooler of our two regimes but the leaves turn bright red in winter, only recovering slowly in the spring, a sure sign that it could do with a little more heat. It superficially resembles narrow-leafed forms of *R. javanicum* but is distinguishable by its completely grooved petioles and impressed mid-vein. It also resembles some forms or *R. multicolor* but that species also has ungrooved petioles and a mid-vein which is distinctly raised above.

244. Rhododendron yongii Argent
Bot. J. Linn. Soc. 1982. 85: 12.
Type: Argent et al. 826, 24 Nov. 1977. Malaysia (Borneo), Sarawak, 4th Div., G. Mulu Nat. Park, G. Mulu W ridge, *c*.2000m (E, SAR).
Derivation: Named in honour of Joseph Yong, former director of the Forest Department, Sarawak, who facilitated the expedition on which this species was collected.

Shrub to 3m. Twigs smooth, rounded, sparsely covered with pale brown, lobed scales; internodes 2–20cm. **Leaves** in tight pseudowhorls of 4–5 large and a similar number

Mary Mendum

Rhododendron yongii.

265

of very small leaves and with well-spaced cataphylls on the internodes when young. **Blade** 60–110 x 20–55mm, elliptic; apex rounded or slightly retuse; margin entire, broadly revolute, the whole leaf being convex; base broadly tapering. Mid-vein impressed in a channel above and strongly raised below throughout its length; lateral veins 5–8 per side, diverging at *c*.45°, slightly raised; above sparsely covered with small, lobed, pale scales with brown centres, quickly glabrescent; below sparsely covered with more persistent scales impressed in shallow depressions. **Scales** small, brown, lobed. **Petiole** 10–25 x 3–5mm, weakly grooved above, especially distally, sparsely scaly.

Flower buds to 15 x 12mm, ellipsoid to ovate, the tips of the scales spreading outwards and dark, shiny, red, remainder pale green flushed with pink, the outermost bracts often becoming brown, with appressed hairs and brown scales outside. Outermost bracts mucronate, main bracts broadly elliptic with rounded apices, scaly and appressed hairy in the distal ½ outside, glabrous inside. Bracteoles *c*.12 x 1mm, filiform but channelled adaxially, sometimes sub-spathulate, with a few scales especially along the margins and occasionally with sparse simple white hairs. Inflorescence 5–10-flowered, in an open umbel, the flowers semi-erect to horizontal. Pedicels 13–18 x 1–1.5mm, dark red with scattered scales and patent white hairs. Calyx disc-shaped, shallowly 5-lobed, patently hairy. **Corolla** 30–36 x 20–30mm, dark purplish-red, without scent; tube 20–25 x 5–6 x 8–9mm, cylindrical, curved, sulcate near the base, shortly patently white hairy outside and with a few small silvery scales; inside with white hairs only in the proximal 2–3mm otherwise glabrous; lobes 10–12 x 9–10mm, overlapping ¼–½, spreading, hairy

outside and with some small silvery scales, rounded or weakly emarginate. **Stamens** clustered on the upper side of the mouth, exserted to *c*.4mm; filaments 22mm, hairy at the base for *c*.3mm, glabrous distally; anthers 1.5–2mm, pale brown. **Ovary** 3–4 x 2–3mm, shortly cylindrical, densely covered with semi-appressed white hairs and white scales, abruptly contracted distally; style 16–18mm, glabrous; stigma disc-shaped. **Fruit** 11–15 x 5–7mm, broadly ellipsoid, the valves spreading to 45° or weakly curving back; placentae adhering to the central column or weakly spreading from the base. Seeds *c*.2.5mm, without tails 0.8–0.9mm, the longest tail to 1mm.

Malaysia (Borneo), Sarawak, Mt Mulu, Mt Tamacu, (Mulu Nat. Park), Mt Murud. Sabah, Crocker Range, Mt Alab, (not yet recorded from Mt Kinabalu); Mt Lumarku and Long Pa Sia area. In mossy montane forest on ridges where it is predominantly terrestrial but it may also grow epiphytically. Flowering in the wild in Oct.–Nov.

It grows easily in cultivation where it flowers irregularly but quite freely. It was first introduced into cultivation to the Royal Botanic Garden Edinburgh in 1967 by Bill Burtt and Adam Martin from Mt Murud and from the RGS expedition in 1977 from Mt Mulu. Both these introductions are tall straggly plants. In 1980 there was a further introduction from Mt Alab. This Alab form is more compact and free flowering but unfortunately suffers from leaf tip 'burn' which can make the plants look unsightly. The flowers are reported to be visited by birds on Mt Murud, which would be the expected pollinators. The dark red corollas, although looking dull in reflected light, shine brightly – like stained glass windows – when viewed with the sun behind the flowers.

Rhododendron yongii.

Vegetatively this species is very similar to *R. praetervisum* from Mt Kinabalu and the Crocker Range (Sabah) but the flowers are smaller, different in colour and disposition and hairy outside. Some earlier collections of this species were ascribed to *R. x keditii* but that taxon is larger with more pointed leaves, longer pedicels, anthers and ovary and much broader pink flowers. Amongst the red-flowered Bornean species this appears to be distinctive in having the stamens tightly clustered on the upper side of the mouth of the flower as is much more common in New Guinea.

245. Rhododendron baconii Argent, A.Lamb & Phillipps
Notes RBG Edinb. 1984. 42(1): 115.
Type: Argent & Walpole 1459, 12 March 1980. Malaysia, Sabah, Kinabalu N.P., G. Tambuyukon (E, SAN).
Derivation: Named in honour of Andrew Bacon, a keen Sabah naturalist, who participated in the ascent of Mt Tambuyukon on which the first flowering material of this species was collected.

Shrub or tree to 9m. Twigs smooth, green, sparsely scaly when young. **Leaves** 4–6 in tight pseudowhorls between which are scattered scale leaves that soon fall off. **Blade** 35–80 x 15–35mm, elliptic to broadly elliptic; apex rounded or retuse; margin entire, strongly recurved even in the fresh state in fully mature leaves; base rounded or broadly tapering; sparsely scaly, quickly becoming glabrescent above and often beneath as well, smooth. **Scales** variable in size, slightly impressed, sub-circular to lobed, mostly with small centres and relatively broad flanges. Mid-vein impressed above and strongly raised below throughout its length; lateral veins 4–6 per side, widely spreading, very slightly raised beneath, almost smooth and fairly obscure above. **Petiole** 1–2 x 2.5–3mm, sparsely scaly, weakly grooved above.

Flower buds to 20 x 13mm, pale green, ovoid, the scales thick and fleshy, the broadly tapering points reflexed well away from the surface of the bud. Outer bracts fringed with minute brown scales along their edges and evenly covered with very fine, minute, patent white hairs on the outer side and also on the inner, near the apex. Bracteoles 11–14 x *c.*1mm, linear, hairy outside. Inflorescence 3–6-flowered, (8 in cultivation), the flowers displayed horizontally to half-hanging in an open umbel. Pedicels 23–32 x *c.*2mm, densely hairy and with a few scales. Calyx 3mm in diameter, a low hairy ring or with broad, well-marked lobes. **Corolla** 30–35 x 33–40mm, pink,

not scented; tube 17–22 x 8–10 x 12–15mm, scaly outside, hairy near the base inside; lobes *c.*18 x 16–20mm, slightly emarginate, spreading almost to right angles, overlapping to *c.*⅔, finely scaly outside. **Stamens** arranged regularly all round the flower, distinctly dimorphic to about ½ the length of the anthers; filaments 15mm, pink, with spreading hairs in the proximal ⅓; anthers 3mm, pale brown. **Ovary** 3.5 x 2.5mm, densely hairy with spreading hairs and a sparse covering of silvery scales; style 6–13mm, hairy in the proximal ⅓; stigma 2mm in diameter, glossy red, central in position. **Fruit** to 14 x 7mm, softly hairy. Seeds 2.4mm, without tails 1.2mm, the longest tail 0.8mm.

Malaysia (Borneo), Sabah, Mt Tambuyukon endemic, occurring between 2000 and 2500m altitude in low ridge forest or more open shrub-covered ridges.

It was in full flower in March 1980 and was seen with some flowers in January 1981; the first collection of the species made by W. Meijer was collected in fruit in July 1961 and thus probably had a similar flowering time. Pollinators are not known and this species remains little tried in cultivation as the early introductions all died. More recent ones have grown slowly but produced well-formed sturdy flowers for the first time in April 2001. This species is known by its large, pink, non-hairy flowers and generally flat, or broadly curved, smooth leaves; it also has very distinctive pale green flower buds with reflexed points to the bracts. *Rhododendron baconii* hybridises in the wild with *R. meijeri* and *R. rugosum*. Wild collected seed produced some attractive vigorous plants with delicate pink flowers which are probably hybrids with *R. meijeri*.

Rhododendron baconii.

Rhododendron praetervisum.

246. Rhododendron praetervisum Sleumer

Blumea 1973. 21(2): 376.

Type: Lajangah SAN 44622, 22 Oct. 1965. Borneo, Sabah, Mt Kinabalu, W trail (L, SAN).

Derivation: Latin – *praetervisus* – overlooked, from the fact that specimens of this species had accumulated in herbaria under *R. longiflorum*.

Shrub to 2m. Twigs green, rounded, at first covered in small pale brown or transparent scales but quickly glabrescent. Lateral buds often distinct, reddish, triangular and pointed. **Leaves** in distinct pseudowhorls of 4–6 large and a few small ones. **Blade** 50–72 x 18–32mm, ovate or elliptic; apex rounded or retuse; margin entire but broadly revolute; base tapering; dark green, quickly glabrescent and shiny above, sparsely scaly, paler and dull beneath. **Scales** lobed, to stellate, brown. Mid-vein impressed above, strongly raised below throughout its length; lateral veins 3 or 4 per side, spreading at *c*.80°, often rather obscure. **Petiole** 2–6 x 3–4mm, weakly grooved, finely scaly, minutely hairy on the upper side, often purplish-red.

Flower buds 14 x 8mm, broadly ellipsoid, smooth, green to dark red, minutely hairy outside and with a few pale brown scales. Bracts broadly ovate with rounded apices which often split so as to become emarginate, the margins densely scaly, inside glabrous. Bracteoles filiform, grooved, with a few scales distally especially on the margins. Inflorescence a 3–7-flowered umbel, the flowers hanging vertically downwards. Pedicels 20–37 x *c*.1.25mm, with patent white hairs and a few scales, green or red. Calyx a low circular or weakly angular disc, densely scaly and with a few simple hairs. **Corolla** 50–80 x 27–30mm, pink or pinkish-violet, without scent; tube 40–60 x 7–8 x 10–12mm, slightly curved and strongly fluted proximally; lobes 21–22 x 10–12mm, sub-erect on opening and overlapping ½–⅔, later spreading and not overlapping. **Stamens** distributed around the lower side of the mouth of the flower; filaments 60mm, glabrous to the base or hairy in the proximal ⅓, mostly white, becoming pink distally; anthers 2.5 x 1mm, exserted to *c*.12mm, pale brown with an outwardly curved point at the end of each cell. **Ovary** 12 x 3.5mm, green, with spreading hairs and some scales; style 50mm, green, white or flushed pink, glabrous; stigma circular, *c*.2mm in diameter. **Fruit** 30–32 x 5–6mm, hairy and scaly, on opening the valves curving back to a wide angle and the placentae separating from the central column. Seeds 3.2mm, without tails 1mm, the longest tail 1.2mm.

Malaysia (Borneo), Sabah, Mt Kinabalu, Mt Alab, along the Crocker Range to near Tenom. 1100–1800m. Montane forest, mostly epiphytic. *Fl.* March, April.

First known to be introduced into cultivation at Kew from material collected by Giles and Wooliams in 1963. It was grown as *R. longiflorum* before *R. praetervisum* was described. Several later introductions were made in 1979 and 1980. The extremely long, hanging, pink flowers are often the subject of comment. Although somewhat lanky in growth it can be very attractive when flowering '*en masse*'. In the wild it flowers best about March and has been seen visited by Whitehead's spiderhunter (*Arachnothera juliae* Sharpe). In Edinburgh it also flowers well in March but can produce a few flowers at any time of the year. Without flowers it is almost identical to *R. yongii* although the scales are more stellately pointed and lack the transparent margin usual in that species if closely inspected. For some years specimens of this species accumulated in herbaria under *R. longiflorum*, and it was a remarkable piece of detective work by Professor Sleumer to analyse the differences between the two species, chiefly on the technicality that *R. praetervisum* had a completely glabrous style. In the field it is surprising that the two species were ever confused, as the flowers of *R. longiflorum* are held semi-erect and are orange-red in colour, and it grows at lower altitude.

247. Rhododendron orbiculatum Ridl.
J. Str. Br. R. As. Soc. 1912. 63: 60.
Type: Moulton *s.n.* Borneo, Sarawak, Mt Batu Lawi, Upper Limbang R., *c*.1740m (SAR, L, fragment).
Derivation: Latin – *orbiculatus* – circular, referring to the often nearly circular leaves.

Shrub or small tree to 4m. Twigs 1.5–2.5mm in diameter, round, green, when young thinly covered in small flat scales; internodes 3–10cm. **Leaves** 4–6 together in tight pseudowhorls, with a few additional small ovate leaves which have very pronounced petioles for their size. **Blade** 32–65 x 35–60mm, broadly ovate to circular; apex obtusely pointed or rounded; margin entire, flat, with a narrow cartilaginous edge; base rounded to cordate; quickly glabrescent and smooth above, laxly to sub-densely scaly below. **Scales** very small, brown, sub-circular, only weakly lobed but with a pronounced central area, impressed in shallow pits. Mid-vein slightly raised but grooved proximally, becoming impressed, extending the full length of the leaf but becoming very narrow distally; beneath very slightly raised proximally but quickly becoming smooth

or even slightly impressed distally; lateral veins 5–7 per side, spreading at 45°, straight or slightly curving, very slightly impressed above, indistinct below, reticulation obscure. **Petiole** green, 2 x 5mm, with small brown scales, weakly or not grooved above.

Flower buds green, narrowly conical, the scales with subulate points. Inflorescence an open, loose, umbel of 2–6 flowers which are held horizontally or slightly hanging. Pedicels 12–17 x 2.5mm, usually conspicuously red in colour, scaly with small brown scales. Calyx a low circular or 5-angled disc. **Corolla** 70–80 x 70–80mm, pale-pink or white, without or just faintly scented; tube 35–50 x 7–12 x 10–18mm, pouched at the base and 5-angled in the lower ½, sparsely scaly outside and shortly hairy towards the base inside; lobes 30–40 x 22–33mm, overlapping to ⅕ of their length and bent back perpendicularly. **Stamens** in a group on the lower side of the corolla; filaments 60–65 x 0.75mm, pink, shortly hairy in the basal ½; anthers 3.5mm, brown. **Ovary** 8 x 3mm, purplish-red with silvery scales and very short, white hairs; style 35–56 x 2mm, shortly hairy and with a few scales in the lower ½, glabrous above; stigma pink, 5mm in diameter, circular. **Fruit** 30 x 6mm, splitting lengthwise from the apex. Seeds 4mm, without tails 0.8mm, the longest tail 1.6mm, crimped.

Malaysia (Borneo), Sarawak, widespread. Sabah. **Brunei**. **Indonesia**, Kalimantan (Borneo), Sulawesi (W and C). Frequently growing as an epiphyte on large trees in mossy forest but also on the ground in suitable open vegetation on mountain ridges and rocky outcrops from 800 to 1800m altitude.

Rhododendron orbiculatum was first collected in 1911, probably on G. Selinguid on the Sabah/Sarawak border,

Rhododendron orbiculatum.

by J.C. Moulton, a former curator of the Sarawak Museum and Director of the Raffles Museum and Library. The species is similar to *R. edanoi*, *R. suaveolens* and *R. lambianum* but all of these species have many more, smaller flowers in the umbel and longer, elliptic rather than orbicular leaves. The species has been moved from section *Solenovireya* (Sleumer 1966) as the corolla lobes are much longer than is usual in this group, often being almost as long as the tube.

This species is first recorded as being in cultivation in 1965 when it was introduced by Mr C.J. Giles to Kew; it first flowered in February 1969 and was written up for *Curtis's Botanical Magazine* (Hunt 1970). There have been various other introductions since then and it is now widely grown. It is not very vigorous but the flowers are often a delightful shell pink and exquisitely delicate. An introduction into Australia is said to be pollen sterile but other introductions appear to be quite normal in pollen production. Specimens collected on G. Penrissen in Sarawak by David Binney and now in cultivation have much smaller lobes, *c*.25 x 19mm, but are still much larger than related species and this is one of the most strongly perfumed forms of this species.

---

248. Rhododendron lanceolatum Ridl.

J. Str. Br. R. As. Soc. 1912. 63: 60.

Type: Moulton *s.n.*, 29 May 1911. Borneo, Sarawak, Mt Batu Lawi, Upper Limbang R., *c*.1125m (SAR, L).

Derivation: Latin – *lanceolatus* – shaped like a spear-head, referring to the shape of the leaves.

Synonym: *R. partitum* J.J.Sm., Bull. Jard. Bot. Buit. III, 1935. 13: 453.

Shrub to 1.2m. Twigs 2–3mm in diameter, green, rounded, smooth apart from a fine covering of pale brown scales becoming glabrescent; internodes 3.5–8cm. **Leaves** 3–7 large, together with several very slender scale leaves in well-marked pseudowhorls at the upper 1–3 nodes. **Blade** 70–120 x 25–45mm, narrowly ovate to elliptic, sub-sessile; apex acuminate, acute, often slightly curved; margin entire, flat or weakly revolute; base obtusely tapering to rounded and highly rugose; very densely scaly on both sides when young, above the scales, sparse and becoming glabrescent but leaving a pitted surface, beneath sub-densely and persistently scaly, especially at the base of the blade. **Scales** small, thin and flat, the marginal zone irregularly sub-stellately lobed; centre minute and shallowly impressed, leaving dark pits. Mid-vein broad and prominent and often coloured red in the proximal ½

above, but flat or slightly raised beneath; lateral veins 7–12 per side, very fine and obscure, wide-spreading, almost at right angles, curved and anastomosing before the margin, the lamina often thrown into folds on either side of the mid-vein, reticulation inconspicuous above, obscure below. **Petiole** 2–3 x 2–3mm, scaly, obscurely defined, (the leaves being almost sessile), without a groove, reddish in colour.

Flower buds (see p.327) to 25 x 15mm, sub-spherical with a broadly pointed apex, brown with the bract tips spreading. Outer bracts subulate to ovate-acuminate, inner ones obovate to spathulate, apiculate, all sub-densely scaly outside. Bracteoles to 15mm, subulate-linear, scaly. Inflorescence 4–10-flowered in an open umbel. **Flowers** *c*.24 x 22mm, white, sometimes scented, horizontal or half-hanging. Pedicels 20–30 x 1–2mm, densely brown-scaly and shortly white-hairy. Calyx *c*.4mm in diameter, disc-shaped, with distinct, very short blunt lobes, scaly and hairy outside. **Corolla** sub-campanulate, lobed to ⅔; tube 7–10 x 4–6 x 10–15mm, densely scaly, glabrous or slightly hairy inside, with broad grooves in the proximal ½; lobes 12–16 x 8–13mm, sub-obovate, erect, not reflexing back, scaly outside where the lobes were not overlapping in bud, variously overlapping ¼–¾. **Stamens** spreading regularly all round the flower, slightly dimorphic; filaments white, hairy for ¾ of their length, *c*.10 and 12mm; anthers 3–4 x *c*.1mm, white, curved, narrowed towards the pores, base obtuse or very shortly bilobed. Disc of 10 rounded, greenish yellow lobes, hairy on the upper side. **Ovary** 4–5 x 3–3.5mm, conical, green but covered with white hairs but without scales, ridged in the proximal ½, obtusely contracted distally; style *c*.5mm, green, hairy in the proximal ½, straight in young flowers but bending to place the stigma at the side of the flower; stigma green, 1.5mm in diameter. **Fruit** *c*.25 x 5mm, not seen mature.

Rhododendron lanceolatum.

Malaysia (Borneo), Sarawak, Mt Batu Lawi at Upper Limbang R., Mt Mulu and Mt Murud, Batu Tiban (7th Div.). Sabah, from the Long Pa Sia area. **Indonesia**, W Kalimantan (Borneo), on Mt Batu Tiban (G. Tiboeng) (as *R. partitum*). *Fl*. March, April, Sept., Oct., Dec.; probably throughout the year. Grows as an epiphyte in the shade of wet mossy forest or occasionally on the ground in open peaty situations from *c*.1000 to 1600m altitude.

Rhododendron partitum was reduced to synonymy by Sleumer (1966) and in almost all respects agrees with *R. lanceolatum* as understood here. It was however described (possibly in error) as having orange-yellow flowers, which *R. lanceolatum* apparently never does. This is a very distinct species with short, almost campanulate flowers, which are a dirty white due to the small but dense brown scales on the outside of the corolla. It has relatively large, nearly sessile leaves which are distinctly rugose at the base and it possesses numerous slender scale leaves associated with the pseudowhorls of normal leaves. Pollinators have not been recorded and hybrids with other species are unknown. Curiously the flowers are distinctly pleasantly scented, unpleasantly scented or quite without scent to different observers of the same plant.

It has been in cultivation on and off since 1967 when it was introduced into the Royal Botanic Garden Edinburgh by Bill Burtt and Adam Martin, which introduction grew very slowly, did not flower regularly and eventually died. It was reintroduced to Edinburgh in 1977 from Mt Mulu, but again the plants eventually died. Keith Adams reintroduced a clone in 1990 from Batu Lawei, in Sarawak, to Pukeiti in New Zealand. Here it thrives in their covered area and has now been distributed to the USA and the UK and is in many collections. It is more of a novelty than an attractive horticultural plant.

249. Rhododendron exuberans (Sleumer) Argent
J. Linn. Soc. Bot. 1982. 85: 12.
Type: Anderson 4596, 30 June 1961. Borneo, Sarawak, 4th Div., G. Mulu, path from Sg. Melinau Paku up W ridge, 1430m (L).
Derivation: Latin – *exubero* – to grow luxuriantly, referring to the wider leaves than those of the related *R. nervulosum*.

Synonym: *R. nervulosum* Sleumer var. *exuberans* Sleumer, Blumea 1963. 12: 113.

Shrub to 4m. Twigs smooth, green, finely and sparsely scaly only; internodes 2–12cm. **Leaves** arranged in tight to loose pseudowhorls of 5–8 large and a few smaller. **Blade** 70–100 x 20–35mm, elliptic to broadly elliptic

rarely somewhat obovate; apex acute, sometimes shortly acuminate; margin entire, flat but somewhat irregular; base tapering; obscurely scaly, the scales being very small and quickly disappearing from the upper side of the leaf. **Scales** sub-stellately lobed with small centres. Mid-vein distinct but smooth, hardly raised above or below; lateral veins 8–10 per side, issuing at an acute angle, very slightly impressed above. **Petiole** 3–5 x 2–3mm, very weakly grooved above, finely covered in scales.

Flower buds (see p.327) to 35 x 15mm, narrowly ovoid, tapering to a very acute point; tips of the bracts only slightly spreading, glabrous, red. Inflorescence 1–3-flowered, an open umbel, the flowers half-hanging, orange becoming red with age, without scent. Pedicels 9 x 2mm, sparsely scaly and occasionally with a few simple hairs. Calyx a low ring, sparsely scaly. **Corolla** 25–38 x 25–35mm; tube *c*.20 x 11 x 19mm, straight, very sparsely and inconspicuously scaly outside, glabrous inside; lobes *c*.19 x 15mm, overlapping for *c*.½ their length. **Stamens** arranged all round the mouth of the flower, not exserted, slightly dimorphic; filaments *c*.15mm, glabrous or with scattered hairs at the base; anthers 5 x 2mm. **Ovary** 6 x 3mm, densely white-hairy and with a few scales; style *c*.12mm, glabrous; stigma *c*.2mm in diameter. **Fruit** 21 x 6mm, narrowly ellipsoidal. Seeds 5.2mm, without tails 0.8mm, the longest tail 2.6mm.

Malaysia (Borneo), Sarawak, Mt Mulu, Mt Murud. Sabah, Mt Kinabalu (Marai-Parai), Mt Trus Madi, Mt Lumarku. **Indonesia**, W Kalimantan (Borneo), Mt Rajah. Epiphytic in mossy forest, 1300–2000m. *Fl*. March, June, Aug., Oct., Nov.

An unusual species confined to very wet mossy forest in the wild. It was introduced into cultivation to the Royal Botanic Garden Edinburgh in 1967 but later lost and reintroduced in 1984. It grows easily and flowers well, usually in March or April in Edinburgh, but often suffers from disfigured contorted leaves and flowers if the humidity drops too low. When grown in poor light the flowers can be yellow.

250. Rhododendron commutatum Sleumer
Reinwardtia 1960. 5: 201.
Type: Beccari P.B. 2322. Borneo, Sarawak, Lundu (Fl, A, K, P, S).
Derivation: Latin – *commutatus* – change, presumably an allusion to the changed status of the original collection.

Synonym: *R. gracile* (*non* Low *ex* Lindl.) Beccari, Malesia 1878. I: 203.

Shrub or small tree to 3m, growing with dense-packed, slender stems. Twigs 2–4mm in diameter, rounded, densely covered with sub-stellate reddish-brown scales when young; internodes 3–12cm. **Leaves** 2–5 together in pseudowhorls. **Blade** 80–170 x 20–55mm, elliptic; apex elongate, sometimes abruptly acuminate, sub-acute; margin flat or very slightly revolute; base broadly and acutely tapering, (never rounded), sometimes the sides unequal, sub-persistently scaly above, minutely rugose by inflated epidermis cells, persistently laxly to sub-densely scaly beneath. **Scales** minute, marginal zone sub-stellately lobed; centres small and slightly impressed. Mid-vein very narrow and distinctly depressed above, as thick as the petiole, and strongly prominent beneath, often more densely scaly than the surrounding leaf; lateral veins 10–14 per side, spreading at almost 90°, straight below, curved and obscurely anastomosing before the margin, with additional less distinct veins, parallel, faintly impressed above, minutely raised or inconspicuous beneath, reticulation dense, visible above only. **Petiole** 10–15 x 1.5–2mm, flattened and grooved above, densely scaly.

Bracts to 20 x 7mm; outer bracts narrowly ovate-acuminate, extended at the apex into a fine sharp point, scaly along the outside middle line distally, glabrous at the margin, inner bracts much narrower, nearly linear. Bracteoles *c*.15mm, filiform, laxly scaly. Inflorescence 3–5-flowered, an open umbel, the flowers semi-erect. Pedicels 10–20 x *c*.1mm, laxly sub-stellately scaly, not hairy. Calyx *c*.4mm in diameter, obliquely disc-shaped, shortly and bluntly 5-lobed, densely scaly outside. **Corolla** 50–65mm, funnel-shaped, bright red with purplish-pink flushed throat, lobed to *c*.⅓; tube 30–40 x 4–5 x *c*.15mm, lobed at the base, laxly minutely sub-stellately scaly outside, laxly short-hairy in the proximal ½ inside; lobes 20–27 x 15–24mm, half-spreading, broadly obovate-spathulate or sub-circular. **Stamens** unequal, exserted to *c*.10mm; filaments linear, sub-densely papillose-hairy proximally, papillose in the middle, glabrous in the distal ⅓; anthers 3–3.5 x *c*.1mm, oblong. Disc glabrous below, shortly hairy on the upper margin. **Ovary** 7–8 x *c*.2mm, sub-cylindrical, greyish long-hairy with distally directed hairs and densely scaly (the scales covered by the hairs), abruptly contracted distally; style thick, densely sub-patently hairy nearly to the top, less densely scaly, nearly as long as the corolla; stigma thick-rounded. **Fruit** *c*.80 x 4mm, narrowly cylindrical, curved, laxly hairy and densely scaly.

Malaysia (Borneo), Sarawak and Sabah. **Brunei**. Mostly terrestrial in swampy jungle or white sand podsols at low elevations in shaded habitats. *Fl.* Jan.–Dec.

Not yet known to have been cultivated.

251. Rhododendron intranervatum Sleumer

Blumea 1961. 11: 129.
Type: Kostermans 12886, 10 Sept. 1956. Borneo (E), W Kutei, Mt Palimasan, near Tabang on Belajan R., 600m (L, BO).
Derivation: Latin – *intra* – inwardly; *nervus* – vein. Alluding to the prominent veins on the leaves.

Shrub to 40cm. Twigs *c*.4mm in diameter, brown scaly; internodes 1.5–3cm. **Leaves** loosely to densely spiral. **Blade** 110–180 x 80–110mm, broadly elliptic to elliptic-obovate, deeply sulcate between the lateral veins; apex rounded-obtuse, or sometimes very shortly apiculate; margin narrowly revolute, often red; base broadly tapering, rounded, truncate, or cordate, glabrescent above when mature, sub-persistently scaly beneath. **Scales** minute, flat, marginal zone variously sub-stellately lobed; centre small, slightly impressed. Mid-vein as wide as the petiole and slightly raised proximally on the upper surface, strongly prominent beneath; lateral veins 12–16 per side, at right angles, straight and parallel, with numerous similar less distinct veins between, prominent above, broadly impressed beneath, anastomosing and united into an inner intramarginal vein, which is connected by numerous transverse veinlets with an outer, less distinct one; reticulation dense, slightly prominent on both sides, especially beneath. **Petiole** *c*.6–12 x 7–10mm, without a groove, flattened above and inconspicuously winged, rounded beneath, densely and finely brown scaly.

Flower buds to 50 x 26mm, narrowly ovoid, acute, pale green sometimes with a pink flush, bracts erect, slightly gaping, not tightly appressed. Bracts to 35 x 9mm, narrowly elliptic, acutely pointed, strongly keeled, with a few scales outside and minutely scaly at first along the margins, otherwise glabrous. Bracteoles to 26 x 4mm, narrowly spathulate, channelled, glabrous. **Flowers** 2–10

Rhododendron intranervatum.

in a loose umbel. Pedicels 40–65 x 1.5–2mm, very densely patently short-hairy, scaly. Calyx disc-shaped, wavy, obtusely 5-lobed, *c.*4mm in diameter, glabrous, lobes sometimes narrowly elongate, appressed. **Corolla** 35–50 x 50–100mm, funnel-shaped, lobed to halfway, light yellow, without scent, commonly with 4- and 5-lobed flowers; tube *c.*21 x 12 x 32mm, densely hairy at the base inside, glabrous outside, base slightly 5-lobed; lobes 25–40 x 35–40, obovate-spathulate, spreading, overlapping to *c.*¼. **Stamens** *c.*30mm, arranged all round the mouth, exserted 6–8mm; filaments linear and densely hairy in the lower ½, filiform and glabrous above; anthers 7–8 x 1.5mm, cream, narrowly oblong, curved, each cell with a basal obtuse swelling. Disc prominent, thickly 10-lobed, glabrous below, laxly hairy above. **Ovary** *c.*6 x 2mm, sub-cylindrical, densely white-hairy and apparently scaly, tapering distally; style slender, glabrous, 10–15mm; stigma green, thick-conical with 5 distinct lobes. **Fruit** 35–40 x 9–10mm. Seeds 5–7mm, with irregularly crimped tails, without tails *c.*0.8mm, the longest tail 3mm.

Indonesia (Borneo), Mt Palimasan, near Tabang on Belajan R. in W Kutei. **Malaysia** (Borneo), Sarawak, Mt Penrissen and Mt Berumput. Epiphytic in *Agathis* forest on waterlogged, white, acid sands or on granite rock faces, 600–1050m.

Introduced into cultivation in 1962 by Bill Burtt and Paddy Woods from seedlings collected on Mt Burumput (Burtt & Woods 2829). Later, a slightly narrower leaf form was introduced by David Binney from Mt Penrissen which was reported with 10 flowers in the inflorescence. This species is often a cause for comment, with its broad and deeply sulcate pale yellowish-green leaves, which are bizarre but not unattractive when it is growing well. The pale yellow flowers are pretty but not especially attractive or particularly freely produced. It does not appear to have a regular flowering time in cultivation, having been recorded in flower in Edinburgh in May, October and November. A curiosity related to the *R. javanicum* complex but quite distinct. It grows slowly in cultivation but responds well to feeding.

252. Rhododendron maxwellii Gibbs

J. Linn. Soc. Bot. 1914. 42: 103.
Type: Gibbs 4254. North Borneo, Mt Kinabalu, 1830–2440m (BM).
Derivation: Named after Mr D.R. Maxwell, Assistant District Officer for North Keppel, who accompanied Miss Gibbs on her ascent of Mt Kinabalu in 1910 when she discovered this species.

Rhododendron maxwellii.

Shrub to 2m. Twigs rounded, or fluted with longitudinal grooves in the youngest parts, 3–4mm in diameter, with small brown indistinct scales; internodes 2–9cm; lateral buds conspicuous, 3mm, conical. **Leaves** 3–5 large, and a few smaller together in distinct pseudowhorls. **Blade** 65–100 x 30–50mm, obovate or elliptic; apex rounded or retuse; margin slightly recurved; base broadly tapering; glabrescent above, laxly scaly but also often glabrescent beneath. **Scales** small, marginal zone variously lobed; centre dark, persistent, deeply impressed. Mid-vein strongly impressed above and raised below throughout its length; lateral veins 5–7 per side also slightly impressed above and raised below, dark-green above, paler green below. **Petiole** 7–12 x 4–6mm, strongly grooved above, initially with fine brown scales, green.

Flower buds 14 x 9mm, ellipsoid, green or yellowish-green, with appressed, rounded or shortly apiculate bud scales. Inflorescence with 11–14 flowers held horizontally or half-hanging in an open umbel. Pedicels green or bright-red, densely scaly, sometimes also with hairs. Calyx a low ring covered in scales. **Corolla** *c.*26 x 30mm, shortly funnel-shaped, pale-yellow, often lightly flushed with pink outside on the tube, very strongly and sweetly scented; tube *c.*12 x 6 x 9mm, covered in scales and hairy inside at the base; lobes *c.*16 x 17mm, densely scaly outside, overlapping to *c.*halfway and broadly spreading nearly to the horizontal. **Stamens** evenly arranged in a circle at the mouth of the tube; filaments *c.*13mm, with patent hairs in the proximal ⅓; anthers 2.5–3.3 x *c.*0.8mm, oblong. Disc hairy at the upper margin. **Ovary** *c.*4 x 2.5mm, sub-conical, densely hairy and scaly; style 4–6 x *c.*2mm, patently hairy near the base only, cream; stigma *c.*2mm in diameter, green. **Fruit** *c.*15 x 7mm, ovoid-cylindrical. Seeds 2.3–2.6mm, without tails 1.0mm, the longest tail 0.8mm.

Malaysia (Borneo), Sabah, Mt Kinabalu. Mossy sub-montane forest from 2300 to 2900m. On Kinabalu it is common in the zone of ultramafic soils dominated by bamboo; it usually grows on emergent trees although seedlings can be commonly found on the ground or amongst moss on tree trunks. *Fl.* Feb.–June.

Rhododendron maxwellii remains one of the Kinabalu endemics and has yet to be found anywhere else. This species appears to hybridise with *R. rugosum* giving rise to forms with pink, less strongly scented flowers but leaves very similar to those of pure *R. maxwellii*. These pink forms always occur on open ridges amongst *R. rugosum* but very close to forest containing typical *R. maxwellii* and it seems reasonable to regard them as hybrids. A beautifully scented plant with extra large flowers and intermediate leaves found on Kinabalu's Eastern Ridge recently is thought to be a hybrid with *R. lowii*.

This species is the most strongly scented Bornean rhododendron and the flowers can often be smelled before they can be seen. It has been tried in temperate glasshouse cultivation for almost 20 years but only flowered for the first time in the collection of Richard Currie in New Zealand in 2004. It has still failed to produce a single flower in Edinburgh whereas the pink hybrid with *R. rugosum* flowered regularly when in cultivation at the Royal Botanic Gardens, Kew.

253. Rhododendron retivenium Sleumer

Reinwardtia 1960. 5: 222.

Type: Clemens 35017, 22 Feb. 1933. North Borneo, Mt Kinabalu, Upper Kinataki R., S Ridge, 2135m (L, A, BM, BO, E, NY).

Derivation: Latin – *rete* – network; *venium* – veins. Alluding to the distinct reticulation on the leaves.

Shrub or small tree to 6m. Twigs 3–5mm in diameter, rounded, smooth, green or reddish, covered in flat brown scales; internodes 3–12cm. **Leaves** spirally arranged or weakly arranged in very loose pseudowhorls. **Blade** 110–160 x 30–50mm, narrowly elliptic; apex acutely pointed; margin entire and flat but strongly rolled back in young expanding leaves; base tapering, often shortly truncate, glabrescent and indistinctly dark punctate above, laxly and persistently scaly beneath. **Scales** minute, shallowly lobed to sub-circular with a broad marginal zone and small centre, weakly impressed. Mid-vein slightly raised above proximally but then becoming slightly impressed, raised below throughout its length; lateral veins numerous, slender, smooth or slightly raised in dried specimens, reticulation obscure when fresh, dense, fine, but

Rhododendron retivenium.

prominent on both sides when dry. **Petiole** 10–20 x 4–5mm, not grooved, green or red, scaly.

Flower buds ovoid, to 30 x 15mm. Outer bracts to 30 x 12mm, ovate, inner ones broadly ovate-oblong, innermost spathulate, obtuse, membranous, all glabrous apart from sparse marginal scales. Bracteoles *c.*20 x 1mm, linear, glabrous. Inflorescence 4–7-flowered in an open umbel, the flowers held horizontally. Pedicels 22–32 x 2mm, red or green, sparsely scaly, not hairy. Calyx 4–5mm in diameter, obliquely disc-shaped, the margin wavy and indistinctly 5-lobed, glabrous. **Corolla** 30–64 x 35–75mm, clear yellow or yellow flushed with orange, usually strongly and sweetly scented; tube 14–34 x 8 x 20mm, funnel-shaped, straight, with a few scattered scales outside, densely short-hairy inside proximally; lobes 20–37 x 21–36mm, broadly obovate to sub-circular, half-spreading, overlapping up to ¾. **Stamens** loosely and irregularly arranged on the lower side of the flower, sometimes in two groups on each side, exserted up to 10mm; filaments *c.*35mm, hairy in the lower ⅓; anthers 4–5 x 1mm, yellow or purple, curved, minutely apiculate. Disc thick and prominent, glabrous, or occasionally shortly hairy at the upper margin. **Ovary** 8–10 x 2–3mm, cylindrical, tapering gradually distally, appearing glabrous, but laxly finely and very shortly hairy and with some sparse scales; style 20–25mm, glabrous or slightly (and minutely) hairy at the very base; stigma *c.*5mm in diameter, yellow or turning red with age. **Fruit** 52 x 9mm, cylindrical but tapering at each end. Seeds 5mm, without tails 1mm, the longest tail 2mm.

Malaysia (Borneo), Sabah, Mt Kinabalu and Mt Alab (Crocker Range). Usually growing terrestrially between 2000 and 2700m in shaded moist valleys often in the ultrabasic zone on Mt Kinabalu. It flowers throughout the year and large bees have been seen visiting the flowers.

Rhododendron retivenium hybridises with *R. lowii* at the zone of overlap on Kinabalu at *c.*2600m, the hybrids having intermediate leaf size between those of the parents. A hybrid with *R. crassifolium* has also been recorded. This species is closely related to the *R. javanicum* complex but is easily distinguished from these when with young expanding leaves as the distinctive rolling is quite different to the flat-expanding leaves of that complex. The minutely hairy ovary and usually strongly and sweetly scented flowers are other distinguishing characteristics. It is similar in some respects to *R. monkoboense* but has much narrower leaves with tapering bases.

Introduced into cultivation in Edinburgh in 1980 and several times subsequently and by Os Blumhart to New Zealand. It grows easily as a lanky shrub, flowering freely and irregularly. It is one of the best yellows, and the sweet-scented flowers are a bonus.

254. Rhododendron polyanthemum Sleumer
Blumea 1963. 12: 111.
Type: Collenette 644, 7 Jan. 1961. North Borneo, Mt Trus Madi, Crest of main ridge, 2135–2285m (K, L).
Derivation: Greek – *poly* – many; *anthos* – flowered. The many-flowered rhododendron.

Tree or shrub to 7m. Twigs 5–8mm in diameter, rounded, at first with a thick covering of reddish-brown stellate scales, quickly glabrescent; internodes 5–11cm. **Leaves** 5–7 together in well-marked pseudowhorls additionally with several very reduced leaves. **Blade** 70–150 x 40–90mm, elliptic or broadly elliptic; apex gradually broadly tapering or sub-acuminate, the extreme tip obtuse; margin entire and flat; base broadly tapering to rounded, or shortly cordate, sometimes 'pinched' into a vertical undulation; when young, densely scaly, at first the scales white but they quickly turn brown before falling off; becoming glabrescent above and often beneath also. **Scales** sub-dendroid, narrowly stellately divided to the minute centre, fragile, leaving no pits. Mid-vein *c.*2mm wide proximally, gradually narrower and slightly impressed distally; lateral veins 9–11 per side, slightly curved, often deeply forked, anastomosing before the margin, faintly though even distinctly impressed above, hardly raised or inconspicuous beneath, reticulation obscure. **Petiole** 20–40 x 4–5mm, grooved above, green but densely brown scaly.

Flower buds to 16 x 15mm, spherical, or top-shaped, smooth with all except the outermost bracts fully appressed, green or pale brown. Outermost bracts subulate, densely brown scaly, other bracts with only a few scales outside, fringed with long-stalked brown scales along the margins, glabrous inside, sub-circular, rounded at the apex but often splitting to become emarginate. Bracteoles *c.*20mm, linear to filiform, glabrous. Inflorescence of 25–30 horizontal to semi-erect flowers in a full umbel. Pedicels 60–80 x 1.5–2mm, orange-red, scaly. **Flowers** brilliant pink, or orange with a yellow centre, very strongly scented. Calyx 4–5mm in diameter, oblique, circular, sometimes shortly and obtusely 5-lobed. **Corolla** 30–35 x 40–48mm; tube 18–20 x 5–7 x 13–20mm, funnel-shaped, strongly angled and slightly grooved proximally, with transparent scales outside and irregular hairs in the

Rhododendron polyanthemum.

Ken Grant

275

proximal ½ inside; lobes 18–20 x 15–18mm, broadly obo-vate-spathulate, slightly retuse, with scales in the central part outside, overlapping to *c*.½, spreading horizontally. **Stamens** irregularly arranged in two groups on either side of the flower; filaments 25mm, sub-densely to laxly hairy in the proximal ⅓, glabrous distally, yellow at the base, passing through pink to red distally; anthers 2.7–3 x *c*.1.2mm, pale-brown. Disc deeply lobed, hairy between the glabrous lobes. **Ovary** 5–6 x 3–4mm, green, with dis-tally pointing hairs which cover scales; style green and hairy in the proximal ⅔, glabrous and pinkish-brown dis-tally, *c*.12mm; stigma pinkish-brown, *c*.2mm in diameter. **Fruit** 21–28 x 7–9mm, fusiform, opening by strong valves, which curve back after the outer coat has peeled off. Seeds 3mm, without tails 1mm, the longest tail 1mm.

Malaysia (Borneo), Sabah, Mt Trus Madi, Mt Kinabalu: Mesilau East R. Basin, Meligan Range. Sarawak, possibly from Mt Murud and Mt Mulu although there is some doubt about the identity of plants from these mountains. Occurring in dense mossy forest, hanging from cliffs, and on ridges, 1300–2300m. *Fl.* Jan., Feb., May, Sept.

This species is easily known by its dark-brown, scaly covering on long-petioled, smooth leaves and bright pink-ish-orange, strongly scented flowers. It is probably most closely related to *R. verticillatum* from Sarawak and West Kalimantan but it has a much shorter corolla tube, only about ½ as long as in that species, and never has simple hairs on the petioles as *R. verticillatum* probably always has. The original collection of this species from G. Trus Madi was a terrestrial tree almost 7m high, growing on a ridge, but subsequent collections demonstrate it is often on cliffs or epiphytic and not necessarily so large. There are no records of any wild hybrids. It was introduced to temperate cultivation in Edinburgh in 1978 by Martin Gardner and grows vigorously. It flowered for the first time in 1982, and has flowered regularly once a year since in late spring with wonderful displays of its bright orange, strongly and sweetly scented flowers on very attractive brown-scaly foliage. It is one of the species which always causes rapturous comment when it is in full bloom.

255. Rhododendron lowii Hook.*f.*

Ic. Pl. 1852. *t*.883 (*lowei*).

Type: Low *s.n.* North Borneo, Mt Kinabalu, 2440–3350m (K, CGE).

Derivation: Named after H. Low, the collector.

Shrub or small tree to 10m, often with long unbranched stems. Twigs 5–10mm in diameter, green but covered in pale brown lobed scales, round; internodes 4–100cm. **Leaves** evenly spirally arranged along the stems, rarely in pseudowhorls of 4–6 leaves. **Blade** 100–200 x 45–100mm, broadly elliptic to elliptic, sub-obovate or broadly ovate; apex obtuse, to rounded; margin entire, flat, often slightly irregularly wavy; base broadly rounded to cordate; initially very densely scaly on both sides, gla-brescent above, more persistently scaly below. **Scales** stellate, irregularly lobed with broad flanges and small centres, not or shallowly impressed. Mid-vein broad, raised in the proximal ½ on the upper side of the leaf, not raised below; lateral veins 9–15 per side, broadly spread-ing, with distinct reticulation which is smooth above and below. **Petiole** 5–22 x 4–8mm, ungrooved and rounded on the upper side, distinctly flattened below, scaly, green sometimes flushed with red.

Flower buds to 60 x 40mm, smooth with the bracts appressed, ovoid-conical, pale green. Outer bracts ovate, obtuse, often splitting to become emarginate, inner ones ovate, shortly acuminate, innermost ones obovate, obtuse, all membranous, glabrous and shiny outside. Bracteoles 30 x 2mm, linear below, sub-spathulate distally. Inflores-cence a full umbel, 8–15-flowered, flowers erect to hori-zontal. Pedicels 20–50 x 2–4mm, laxly sub-stellately scaly, without hairs, yellow or flushed with red or orange. Calyx 5–6mm in diameter, a low wavy ring or obscurely 5-lobed, sub-glabrous. **Corolla** 60–110 x 70–80mm, funnel-shaped (wax-like when fresh), yellow or orange, sometimes flushed with orange or pink, scentless or delicately scented, glabrous outside; tube 30–35 x 6–8 x 12–15mm, straight; lobes 35–56 x 40–50mm, spreading to slightly reflexed, broadly obovate, sometimes retuse, overlap-ping ⅓–½. **Stamens** usually all on the lower side of the flower, somewhat irregular, exserted to *c*.15mm; filaments linear, long hairy in the proximal ⅓, sub-filiform and gla-brous above; anthers *c*.6 x 2mm, cream, curved, with the pores turned upwards and with minute basal append-ages. Disc thick, very prominent, glabrous or shortly hairy on the upper margin. **Ovary** 12 x 5.5mm, columnar, but tapering more gradually proximally than distally, covered with white hairs and densely scaly, although most scales are hidden by hairs; style 20–25mm, thick, glabrous, or with some hairs at the base; stigma 3–8mm in diameter, obtusely lobed. **Fruit** 30–80 x 8–12mm, fusiform, shortly hairy to glabrescent, with scattered, minute, elliptic-oblong, lenticel-like warts. Seeds 5–6mm, without tails *c*.1mm, the longest tail *c*.2.2mm.

Malaysia (Borneo), Sabah, Mt Kinabalu, Mt Trus Madi and Mt Alab. Terrestrial in gullies in mossy forest and on open shrub-beries on rocky ridges, 2700–3650m. *Fl.* Jan.–Dec. Old reports of this species from New Guinea are without foundation and

Rhododendron lowii.

reports from Mt Monkobo are now referable to *R. monkoboense* (for differences see under that species).

This beautiful species is very conspicuous on Mt Kinabalu: the umbels are up to 35cm in diameter and can be found at almost all times of the year. Some flowers have a delicate scent reportedly like that of roses. It grows slowly in cultivation having been grown since 1980 at the Royal Botanic Garden Edinburgh, but the first flowering of the species is claimed by Peter Cox in 1989 at Glendoick, in Scotland. Once large enough, the plants flower irregularly whenever they have built up sufficient resources. They then produce some attractive flowers but nothing like the wonderful displays that can be seen in the wild: great balls of yellow or orange sometimes terminating 6m, unbranched canes growing out of gloomy mossy ravines.

256. Rhododendron mendumiae Argent
Gardens Bull. Sing. 2004. 56(1&2): 82, *f.*2.
Type: Argent, Chavez, Cronk, Fuentes, Mendum, Middleton & Wilkie 53, 22 Jan. 1998. (Cultivated collection: 20 Sept. 2003, Acc. No. 19981815), Philippines, Palawan, Cleopatra Needle (PNH, E).
Derivation: Named in memory of Mary Mendum (1945–2004) who was on the expedition which collected this species: a tireless enthusiast for SE Asian botany and respected research worker.

Shrub to *c.*1m. Stems pale green, rounded, *c.*3mm in diameter, moderately densely covered in brown stellate scales. **Leaves** in loose pseudowhorls 3–8cm apart. **Blade** 40–75 x 17–30mm, narrowly obovate, occasionally elliptic; apex obtuse with a somewhat obscure, white, non-protruding, gland-like structure at the point; margin entire, flat or slightly and narrowly recurved; base tapering, often slightly decurrent. Mid-vein narrowly impressed above, distinctly prominent in the proximal ½–⅔ beneath, pink especially towards the base; lateral veins smooth, indistinct, 5–8 per side, the basal arising at an acute angle, the upper ones wide-spreading, all disappearing before the edge of the leaf: at first scaly with silvery or brown scales above but quickly glabrescent; below persistently brown scaly. **Scales** rounded to weakly lobed with darker centres which are often as broad in diameter as the flanges, distributed 1–2 diameters apart in the mature leaves. **Petiole** 4–7 x 2–3mm, faintly grooved above, pale green or pale pink with brown scales.

Flower buds green, becoming almost white in the distal ½ just before opening, to 40 x 22mm, conical, but contracted near the base, acutely pointed, imbricate with the tips of the bracts reflexed. Bracts minutely hairy and with a few small, scattered brown scales outside and scales along the margins, inner bracts often shortly emarginate. Pedicels 18–22 x 2–3mm, green, laxly scaly but without simple hairs. **Flowers** 1 or 2 together, terminal, held more or less horizontally, white with a cream throat, very strongly and sweetly scented. Calyx a lobed disc, densely scaly below, less so near the perimeter. **Corolla** 52–60 x 102–105mm; tube 26–30 x *c.*15 x 17–24mm, glabrous outside but with retrorse white hairs in the proximal ½ inside; lobes *c.*46 x 35–46mm, spreading horizontally, overlapping to *c.*½ their length, with a rather irregular 'frilled' margin. **Stamens** clustered on the lower side of the flower, exserted 20–25mm from the mouth; filaments 38–43 x 0.2mm wide expanded suddenly for the basal 2.5mm to *c.*1.4mm wide, glabrous but densely white hairy in the basal expanded portion, white, slightly dimorphic; anthers *c.*7mm, brown, shortly but distinctly apiculate at the base. Disc green with dense short, white, erect hairs. **Ovary** *c.*6 x 5mm, broadly trapezoid in outline, densely silvery scaly and with sparse short patent hairs mostly towards the top; style *c.*50mm, cream, lying on the lower side of the corolla tube but curving upwards when the stigma becomes receptive, densely patent-hairy and sparsely scaly in the proximal ⅓, the scales arising on low papillae; stigma 4–7mm in diameter, white, crown-shaped, exserted up to 15mm beyond the anthers. **Fruit** 25 x 12mm, pale-green with a covering of dense brown scales,

Rhododendron mendumiae.

the outer skin only weakly separating from the valves which curve outwards on opening without twisting, the placentae separating from the central column. Seeds *c.*2.3mm, without tails 1mm, the longest tail 0.8mm.

Philippines, Palawan, Cleopatra Needle at *c.*1600m in mossy sub-montane forest. Known only from the type locality.

Rhododendron mendumiae is similar to *R. madulidii* from Mt Mantalingajan near the southern tip of Palawan but that species has many more flowers in the inflorescence, shortly hairy stems and pedicels, and very different flower bud morphology with erect not reflexed tips to the bracts. Vegetatively, it looks very similar to *R. jasminiflorum* var. *copelandii*, but the massive flowers of this new species are totally different to the slender flowers with very small lobes of that species and the bud morphology again is also very different.

This very distinctive species is associated with section *Euvireya* on the basis of its short, broad, corolla tube relative to the enormous lobes and the well-spaced, stellate scales on the leaves. It is anomalous in that, from the single observation of fruit dehiscence, the outer skin remains closely attached to the valves, only weakly separating near the tips, but it clearly does not belong in the groups with adherent outer skins from the scale morphology. When this species flowered in cultivation for the first time in 2002 with a single flower, it was thought this must be an anomalous peloric form but the following year 2-flowered inflorescences were produced on several plants and it was concluded that these large flowers are normal. The seeds are unusual in having such short tails; these are characteristic of vireyas which occur in open situations on mountain peaks – *R. retusum*, *R. adinophyllum*

and *R. abietifolium* have similar seeds with very reduced tails. Since this species was collected near the summit of Cleopatra Needle where the vegetation was dense, mossy forest, this is a surprising character. Plants have been raised from both seed and cuttings collected in the wild and from the isolation of the peak it seems virtually impossible that these are hybrids.

Given the isolation of the habitat and the very restricted area of mossy forest on the mountain, the population of this species is very small and must be vulnerable to any kind of habitat disturbance. Cultivated since 1998 it grows as an erect, sparingly branched shrub so far to about 50cm. It flowers towards the end of the Edinburgh summer and different plants flower at differing times well into the autumn. A single bloom brought into a room is enough to fill it with its delightful sweet perfume.

257. Rhododendron kochii Stein
Gartenflora 1885. 34: 193, *t.*1195.
Type: Schadenberg *s.n.*, Aug. 1909. Philippines, Mindanao, Mt Apo, Seriban Creek (B†, MA). Neotype: Elmer 11435, Aug. 1909. Mt Apo (L, A, BM, BO, E, FI, GH, K, NY, U).
Derivation: Named after Otto Koch, collector of plants and animals in the Philippines and nephew of the collector of the type.

Shrub, or small tree, to 10m. Twigs 3–5mm in diameter, rounded, scaly; internodes 5–9cm. **Leaves** 4–8 together in tight pseudowhorls. **Blade** 70–160 x 25–50mm, elliptic, broadly elliptic to obovate; apex shortly and abruptly acuminate, the tip acute, often shortly deflexed; margin entire or slightly wavy, very slightly, or not revolute; base broadly tapering, rarely sub-rounded, densely scaly on both sides initially, becoming glabrescent above, laxly sub-persistently scaly beneath. **Scales** flat, small, with a relatively wide marginal zone sub-stellately lobed; centre small and shallowly impressed. Mid-vein dilated at the base, suddenly narrowed and a little impressed above, as thick as the petiole and obtusely prominent in the proximal part beneath; lateral veins 8–10 per side, spreading and ascending, inarching near the margin, slightly impressed or raised above, distinctly prominent beneath, reticulation dense, smooth when living, raised slightly on both sides, when dry or at least underneath. **Petiole** 15–20 x 2–3mm, almost rounded, not grooved, flushed with red.

Flower buds (see p.327) 25–40 x 18mm, sub-spherical to obovoid; apex rounded, or broadly acute to obtuse, glossy white with pale green or red margins to the bracts and a light pink flush along the centre line, smooth in outline, the bracts tightly appressed except for a collarette of small broad dead bracts spreading at a wide angle around the base. Bracts to 20 x 12mm; outer ovate, obtuse, inner ones obovate to spathulate, sometimes retuse, with a small gland-like apiculus, often splitting apically to become emarginate, laxly scaly apically outside or glabrous, often rugose by minute tubercles; margins with a few fragile scales. Bracteoles to 20mm, filiform to linear-spathulate. Inflorescence 10–20-flowered, an open umbel, the flowers mostly horizontal but also semi-erect, to half-hanging. Pedicels 20–30 x *c*.2mm, densely covered with pale sub-stellate scales, without hairs. Calyx 3–4mm in diameter, obliquely disc-shaped, shortly obtusely 5-lobed, lobes occasionally up to 8mm, densely scaly outside. **Corolla** 35–47 x 45–47mm, narrowly funnel-shaped, white, not or sweetly scented; tube 30–33 x 9 x 14–17mm, laxly covered with sub-stellate scales outside, sub-densely short-hairy inside; lobes 19–20 x 22–23mm, spreading nearly to the perpendicular, overlapping to *c*.¾, obovate-sub-circular, often emarginate. **Stamens** arranged all round the mouth of the flower, at first thrust forward in a group, exserted 6–8mm, later wide-spreading, reflexed back against the corolla lobes; filaments linear, white and sub-densely patently hairy in the proximal ½–¾, glabrous and filiform distally; anthers 3–3.5 x 1mm, white, obovate-oblong; base shortly though distinctly possessing 2 appendages. Disc glabrous. **Ovary** 5–6 x 2.5mm, sub-cylindrical, white-hairy, the hairs patent or slightly distally directed, covering small, silvery scales, gradually narrowed distally; style deep within the tube, lying on the lower side when the flower first opens, later elongating, becoming exserted to 15mm, the distal part curving upwards to present the stigma on the upper side of the flower, green at the base, white distally and sub-densely to sparsely hairy to the lower ½–¾, glabrous distally and totally without scales; stigma 2.5–3mm in diameter, green. **Fruit** 25–40 x 6–10mm, sub-cylindrical, laxly scaly but densely grey-hairy, green strongly flushed with purplish red; valves splitting and opening to the perpendicular or a little beyond, not or only slightly twisting; placentae opening slightly. Seeds 3–4.5mm, without tails *c*.1mm, the longest tail to 2mm, the tails both crimped and with one sometimes broader than the other.

Philippines, Luzon, Mindoro, Negros, Mindanao. On ridges in mossy forest, 1000–2300m. *Fl.* Jan.–Dec.

This species is widespread in the Philippines and somewhat variable but has a distinctive habit with shorter, more acuminate leaves on longer petioles than most of the other large-leafed Philippine species. All the material examined has distinctive, glossy white, sub-spherical flower buds with the bracts all closely appressed which is like no other species. Sleumer states the flowers are without scent but there is at least one accession in cultivation which is sweetly scented and P. Wilkie noted scented flowers in this species on Negros. This was one of the species illustrated by Stein (1885) in the *Gartenflora* but there is no evidence that it was cultivated then. It was probably first introduced into cultivation in America but there appears to be no record of this early introduction. It has been cultivated in Edinburgh since 1990 from an unknown source. It flowers irregularly throughout the year, but mostly in the winter months. The plant is large and leggy but the flowers are very attractive and freely produced.

258. Rhododendron williamsii Merr. *ex* H.F.Copel.
Phil. J. Sc. 1929. 40: 163, *t*.9, *t*.11, *f*.2.
Type: Elmer 6519, June 1904. Philippines, Luzon, Mountain Province, Benguet, Baguio (US, K, L, NY, P).
Derivation: Named after one of the early collectors of this species, Robert S. Williams, an American whose main interests were birds and mosses.

Tree to 6m. Twigs 2–3mm in diameter, rounded, at first laxly scaly, later glabrescent, often whitish; internodes 3–10cm. **Leaves** 3–4 together in pseudowhorls. **Blade** 80–110 x 30–50mm, elliptic-ovate, or elliptic; apex mucronate, acute; margin entire, narrowly or not revolute; base broadly to narrowly tapering, glabrescent above with age, laxly scaly beneath initially. **Scales** small, flat, irregularly lobed in the very thin, fragile marginal zone; centre slightly darker, weakly impressed, finally glabrescent beneath also, leaving shallow dark pits. Mid-vein broad (1.5–2mm) at the base, quickly narrowed distally, impressed in the upper ⅔ above, prominent below throughout its length; lateral veins 6–10 per side, diverging at *c*.45° somewhat ascending, slightly impressed or raised above, more conspicuously prominent beneath, obscurely anastomosing before the margin, reticulation inconspicuous. **Petiole** 10–20 x 1.5–2.5mm, somewhat flattened, scaly.

Bracts to 20 x 10mm; outer bracts broadly ovate, mucronate, *c*.15 x 12mm, with a few scales outside; inner ones broadly elliptic or elliptic, obtuse, margin very shallowly impressed with the attachments of fragile scales. Bracteoles to 20 x 0.5mm, linear, glabrous. Inflorescence a 5–8-flowered open umbel. Pedicels 20–25 x *c*.1mm, very densely covered with reddish-brown flat scales, especially towards the apex, without hairs. Calyx 4–5mm in diameter, oblique, disc-shaped, shortly irregularly 5-lobed, the lobes up to 1mm. **Corolla** 25–40 x *c*.30mm, funnel-shaped, white, sparsely scaly or glabrous outside, glabrous inside; tube 18–23 x 6–7 x 10–16mm, base 5-pouched; lobes 10–15 x 10–15mm, obovate-sub-circular. **Stamens** exserted to *c*.5mm; filaments linear, glabrous; anthers *c*.3 x 1mm, oblong, each cell with a short basal apiculus. Disc glabrous, prominent, deeply lobed. **Ovary** 5–8 x 2.5–3mm, sub-ovoid-cylindric, initially with dense, flat, reddish-brown, stellate scales, becoming glabrescent, sub-abruptly contracted distally; style *c*.20mm, scaly in the proximal ½–⅔, glabrous distally; stigma 3mm in diameter, thick. **Fruit** 25–30 x 6–7mm, fusiform. Seeds 5–6 x 0.2mm including the tails.

Philippines, Luzon, Mountain and Zambales Provinces. Along streams, in ravines, 1500–2200m.

Often reported in cultivation but all material examined with this name has turned out to be *R. kochii* which is easily distinguished by its hairy ovary and filaments.

259. Rhododendron mindanaense Merr.

Publ. Gov. Lab. Philip. 1905. 29: 41.
Type: Copeland 1042, April 1903. Philippines, Mindanao, Davao, Mt Apo near summit, *c*.2895m (PNH†). De Vore & Hoover 73 (PNH†, paratype, A, E).
Derivation: Named after the island of Mindanao from where it originated.

Erect shrub or sparingly branched tree to 10m. Twigs rounded, reddish and sparingly scaly at the upper internodes, glabrescent and often greyish or often whitish below, 4–5mm in diameter; internodes 2–7cm. **Leaves** 5–9 together in loose pseudowhorls at the upper 1–2 nodes, often with small but well-formed reddish purple buds in the leaf axils. **Blade** 50–100 x 25–50mm, obovate-elliptic or elliptic; apex obtuse, rounded, or emarginate; margin entire and flat; base tapering, glabrescent above when mature, more persistently and laxly scaly beneath. **Scales** small, with the marginal zone irregularly lobed and the minute dark centre slightly impressed. Mid-vein broad, raised for up to 10mm above, slightly grooved for most of its length otherwise flat; slightly raised proximally below; lateral veins 8–10 per side, at an acute angle, rather high-ascending, anastomosing before the edge, smooth when fresh, slightly but distinctly impressed above and raised beneath when dry, as is the reticulation, dark green above, paler beneath. **Petiole** 6–18 x 2–3.5mm, red, weakly grooved above, persistently silvery scaly.

Flower buds to 45 x 15mm, conical or narrowly ellipsoid, imbricate, glossy purplish-pink with pale areas, smooth, with the bract points appressed. Outer bracts ovate, inner ones ovate-oblong, obtuse, glabrous and shining outside, to 35 x 15mm. Bracteoles to 40 x 3mm, linear below, sub-spathulate at the apex, glabrous. Inflorescence an open umbel with 8–12, half-hanging flowers. Pedicels 25–32 x *c*.2mm, pale green, laxly and obscurely scaly, more densely scaly distally. Calyx oblique, a narrow rim or shortly obtusely 5-lobed, 3.5mm in diameter, scaly. **Corolla** 40–50 x 45–50mm, pure white, without scent; tube 25–30 x 6–8 x 12–15mm, very laxly scaly or glabrous outside, laxly patent hairy in the proximal ¾ of the tube inside, slightly sulcate near the base, cylindrical in the lowest ½–⅔ before expanding to the mouth; lobes 20–22 x 18–20mm, obovate, reflexed to a right angle, overlapping *c*.halfway. **Stamens** sub-equal, 25–30mm, clustered regularly around the mouth, exserted to *c*.3mm; filaments white, linear, laxly hairy in the lower ⅓, glabrous distally; anthers 3.5–4 x 1mm, pale brown, oblong, cell bases minutely apiculate. Disc prominent, hairy at the upper margin. **Ovary** sub-ovoid-cylindrical, densely silvery to yellowish-brown hairy, the hairs covering numerous, minute scales, 6–7 x 2.5mm, tapering distally; style sparsely hairy in its lower ⅙–⅓, as long as the stamens, lying on the lower side of the tube; stigma sub-globose. **Fruit** 30–35 x *c*.7mm, fusiform, slightly curved, warty, sub-densely hairy and scaly, with 5 deep longitudinal grooves. Seeds 4–5mm, without tails 0.7–0.9mm, the longest tail to 2mm.

Philippines, Mindanao, Mt Apo. Mossy forest near the summit, 2700–2895m. *Fl*. July, Aug.

Introduced into cultivation in 1992, it grows easily and flowers when surprisingly small (at *c*.25cm) given that it

Rhododendron mindanaense.

grows into a substantial tree in the wild. In cultivation it flowers mostly in the summer months in Edinburgh but will occasionally flower at other times of the year.

260. Rhododendron reynosoi Argent

Gardens Bull. Sing. 2004. 56(1&2): 84, *f*.3.
Type: Argent, Chavez, Fuentes, Cronk, Mendum, Middleton & Wilkie 44A, 22 Jan. 1998, 1600m. (Cultivated collection: 29 Aug. 2002, Acc. No. 19981806), Philippines, Palawan, Cleopatra Needle, just below summit. Moss forest (PNH, E).
Derivation: Named in memory of Eston Reynoso, who was a wonderful companion on several expeditions and made a considerable contribution to Philippine botany working for the National Museum, Manila.

Shrub to *c*.80cm. Stems green, rounded, *c*.3mm in diameter, moderately densely covered in brown stellate scales. **Leaves** in close pseudowhorls 1–2cm apart, consisting mostly of 6–7 leaves. **Blade** 50–80 x 15–30mm, elliptic to slightly obovate; apex acute to broadly acute, sometimes shortly acuminate or apiculate; margin entire, flat, narrowly cartilaginous; base broadly tapering; with sparse silvery, sub-circular scales at first above but quickly glabrescent; below moderately brown scaly. **Scales** rounded or weakly lobed, slightly impressed; centres small, 1–3 diameters apart in the mature leaves. Mid-vein narrowly impressed above although slightly prominent just above the petiole where it is also faintly grooved; beneath broadly raised for *c*.¾ of the length proximally; lateral veins 6–10 per side, smooth, spreading broadly but then curving upwards to link with the vein above before the margin, distinct above but obscure below. **Petiole** 6–10 x 1.5–2mm, not grooved above, pale green with brown stellate scales.

Flower buds to 40 x 20mm, ovoid, green, acutely pointed with a gradual transition from foliage leaves to bracts, these transitional forms having a smaller but distinct foliar blade with broad translucent decurrent margins instead of a petiole; inner bracts narrowly ovate to subulate with spreading points. Bracts glabrous or with a few, scattered scales outside and along the margins but no simple hairs. Pedicels 9–15 x 1–2mm, orange, moderately scaly but without simple hairs. Inflorescence of 6–10 flowers in a complete umbel. **Flowers** 32–40 x 30–40mm, held erect or semi-erect, bright orange with a red star in the throat, the points extended as lines along the lobes, without scent. Calyx a low scaly disc. **Corolla** tube *c*.15 x 6 x 13mm, glabrous outside, white hairy in the proximal ½ inside; lobes 15–30 x 12–22mm, semi-erect, overlapping

½–¾ of their length, rounded or weakly emarginate at the apex. **Stamens** regularly arranged around the mouth of the flower, exserted to *c*.5mm, distinctly dimorphic; filaments pale orange, with long white hairs in the proximal ⅓, glabrous distally; anthers *c*.3 x 1.5mm, dark purple. Disc green, almost glabrous but with a few short hairs on the upper margin. **Ovary** *c*.6.5 x 3mm, ellipsoid, silvery-scaly and densely white hairy; style *c*.14 x 0.8mm, orange, at first lying on the lower side of the corolla tube, rising to a central position as the flower ages, glabrous; stigma *c*.3mm in diameter, purplish-red, hardly expanded from the style. **Fruit** sub-cylindrical, tapering distally to the style, grooved longitudinally in the proximal ⅔, 20–25 x *c*.6mm, the calyx slightly accrescent; on splitting the outer layer peeling back irregularly, the valves spreading to *c*.45°, the placentae remaining adherent to the central column. Seeds *c*.3.7mm, without tails *c*.0.8mm, the longest tail 1.5mm.

Philippines, Palawan, Cleopatra Needle, mossy forest, *c*.1600m.

Similar in some respects to *R. leytense* but differing not only in the colour of the flowers, which is yellow in *R. leytense*, but also in the non-hairy pedicels. This species also has more flowers in the inflorescence than *R. leytense*. A unique feature, at least amongst the Philippine rhododendrons, is the gradual transition from foliage leaves to bracts, the intermediates having broad sheathing bases and a smaller blade.

Rhododendron reynosoi is very distinct with its bright vibrant orange flowers in a tight, erect umbel; this alone distinguishes it from all other Philippine species as those with several-flowered umbels either have very differently sized flowers or have a totally different disposition. It is much smaller leaved than *R. javanicum* ssp. *schadenbergii* as conceived by Sleumer (1966). Cultivated since 1998, it first flowered in 2000, the flowers being very bright and showy, but it has not grown strongly.

261. Rhododendron brachygynum H.F.Copel.

Phil. J. Sc. 1929. 40(2): 165, pl.11, *f*.4–6.
Type: Sudlon, Cenabre & De la Cruz F.B. 28346. Philippines, Cebu (PNH†).
Derivation: Greek – *brachus* – short; *gynum* – ovary. Alluding to the very short pistil.

Shrub to 1m. Twigs red-brown. **Leaves** either in pseudowhorls at the end of the branchlets or scattered and spiral. **Blade** *c*.100 x 45mm, elliptic; apex shortly acuminate; base obtuse, decurrent into the petiole, shining and minutely blackish pitted above, sparsely covered with pale scales beneath. **Petiole** 15mm.

Inflorescence 5-flowered. Pedicels *c.*20mm, strong, hairy. **Corolla** 40mm, narrowly obconical, yellow; lobes *c.*15mm, rounded. **Stamens** *c.*30mm; filaments minutely hairy in the proximal part; anthers *c.*3mm, oblong, base minutely appendaged. Disc hairy, at the upper margin. **Ovary** *c.*8 x 3mm, sub-cylindrical, densely hairy, abruptly contracted distally; style *c.*9mm, glabrous; stigma 2mm in diameter, rounded.

Philippines, Cebu, once found.

This species is based on a single specimen that has since been destroyed; Sleumer saw no material. The description here is modified from Sleumer's translation of the original Latin. Copeland in discussing this species (1929) regarded it as related to *R. teysmannii* (*R. javanicum* ssp. *teysmannii*) and *R. kochii*. It would appear to belong to the *R. javanicum* complex but it is clearly distinct from *R. kochii* in both flower colour and leaf shape. Copeland also states: 'On the other hand this species represents a transition from the ones just mentioned to *R. leytense* and *R. loheri*, which share the yellow flowers and appendaged anthers, but have somewhat smaller leaves, not at all acuminate, and drying to a dark brown colour. All the species here mentioned are alike in the hairiness of the ovary and filaments. *Rhododendron brachygynum* differs from all the others in the fact that the pistil is only about half as long as the stamens'.

The status of this species will not be satisfactorily evaluated without further collections from the type locality. It probably will turn out to be a minor variant of *R. leytense* (itself very similar to the *R. javanicum* complex). The very short pistil, the character to which Copeland appears to give most significance, may well be the result of examining very young flowers. The style elongates substantially in many species as flowers age and pass from the early unreceptive stigma phase to the later receptive one.

262. Rhododendron leytense Merr.

Phil. J. Sc. Bot. 1915. 10: 55.
Type: Ramos B.S. 15252, 23 Aug. 1912. Philippines, Leyte, Mt Ibuni, back of Dagami (PNH†, BM, E, K, L, P).
Derivation: Named after the island on which it was first found.

Synonym: *R. flaviflorum* Elmer *ex* Merr., En. Philip. 1923. 3: 244, *in obs. pr. R. leytense*.

Var. **leytense**

Shrub to 2m. Twigs 3–4mm in diameter, rounded, green, laxly to densely covered with brown scales, glabrescent; internodes 1.5–5cm. **Leaves** 3–6 together in dense to lax pseudowhorls. **Blade** 40–100 x 15–38mm, elliptic to sub-obovate-elliptic; apex shortly and bluntly acuminate; margin entire, flat, often red; base tapering, sometimes slightly decurrent; laxly sub-stellately scaly on both sides at first, glabrescent above, laxly and sub-persistently scaly beneath, the scales denser along the mid-vein. **Scales** small, marginal zone deeply and irregularly lobed; centre shallowly impressed. Mid-vein slightly prominent in the proximal ½ above, and minutely hairy, becoming glabrous, smooth or narrowly impressed into a groove distally, beneath shallowly and broadly raised for most of its length; lateral veins 5–8 per side, straight or ascending, inconspicuous especially beneath, reticulation not visible. **Petiole** 6–16 x 2–3mm, not grooved, scaly, densely shortly hairy above and sometimes with a few minute papillae, slightly flattened.

Flower buds to 30 x 20mm, narrowly ovate, acute, pale green. Bracts ovate, acuminate, glabrous, to 25 x 10mm. Bracteoles linear, to 11 x 0.5mm, glabrous. Inflorescence an open umbel of 3–5 flowers, held semi-erect to horizontal. Pedicels 10–15 x 2mm, shortly hairy, without, or with just the occasional scale. Calyx *c.*3mm in diameter, rim-like, densely short-hairy. **Corolla** 33–35 x 35–40mm, broadly tubular-funnel-shaped or sub-campanulate, yellow, without scent, lobed *c.*⅓–½; tube 20–21 x 5–6 x 12–15mm, straight, sulcate near the base, glabrous outside, very laxly hairy proximally inside; lobes 15–18 x 12–15mm, obovate, overlapping ⅓–½, spreading, the distal ½ reflexed. **Stamens** 27–30mm, irregularly arranged all round the mouth or sometimes in two groups on either side towards the lower side of the mouth, unequal, exserted to *c.*10mm; filaments broad and hairy at the base or up to ⅓, filiform and glabrous distally; anthers 2–2.5mm, oblong, yellow, base rounded or minutely apiculate. Disc hairy on the upper side or occasionally all over. **Ovary** *c.*7 x 2mm, sub-cylindrical, tapering distally, densely short-hairy and with minute scales hidden by the hairs; style hairy and scaly in the lower ¼, glabrous distally or completely glabrous, lying on the lower side of the mouth; stigma *c.*2mm in diameter, rounded or deeply 5-lobed. **Fruit** 30 x 6mm, fusiform, the valves spreading and twisting. Seeds 7mm, without tails 0.9mm, the longest tail *c.*3mm.

Philippines, Luzon, Leyte, Mt Lobi near Dagami; Mindanao, Camiguin Island, Mt Hibok-hibok. Mossy forest, and open shrubberies, both terrestrial and epiphytic, *c.*1000m.

Rhododendron leytense var. *leytense*.

Introduced into cultivation to Edinburgh in 1999 from the surprising discovery on Mt Hibok-hibok, it has flowered so far in October and November with bright pale yellow flowers. It is not particularly vigorous but has not yet really demonstrated its potential.

Var. **loheri** (H.F.Copel.) Sleumer
Reinwardtia 1960. 5: 218.
Type: Loher 14769, 27 March 1913. Philippines, Luzon, Rizal, Guinuisan (PNH†, E, UC).
Derivation: Named after the collector, August Loher, a German who lived for many years in the Philippines and made many collections of plants there.

Synonym: *R. loheri* H.F.Copel., Phil. J. Sc. 1929. 40(2): 166, pl.11, *f*.10–12.

Differs from the type by the shorter corolla, only *c*.30mm long, and anthers with appendages at the base.

Philippines. Known only from the type collection.

263. Rhododendron loboense H.F.Copel.
Phil. J. Sc. 1929. 40: 172, *t*.15, *f*.3, *t*.16, *f*.5–6.
Type: Mabesa F.B. 28045. Philippines, Luzon, Batangas, Lobo Mts (PNH†, A, E).
Derivation: Named after the Lobo Mts where it was first collected.

Shrub to 1.5m. Twigs *c*.5mm in diameter, rounded, glabrous or sparsely scaly, with large flat fragile scales. **Leaves** spirally arranged with conspicuous, spherical buds in the upper axils. **Blade** 100–120 x 40–60mm, elliptic, apex sometimes shortly acuminate, broadly acute to obtuse; margin narrowly but distinctly revolute; base broadly tapering, occasionally rounded, glabrescent above at maturity; laxly and more persistently scaly beneath. **Scales** small, marginal zone irregularly lobed; centre weakly or not impressed. Mid-vein strong, raised above in the proximal ½, smooth distally, raised beneath throughout, as broad as the petiole proximally, gradually narrowed upwards; lateral veins 12–15 per side, at an acute angle, indistinctly anastomosing, prominent or barely distinct on both sides, reticulation mostly visible beneath only. **Petiole** 10–20 x 2.5–3mm, without a groove, scaly, somewhat flattened.

Rhododendron loboense.

Flower buds to 40 x 20mm, shortly ovoid, shortly pointed, pale yellowish-green, smooth with the bracts appressed. Bracts broadly ovate, glabrous except for minute, fragile scales on the margins. Inflorescence 4–7-flowered, in slightly open umbels. Pedicels 10–20 x *c*.2mm, expanded to *c*.5mm just below the calyx, glabrous to laxly scaly. Calyx 4–5mm in diameter, disc-like, margin thickened, wavy and faintly lobed, glabrous. **Corolla** 35–40 x 50–60mm, funnel-shaped, held horizontally to semi-erect, yellow, without scent; tube 20–22 x 9–11 x 24–30mm, glabrous on both sides; lobes 20–29 x 20–24mm, unequal, oval, reflexed to horizontal, overlapping to *c*.½. **Stamens** irregularly arranged, exserted 5–8mm, slightly dimorphic; filaments linear, glabrous, *c*.25mm; anthers 4 x 1mm, strongly incurved, yellow, oblong, base obtuse. Disc glabrous or with a few sparse hairs, deeply lobed. **Ovary** 7–10 x 3–5mm, sub-obovoid-cylindrical, glabrous or with a few scattered scales, abruptly contracted distally; style 13–17 x 1.25mm, glabrous; stigma 5mm in diameter, yellow, circular, thick and lobed. **Fruit** 25–45 x 6–9mm, fusiform. Seeds 6–7mm, without tails *c*.1.2mm, the longest tail 3.8mm.

Philippines, Luzon, Batangas Province, Lobo Mts; Camiguin Island, Mt Hibok-hibok, Misamis Oriental Province; Mt Halcon, Mindoro. Epiphytic or terrestrial. *Fl.* April, Nov.

The description above has been greatly amplified with the additional recent collections from locations far removed from that of the type collection but it remains a poorly known species. The differences between the three known locations do not appear to warrant any subspecific recognition. It is very similar to *R. leytense* and differs chiefly in the lack of hairs on the ovary. It is hardly distinguishable from the *R. javanicum* complex

but retained here as the number of collections is still very limited. It has been in cultivation in Edinburgh since 1997 and has flowered so far in September, with handsome yellow flowers.

264. Rhododendron xanthopetalum Merr.
Publ. Gov. Lab. Philip. 1905. 29: 41.
Type: Whitford 322. Bataan, Mt Mariveles (PNH†).
Derivation: Greek – *xantho* – yellow; *petalum* – petals. Alluding to the yellow colour of the flowers.

Epiphytic shrub, to 80cm, with a thick, simple or but slightly branched stem. Twigs *c*.4mm in diameter, scaly. **Leaves** spirally arranged. **Blade** 90–120 x 35–50mm, elliptic; apex acuminate or acute; margin flat; base broadly tapering to almost rounded, glabrescent above, scaly below. Mid-vein thick and prominent, raised above in the proximal ½, raised below almost to the apex. **Petiole** 12–15 x 3–4mm, ungrooved, scaly.
Inflorescence 3–4-flowered. Pedicels *c*.15mm, glabrous. Calyx reduced to an obscure disc. **Corolla** 30–40 x 30–55mm, campanulate, yellow flushed with orange; tube 15–25 x 12 x 25mm, glabrous both outside and inside; lobes *c*.30 x 22mm, sub-circular. **Stamens** *c*.18mm, distributed irregularly around the mouth, exserted 2–3mm; filaments hairy proximally; anthers *c*.4mm, linear, without any basal apiculus. Disc with a few hairs at the top. **Ovary** 8mm, scaly, without hairs, abruptly contracted distally; style *c*.12mm, glabrous, lying on the lower side of the tube.

Philippines, Luzon, Bataan Province, Mt Mariveles; Rizal Province, Montalban; Nueva Vizcaya Province, Carballo Sur Mountains. Possibly also from Mindoro at Ibolo (Copeland 1929). Camiguin Island, near Mindanao. Epiphyte in moss forest, or terrestrial in montane grassland, 1200m, apparently rare.

An imperfectly known species of which Sleumer had examined only the single leaf in the Edinburgh herbarium. It appears to be characterised by the spiral leaf arrangement, and a calyx that is much broader than the base of the scaly but non-hairy ovary. A recent expedition to Mt Mariveles failed to find this species in the type locality, but surprisingly material closely matching the description was collected on Camiguin Island off Mindanao in 1999. This has been cultivated and the description above is augmented from this material. The chief differences from the type description are that the stems are not glabrous (which is likely to have been inaccurate in the original), the leaf bases not acute and the margins flat and not revolute. The flower measurements are considerably larger,

Rhododendron madulidii.

which is understandable as they have been made from living material. The species grows slowly and flowered for the first time in the Royal Botanic Garden Edinburgh in 2003. It would appear to be very similar to *R. javanicum* ssp. *schadenbergii*.

265. Rhododendron madulidii Argent

The New Plantsman 1998. 5(4): 204.
Type: Argent GAM 4 (19922782). Philippines, Palawan, Brooks Point, Mt Mantalingajan, 1600–1800m (PNH, E).
Derivation: Named after Domingo Madulid, Chief of the Division of Botany in the National Museum, Manila, who greatly facilitated the collection of this species.

Shrub to 1.5m. Twigs rounded, distinctly brown-scaly and minutely hairy, becoming glabrescent; internodes 2–10cm. **Leaves** 10–14 in loose pseudowhorls. **Blade** 40–80 x 13–40mm, narrowly to broadly elliptic, occasionally obovate; apex broadly acute, obtuse or rounded; margin entire, slightly revolute and with a narrow cartilaginous edge; base narrowly to broadly tapering, often decurrent; above with silvery small scales but quickly glabrescent; below with brown, more persistent impressed scales. **Scales** laxly arranged, rounded to weakly lobed, with a broad, striate marginal flange and a relatively large, slightly swollen centre. Mid-vein grooved and slightly raised or impressed in the proximal part, distally shallowly impressed above, slightly raised beneath and distinct to the apex; lateral veins 4–8 per side, spreading at 45–90°, moderately distinct and minutely impressed above, obscure to invisible

beneath, reticulation inconspicuous. **Petiole** 3–8 x 1–3mm, distinctly grooved above, brown-scaly.

Flower buds (see p.327) to 50 x 30mm, green or green strongly flushed with red, the outer bracts recurving but with the lateral margins strongly inrolled distally, appearing acute but slightly retuse if flattened out, with a few scales outside in the proximal ½, mainly in the central area. Inner bracts to 50 x 17mm, glabrous except for marginal scales near the apex, standing out vertically away from the bud to completely enclosing and ensheathing, ovate to elliptic with hooded apices. Pedicels 25–28 x 2–3mm, green to strongly flushed with red, especially in the proximal ½, scaly and shortly white-hairy. Inflorescence of 5–10, semi-erect to slightly hanging flowers in an open umbel. **Flowers** white with a greenish tinge on the tube or flushed very pale pink, without scent. **Corolla** 50–56 x 65–70mm; tube 30–33 x 6–8 x 16–20mm, glabrous outside, or with some short hairs near the base, hairy inside; lobes 30–36 x 23–29mm, at first semi-erect, later spreading horizontally, overlapping to *c*.¼, often with an irregular margin and retuse at the apex. **Stamens** mostly clustered in the lower ⅔ of the flower, sometimes arranged all round the mouth, exserted to *c*.6mm; filaments *c*.35mm, white with distally pointing hairs in the basal ⅓; anthers *c*.3 x 1mm, cream, becoming pale brown with age. Disc 10-lobed, with dense, white, erect hairs on the upper side. **Ovary** *c*.10 x 3mm, covered in short, white, slightly distally pointing hairs and pale translucent scales; style up to 25mm, glabrous except for the proximal 1–2mm which is densely hairy; stigma 3–5mm in diameter, white, 5-lobed, at first on the lower side of the mouth, rising to central position as it becomes receptive.

Fruit 35–40 x 6–8mm, fusiform, often slightly curved and shallowly longitudinally grooved, green to purplish-red.

Philippines, Palawan, Mt Mantalingajan, known only from the type locality, 1600–1800m, common in sub-montane shrubbery on ultramafic rocks. *Fl.* March.

This species was introduced into cultivation to Edinburgh in 1992 and has proved easy to grow and flower but it has a somewhat 'leggy' habit. The flowers so far have always been a beautiful clear white and the delicate pink-flushed flowers seen in the wild have not so far been produced.

266. Rhododendron impressopunctatum J.J.Sm.
Fedde Rep. 1932. 30: 164.
Type: Toxopeus Ac. Moluccas, Buru, Kenturun, 1075m (BO, L).
Derivation: Latin – *impressi* – sunken or impressed; *punctatus* – marked with dots or spots. Alluding to the impressed scales on the leaves.

Shrub to 1.2m. Twigs semi-rounded, densely covered with stellate scales, becoming glabrescent; internodes 2–10cm. **Leaves** 4–5 together in pseudowhorls. **Blade** 62–83 x 24–32mm, elliptic; apex shortly acuminate, sub-acute or rarely obtuse; margin slightly recurved; base broadly tapering to nearly rounded; above sub-densely covered with small, flat, non-impressed scales which become silvery and persist for a long time, especially on the midvein, eventually glabrescent; more densely and more persistently scaly beneath. **Scales** dense, but mostly not touching, orange-brown, small, marginal zone irregularly lobed; centre dark, distinctly impressed. Mid-vein grooved above, strongly and obtusely prominent beneath; lateral veins 8–10 per side, spreading, obscurely anastomosing, very slightly impressed above, hardly raised beneath, reticulation inconspicuous. **Petiole** 8–10 x 1.5–2mm, densely scaly, the scales touching initially as they do on the proximal area of the mid-vein beneath, semi-rounded, grooved above.

Inflorescence 5–7-flowered. Pedicels 10–19 x 0.7mm, sparsely scaly. Calyx *c.*4mm in diameter, obliquely disc-shaped, unequally 5-angular. **Corolla** 30–35mm, tubular-funnel-shaped, red, glabrous inside and out; tube 20–23 x *c.*5 x *c.*7mm, straight, lobed at the base; lobes 10–13 x 7–12mm, spreading, obovate to sub-circular. **Stamens** somewhat exserted from the mouth; filaments linear, densely patently hairy in the proximal 5–7mm; anthers *c.*3.5 x 1mm, oblong, the base obtuse. Disc prominent, glabrous. **Ovary** 5–6 x 2–2.5mm, conical-sub-cylindrical,

densely stellate-scaly, without hairs, abruptly contracted distally; style as long as the stamens, glabrous; stigma rounded.

Indonesia, Maluku, Buru, known only from the type collection. Terrestrial on a peat moor at Kunturun, 1075m. *Fl.* Feb.

Sleumer (1966) noted that 'Size and colour of the scales suggest that *R. impressopunctatum* is a hybrid of *R. malayanum* with another species of the *Javanicum* group, presumably *R. seranicum*; these three species grow together at Kunturun'. There are no recent observations to confirm or refute this.

267. Rhododendron seranicum J.J.Sm.
Fedde Rep. 1932. 30: 165.
Type: Stresemann 360, Sept.–Dec. 1911. Moluccas, Ceram (C), Hatu Soka Plateau, 1450m (L).
Derivation: Named after Seram, the island on which it was first found.

Shrub to 5m. Twigs 2.5–4mm, rounded, laxly scaly but quickly glabrescent, smooth; internodes 2–11.5cm. **Leaves** spirally arranged. **Blade** 50–85 x 20–40mm, elliptic, sub-ovate; apex shortly acuminate, acute; margin entire, shortly and narrowly recurved; base broadly tapering to nearly rounded; quickly glabrescent above; more persistently laxly scaly beneath but eventually glabrescent. **Scales** small, flat, marginal zone irregularly lobed; centre weakly or not impressed. Mid-vein raised above in the proximal ½, then smooth or very slightly impressed, strongly raised beneath almost to the apex; lateral veins 8–10 per side, spreading at *c.*45°, straight at the base, then sharply curving upwards before the margin and obscurely anastomosing, slightly prominent or smooth on both sides, reticulation faint or obscure. **Petiole** 5–20 x 2–3.5mm, without a groove, laxly scaly.

Bracts to 35 x 10mm, elliptic to narrowly elliptic, obtuse, membranous, glabrous. Bracteoles *c.*25 x 1mm, linear, glabrous. Inflorescence 7–11-flowered in a complete umbel. Pedicels 20–34 x 2–3mm, thickened at the apex, sparsely scaly or practically glabrous. Calyx *c.*5mm in diameter, oblique, shortly cup- or disc-shaped, thickened, obscurely or not lobed, occasionally with slender petaloid lobes up to 40mm, laxly scaly outside. **Corolla** 50–56 x 80mm, broadly funnel-shaped, light violet, orange, yellow or red; tube 18–26 x 6–10 x 15–20mm, base lobed, glabrous outside and inside; lobes 35–40 x 22–23mm, unequal, elliptic to obovate, spreading, overlapping up to ⅕. **Stamens** exserted to *c.*10mm, irregularly arranged mostly in the lower ½ of the mouth; filaments yellow, flat, linear, glabrous; anthers 3–4 x *c.*1mm, cream, oblong, somewhat curved, base blunt or minutely apiculate. Disc prominent, glabrous. **Ovary** *c.*6 x 3mm, oblong-conical, glabrous, minutely rugulose, abruptly contracted distally; style 15–20mm, green, glabrous, at first on the lower side of the corolla tube, curving in the distal ¼ so that the stigma is presented centrally; stigma 3–4mm in diameter, lobed. **Fruit** 35–40 x 7–8mm, fusiform, glabrous.

Indonesia, Maluku, (Seram, Buru, and Ambon); Sulawesi, pass between Lake Poso and Wotu; Mt Wawonoeru, SW of Soroako. Light forest and gaps in primary forest, 900–1700m, often in limestone areas, locally abundant. *Fl.* Aug.–Feb. Sleumer (1960) recorded a specimen from C Sulawesi (Palopo–Rantepao road at 900m) differing by 35mm corollas and distinctly appendaged anthers.

Introduced into cultivation from Mt Binaia in Seram in 1988, it flowered for the first time in July 1999 at the Royal Botanic Garden Edinburgh. It has not grown well and is grown with some difficulty.

---

268. Rhododendron celebicum (Blume) DC.

Bijdr. 1826. 855.

Type: Reinwardt *s.n.*, 1821. Celebes, Menado: Mt Klabat, top, 1800–2000m (L, P).

Derivation: Named after the island on which it was found, Celebes (now Sulawesi).

Shrub to 1.5m; roots sometimes swollen and tuber-like. Twigs rounded, 1.5–3mm in diameter, sub-densely sub-stellately scaly, older stems glabrescent, smooth, often red; internodes 1.5–6cm. **Leaves** 3–7 together in distinct but loose pseudowhorls. **Blade** 30–70 x 15–30mm, elliptic to narrowly ovate-elliptic; apex shortly acuminate, sub-acute or obtuse; margin entire, narrowly cartilaginous, flat when fresh, slightly and narrowly revolute when dry; base broadly tapering; glabrescent and slightly rugose above at maturity, sub-densely scaly beneath. **Scales** small, flat or impressed, marginal zone thin, pale, silvery, large, angled or sub-stellately lobed; centre small, brown. Mid-vein narrow and slightly impressed above, strong and prominent beneath; lateral veins 5–7 per side, sub-patently spreading, anastomosing, faintly impressed above, very slightly or not raised beneath, without clear reticulation. **Petiole** 4–12 x 1–1.5mm, flattened, red, shallowly grooved above, scaly.

Flower buds to 15 x 6mm, ellipsoid, smooth, except for low protuberances at the apices of the bracts, minutely pale-brown scaly outside and along the bract margins. Bracts 5–12 x 4–7mm, ovate to obovate, minutely pale-brown scaly outside or glabrous; margin with brown, stellate scales. Bracteoles *c.*15 x 1–2mm, linear below, sub-spathulate, dilated and irregularly impressed distally, glabrous. Inflorescence 3–8-flowered, an open umbel, the flowers hanging vertically downwards. Pedicels 15–20 x *c.*1mm, slender, densely stellate-scaly and papillose, not properly hairy. Calyx 2.5–3mm in diameter, disc-shaped, oblique, shortly obtusely 5-lobed, densely scaly outside. **Corolla** 35–46 x 20–25mm, tubular, pink to red, without scent; tube 30–35 x 6–8 x 9–11mm, cylindrical, straight, often angular and strongly pouched at the base, laxly to very laxly scaly outside, glabrous inside; lobes 8–11 x 6–10mm, sub-circular, mostly not overlapping, half-spreading to almost horizontal. **Stamens** irregularly spread around the mouth of the flower, or exserted to 8mm; filaments pink, glabrous; anthers 2–2.5 x 1mm, dark, brown, pores up to ½ the length of the anthers. Disc green, prominent, glabrous. **Ovary** 5–6 x 2mm, sub-cylindrical, pink, very densely silvery stellately scaly, tapering gradually distally; style glabrous or scaly at the base, as long as the corolla; stigma thick-globose. **Fruit** 25–38 x 35mm, fusiform-cylindrical, scaly. Seeds 7–8mm, without tails *c.*1mm, the longest tail to 4.5mm, the tails strongly crimped.

Indonesia, Sulawesi, Minahasa: Mt Klabat, Lake Poso area, Mt Rantemario, Mt Gambuta. Epiphytic in mossy forest, 1800–2600m. *Fl.* Jan., June, July, Nov.

Introduced into cultivation in 1854 by Thomas Lobb collecting for the nurseryman Veitch. These collections disappeared at an unspecified time probably before 1900. Recently reintroduced by several collectors, probably first by Hank Helm and John Farbarik (1997), also by Keith Adams, David Binney, Paul Smith and Louise Galloway. Two

Rhododendron celebicum.

distinct colour forms are in cultivation, the commoner pink and a deep red. This species flowers profusely but irregularly in cultivation, remains small and is easy to grow. The pink form is said to be more vigorous than the red.

269. Rhododendron rhodopus Sleumer

Reinwardtia 1960. 5: 199.

Type: Eyma 643, 16 June 1937. Indonesia, Celebes (C), Enrekang, Pokapindjang-Tinábang (BO, L).

Derivation: Greek – *rhodo* – rose or red; *podus* – footed or based. Alluding to the pink pedicels.

Shrub. Twigs 4–5mm in diameter, rounded, laxly sub-stellately scaly when young, quickly glabrescent and often whitish when older; internodes 13–15cm. **Leaves** mostly 5 in pseudowhorls with some reduced ones on the internodes. **Blade** 90–160 x 20–45mm, narrowly ovate, sometimes with slightly unequal sides; apex long-acuminate, acute; margin entire, flat or minutely and narrowly revolute; base broadly tapering, glabrescent above, laxly scaly beneath. **Scales** small, flat, mostly shortly lobed in the marginal zone; centre minute, hardly impressed. Mid-vein broadened above and slightly raised proximally, narrowed and impressed distally, beneath thick and obtusely prominent proximally; lateral veins *c.*8 per side, at an acute angle, high-ascending, indistinctly anastomosing, slightly depressed above, hardly raised beneath. **Petiole** 15–20 x 2–3mm, laxly scaly, semi-rounded.

Bracts to 40 x 20mm. Outer bracts broadly ovate-elliptic, densely and very shortly coarsely hairy outside, glabrous inside. Bracteoles *c.*20 x 1mm, linear, laxly hairy towards the apex. Inflorescence an 8–9-flowered open umbel. Pedicels 15–20 x *c.*1mm, laxly scaly, not hairy, pink. Calyx *c.*4mm in diameter, disc-shaped, wavy, hardly lobed, scaly outside. **Corolla** 65–70mm, tubular, lobed in the upper ⅓, white, scented; tube 40–50 x *c.*5 x *c.*8mm, straight, lobed at the base, glabrous outside or with very sparse fragile scales, sub-densely hairy inside; lobes 20–25 x 15–20mm, spreading, sub-circular. **Stamens** sub-equal, exserted to 10mm; filaments linear hairy in the lower ⅔, filiform and glabrous distally; anthers 4–5 x 1.3mm, oblong. Disc glabrous. **Ovary** *c.*10 x 2.5mm, cylindrical, yellowish hairy and minutely scaly, gradually narrowed distally; style nearly as long as the corolla tube, yellowish hairy in the lower ¾, without scales, glabrous below the rounded stigma. **Fruit** (sub-mature) 50–70 x 7–8mm, cylindrical, tapering at the base, mostly curved, shortly yellowish hairy and minutely scaly, with a persistent hairy style.

Indonesia, Sulawesi, Latimodjong Range, Pokapindjang, Luwuk, in Latimodjong, apparently terrestrial at 2800–3000m. *Fl.* June, *fr.* Sept.

First collected as living material by Keith Adams in 1997; also collected by Craven and Brown in 2002 and growing in Australia.

270. Rhododendron bloembergenii Sleumer

Reinwardtia 1960. 5: 204.

Type: Bloembergen 3972, 9 July 1939. Indonesia, Celebes, Central, E of Lake Lindu, towards the top of G. Ngilalaki, 2335m (BO, A, L).

Derivation: Named after the collector, Siebe Bloembergen, a Dutch botanist who worked in Indonesia.

Tree to *c.*3m. Twigs 4–9mm in diameter, sub-angular, sparsely appressed-scaly when young, becoming glabrescent and often whitish; internodes 5–20cm. **Leaves** 2–3 together in loose pseudowhorls with additional leaves on the internode. **Blade** 90–190 x 30–48mm, broadly elliptic; apex shortly and abruptly acuminate, sub-acute; margin narrowly revolute when dry; base broadly tapering, often unequal; sparsely scaly to glabrescent above, sub-persistently laxly to sub-densely scaly beneath. **Scales** minute, flat, the broad marginal zone irregularly sub-stellately lobed and breaking up early; centre small, hardly impressed. Mid-vein as wide as the petiole proximally, flat or shallowly impressed above, thick and obtusely prominent beneath; lateral veins 9–12 per side, high-ascending, at an acute angle, curved and anastomosing before the margin, with several intermediate smaller veins, all parallel, faintly impressed or raised above, distinctly prominent beneath, reticulation slightly raised beneath only. **Petiole** 10–20 x *c.*3mm, flattened, scaly, striate lengthwise.

Rhododendron bloembergenii.

Bracts to 60 x 25mm, outer bracts 15–20 x 10mm, ovate, obtuse, initially hairy outside especially at the base, later glabrescent, distinctly rough to the touch, inner bracts elliptic to spathulate, very densely hairy outside. Bracteoles *c*.20 x 1–1.5mm, linear to sub-spathulate, densely hairy. Inflorescence *c*.10-flowered in a complete umbel. Pedicels 12–17 x 1.5mm, sub-densely sub-stellate-scaly. Calyx *c*.3mm in diameter, disc-like, short. **Corolla** 65–75mm, tubular below, expanded distally, white, scented; tube 45–50 x 5–6 x 6–7mm, cylindrical, straight, the base lobed, glabrous outside, densely shortly hairy inside; lobes 20–25 x 15–20mm, broadly obovate-spathulate or sub-circular. **Stamens** exserted to *c*.10mm; filaments linear and densely patently hairy in the proximal ⅔, glabrous and filiform distally; anthers 6–7 x 1.5mm, oblong, each cell contracted into a short basal apiculus. Disc prominent, glabrous. **Ovary** 9–10 x 3–4mm, sub-cylindrical, yellowish hairy (scales not visible), tapering distally; style thick, slightly exceeding the stamens, densely hairy proximally, sub-densely or laxly so and minutely scaly distally, glabrous for the terminal 6–8mm; stigma *c*.3mm in diameter, thick-knob-like. **Fruit** 35–40 x 7–8mm, thickly fusiform-cylindric, laxly shortly hairy, somewhat rugose, slightly curved.

Indonesia, Sulawesi, Ngilalaki, E of Lake Lindu; Latimodjong Mts. Summit vegetation, 2200–2335m. *Fl.* July, *fr.* Aug.

Not known to have been cultivated.

---

271. **Rhododendron poromense** J.J.Sm.

Bot. Jahr. 1937. 68: 203.
Type: Kjellberg 2627, 24 Oct. 1929. Celebes (SE), B. Porema (in the north part of the Mengkoka Mts), 1400m (S, BO, L, fragment).
Derivation: Of Porema, the place where this species was collected.

Shrub to 1m. Twigs 1.5–2.5mm in diameter, very laxly covered with appressed scales, quickly glabrescent; internodes 4–9cm. **Leaves** 3–6 together in pseudowhorls. **Blade** 65–110 x 29–46mm, obovate- to elliptic; apex shortly acuminate or obtuse; margin narrowly revolute; base acutely tapering, glabrescent but densely blackish punctate above when mature, laxly appressed-scaly beneath. **Scales** minute, marginal zone narrow, irregularly lobed; centre slightly impressed, becoming glabrescent beneath also. Mid-vein flat, slightly, or not raised above, obtuse and much more prominent proximally beneath; lateral veins 7–9 per side, narrow and sub-parallel, curved-ascending and obscurely anastomosing along the margin,

slightly raised on both sides, reticulation obscure. **Petiole** 7–9 x *c*.2mm, grooved above, rounded, scaly.

Inflorescence 5–6-flowered. Pedicels *c*.15mm, thick, densely scaly, without hairs. Calyx *c*.4mm in diameter, obliquely disc-shaped, crenulate or obtusely lobed, scaly outside. **Corolla** *c*.40mm, funnel-shaped, red; tube *c*.20 x 4 x 6–8mm, sulcate at the base, sparsely, sub-stellately scaly outside, finely hairy in the proximal ½ inside; lobes 18–20 x 14–16mm, obovate-spathulate, often retuse, spreading. **Stamens** exserted; filaments linear, laxly hairy in the proximal ½, glabrous distally; anthers *c*.4 x 1mm, oblong, base obtuse. Disc low, glabrous. **Ovary** *c*.5 x 2mm, sub-cylindrical, tapering distally, finely shortly hairy, and sub-densely covered with minute, sub-entire scales; style 17–20mm, glabrous; stigma thick, globose.

Indonesia, Sulawesi (SE), Mengkoka Mts, Mt Porema, at 1400m. Epiphytic. *Fl.* Oct.

Known only from the type collection. Never cultivated.

---

272. **Rhododendron leptobrachion** Sleumer

Reinwardtia 1960. 5: 203.
Type: Eyma 647, 16 June 1937. Celebes (C): Enrekang, Pokapindjang-Tinábang (L, A, BO, K, SING).
Derivation: Greek – *lepto* – thin or slender; *brachium* – arm. Described as having slender branches.

Shrub or small tree with slender branches to 3m. Twigs rounded, 1.5–3mm in diameter, laxly silvery scaly, becoming glabrescent, often pink when fresh, whitish in dry specimens, with distinctive slender, acutely pointed lateral buds with subulate tips to the scales; internodes 3.5–12cm. **Leaves** 4–7 together in tight pseudowhorls at the upper 1–2 nodes, 1–2 additional sometimes on the internodes. **Blade** 55–90 x 18–28mm, narrowly elliptic; apex shortly acuminate, acute; margin entire, flat or only very slightly revolute; base acutely tapering, densely scaly on both sides when young, glabrescent and minutely blackish punctate above with age, more persistently and laxly scaly beneath. **Scales** small, with a relatively wide marginal zone which quickly disintegrates, sub-stellately lobed; centre minute and slightly impressed, blackish with age. Mid-vein narrow and impressed above, strongly and obtusely prominent beneath, often pale whitish; lateral veins 6–10 per side, irregular, spreading, obscurely inarching, with additional shorter intermediate veins all minutely impressed, inconspicuous above, more distinct beneath. **Petiole** 10–20 x 1.5–1.8mm, compressed and grooved above.

Rhododendron leptobrachion.

Flower buds to 20 x 11mm, ovoid, or narrowly ovoid, smooth, bright red. Outer bracts to 20 x 10mm, ovate to ovate-oblong, inner ones spathulate, very densely hairy outside, glabrous except for the sparsely hairy base inside. Bracteoles 15–20 x *c*.0.6mm, linear, densely hairy. Inflorescence 4–10-flowered, an open umbel, the flowers half-hanging. Pedicels 10–24 x *c*.1.25mm, pink, slender, laxly scaly, without hairs. Calyx 3–4mm in diameter, obliquely disc-shaped, shallowly 5-lobed, densely scaly outside. **Corolla** 30–40 x *c*.30mm, tubular, bright glossy red; tube 25–27 x 6–8 x 6–8mm, cylindrical, straight, very prominently and deeply sulcate in the proximal ½, laxly or very laxly scaly especially towards the base outside, sub-densely very shortly hairy inside; lobes 10–14 x 9–11mm, broadly obovate or sub-circular, ⅓–½ overlapping, half-spreading. **Stamens** irregularly arranged, exserted to *c*.10mm; filaments linear, pink, densely sub-patently hairy in the proximal ⅔, glabrous distally; anthers 2–3 x *c*.1mm, obovate-oblong. Disc prominent, glabrous. **Ovary** 4–6 x 2–3mm, sub-ovoid-cylindrical, densely sub-patently hairy and scaly, tapering distally; style slender, pale pink, nearly as long as the stamens and depressed to the lower side of the tube, hairy in the proximal ½, sparsely, or not scaly; stigma globose. **Fruit** 20–30 x 5–6mm, cylindrical, slightly curved, sub-densely hairy and scaly. Seeds 3.8mm, without tails 0.8–1mm, the longest tail 1.8mm, the tails highly crimped.

Indonesia, Sulawesi (C), Mt Pokapindjang, Mt Rantemario. In mossy forest, 2000–3000m, locally common. *Fl.* May–June.

Recently introduced into cultivation in both the USA and the UK. It grows well and produces its bright red glossy flowers freely.

273. Rhododendron vanvuurenii J.J.Sm.

Bull. Jard. Bot. Buit. III, 1920. 1: 399, *t*.48.
Type: Rachmat 878, Nov. 1913. Celebes (C), G. Pelali (lectotype) (BO, L).
Derivation: Named after Louis van Vuuren, who led the expedition to Celebes (Sulawesi) on which this species was discovered.

Shrub or small tree to 4m. Twigs 2–5mm in diameter, rounded, at first covered with dense, scurfy, deeply stellate and sub-dendroid, reddish-brown scales, quickly glabrescent; internodes 3–15cm. **Leaves** mostly spirally arranged, sometimes in loose pseudowhorls. **Blade** 50–140 x 15–40mm, elliptic to narrowly elliptic or ovate elliptic; apex shortly acuminate, sub-acute; margin entire, slightly or not revolute; base broadly tapering to rounded; densely stellate-scaly on both sides at first, quickly glabrescent above and also below, the fragile, loose scales often only persisting close to the mid-vein or in other protected areas. **Scales** with the marginal zone deeply and narrowly stellately divided; centre depressed, sub-dendroid. Mid-vein narrowly impressed above, broader and very prominent beneath; lateral veins 6–9 per side, somewhat irregular, spreading at *c*.45°, straight below, curved-anastomosing before the edge, mostly faintly raised, reticulation obscure. **Petiole** 5–10 x 1–1.5mm, semi-rounded, densely scaly.

Flower buds *c*.40 x 20mm, narrowly ellipsoid, smooth, green. Bracts to 30 x 6mm, outer bracts ovate, becoming ovate-elliptic to broadly elliptic, innermost ones elliptic-spathulate, all densely shortly appressed-hairy and scaly outside, laxly hairy inside. Bracteoles to 22mm, filiform to linear-spathulate, laxly hairy. Inflorescence a complete umbel of 5–15 flowers. Pedicels 9–25 x *c*.1mm, densely, or more rarely laxly sub-patently hairy and scaly but the scales fragile tending to persist near the ends, occasionally only laxly to sub-densely scaly and without hairs. Calyx *c*.5mm in diameter, oblique, shortly obtusely 5-lobed, densely hairy and scaly. **Corolla** 40–60 x 50–55mm, funnel-shaped, orange to yellow, also occasionally white or pink; tube 25–35 x 6–8 x 13–20mm, obtusely 5-angled, and lobed at the base, laxly, minutely stellate-scaly outside, hairy inside; lobes 20–25 x 15–20mm, broadly obovate. **Stamens** exserted to *c*.10–12mm, sub-equal; filaments linear and hairy proximally, filiform and glabrous in the distal ½; anthers 3–5mm, oblong, base obtuse. Disc densely hairy on the upper margin only. **Ovary** 5–9 x 2–2.5mm, sub-cylindrical, densely long-hairy and scaly, tapering distally; style slender, equalling the stamens, densely hairy and scaly proximally, becoming less so distally, glabrous in the ultimate area; stigma thick-rounded.

Fruit 55–70 x 6–7mm, sub-fusiform-cylindric, sub-densely hairy and scaly.

Indonesia, Sulawesi (C), Mt Masawa, Mt Taburone, Mt Balapioe, Mt Pelali, Mt Rantemario and Mt Lompoh; Lore Lundu (Lake Kalimpaa). Terrestrial in light dry forest, grass and fern shrubberies, on rocks or bare slopes, locally common and gregarious, 600–1600m. *Fl.* June, July, Aug., Nov.; probably throughout the year.

The showy flowers vary in colour and are used for decoration by local people, but it is also known to be poisonous to livestock and sometimes actively removed (Binney 2003). Collected as living material by Craven and Brown in 2002 and being grown in Canberra. A white form has flowered in New Zealand; the coloured forms have the potential to be really good horticultural plants.

274. Rhododendron stresemannii J.J.Sm.
Fedde Rep. 1932. 30: 166.
Type: Stresemann 1, May 1911. Moluccas, Ceram (W), Ora Mts, 1000m (L).
Derivation: Named after the collector, Erwin Stresemann, a German ornithologist.

Shrub. Twigs 2–3mm in diameter, rounded, brown, sub-densely covered with appressed scales at first, laxly so later. **Leaves** 3–5 together in pseudowhorls. **Blade** 85–100 x 42–53mm, ovate- or elliptic; apex shortly acutely acuminate; margin flat; base cordate with rounded lobes; glabrescent above when mature and then covered with minute black pits, laxly to sub-densely scaly beneath. **Scales** small, marginal zone sub-stellately lobed; centre impressed, finally glabrescent beneath also, leaving dark pitted spots. Mid-vein flat, broad proximally, narrower and slightly impressed for the distal ⅓ above; below as large as the petiole proximally, obtusely prominent; lateral veins 7–8 per side, spreading, inarching before the margin, slightly impressed above and raised beneath, reticulation inconspicuous. **Petiole** 5–6 x *c.*2mm, flattened, scaly.

Inflorescence *c.*7-flowered. Pedicels 24–27 x *c.*1mm, laxly sub-stellately scaly with flat scales and minute white hairs. Calyx *c.*4mm in diameter, oblique, disc-shaped, obscurely lobed, fleshy, outside scaly and with short, fine hairs. **Corolla** 40–45mm, tubular-funnel-shaped, slightly oblique, dark-red; tube 20–23 x 5–6 x 12–15mm, glabrous outside, practically so inside, base dilated and 5-lobed; lobes 20–23 x 15–18mm, obovate-spathulate. **Stamens** sub-equal, 24–28mm; filaments linear, with sparse, long, spreading hairs in the proximal ⅓, glabrous distally; anthers *c.*3 x 1mm, oblong. Disc low, hairy, except for the

base. **Ovary** 6–7 x *c.*3mm, sub-ovoid-cylindrical, densely covered with white, forwardly directed hairs, which cover small scales, abruptly contracted distally; style *c.*20mm, thick, hairy at the base; stigma thick, rounded.

Indonesia, Maluku, Ora Mts. On steep limestone ridge in *Rhododendron* copse with a few high *Casuarina, c.*1000m. *Fl.* May.

Known only from the type collection. Never cultivated.

275. Rhododendron impositum J.J.Sm.
Fedde Rep. 1937. 68: 201.
Type: Kjellberg 4149. Indonesia, Sulawesi, Enrekang, Bukit Pokapindjang (S, E).
Derivation: Latin – *impositus* – placed upon, alluding to the abrupt junction between ovary and style in this species.

Shrub or small tree to 4m. Twigs rounded, *c.*5mm in diameter, young parts with pale brown scales, quickly glabrescent; internodes 4–5cm, shorter than the leafy area. Lateral buds conspicuous, spherical. **Leaves** loosely spirally arranged. **Blade** 40–100 x 25–55mm, broadly elliptic to obovate or ovate; apex shortly and abruptly acutely acuminate, rarely obtuse; margin entire although finely crenulate by impressed scales if viewed with a lens, narrowly cartilaginous, often broadly revolute; base broadly tapering to rounded, sometimes sub-cordate. Initially densely scaly on both sides, the scales often touching each other on the upper side, glabrescent and remaining minutely pitted above, densely to sparsely scaly beneath. **Scales** mostly transparent or pale brown with small darker centres, sub-stellate, slightly impressed. Mid-vein broad, but quickly tapering, raised above in the proximal ½ and more weakly raised below for *c.*¾ of its length; lateral veins 4–9 per side spreading at an angle of *c.*45°, high-ascending, curved-anastomosing before the margin, slightly raised and often minutely grooved above, smooth beneath, reticulation obscure above, moderately visible beneath. **Petiole** 5–10 x 4–5mm, robust, silvery scaly initially, without a groove, becoming rugulose when dry.

Flower buds to 50 x 23mm, ovate or narrowly ovate, with an acute apex, smooth with all the bracts appressed, green flushed with red. Bracts ovate, obovate to spathulate, appressed hairy outside and with small pale brown scales in a central band, glabrous inside, fringed with brown often dendroid scales. Bracteoles 17–22mm, filamentous but slightly broadened upwards, laxly sub-appressed hairy throughout. Inflorescence an open umbel of 6–15 flowers, these horizontally displayed or half-hanging, not or only very faintly scented. Pedicels 25–50 x *c.*2.5mm,

Debbie White

Rhododendron impositum.

densely to sparsely stellate-scaly, strongly flushed pink. Calyx *c*.4mm in diameter, obliquely disc-shaped, normally shortly lobed or occasionally with one or two elongate deflexed teeth up to 5 x 1mm, scaly outside, glabrous inside. **Corolla** 35–45 x 35–55mm, funnel-shaped, white, pink or red; tube *c*.24 x 5 x 10mm, white, straight, glabrous or sparsely scaly outside, hairy in the basal ½ inside; lobes 23–26 x 17–22mm, reflexed to the horizontal, overlapping ½–⅔, rounded or slightly retuse. **Stamens** at first clustered together in the mouth of the flower, becoming a little exserted (to *c*.3mm), strongly incurved; filaments linear and laxly hairy below, narrower to filiform and glabrous upwards, white; anthers cream, oblong, 3–3.5 x *c*.1mm, the base obtuse or minutely apiculate. Disc glabrous, or hairy at the upper margin. **Ovary** 5–7 x 2.5–3mm, ovoid-conical or somewhat cylindric-obovoid, densely covered with appressed, long white, (brown on drying), hairs which cover the scales, abruptly contracted distally; style slender, white, lying on the lower side of the tube but curving upwards, with some sparse hairs at the very base or glabrous, remaining distinctly shorter than the stamens; stigma globose, deeply lobed, white. **Fruit** 25–30 x 7–8mm, cylindrical, densely and persistently short brown hairy, the outer layer peeling irregularly and then the valves reflexing and the placentae weakly splayed and breaking away at the base. Seeds 3–3.5mm, without tails *c*.0.9mm, the longest tail 1.2–1.5mm.

Indonesia, Sulawesi (SW Central), Latimodjong Range. In low forest, 2400–3000m. *Fl*. June & Feb. in the wild.

First introduced into cultivation by Martin J. Sands to Kew in 1969 where it flowered in February 1980 and was painted for *Curtis's Botanical Magazine* by Cristabel King (Hunt 1981b). Reintroduced in 1998 to New Zealand by David Binney and in 2000 to Edinburgh by Smith and Galloway where it first flowered in May 2004. All the introductions to cultivation appear to have been white-flowered. At present this species appears to be slow growing but the large truss of flowers is impressive and it will be interesting to see how this species performs as more plants come to maturity.

276. Rhododendron buruense J.J.Sm.
Fedde Rep. 1932. 30: 168.
Type: Stresemann 38. Moluccas, Buru, G. Toga, 1900m (L).
Derivation: Named after the island from which it was collected.

Synonym: *R. lompohense* var. *grandifolium* J.J.Sm., Fedde Rep. 1932. 30: 169.

Shrub to 3.5m. Twigs 3–4mm in diameter, rounded, laxly appressed-scaly, often whitish; internodes 3–16cm. **Leaves** 4–6 together in lax pseudowhorls with 1–2 additional ones on the internodes. **Blade** 70–160 x 4–75mm, ovate-elliptic to elliptic; apex shortly acuminate, obtuse; margin very slightly or not revolute; base broadly tapering, sometimes nearly rounded, glabrescent above when mature, laxly persistently scaly beneath. **Scales** small, marginal zone variously lobed, fragile and disappearing, leaving dark spots; centre small, shallowly impressed. Mid-vein grooved above, obtusely prominent beneath; lateral veins 8–12 per side, straight below, curved and anastomosing before the margin, minutely impressed above, distinctly raised beneath, reticulation lax, faintly prominent beneath. **Petiole** 10–20 x 1.5–2mm, slightly flattened, rugose, often white.

Inflorescence 7–10-flowered. Pedicels 20–33 x *c*.1mm, laxly scaly and hairy. Calyx 4–5mm in diameter, obliquely disc-shaped, scaly and with some short hairs outside. **Corolla** 40–50mm, broadly funnel-shaped, tubular below, white; tube 20–26 x 5–6 x 7–8mm, distinctly 5-pouched at the base, straight, with some scattered scales, (almost glabrous), outside, shortly hairy inside; lobes 12–23 x 12–20mm, spreading, broadly obovate to sub-circular. **Stamens** unequal, exserted to *c*.6mm; filaments linear and sub-densely patently hairy in the proximal ⅓–½, filiform and glabrous distally; anthers 3–4 x 1mm, oblong, the base slightly thickened. Disc prominent, glabrous or shortly hairy on the upper margin. **Ovary** 6–7 x 2.5–3mm, sub-cylindrical, densely covered with sub-patent short hairs which cover small scales, abruptly contracted distally; style densely hairy and laxly scaly to the lower ⅔, glabrous distally; stigma rounded.

Indonesia, Maluku, Buru, Mt Toga and between Leksula and Mnges Waen. Terrestrial on loamy limestone soil, 1290–1900m. *Fl.* Feb., April.

Not recollected recently, and never cultivated.

---

277. Rhododendron toxopei J.J.Sm.
Fedde Rep. 1932. 30: 168.
Type: Toxopeus Ab. *s.n.*, 6 Feb. 1922. Moluccas, Buru, Kunturun, 1075m (BO, L, fragment).
Derivation: Named after the collector, L.J. Toxopeus, a Dutch entomologist who led the Boeroe Expedition on which this species was collected.

Shrub. Twigs 2–3mm in diameter, rounded, initially scaly, early glabrescent; internodes 2–4cm. **Leaves** *c*.4 together in pseudowhorls. **Blade** 62–100 x 20–46mm, broadly elliptic to ovate; apex gradually and shortly acuminate, broadly acute; margin very narrowly or not revolute; base very broadly tapering to rounded, slightly unequal, glabrescent above, the scale attachments remaining recognisable as numerous minute, blackish pits; laxly sub-persistently scaly beneath. **Scales** small, marginal zone variously and shortly lobed, but later circular as the marginal zone disintegrates; centre slightly impressed. Mid-vein broadened proximally, wrinkled lengthwise, flat or a little impressed above, distinctly prominent beneath; lateral veins 10–12 per side, curved, spreading, inarching near the margin, clearly visible, impressed above, slightly

raised beneath, reticulation dense, finely prominent beneath only. **Petiole** 7–11 x 2–2.5mm, rugose, flattened.

Bracteoles linear, glabrous. Inflorescence *c*.8-flowered. Pedicels 17–21 x 1mm, sparsely scaly at both ends. Calyx 3–4mm in diameter, oblique, disc-shaped, obtusely angled or very shortly lobed, almost glabrous. **Corolla** 45–50mm, tubular-funnel-shaped, pale pink; tube 20–24 x 5–6 x *c*.10mm, glabrous outside, laxly hairy in the lower ⅔ inside; lobes 23–27 x 10–16mm, spathulate, spreading. **Stamens** shortly exserted; filaments linear and sub-densely patently hairy proximally, narrower and glabrous in the distal ½; anthers *c*.4 x 1mm, oblong, curved, base obtuse. Disc prominent, shortly hairy. **Ovary** 6–8 x *c*.2.5mm, sub-cylindrical, densely hairy, with numerous minute scales clearly visible between the hairs, gradually tapering distally; style slender, hairy in the lower ¼–⅓, *c*.20mm; stigma *c*.2.5mm in diameter, rounded.

Indonesia, Maluku, Buru, near Kunturun, in moorland peat with *Sphagnum*, 1075m. *Fl.* Feb.

Not recently recollected and never cultivated.

---

278. Rhododendron lompohense J.J.Sm.
Bull. Jard. Bot. Buit. III, 1920. 1: 402, *t*.50.
Type: Rachmat 943, Dec. 1913. Indonesia, Celebes (C), G. Lompoh (BO, L).
Derivation: Lompoh – the mountain on which this was found; *ense* – the place of origin.

Shrub. Twigs rounded, 2.5–4mm in diameter, densely scaly when young, becoming glabrescent; internodes 2.8–9cm. **Leaves** 4–7 together in pseudowhorls. **Blade** 70–105 x 28–44mm, elliptic-ovate; apex gradually acuminate, broadly acute; margin flat or weakly revolute; base rounded; initially densely scaly on both sides, glabrescent above at maturity, persistently and sub-densely scaly beneath. **Scales** flat, small marginal zone irregularly lobed; centre slightly impressed. Mid-vein broad proximally, flat above, strongly raised beneath; lateral veins 8–12 per side, spreading, straight at the base, curved upwards and inarching distally; a little raised above, more distinctly so beneath, reticulation indistinct above, densely and minutely prominent beneath. **Petiole** 6–12 x 1.5–2mm.

Bracts to 30 x 15mm, circular to broadly ovate-acuminate, scaly and shortly hairy near the base outside, scaly on the margins, becoming glabrescent but remaining a little rough. Inflorescence a 6-flowered umbel. Pedicels 12–16mm, thick, sub-densely scaly, without hairs. Calyx *c*.3mm in diameter, inconspicuous, disc-shaped, oblique. **Corolla** tubular below, funnel-shaped distally, white; tube 26–31 x 4–5 x 5–6mm, strongly 5-lobed at the base, glabrous outside, hairy inside; lobes *c.*15 x 12–13mm, obovate, half-spreading. **Stamens** somewhat exserted; filaments linear, densely hairy in the proximal ⅔, glabrous distally; anthers *c.*3 x 1mm, oblong, base obtuse. Disc glabrous below but with short white hairs on the upper margin. **Ovary** *c.*9 x 2mm, cylindrical-conical, 5-angled, appressed-hairy, the hairs covering scales, gradually tapering distally; style *c.*20mm, densely hairy and laxly scaly in the proximal ⅔, glabrous distally; stigma large, 5-lobed.

Indonesia, Sulawesi (C), Mt Lompoh. *Fl.* Dec.

An intermediate specimen between this and *R. bloembergenii* at Kew casts doubt on the distinctness of this species. Never cultivated.

279. Rhododendron subulosum Sleumer

Reinwardtia 1960. 5: 143.
Type: Lam 1906, 5 Nov. 1920. New Guinea (NW), Doormantop, *c.*1450m (BO, L).
Derivation: Latin – *subula* – a fine sharp point; *osum* – full or marked development. Alluding to the narrow 'awl-shaped' leaves.

Weak shrub to 30cm. Twigs to 1.5mm in diameter, at first sub-densely covered with star-shaped and shortly stalked, fragile scales, becoming glabrescent but remaining minutely warty near the tips; internodes 1–4cm. **Leaves** 3–5 together in pseudowhorls. **Blade** 35–80 x 1.5–3mm, linear; apex acute or nearly so; margin slightly revolute; base narrowly tapering; glabrescent above, more persistently scaly beneath. **Scales** the marginal zone angular or obtusely lobed; centre much darker and hardly impressed. Mid-vein distinctly impressed above, prominent beneath, red; lateral veins obscure. **Petiole** 2–4 x 0.5mm, rounded, red, much darker than the lamina in dry specimens.

Bracts to 20 x 5mm; outer bracts subulate, inner ones, ovate-subulate, innermost ones ovate, abruptly subulate-acuminate in the upper ½ and acute, glabrous outside, reddish. Inflorescence 1–3-flowered. Pedicels 5–7mm, slender, densely stellate-scaly. Calyx *c.*2mm in diameter, obliquely disc-shaped, margin membranaceous, shortly 5-lobed, scaly outside. **Corolla** *c.*15mm, probably red; tube *c.*10 x 2–3 x 3–4mm, cylindrical, glabrous inside and out; lobes *c.*4 x 4mm, broadly obovate-sub-circular. **Stamens** 14–16mm; filaments filiform, glabrous; anthers sub-globose, *c.*1.5mm in diameter. Disc prominent, glabrous. **Ovary** *c.*3 x 1.3mm, sub-cylindrical, densely stellately scaly, abruptly contracted distally; style 5–6mm,

slender, glabrous; stigma club-shaped. **Fruit** *c.*15 x 4mm, valves reflexed and twisted. Seeds narrow, tailed at both ends, 2–3mm.

Indonesia, New Guinea (W), Doormantop, epiphytic on ridge at 1450m. *Fl.* Nov.

Known only from the type collection; never cultivated.

280. Rhododendron glabriflorum J.J.Sm.

Med. Rijksherb. 1915. 25: 6.
Type: Pulle 1030. New Guinea, SW, top of the Wichmann Mts, 3100m (L).
Derivation: Latin – *glaber* – glabrous; *florum* – flower. The flowers being without hairs or scales.

Shrub to 3m. Twigs 4–7mm in diameter, rounded, at first sub-densely scaly, often white, minutely warty; internodes 4–5cm. **Leaves** 6–7 together in lax pseudowhorls. **Blade** 60–90 x 20–40mm, elliptic; apex broadly acute to obtuse; margin narrowly cartilaginous, narrowly revolute; base tapering or broadly tapering; glabrescent and rugulose above; laxly to sub-densely scaly beneath. **Scales** flat, thin, marginal zone relatively large, irregularly sub-stellately lobed; centre minute, dark, hardly impressed. Mid-vein narrow and deeply impressed above, strong and prominent proximally beneath, gradually narrowing distally; lateral veins 8–10 per side; lowest from the base, steeply ascending, anastomosing, slightly impressed above, raised beneath, reticulation dense, not or faintly impressed above, distinct and prominent beneath. **Petiole** 8–12 x 20–25mm, grooved above, a little flattened, densely scaly.

Flower buds to 35 x 32mm, sub-spherical, smooth, pale translucent whitish-green. Bracts to 28 x 25mm,

Rhododendron glabriflorum.

broadly ovate, the apices rounded, densely scaly along a broad middle line outside, with fragile scales on the margins, without hairs, glabrous inside. Inflorescence 9–22-flowered, at first tightly clustered, later a lax open one-sided umbel. Pedicels 11–18mm, thick, very densely scaly, without hairs. Calyx *c*.3.5mm in diameter, disc-shaped, but slightly oblique, obscurely and very obtusely 5-lobed, scaly outside. **Corolla** 45–52mm, tubular-campanulate, fleshy, yellow (possibly sometimes red); tube *c*.35 x 6–7 x *c*.15mm, straight, glabrous inside and out; lobes 14–20 x 14–20mm, spreading, sub-circular. **Stamens** *c*.35mm, regularly arranged around the mouth of the corolla, not exserted; filaments linear, glabrous; anthers 4–4.5 x 2–2.2mm, obovoid, narrowed towards the base, each cell ending in a narrow apiculus. Disc glabrous. **Ovary** 6–7 x *c*.3mm, sub-ovoid-conical, densely scaly, abruptly narrowed distally; style *c*.20mm, scaly up to the proximal ⅓, glabrous distally; stigma rounded, yellow, deflexed to the side of the mouth, not exserted. Seeds 4.3–4.5mm, without tails 0.9–1.2mm, the longest tail 2.1mm.

Indonesia, New Guinea (W), Wichmann Mts; Lake Habbema near Wamena, 3000–3200m. *Fl.* Jan.–Feb.

Recollected and grown from seed by Hansjörg and Margot Brentel in 2003. It has not yet flowered in cultivation but promises to be a really stunning addition to vireya collections. The flowers were originally described as red but all the plants recently collected have been yellow. It is possible that the colour recorded on the type collection is an error and that this species always has yellow flowers.

281. Rhododendron pachycarpon Sleumer

Reinwardtia 1960. 5: 186.
Type: Clemens 41390, 18–20 May 1940. New Guinea (NE), Morobe District, Rawlinson Range, 2135–3655m (A, E, L, fragment).
Derivation: Greek – *pachy* – thick; *carpo* – relating to the fruit. Alluding to the thick broad fruits of this species.

Shrub to 2m. Twigs 4–6mm in diameter, rounded, or weakly 4-angled, with conspicuous, spherical lateral buds, laxly scaly at first, glabrescent and whitish later; internodes 3–6cm. **Leaves** spiral or *c*.3 together in loose pseudo-whorls. **Blade** 40–80 x 25–45mm, obovate; apex obtuse or rounded, sometimes slightly emarginate; margin narrowly cartilaginous, flat, sub-serrulate-crenulate; base tapering; glabrescent above at maturity, sub-densely scaly below. **Scales** small, rounded, large, marginal zone variously angular or lobed; centre minute and distinctly impressed.

Rhododendron pachycarpon.

Mid-vein narrowly impressed above, thick, flattened and obtusely prominent beneath; lateral veins 6–8 per side, lower two from near the base, the others at an angle of *c*.45°, all high-ascending and curved-anastomosing before the margin, slightly impressed above and raised beneath, reticulation inconspicuous. **Petiole** 3–6 x 2.5–3.5mm, grooved above, scaly.

Bracts to 18 x 13mm, ovate, laxly scaly outside, apices obtuse or rounded; inner bracts obovate-spathulate, to 25 x 10mm. Bracteoles to 30mm, linear, glabrous. Inflorescence 3–9-flowered open umbels. Pedicels 9–16 x *c*.1mm, densely scaly, without hairs. Calyx *c*.5mm in diameter, disc-shaped, scaly outside. **Corolla** 45–70mm, half-hanging, tubular or narrowly funnel-shaped, greenish-yellow to light yellow; tube 30–45 x 6–10 x 10–12mm, straight, fleshy, glabrous inside and out, sulcate at the base; lobes *c*.15 x 15mm, sub-circular, erect to half-spreading. **Stamens** unequal, not exserted; filaments glabrous, linear; anthers 2.5–4 x 1.5–2.5mm, brown, broadly obovoid-cordate, distinctly narrow towards the base and ending in a small basal appendage. Disc prominent, glabrous. **Ovary** *c*.6 x 3.5–4mm, ovoid-cylindrical, densely covered with reddish-brown scales, abruptly contracted distally; style *c*.30mm, sub-densely scaly at the base, glabrous distally; stigma globose, shortly 5-lobed. **Fruit** 20–25 x 8–9mm, obliquely obovoid-cylindrical, scaly.

Papua New Guinea, Madang District, Finisterre Mts; Morobe District, Saruwaket Mts, Mt Enggan, Rawlinson Mts. In open sub-alpine forest often in limestone areas, 2135–3655m. *Fl.* March–Aug.

Introduced into cultivation in 1986 to the Royal Botanic Garden Edinburgh but subsequently lost and not known to be cultivated elsewhere. Van Royen & Kores (1982) note the similarity of this species to *R. brassii* and suggest that they may have to be united if intermediates are collected. At present *R. brassii* may be distinguished by its acutely, or sub-obtusely pointed, smaller leaves (up to 50 x 27mm).

282. Rhododendron pachystigma Sleumer

Blumea 1963. 12 : 110.

Type: Versteegh BW 10464, 25 June 1961. New Guinea (C), Balim R. valley, Wiligimaan, *c.*1800m (L, CANB).

Derivation: Greek – *pachy* – thick; *stigma* – the stigma. Alluding to the large stigma of this species.

Shrub to 1.5m. Twigs 3–5mm in diameter, semi-rounded, densely scaly at first, older parts often whitish; internodes 4–13cm. **Leaves** in loose pseudowhorls. **Blade** 50–90 x 25–50mm, obovate or elliptic-obovate; apex rounded, sometimes slightly retuse; margin entire, revolute proximally, otherwise flat; base broadly tapering; at first densely scaly on both sides, quickly glabrescent both above and below. **Scales** small, reddish, sessile and flat, fragile, marginal zone irregularly sub-stellately lobed; centre minute, hardly or not impressed. Mid-vein thick and grooved proximally above, as strong as the petiole proximally beneath; lateral veins 8–9 per side, straight, at an angle of *c.*45° and sub-parallel proximally, curved and joining before the margin, faintly impressed above, a little raised beneath, reticulation obscure. **Petiole** 10–25 x *c.*2mm, densely scaly initially.

Immature bracts laxly scaly outside, without hairs. Bracteoles to 15mm, filiform, glabrous. Inflorescence 2–3-flowered. Pedicels 8–14 x 1.5–2mm, with dense, small brown scales and fine short hairs in the proximal ¾, distally more densely and with longer hairs. Calyx 6–7mm in diameter, an oblique rim with irregular spreading, triangular lobes, up to 4mm, hairy and scaly along the margin. **Corolla** 70–80mm, funnel-shaped, deeply 6–7-lobed, light orange on the tube outside, white at the lobes, fleshy; tube 25–30 x 8–9 x 20–25mm, straight, pouched at the base, glabrous outside, densely white-hairy proximally inside; lobes 45–50 x 25–35mm, obovate-spathulate, spreading. **Stamens** 12–14, unequal, exserted; filaments linear, proximally densely white-hairy, filiform and glabrous distally; anthers *c.*8 x 1–1.2mm, hinged, elongate-oblong, base obtuse. Disc prominent, densely white-hairy on the margin. **Ovary** 8–9 x *c.*4mm, thickly cylindrical, with reddish-brown stellate scales, without hairs, tapering distally; style *c.*40 x 1–1.5mm, glabrous; stigma rounded, 6–9mm in diameter, with 6–7 thick, sub-globular lobes.

Indonesia, New Guinea (W), Balim R. Valley near Wiligimaan. Young secondary forest, terrestrial on stony clay, *c.*1800m. *Fl.* June.

Known only from the type collection and never cultivated.

283. Rhododendron angulatum J.J.Sm.

Bull. Jard. Bot. Buit. II, 1912. 8 : 50.

Type: De Kock 177. New Guinea (SW), Mt Goliath, Juliana Range, 1500m (BO).

Derivation: Latin – *angulatus* – angled, alluding to the distinctly angled corolla.

Shrub to *c.*75cm. Twigs robust, rounded, laxly scaly. **Leaves** *c.*5 in pseudowhorls. **Blade** 110–180 x 35–58mm, ovate-elliptic; apex gradually long-acuminate, acute; margin flat or weakly recurved; base obtuse, rounded or slightly cordate; glabrescent above with age, sub-densely scaly beneath. **Scales** stellately lobed in the marginal zone; centre impressed, leaving minute pits when scales are gone. Mid-vein narrowly grooved above, thick and obtusely prominent beneath in the proximal part; lateral veins 12–15 per side, ascending, anastomosing, very slightly raised or impressed above, obscure beneath; reticulation obscure. **Petiole** 10–12 x 3mm, strong, grooved above, flattened, transversely rugulose, minutely scaly.

Inflorescence of *c.*6 flowers. Pedicels 40–50 x *c.*2.5mm in diameter, laxly minutely scaly, more densely so below the calyx, without hairs. Calyx *c.*4.5mm in diameter, oblique, obtusely and inconspicuously 5-angular, ciliate. **Corolla** 55–66mm, funnel-shaped, lobed in the upper ⅔, red, fleshy; tube *c.*20 x 8 x 9mm, sparsely minutely scaly outside, laxly hairy inside, distinctly 5-angular or pouched at the base outside, deeply 5-grooved lengthwise in the proximal part inside, the ribs extending upwards to the middle of the corolla lobes; lobes 35–40 x *c.*20mm, sub-ovate-elliptic, obtuse, spreading. **Stamens** nearly as long as the corolla; filaments linear and shortly patently hairy below, narrower and glabrous distally; anthers 5.5–6 x *c.*1mm, linear-oblong, obtuse at the base. Disc prominent, practically glabrous. **Ovary** *c.*10 x 3mm, conical-cylindrical, densely covered with thick, nearly round, scales, no hairs, tapering distally; style *c.*48mm, scaly and sparsely minutely hairy, or nearly papillose, at the base, glabrous distally; stigma thick-rounded.

Indonesia, New Guinea (W), Oranje Mts, Mt Goliath, common terrestrial in shady peat swamps at 1500m. *Fl.* April.

Known only from the type collection; never cultivated.

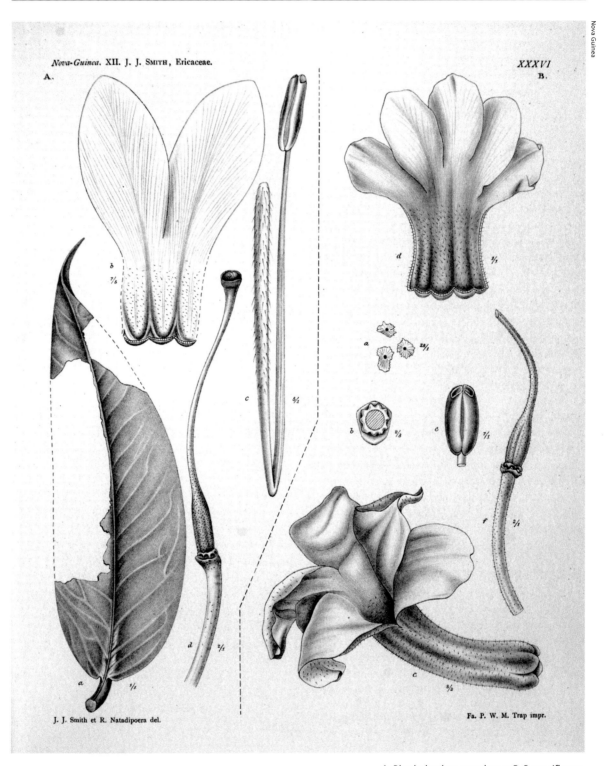

Nova-Guinea. XII. J. J. Smith, Ericaceae.

XXXVI

J. J. Smith et R. Natadipoera del.

Fa. P. W. M. Trap impr.

A, *Rhododendron angulatum*; B, *R. curviflorum*.

284. Rhododendron alticola Sleumer

Reinwardtia 1960. 5: 164.

Type: Brass 4332, May–July 1933. New Guinea (SE), Mt Albert Edward, Central District, *c.*3600m (L, BO).

Derivation: Latin – *alte* – high up; *cola* – dweller. Alluding to the high altitude at which it was found.

Shrub or small tree to 3m. Twigs 2–4mm in diameter, appressed scaly at first, quickly glabrescent and smooth; internodes 1.5–2.5cm. **Leaves** 3–6 together in tight pseudowhorls. **Blade** 30–90 x 12–25mm, obovate or elliptic; apex broadly tapering, obtuse to rounded, sometimes apiculate with a terminal gland; margin narrowly cartilaginous, slightly revolute; base broadly tapering, rarely rounded; densely scaly at first on both sides, glabrescent above, laxly persistently scaly beneath. **Scales** small, marginal zone very thin, quickly disappearing, lobed; centre minute, dark and impressed. Mid-vein deeply impressed above, prominently raised below, often becoming broader near the base; lateral veins 6–8 per side, irregularly curved-upwards, anastomosing, faintly impressed in old leaves above, a little prominent beneath, reticulation lax, visible beneath only. **Petiole** 5–9 x 1–1.5mm, grooved above, flat, laxly scaly.

Bracts to 12 x 5mm, ovate-acuminate, laxly scaly outside or glabrous. Bracteoles *c.*10mm, filiform below, slightly dilated distally. Inflorescence 3–6-flowered open umbels, the flowers hanging. Pedicels 8–20mm, slender, laxly to sub-densely scaly. Calyx *c.*4mm in diameter, disc-shaped, irregularly and shortly 5-lobed, glabrous. **Corolla** 20–60mm, tubular-funnel-shaped, bright red; tube 18–50 x *c.*4 x 7–12mm, laxly scaly outside, glabrous inside or laxly hairy, tube slightly to distinctly curved; lobes 12–15 x 10–13mm, spreading, broadly obovate-spathulate, sometimes with a few scales outside. **Stamens** clustered on the upper side of the flower, at the mouth or exserted to 6mm; filaments linear and laxly papillose-hairy proximally for *c.*⅔, glabrous and filiform distally; anthers *c.*2.5 x 1mm, oblong. Disc very prominent, glabrous. **Ovary** *c.*7 x 2mm, obovoid-cylindrical, densely scaly, but without hairs, gradually tapering distally; style slender, scaly at the base, glabrous distally, becoming slightly exserted; stigma thick, rounded. **Fruit** 40–50 x 5–7mm, sub-cylindrical, slightly curved, sub-densely scaly. Seeds 3mm, without tails *c.*0.8mm, the longest tail 1.3mm.

Papua New Guinea, Fatima River, Spreader Divide, Bulldog Road, Mt Kaindi, Mt Missim, Mt Albert Edward, Mt Victoria, Mt Yule, 2600–3600m. *Fl.* April–July.

Kores & van Royen (1982) regarded *R. alticola* as a widespread and polymorphic species, transferring it to

Rhododendron alticola.

series *Javanica* (of Sleumer 1966) as the leaves of many collections exceed 40mm in length. It is certainly very similar to *R. culminicola* and differs from that variable species in that the ovary is said always to be without hairs. Material in Edinburgh has been cultivated under this name since 1967; this was collected by Michael Black (no. 81) from the Fatima River area and agrees with the informal description in Kores & van Royen (1982) of the form from that area, except that it has hairs on the inside of the corolla tube. Hairs inside the corolla have also been found on specimens from Mt Yule and the Bulldog Road – these may represent a different taxon. A Woods specimen (3064A) from the Mt Albert Edward area has sparse hairs on the ovary also and may represent a hybrid. The hybrid *R. alticola* x *R. spondylophyllum* was collected by Paul Kores from Mt Victoria and it would be surprising if hybrids with *R. culminicola* did not occur. High altitude species tend to be the most difficult to cultivate. The 'Black' collection grows well, with beautiful deep red flowers which are for some time held semi-erect due to the persistence of the bracts at the base in a collarette. It flowers once a year in late spring in Edinburgh and can look most attractive.

285. Rhododendron sayeri Sleumer

Reinwardtia 1960. 5: 188.

Type: Sayer *s.n.*, Aug. 1887. New Guinea (SE), Central District, Mt Obree, Howers Lake, *c.*2135m (MEL, L).

Derivation: Named after the collector, W.A. Sayer, an Australian naturalist.

Shrub, *c.*1.8m. Twigs 1.5–3mm in diameter, rounded, at first densely reddish-stellate-scaly, quickly glabrescent and smooth; internodes 3–7cm. **Leaves** 3–5 together in pseudowhorls. **Blade** 35–65 x 20–40mm, broadly elliptic, sometimes obovate-elliptic or obovate; apex broadly tapering, obtuse to rounded; margin slightly revolute proximally or quite flat; base rounded or broadly tapering; glabrescent above, sub-persistently densely reddish-scaly beneath. **Scales** small, deeply stellately lobed in the marginal zone; centre minute, dark and very slightly impressed. Mid-vein slightly impressed above, markedly prominent proximally beneath; lateral veins 6–8 per side, irregular, spreading, anastomosing before the margin, somewhat impressed or raised above, prominent beneath, reticulation distinct. **Petiole** 4–7 x 1–1.5mm, flattened and grooved above, scaly.

Bracts to 10 x 8mm, ovate to obovate, obtuse, glabrous outside, very shortly fringed with scales. Bracteoles to 12 x 0.5–1.5mm, linear below, sub-spathulate distally. Inflorescence 1–4-flowered. Pedicels 15–23 x *c.*0.6mm, densely reddish-stellate-scaly. Calyx obliquely disc-shaped, irregularly 5-toothed, with triangular sub-acute teeth 0.5–3mm, scaly at the base outside, spreading. **Corolla** 40–45mm, tubular below, sub-oblique; tube *c.*30 x 4–5 x 7–8mm, curved, lobed at the base, laxly stellate-scaly outside, laxly and long patent-hairy inside; lobes 9–13 x 9–13mm, sub-circular. **Stamens** as long as the corolla tube; filaments linear, laxly patently long-hairy in the proximal ⅔; anthers 2.5 x *c.*1.2mm, sub-obovoid obtuse at the base. Disc prominent, sparsely hairy on the upper margin. **Ovary** 5–6 x 2–2.5mm, sub-cylindrical, abruptly narrowed distally, densely stellate-scaly, without hairs; style as long as the stamens, laxly stellate-scaly in the proximal ⅓, glabrous distally; stigma thick-rounded.

Papua New Guinea, Central District, Mt Obree, growing in profusion on brink of precipitous cliffs at Howers Lake, *c.*2135m. *Fl.* Aug.

Known only from the type collection; never cultivated.

286. Rhododendron aurigeranum Sleumer

Reinwardtia 1960. 5: 214.
Type: Lam 7753, 4 Oct. 1954. Papua New Guinea, Morobe District, Lae–Bulolo road above Patop Creek (L, CANB, SING).
Derivation: Latin – *aurum* – gold, alluding to the gold-mining area in which it was found to be abundant.

Ssp. **aurigeranum**

Shrub or tree to 4m. Twigs 2–4mm in diameter, green, a little flattened and densely brown scaly; internodes 5–15cm. **Leaves** 4–7 in dense pseudowhorls at the upper 1–2 nodes and with 2–4 much smaller leaves associated. **Blade** 70–140 x 30–60mm, elliptic or broadly elliptic; apex

acute, sub-acute or shortly acuminate; margin entire, slightly revolute; base tapering into the petiole, glabrescent above when mature, densely scaly beneath when young, less so in mature leaves. **Scales** small, brown, fragile, sessile or very shortly stalked, marginal zone irregularly and deeply stellate-incised; centre often extended into a short stalk, not or hardly impressed. Mid-vein broad at the base, narrowed and slightly impressed above, thick and prominent beneath; lateral veins 6–8 per side, rather straight below, curved and obscurely anastomosing before the edge, nearly smooth above, slightly raised beneath, reticulation inconspicuous on both sides. **Petiole** 7–12 x 3–5mm, grooved above, scaly.

Flower buds to 34 x 6mm, broadly ovate, with the outermost bracts narrowly triangular, spreading and reflexing, as a collarette inside the foliage leaves, tips of the main bracts shortly triangular, spreading and reflexing, green, scaly. Bracts 15–20 x 4–10mm, ovate-acuminate, apex blunt or very shortly contracted into a sharp point, densely scaly on both sides at the apex, glabrous elsewhere, inner bracts obovate-elliptic to sub-spathulate, glabrous outside, all initially with scales along the margins. Bracteoles 10–15 x 1–2mm, linear-sub-spathulate. Inflorescence an 8–14-flowered complete umbel. Pedicels thick, 20–50 x 1–1.5mm, sub-densely stellately scaly, very laxly though distinctly shortly hairy. Calyx disc-shaped, wavy, *c.*3mm in diameter. **Corolla** funnel-shaped, orange or orange-yellow initially, fading to yellow, 60–80mm, laxly stellately scaly outside, laxly hairy in the lower ½ of the tube inside; tube 30–40 x 4–5 x 10–15mm, straight, markedly 5-angled; lobes 20–30 x 18–25mm, obovate, spreading. **Stamens** sub-equal, exserted to 15mm; filaments linear, sub-densely hairy in the proximal ⅓, glabrous distally; anthers 3.5–4 x *c.*1.3mm, broadly oblong, base obtuse. Disc very prominent, white-hairy at the

Rhododendron aurigeranum ssp. *aurigeranum*.

upper margin. **Ovary** *c.*10 x 2.5mm, sub-conical-cylindrical, densely and shortly hairy and scaly, tapering distally; style densely hairy and scaly for the proximal ¾, densely and exclusively scaly for the subsequent *c.*2mm, glabrous for the upper *c.*10mm; stigma thick-globose and deeply 5-lobed. **Fruit** elongate-cylindrical, shortly tapering at the base, more gradually so at the apex, hairy and scaly, often curved, 60–100 x 5–6mm, the valves becoming twisted. Seeds 7–12mm including the tails.

Papua New Guinea, Morobe District, Mt Misim, Wagau, Mapos and in the Wau–Bulolo area. Occasionally in floating immature peat swamps in forest clearings, generally in dry grassy or shrubby hillsides together with *Grevillea papuana* Diels. or on schistes or steep rock, 915–1740m, locally common. *Fl.* Feb.–Oct., *fr.* July–Sept.

The flower buds are very distinctive in this species, with short reflexed tips which are scaly both inside and out. Long established in cultivation for its very showy flowers, it remains one of the best 'yellows'. Introduced into Australia in the 1950s by an unknown person (Craven 1973) and in 1965 by Mrs H. Johnston. Seed was sent to Kew by Tom Lelliot from Australia in 1966 where it was grown and painted for *Curtis's Botanical Magazine* (Hunt 1979). Michael Black reported seeing 'two large bushes smothered in flower – glowing on a hillside near Bulolo. The visual impact was almost overpowering' (Black 1969). He and Paddy Woods introduced this species to the UK in 1968 from where it was distributed. Reported to be cultivated in the town of Wau (Papua New Guinea) by Sleumer (1973). Parent of many fine hybrids.

Ssp. **hirsutum** Argent
Folia Malaysiana 2003. 4(2): 120.
Type: Woods & Black 1121, 12 May 1968. Papua New Guinea, Morobe District, above Garaina, Saureli Bubu to Arabuka (E, A, L, LAE, SYD).
Derivation: Latin – *hirsutus* – covered with long stiff hairs, alluding to the hairs on the outside of the corolla.

Differing from the type subspecies by having both white hairs and scales on the outside of the corolla tube.

It was growing at *c.*1520m in grassland above lower montane forest and appears to be well established as two collections were made 12 years apart from similar localities. The flowers are described as yellow in one collection but with a yellow tube and salmon pink lobes in the other. Remaining colour in one of the herbarium sheets clearly indicates a yellow tube and pink or orange lobes. Not known to have been cultivated.

287. **Rhododendron laetum** J.J.Sm.
Nova Guinea 1914. 12: 139, *t.*35.
Type: Gjellerup 1136, 20 April 1912. New Guinea, NW, Arfak Mts, Angi Lakes, 1800–2135m (BO, A, L).
Derivation: Latin – *laetus* – cheerful or bright, an allusion to the bright flowers.

Synonym: *R. uliginosum* J.J.Sm., Nova Guinea 1914. 12: 136, *t.*33.

Shrub to 3m. Twigs 3–6mm in diameter, sub-angular to rounded, laxly scaly; internodes 2.5–16cm. **Leaves** 4–6 together in tight pseudowhorls. **Blade** 40–95 x 25–53mm, broadly elliptic or sub-ovate-elliptic; apex very shortly acuminate or sub-cuspidate, more rarely broadly tapering, sub-acute or obtuse to rounded; margin entire, flat; base rounded, rarely broadly tapering or sub-cordate, dark green and glossy above, paler beneath, sub-densely scaly on both sides at first becoming glabrescent above, more persistently and laxly scaly beneath but eventually glabrescent there also but spotted from the persistent bases. **Scales** small, marginal zone irregularly sub-stellately lobed; centre minute, shallowly impressed. Mid-vein narrow and grooved above, as wide as the petiole and obtusely prominent proximally beneath; lateral veins 6–8 per side, spreading, obscurely anastomosing before the margin, faintly impressed, or inconspicuous above, slightly to distinctly raised beneath, reticulation lax, a little prominent beneath, or invisible. **Petiole** 2–7 x 2–3mm, grooved above, laxly scaly.

Flower buds *c.*45 x 25mm, ovoid, smooth, green. Outer bracts 35–50 x 15–20mm, rounded to ovate, apiculate or obtuse, with short appressed hairs initially outside, glabrescent and smooth finally; inner ones ovate-oblong to sub-spathulate, glabrous or nearly so. Bracteoles filiform, sub-spathulate at apex, very laxly hairy or glabrous, *c.*40 x 0.5–1mm. Inflorescence an open to full umbel of 5–12 horizontal or semi-erect flowers. Pedicels 25–55 x *c.*1mm, sub-densely stellately scaly and minutely hairy. Calyx obliquely disc-shaped, shortly obtusely 5-lobed, scaly and minutely hairy outside, *c.*4mm in diameter. **Corolla** 50–70 x 50–60mm, broadly funnel-shaped, fleshy, sometimes fragrant, pure deep yellow first, becoming suffused with red or orange with age; tube 28–35 x 8–12 x 15–20mm, straight, distinctly 5-angular and often pouched at the base, laxly stellately scaly and sometimes with some hairs at the base outside, shortly hairy inside; lobes broadly obovate, 20–30 x 15–22mm. **Stamens** dimorphic, exserted 5–10mm, irregularly arranged but with a tendency to be spread around the lower ½; filaments linear, sub-densely short-hairy in the proximal ½, narrower and glabrous

Ken Grant

Rhododendron laetum.

distally; anthers 4–5 x *c.*1.5mm, broad-oblong, base obtuse. Disc prominent, hairy on the upper margin other- wise glabrous. **Ovary** 6–8 x 2.5–3mm, sub-cylindrical, sub-abruptly contracted distally, white-hairy, the hairs covering minute scales; style thick, hairy at the base, laxly hairy above to the lower ½–⅔, usually without scales, gla- brous distally, mostly lying close to the lower side of the flower; stigma thick-globose, green, becoming exserted to 10mm. **Fruit** sub-fusiform or cylindrical, curved, densely hairy and scaly, 35–55 x *c.*0.8mm. Seeds 4–6mm including the tails.

Indonesia, New Guinea (W), Anggi Lakes area in Arfak Mts. Terrestrial on the edge of primary and secondary forest, in open marsh and in swamps at the edge of lakes, 1800–2300m. *Fl.* Jan.– Dec.

Introduced into cultivation from material distrib- uted by Professor Sleumer in 1967. It grows well, is one of the best yellows and is fairly heat tolerant. Sleumer comments that this species is 'Much related to *R. zoelleri'*. It differs mainly in the pure yellow colour of the flowers, at least when they first open, and the shorter pedicels. The anther length difference breaks down when one considers the forms of *R. zoelleri* found at the eastern end of New Guinea.

288. Rhododendron christi Foerster
Fedde Rep. 1914. 13: 222.
Type: Keysser *s.n.*, Oct. 1912. New Guinea (NE), Morobe District, Mt Saruwaged, Bolan, 2400–3000m (B†); ibid. Key- sser 176 (BM, neotype).
Derivation: Named after Konrad H. Christ, Swiss fern specialist who was professor of botany at Basel.

Synonyms:
R. christi var. *loniceroides* Schltr., Bot. Jahr. 1918. 55: 155.
R. aff. wentianum Stonor, Rhod. Yearbook 1951. 6: 50, *f.*54.
R. christii Foerster *orth. var.*, Chamberlain et al., The Genus Rhododendron 1996. 17, 103.

Small shrub to 1.2m. Twigs 1.5–2mm in diameter, rounded, laxly scaly, becoming glabrescent, smooth; internodes 4–11cm. **Leaves** 2–4 together in tight pseudo- whorls at the upper 2 or 3 nodes, sub-sessile. **Blade** 40– 110 x 25–65mm, ovate; apex shortly or long-acuminate; margin entire, flat, slightly recurved when dry; base cord- ate to rounded; laxly scaly initially, glabrescent above, persistently scaly beneath. **Scales** flat, small, the thin marginal zone large, irregularly and deeply divided; cen- tre darker, small, slightly impressed. Mid-vein narrow and deeply grooved above, strong and prominent beneath;

lateral veins 4–6 per side, curved-ascending and join-ing, weakly or not impressed above, slightly prominent beneath; densely reticulate. **Petiole** 1–2 x 1–2mm, flat-tened, scaly.

Flower buds to 20 x 12mm, ovate, smooth. Bracts to 20 x 8mm, outer ovate, the apex abruptly subulate or mucronate, very shortly appressed hairy outside and with a few scales distally in the central area; inner ones ovate, apiculate or obtuse, appressed-hairy in the upper part outside, margin minutely irregular and with fragile scales. Bracteoles to 20 x 5mm, linear below, spathulate towards the apex, laxly hairy, often with a few irregular teeth apically and with a few stalked scales on the mar-gins. Inflorescence an open umbel of 2–5 flowers. Pedi-cels 15–25 x *c.*2mm, red, densely patently hairy, with few or no scales. Calyx 3–4mm in diameter, disc-shaped, densely hairy outside, with 5 short, obtuse ciliate lobes or occasionally longer up to 5mm. **Corolla** 30–45 x 25–35mm, tubular below, expanded and oblique at the lobes, bicoloured with a yellow tube and orange lobes, without scent; tube 20–25 x 6–7 x 12–18mm, yellow at the base or throughout, orange distally, densely long-hairy both inside and out, without scales; lobes 13–18 x 10–18mm, obovate-spathulate or sub-circular, hairy out-side. **Stamens** exserted to 12mm, clustered on the upper side, unequal; filaments linear, densely patently hairy in the proximal ¼–⅓, glabrous distally; anthers 2–2.5mm, obovoid, apex truncate. Disc densely hairy in the upper ½. **Ovary** 5–7 x 2.5–3mm, cylindrical, continuous with the style, shortly hairy; style as long as the stamens, densely hairy to nearly the top; stigma oblique, rounded or weakly lobed. **Fruit** 30–35 x *c.*5mm, sub-cylindrical, widest in the upper ⅓, slightly curved, laxly hairy, valves thin, becoming twisted. Seeds 6–7mm, without tails 0.8mm, the longest tail 3.5mm.

Papua New Guinea, New Guinea (E), Mt Saruwaged and vicinity; Eastern, Western and Southern Highlands; Simbu District; Wharton Range; Finisterre Mts (Madang District). **Indonesia**, New Guinea (W), Wamena R.; Ibele valley. Mostly epiphytic in mossy forest and on grassland tree-ferns, or terrestrial in open forest or rock faces on cliffs, 1200–3000m. *Fl.* May–Jan.

The records from near Wamena are a surprising exten-sion to the range of this species which had previously been known only from Papua New Guinea; some of these plants differ in having broadly tapering leaf bases but others are quite typical with cordate bases. Those with tapering leaf bases could be hybrids with *R. curviflorum*. It is reported hybridising with *R. beyerinckianum* (Kores & van Royen 1982), these hybrids having uniformly pink

flowers (see *R.* x *schoddei*). This species has been in cultiva-tion for many years. Captain Stonor collected this species in 1949 and had it painted in Edinburgh but it was obvi-ously done from the herbarium collection and Stonor's recollections of what it looked like in the wild. The earli-est collection in Edinburgh still growing is that made by Paddy Woods from the Mt Albert Edward area in 1968. D.B. Stanton introduced this species to Australia in 1971 and there have been several introductions subsequently. It flowered at Kew in January 1983 and was figured in the *Kew Magazine* (Halliday 1985). Several different forms are in cultivation. In Edinburgh we have a large-leafed and a small-leafed form. These forms remain true to type grow-ing side by side and Graham Snell reports growing at least two different forms in Queensland. In cultivation it has a sprawling habit and is more suitable as a hanging basket plant or grown on blocks of tree-fern trunk, but it flowers well at irregular times, often in the dark months of winter. The bright, hairy, bicoloured flowers look extremely hand-some against the dark-green glossy foliage.

289. Rhododendron villosulum J.J.Sm.
Med. Rijksherb. 1915. 25: 5.
Type: Pulle 589, 2 Dec. 1912. New Guinea (W), Hellwig Mts, 2500m (BO, lectotype, L).
Derivation: Latin – *villosus* – with long soft hairs; *ulum* – diminutive. Alluding to the shortly hairy flowers.

Erect shrub to *c.*1m. Twigs rounded, 2–4mm in diam-eter, at first rough with fragile, brown stellate scales, quickly glabrescent and smooth; internodes 4–16cm. **Leaves** 3–5 together in tight pseudowhorls, often with 1 or 2 much smaller leaves. **Blade** 40–70 x 25–40mm, ovate or broadly elliptic; apex shortly to long acuminate, characteristically decurved, obtuse to acute; apex often slightly mucron-ate with the protruding mid-vein; margin entire, broadly recurved; base broadly tapering to rounded; glabrescent above at maturity; persistently and sub-densely scaly beneath. **Scales** flat, marginal zone variously and irregu-larly sub-stellately lobed; centre dark, slightly impressed. Mid-vein narrow, strongly impressed above, strong and very prominent beneath; lateral veins 4–8 per side, irregu-lar, spreading and anastomosing, faintly or not impressed above and weakly raised beneath, reticulation dense and prominent on both sides. **Petiole** 5–7 x 2–3mm, grooved above, densely scaly, held at 45° to the stem.

Flower buds to 25 x 14mm, ovoid, smooth with the bract tips appressed, pale green or pink; outer bracts broadly ovate, apex shortly subulate or apiculate, with a few scales along the midline near the apex and along the margins otherwise glabrous; inner ones to 25 x 10mm, ovate to obovate-spathulate, obtuse, densely appressed-hairy outside, the innermost narrowly spathulate. Bract-eoles to 20 x 1mm, linear, hairy throughout and with a few scales at the apex. Inflorescence 2–5 flowers in an open umbel, half-hanging to hanging. Pedicels 12–29 x 1.25–2mm, red, densely patently hairy and sparsely scaly. Calyx *c.*4mm in diameter, disc-shaped, obliquely 5-angular, densely hairy. **Corolla** 35–40 x 35–40mm, tubular below, expanded distally, oblique, dark to light red, without scent; tube 20–26 x 7–8 x 10–13mm, curved, laxly to densely, shortly patently hairy all over, outside and at the base inside; lobes 15–16 x 14–18mm, sub-circular, slightly retuse, spreading horizontally, overlapping ½–⅔, hairy outside in the basal central region. **Stamens** tightly clustered on the upper side of the mouth, exserted to 8mm; filaments red, filiform, hairy in the proximal ⅓–½; anthers 2–3 x 1–1.5mm, brown. Disc densely hairy at the upper margin only. **Ovary** 5–6 x 2.5–3mm, sub-ovoid-cylindrical, densely patently white hairy, the hairs covering scales, gradually tapering distally; style white patent-hairy almost to the top, without scales, held on the upper side of the corolla tube; stigma broad, distinctly lobed. **Fruit** 25–35 x 4–5mm, fusiform, persistently hairy. Seeds 5mm, without tails 0.9mm, the longest tail 2.4mm.

Indonesia, New Guinea (W), Wissel Lakes region, Oranje and Nassau Mts, Mt Trichora. **Papua New Guinea**, Eastern Highlands. Epiphytic in moss forest, 2000–3000m.

Sleumer (1966) noted that this species is 'much related to *R. christi*, distinguished mainly by the non-cordate, more distinctly petioled leaves'. In cultivation it has a much more erect habit than *R. christi* and has uniformly red, not bicoloured, flowers but it is certainly very similar. Introduced into cultivation by Paul Smith in 1992, it grows vigorously and flowers usually in August.

290. Rhododendron curviflorum J.J.Sm.

Bull. Jard. Bot. Buit. II, 1912. 8: 50.

Type: Cocq d'Armandville 233, Dec. 1912. New Guinea (SW), Johannes Keyts Mts (BOG†). Neotype: Brass 11215. New Guinea (W), Bele R., *c.*18km NE of Lake Habbema (L).

Derivation: Latin – *curvi* – curved; *florum* – with flowers. Alluding to the curved flowers.

Shrub to 2.5m. Twigs semi-rounded, 2.5–4mm in diameter, tips sub-densely sub-stellately scaly, older parts glabrescent; internodes 4–17cm. **Leaves** 4–7 together in tight pseudowhorls. **Blade** 100–130 x 50–70mm, ovate

to ovate-elliptic; apex shortly apiculate, broadly acute; margin entire or slightly sinuate, flat or weakly recurved; base rounded or occasionally broadly tapering, dark green and glabrescent above, sub-densely brown-scaly beneath. **Scales** dense, small, irregularly and deeply stellate; centre dark brown, finally blackish, faintly impressed but with occasional long-stalked scales from the flat surface. Mid-vein narrowly impressed above, strongly raised below; lateral veins 5–8 per side, spreading at a wide angle, straight below, curved upwards and anastomosing, slightly impressed above, prominent beneath, reticulation dense, faintly impressed or raised above, much more distinct and prominent beneath at least when dry. **Petiole** 7–17 x 2–3mm, grooved above, densely brown scaly but becoming glabrescent.

Flower buds to 40 x 25mm, ovate, smooth with all the bracts appressed, dull pale green except for brown marks at the apices of the bracts, minutely hairy outside and with areas of small brown scales towards the bract apices. Outermost bracts broadly ovate and apiculate; central bracts to 20mm, hemispherical to broadly ovate, shortly emarginate, minutely hairy outside, scaly distally near the apex and fringed with small brown scales, glabrous inside; innermost bracts spathulate. Bracteoles 36 x *c.*1mm, linear becoming slightly broadened towards the apex, white hairy throughout and with slender, brown, long-stalked scales near the apex. Inflorescence an open 5–11-flowered umbel, the flowers mostly horizontal but the mouth facing downwards due to the curvature of the tube. Pedicels 20–35 x 2–3mm, densely shortly hairy, without scales, except for a few distally just under the calyx. Calyx 4–6mm in diameter, disc-shaped, patently white hairy outside but fringed on the margin with scales, the lobes *c.*1mm, shortly triangular, obtuse. **Corolla** 60–65 x 40–50mm, tubular, oblique, unequally 5-lobed, yellow (or mauve; see note below), without scent; tube 35–40 x 9–11 x 11–17mm, cylindrical but sulcate and 5-angled

Rhododendron curviflorum (see also p.297).

in the proximal ½, slightly compressed laterally in the upper ½, densely shortly patent hairy outside and without scales, hairy in the lower ½ of the tube inside; lobes 22–25 x 18–20mm, hairy outside except near the margins, all lobes spreading to the horizontal, the three upper lobes overlapping to halfway, the two lower lobes not overlapping. **Stamens** clustered on the upper side of the mouth, exserted to *c*.12mm; filaments linear, densely to sparsely patently hairy below, more slender and glabrous towards the top; anthers *c*.4 x 1.8–2mm, brown, broadly oblong, the base obtuse. Disc prominent, deeply lobed, densely hairy above, less so below. **Ovary** 6–7 x 4–5mm, elongate-conical, tapering distally, densely hairy with slightly forward-pointing white hairs; style deep within the tube on the flower opening, becoming exserted to 15mm, green, densely patently hairy nearly to the top; stigma thick, lobed, reddish-brown. **Fruit** 40–50 x 6–7mm, fusiform, often curved and longitudinally grooved. Seeds 60–70mm, without tails *c*.1mm, the longest tail 3.8mm.

Indonesia, New Guinea (W), Keyts Mts and Bele R. around Pabililo and the Ibele valley, near Wamena. Epiphytic or terrestrial in secondary forest or landslips, 1900–2700m. *Fl.* Nov.–Dec.

Sleumer (1966) notes: 'The size of the corolla in Smith's description of 1914 differs from that in *t*.36 B; unfortunately, the type material, conserved in formaline at Bogor, is practically useless. I have drawn a new description of it based on good and apparently conspecific specimens (BRASS 11215 AND 11536) from the Bele R., which have yellow flowers instead of "lilac" as said of the type material, which came from the Keyts Mts. Also the description of the perulae [bracts], not given in the original diagnosis, is made after the BRASS collections'. I have followed Sleumer's interpretation of this species; the anatomical characters certainly agree closely with Smith's descriptions but I cannot find the discrepancy in measurements that he mentions. *Rhododendron curviflorum* was common around the village of Pabilio above Wamena and was all very uniform yellow in colour. It would be odd for this species to occur in the lilac mentioned in the original type description. This may have been an error in the field descriptions or we may still be dealing with two different species. Further collecting in the Keyts Mts will need to be done to resolve this.

Introduced into cultivation in Edinburgh in 1992 from where it has been distributed. It grows well but is of a rather lanky habit; however, the bright yellow, softly hairy flowers are produced in great profusion in the dark days of December in Edinburgh (occasionally at other times), which makes it well worth growing.

291. **Rhododendron milleri** *sp. nov.*

Type: Argent, Johns & Utteridge 00619, 11 Nov. 2000. Indonesia, Papua, Darnell ridge, Timika to Tembagapura road, *c*.4°16′S 137°01′E, 1600m (BO, E, K).

Derivation: Named after Mr H.A. Miller, consultant for the Freeport Mining Company, who did so much to aid the Kew expeditions to the mining area where this species was found.

R. flavoviridi J.J.Sm. similis et ab omnibus aliis speciebus in sectione *Vireya* cognitis colore floris pallide viridi distincta. A *R. flavoviridi* J.J.Sm. staminibus in facie abaxiali (haud adaxiali) corollae deorsum (haud sursum) curvatae fasciculatis, pedicellis et pilis et squamis indutis, ovario multo longiore, foliis tenuioribus et forsan ramulis glaucis recedit.

A much-branched, erect, terrestrial shrub or small tree to 2m. Twigs rounded, glaucous-white with tiny brown scales, becoming glabrescent, 2–4mm in diameter; internodes 3.5–10cm. **Leaves** 3–6 together in tight pseudo-whorls at the upper 1–3 nodes. **Blade** 40–85 x 18–33mm, elliptic; apex broadly acute to obtuse; margin narrowly revolute; base tapering; initially scaly on both sides, above the scales persisting as very small dark brown points, more persistently and sub-densely scaly beneath. **Scales** very varied in both size and morphology, the smallest mostly circular, pale brown and flat, the larger ones stellately lobed and dark brown and distinctly raised. Midvein narrow and impressed above, grooved proximally for *c*.10mm, beneath strongly raised almost to the apex; lateral veins 5–8 per side, spreading at *c*.45°, or somewhat obscure, irregular, anastomosing, slightly depressed above and raised beneath in dried leaves, reticulation indistinct. **Petiole** 6–10 x 1–2mm, not or hardly grooved above when fresh, densely scaly.

Inner bracts spathulate with marginal scales on long stalks otherwise glabrous. Bracteoles to 22 x *c*.1mm, linear to linear-spathulate, glabrous, irregularly toothed at the apex. Umbels 2–6-flowered, the flowers held semi-erect. Pedicels moderately densely covered with pale brown appressed, sub-stellate scales and minutely patently hairy, 15–17 x *c*.2mm. Calyx obliquely disc-shaped, very shortly and obtusely 5-lobed, 4–5mm in diameter, with brown scales and minutely hairy. **Corolla** 45–50 x *c*.35mm; tube 30–35 x 6–8 x 12–14mm, sub-cylindrical, sulcate at the base, distinctly downwardly curved, laxly but obscurely sub-stellate-scaly outside and sparsely to densely hairy in the proximal ½, shortly hairy inside, the lobes 15 x 12mm, sub-circular, spreading horizontally or sometimes a little reflexed, overlapping to *c*.½ their length, with a few very

Rhododendron milleri.

small scales near the base outside. **Stamens** exserted to 10mm, clustered around the style on the upper side of the mouth of the corolla; filaments green, filiform, sub-densely hairy in the proximal ½, laxly hairy almost to the top; anthers *c.*3.5 x 1.3mm, pale brown, oblong, curved, the base obtuse. Disc densely hairy. Ovary *c.*7 x 3mm, sub-cylindric-conical, base tapering, apex tapering distally, green but densely covered with silvery, sub-patent hairs and scales; style at first with the stigma just below the anthers in the mouth of the flower, later exserted to *c.*10mm, hairy and scaly in the proximal ⅔, glabrous above; stigma globose, *c.*3mm in diameter.

Indonesia, New Guinea (W), Darnell ridge, Timika to Tembagapura road. Known only from the type collection. Open sub-alpine shrubbery by roadside, *c.*1600m. *Fl.* Nov.

This species is superficially similar to *R. flavoviride* J.J.Sm. as it has the same distinctive pale green flowers. However, the flowers are curved downwards not upwards and are horizontally disposed not hanging, and the stamens are clustered on the upper side of the mouth of the corolla not the lower. Other small differences are that the stems are pale glaucous, not dark green, the leaves are narrower and always with tapering bases never the rounded bases which are common in *R. flavoviride*, the petioles are without grooves for the greater part of their length not clearly grooved as in *R. flavoviride*, the pedicels and calyx are distinctly hairy, not scaly only, and the corolla often has hairs outside as well as within. The scales of this new species are also distinctive in the great variation in size and shape and their dark brown colour; the scales in *R. flavoviride* are more uniform and paler and mostly translucent.

Flowering for the first time in cultivation at the Royal Botanic Garden Edinburgh in July 2005, this was only a newly rooted cutting and it is too early to assess its horticultural potential.

292. Rhododendron macgregoriae F.Muell.

J. Bot. 1891. 29: 177.

Type: Bedford *s.n.*, 1891. New Guinea (E), Mt Yule, top, *c.*3350m (MEL, BM, K).

Derivation: Named after Lady MacGregor, wife of the former Administrator of New Guinea and Lieutenant Governor of Papua, explorer and collector of natural history objects who promoted the expedition on which this species was first collected.

Synonyms:
R. hansemanni Warb., Bot. Jahr. 1892. 16: 26.
R. vonroemeri Koord., Nova Guinea 1912. 8: 879, *t.*155.
R. lauterbachianum Foerster, Fedde Rep. 1914. 13: 224.
R. calceolarioides Wernham, Trans. Linn. Soc. London, II, Bot. 1916. 9.
R. gorumense Schltr., Bot. Jahr. 1917. 55: 142.

Shrub or tree to 15m. Twigs 2–4mm in diameter, rounded, sparsely scaly, quickly glabrescent; internodes 2–10cm. **Leaves** 3–7 together in tight pseudowhorls. **Blade** 40–140 x 25–50mm, elliptic, ovate-elliptic, or obovate-elliptic; apex shortly acuminate, acute or obtuse to rounded; margin entire, flat or weakly and narrowly revolute; base tapering to broadly tapering, laxly scaly and quickly glabrescent above; laxly to sub-densely scaly below. **Scales** rounded to weakly sub-stellately lobed, flat, with a broad margin and small slightly impressed centre. Mid-vein narrowly impressed above, weakly to strongly raised below; lateral veins 4–10 per side, spreading at 45–90°, curving before the margin, minutely impressed above, and smooth to weakly raised below, reticulation obscure to faintly visible on both sides. **Petiole** 5–12mm, grooved above, scaly.

Flower buds to 15 x 12mm, spherical, often with an outer collarette of narrow subulate spreading or reflexed bracts, these often disappearing near maturity so that the bud is then smooth. Outer bracts ovate, inner ones sub-circular, obovate to spathulate with rounded or apiculate apices, all laxly scaly and minutely hairy outside and fringed with scales. Bracteoles to 15 x 1mm, linear to filiform, sub-spathulate distally, very laxly hairy or glabrous. Inflorescence of 5–15 flowers in a complete umbel. Pedicels 25–50 x *c.*1mm, slender, sparsely scaly, normally without hairs, but sometimes laxly covered with very fine, short hairs. Calyx 2–3mm in diameter, oblique, rounded, the lobes indistinct, margin often scaly. **Corolla** 10–25 x 20–30mm, shortly tubular or tubular-campanulate, light yellow to orange or yellow at the tube and/or centre, reddish orange at the lobes, variable in size, mostly scentless; tube 10–12 x 3–5 x 4–6mm, straight, 5-angular, lobed at

Rhododendron macgregoriae (yellow form).

Rhododendron macgregoriae (pink form).

the base, laxly scaly outside, densely hairy inside; lobes 12–20 x 8–14mm, broadly obovate-spathulate, laxly scaly outside, glabrous inside. **Stamens** strongly exserted to 15mm, spreading around the mouth of the flower, unequal; filaments linear and densely covered with spreading hairs in the proximal ½, glabrous and narrower distally; anthers 2.5–3.2 x *c*.1mm. Disc with thick lobes, mostly glabrous, rarely shortly hairy in the upper ½. **Ovary** *c*.4 x 1.8mm, elongate-conical, densely covered with sub-appressed hairs, which completely cover scales, tapering distally; style 10–15mm, densely to laxly hairy and scaly in the proximal ½, glabrous distally; stigma rounded to distinctly lobed. **Fruit** 35–45 x 3–5mm, fusiform, often slightly curved, strongly 5-ribbed, hairy and scaly. Seeds *c*.4mm including the long tail at both ends.

Indonesia and **Papua New Guinea**. Widespread over the whole mainland of New Guinea, common and locally abundant, sometimes colouring hillsides with its flowers, mostly terrestrial, occasionally epiphytic, both in primary mossy forest, secondary shrubberies and often persisting in anthropogenic grassland in dry sunny situations, 120–3000m. *Fl.* Jan.–Dec.

This species is well known to the local people in many places as poisonous to grazing animals and therefore it is often removed. A bizarre use was recorded by Clyde Smith (1984) who stated that the local people in the Western Highlands were mixing parts of *R. macgregoriae* with sweet potato and using this mixture to poison rats. He notes that the flowers are considered particularly poisonous. Natural hybrids are common, especially with *R. zoelleri*, the two species sometimes forming hybrid swarms in disturbed areas where the forest has been cleared. These hybrids have intermediate-sized flowers between those of the parents. Hybrids with longer tubes and scented flowers have been attributed to crossing with *R. herzogii*. Records of this species with pink flowers and corollas

which are glabrous inside are now referable to *R. glabrifilum*; plants with pink flowers and hairy corollas may be hybrids with that species but more careful observations are needed.

The first recorded introduction was from seed sent by Professor Sleumer from the hills above Kundiawa in 1961 to various botanic gardens. It flowered at Kew in 1964 from material sent from Longwood, possibly from this same introduction. Many introductions have been made since: Michael Black 1965, Lyn Craven and E. Wadell 1966 are recorded by Withers (1991). A variety of colours are now cultivated, from pure yellow to intense orange, pink and a bicoloured form with a yellow tube and red lobes. It is a very tough species, its low altitude distribution means it is more heat tolerant than most vireyas and it gives exceptional displays of flowers. The fact that it is so common in the wild means it is often looked down upon by collectors and growers but it deserves to be grown more widely, especially in tropical and sub-tropical areas where it can be grown outside.

293. **Rhododendron christianae** Sleumer
Reinwardtia 1960. 5: 211.

Type: Cruttwell 410, 8 May 1954. New Guinea (SE), Milne Bay District, Kanasura, *c*.775m (E, K, L).

Derivation: Named after Canon Cruttwell's mother Christian Cruttwell, who went out to New Guinea to work as a missionary at the age of 55 and remained there for some 25 years.

Shrub to 3m. Twigs 2–3mm in diameter, rounded, sparsely scaly when young; internodes 2–12cm. **Leaves** 3–5 together in tight pseudowhorls. **Blade** 40–75 x 30–45mm, broadly elliptic or sub-obovate-elliptic, apex abruptly and shortly or gradually acuminate, obtuse, sometimes rounded or slightly emarginate, terminal gland thick, not protruding; margin flat; base broadly tapering or tapering; laxly scaly on both sides when young, glabrescent above, persistently laxly scaly beneath. **Scales** small, marginal zone variously lobed; centre slightly impressed. Mid-vein slightly or faintly impressed above, bluntly prominent in the proximal ½ beneath; lateral veins 5–7 per side, spreading, divided and curved-anastomosing before the margin, obscure above, a little raised beneath, reticulation inconspicuous. **Petiole** 5–10 x 1–1.5mm, grooved above, somewhat rugose, glabrous.

Outer bracts to 15 x 8mm, ovate to obovate, innermost ones elliptic-spathulate, hairy on the outer middle line and at the apex, margin with fragile scales. Bracteoles *c.*15mm, linear-sub-spathulate to filiform, laxly hairy. Inflorescence 2–5-flowered, an open umbel. Pedicels 10–27 x *c.*1mm, densely, shortly hairy, laxly scaly at both ends. Calyx *c.*4mm in diameter, oblique, disc-shaped, shortly obtusely 5-lobed, scaly and hairy outside. **Corolla** tubular, yellow shading to orange, especially at the lobes, and yellow or green on the tube; tube 25–35 x 7–10 x 15–20mm, straight, the base lobed, sparsely scaly outside, laxly hairy in the proximal ⅓ inside; lobes 15–25 x *c.*20mm, broadly obovate or sub-circular. **Stamens** unequal, regularly arranged around the flower, short ones at or a little beyond the mouth, longer ones exserted to *c.*12mm; filaments linear, yellow, densely and very shortly hairy in the proximal ⅓, glabrous distally; anthers 3–5 x *c.*1mm, blackish-purple, narrow-oblong, base shortly biappendiculate. Disc slightly prominent, white-hairy on the upper margin. **Ovary** *c.*6 x 2.5mm, sub-cylindrical, abruptly contracted distally, white-hairy and scaly (scales hidden by the hairs); style 30–40mm, as long as the corolla tube, densely hairy and scaly proximally, becoming laxly so distally, glabrous for the 5–7mm below the stigma; stigma thick, 5-lobed. **Fruit** 30–34 x *c.*6mm, persistently appressed hairy, fusiform with longitudinal grooves.

Papua New Guinea, Milne Bay District, Daga country; Mt Simpson area, Mt Dayman area. Compact terrestrial shrubs on precipitous rock faces or cliffs, overhanging deep gorges, in full sun. Locally abundant, 600–1525m. *Fl.* May–Oct.

'When in flower (probably about June), it is a mass of orange and a conspicuous sight for miles, even from an aeroplane' (Cruttwell 1971). Introduced into cultivation by N.E.G. Cruttwell first in 1959 to Australia and the UK but also with a later introduction in 1967; he also had it growing in Goroka, Papua New Guinea in 1981. Introductions were also made by Paddy Woods (1971) and Paul Kores (1974). It grows as a lanky shrub, contrasting with the wild description of the plant as compact. It has good heat tolerance and has performed well in Queensland, Australia, and is the parent of many hybrids. The flowers are varied in colour, the best forms having a strong orange flush to the lobes with a yellow tube; poorer forms or perhaps the species growing in poor light conditions give greenish-yellow flowers with very little orange. The stems have been noted to swell and split in a very characteristic way in cultivation in Queensland and Edinburgh – it is not known whether this is just an odd condition or some disease but it does not appear to be passed to other plants in close proximity.

Rhododendron christianae.

294. Rhododendron rosendahlii Sleumer

Reinwardtia 1960. 5: 207.

Type: Rosendahl BW 3254, 9 Sept. 1955. New Guinea (W), Wissel Lake, Ulida, c.1800m (L).

Derivation: Named after the collector, M. Rosendahl, who collected for the Forest Service at Hollandia (now Jayapura).

Erect shrub, c.1.5m. Twigs 1.5–2mm in diameter, laxly sub-stellately scaly when young; internodes 1.5–10cm. **Leaves** 3–6 together in tight pseudowhorls, often with 1–2 much smaller leaves. **Blade** 50–105 x 25–50mm, ovate to ovate-elliptic; apex often long-acuminate, acute, obtuse, sometimes almost rounded and minutely emarginate; margin entire, narrowly revolute; base rounded to slightly cordate, glabrescent above, laxly to sub-densely scaly beneath. **Scales** variable in size; margin sub-stellately lobed, transparent and fragile; centre minute, impressed. Mid-vein narrowly impressed above, strongly raised beneath; lateral veins 6–8 per side, wide-spreading, curved-anastomosing before the margin, slightly raised above and beneath or almost inconspicuous, reticulation obscure. **Petiole** 1–4 x 1.5–2mm, grooved above.

Flower buds to 27 x 17mm, minutely but densely hairy outside and laxly scaly. Bracts to 20 x 10mm, ovate, shortly acuminate, to obtuse, often splitting to appear emarginate, laxly scaly and minutely hairy outside, inner bracts obtuse, elliptic to sub-circular, densely hairy, not scaly. Bracteoles to 15 x 1mm, filiform below, sub-spathulate distally, densely hairy. Inflorescence an open umbel of 3–6 half-hanging to hanging, dark red flowers, without scent. Pedicels 25–38 x c.1mm, densely sub-patently hairy and very laxly or not scaly. Calyx c.3mm in diameter, disc-shaped, shortly obtusely angled, shortly hairy outside. **Corolla** 40–45 x 25–30mm, tubular-funnel-shaped; tube 25–35 x 5–6

Rhododendron rosendahlii.

x 12–14mm, slightly oblique, sparsely sub-stellately scaly outside, glabrous inside; lobes 10–12 x 8–10mm, broadly spathulate or sub-circular. **Stamens** unequal, exserted to c.8mm; filaments linear, glabrous. Disc hairy especially at the upper margin. **Ovary** 6–7 x c.2.5mm, sub-cylindrical, tapering distally, densely patently hairy, the hairs hiding minute scales; style patently white-hairy proximally becoming less densely so and glabrous for the distal 2–4mm; stigma thick rounded. **Fruit** 40–48 x 5–6mm, fusiform, the outer layer peeling irregularly, the valves spreading widely and twisting when dry, the placentae irregularly breaking away from the base. Seeds 5–7mm, without tails 0.7–0.8mm, the longest tail c.4mm, the tails slender and wavy.

Indonesia, New Guinea (W), Wissel Lakes region, Valentin Mts, and Mt Jaya (Carstensz). Terrestrial, in peaty swamps and on cliffs, epiphytic in sub-alpine shrubberies, 1380–2600m. *Fl.* Sept., Oct., Jan.

Introduced into cultivation in Edinburgh in 2000, it has yet to demonstrate its worth as a horticultural plant. The flowers are an extraordinarily dark red.

295. Rhododendron culminicola F.Muell.

Trans. R. Soc. Vict. n.s. 1889. 1(2): 23.

Type: MacGregor *s.n.*, 1889. New Guinea (E), Mt Victoria (MEL).

Derivation: Latin – *culmen* – summit; *cola* – inhabiting. Summit-dwelling.

Synonyms:

R. culminicolum F.Muell., Trans. R. Soc. Vict. n.s. 1889. 1(2): 23 (orthographic variant).

R. nodosum C.H.Wright, Kew Bull. 1899. 103.

R. keysseri Foerster, Fedde Rep. 1914. 13: 223.

R. angiense J.J.Sm. in Gibbs, Phyto. Fl. Arfak Mts, 1917. 169, *non* J.J.Sm. (1914).

R. convexum Sleumer, Reinwardtia 1960. 5: 218.

R. gregarium Sleumer, Reinwardtia 1960. 5: 221.

Var. **culminicola**

Shrub or tree to 8m. Twigs 2–5mm in diameter, scaly but early glabrescent; internodes 2–10cm. **Leaves** 3–7 together in tight pseudowhorls. **Blade** 25–80 x 1–45mm, elliptic, broadly elliptic, obovate or more rarely ovate; apex obtuse to rounded, sometimes abruptly sub-acuminate; margin revolute; base broadly tapering, rounded to sub-cordate; at first densely covered on both sides with flattish, pale scales, glabrescent above at maturity, laxly scaly

Rhododendron culminicola var. *culminicola*.

beneath. **Scales** small, flat, shallowly and irregularly lobed with a broad flange and small slightly impressed centre. Mid-vein narrowly impressed above, broadened, wrinkled, and prominent in the proximal part; lateral veins 4–8 per side, curved-spreading and indistinctly anastomosing before the margin, slightly impressed above, somewhat raised beneath, reticulation sub-dense, obscure above, slightly raised beneath. **Petiole** 2–9 x 1–3mm, grooved above, scaly.

Flower buds to 25 x 15mm, ovoid or broadly ovoid, smooth with all bracts appressed. Outer bracts sub-circular to ovate, sometimes with a short narrow acumen, inner ones ovate to obovate, laxly scaly and sometimes hairy at the base outside, glabrous or laxly to sub-densely hairy inside. Bracteoles filiform to linear, glabrous, to 20 x 3mm. Inflorescence 4–9 flowers in an open umbel, curving downwards. Pedicels 15–24 x *c.*1mm, laxly to sub-densely scaly, sometimes also hairy. Calyx obliquely disc-shaped, wavy, obtusely and shortly lobed, *c.*4mm in diameter, scaly outside, occasionally fringed with hairs. **Corolla** 35–45 x 12–25mm, obliquely tubular, red to purple, sometimes pink; tube 25–40 x 4–6 x 8–15mm, distinctly curved, laxly to sub-densely scaly outside, sparsely to sub-densely hairy in the lower part of the tube inside; lobes 8–18 x 8–15mm, broadly obovate to sub-circular, sub-erect or spreading, overlapping ⅓–⅔. **Stamens** sub-equal, not or only weakly exserted; filaments linear, laxly to sub-densely hairy in the lower ½, glabrous distally; anthers 2–3.5 x 1–1.5mm, obovate to broadly oblong, base often minutely apiculate. Disc prominent, shortly hairy at the upper margin. **Ovary** 5–7 x 2–3mm, sub-cylindrical, white or yellowish hairy, and densely (but obscurely) scaly, gradually tapering distally; style slender, mostly with some sparse hairs and scales at the base, rarely so up to the proximal ⅓, becoming exserted; stigma round. **Fruit** 25–40 x 6–8mm, sub-cylindrical, tapering at both ends, scaly and laxly hairy.

Indonesia and **Papua New Guinea**. Widespread on the island of New Guinea on the Main Range, from Mt Jaya (Carstensz) to the Southern and Western Highlands and in the Owen Stanley Range, also in the Mt Saruwaged–Rawlinson Range area. Low mossy forest or the margins of sub-alpine shrubberies, open slopes or summit vegetation, also found in alpine pasture, in both primary and secondary communities, often as part of the forest undergrowth, locally plentiful, 2400–4000m. *Fl.* Jan.–Dec.

Rhododendron culminicola is conceived here in the broad sense of Sleumer (1966) with the exception that the variety *nubicola* has been reinstated as a good species. Specimens from the upper montane forest (at the lower elevations from *c.*2400m) tend to have larger flowers and tapering leaf bases. Forms at higher elevations (3200–4000m) have smaller flowers and smaller, stiffer, short-petioled or sub-sessile leaves with rounded or sub-cordate bases. It is one of the small number of variable species which are distributed all over the mountainous part of New Guinea.

Var. **angiense** (J.J.Sm.) Sleumer
Blumea 1963. 12: 114.
Type: Gjellerup 1217. New Guinea (W), Arfak Mts, Anggi Lakes, 1900m (BO, L).
Derivation: Named after the lakes where the type specimen originated.

Synonym: *R. angiense* J.J.Sm., Nova Guinea 1914. 12(2): 133, *t.*30b.

Differs from var. *culminicola* in having smaller more rounded scales, corollas 25–35mm and smaller fruits, 4–5mm in diameter.

Indonesia, New Guinea (W), Vogelkop Peninsula, Arfak, Nettoti and Tohkiri Mts. **Papua New Guinea**, Star Mts, Tel Basin. In disturbed *Nothofagus/Tristania* forest or forest margins and open summit areas, 900–2300m, locally common, but often sterile, mostly terrestrial. *Fl. fr.* Jan.–Dec.

296. Rhododendron arfakianum Becc.
Malesia 1878. I: 201.
Type: Beccari 5792. New Guinea, W Arfak Mts, Hatam (FI).
Derivation: Named after the mountains from where this species was described.

Synonym: *R. undulaticalyx* J.J.Sm. in Gibbs, Phyto. Fl. Arfak Mts. 1917. 168.

Shrub to 2.5m. Twigs 2–3mm in diameter, sparsely scaly and papillose-hairy in the youngest parts, becoming glabrescent; internodes 2–10cm. **Leaves** 3–5 together in tight pseudowhorls. **Blade** 40–100 x 15–45mm, obovate-elliptic; apex obtusely tapering or nearly rounded; margin entire, slightly revolute in dry specimens; base tapering or broadly tapering, glabrescent above when mature, sub-persistently and sub-densely to laxly scaly beneath. **Scales** small, with the marginal zone irregularly lobed and a minute dark centre, slightly impressed, each scale surrounded by a dark halo, also very finely punctate by minute emergences of the epidermis beneath. Mid-vein slightly depressed and with minute, papillose, spreading hairs above, as wide as the petiole and obtusely prominent in the lower part beneath; lateral veins 6–10 per side, spreading, obscurely inarched at the margin, slightly prominent on both sides, reticulation inconspicuous. **Petiole** 6–12 x 1–1.5mm, with minute, papillose, spreading hairs above.

Outer bracts to 15 x 8mm, ovate, obtuse, inner ones oblong-obovate, laxly scaly and minutely hairy outside, becoming glabrescent, fringed with scales. Bracteoles to 23 x 0.5–4mm, filiform below, spathulate distally, papillose. Inflorescence a 4–10-flowered umbel. Pedicels 8–12mm, slender, laxly to sub-densely scaly and finely patently hairy. Calyx *c.*3mm in diameter, disc-shaped, membranous, sub-obtusely and very shortly unequally lobed, wavy, spreading to reflexed, glabrous outside, distinctly ciliate. **Corolla** 25–35mm, tubular below, expanded upwards, oblique, deep pink; tube 15–20 x 3–4 x *c.*5mm, sub-cylindrical, straight or slightly curved, glabrous outside, laxly hairy inside; lobes 7–10 x 5–8mm, sub-erect, or somewhat spreading, obovate-spathulate. **Stamens** spreading all round the mouth, unequal, the longest as long as the corolla; filaments linear and laxly hairy below, filiform and glabrous distally; anthers 2mm, obovate. Disc shortly hairy. **Ovary** *c.*4 x 2mm, sub-cylindrical, densely short-hairy and minutely scaly (the scales covered by hairs), abruptly contracted distally; style slender, sometimes with some hairs at the very base, equalling the stamens in length; stigma club-shaped, obconical, oblique. **Fruit** (sub-mature) 20 x 4mm, fusiform, densely hairy, surmounted by the glabrous, 20mm style.

Indonesia, New Guinea (W), Arfak and Nettoti Mts. At the edge of forest, 1200–2135m, locally common, epiphytic or more rarely terrestrial. *Fl.* Jan.–Dec.

Said to be close to *R. angiense* J.J.Sm. but differing in the shortly hairy pedicels and non-scaly corolla. Introduced into cultivation from seed sent by Professor Sleumer to the Australian Rhododendron Society in 1962. Doubtfully still in cultivation. A plant cultivated under this name in Bremen differs in that the corolla is much larger

than described, scaly outside and with hairs on the style almost the whole length. It is probably a hybrid but it does have the minute hairs on the petiole and mid-vein described for this species.

297. Rhododendron blackii Sleumer
Blumea 1973. 21: 375.
Type: Vink 17280, 28 July 1966. New Guinea (E), Southern Highlands District, Tari subdistrict, Mt Ambua, 3390m (LAE, L, K).
Derivation: Named after Michael Black, an English medical doctor who collected in New Guinea and grew vireya rhododendrons at his home in Grasmere.

Synonym: *R. sleumeri* A.Gilli, Ann. Naturh. Mus. Wien 1980. 83: 435.

Shrub to 3m. Twigs 3–4mm in diameter, rounded, sub-densely scaly, longitudinally striate when dry; internodes 5–13cm. **Leaves** in tight pseudowhorls of 3–4, but inserted over 1–2cm. **Blade** 40–75 x 30–65mm, ovate to circular, rarely obovate; apex obtuse to rounded; margin cartilaginous, entire, narrowly revolute; base auriculate, the sides broadly turned down; laxly silvery scaly above, quickly becoming glabrescent; below laxly to sub-densely and more persistently scaly. **Scales** sub-circular to broadly sub-stellately lobed; the marginal flange broad, thin and transparent, the centres moderately small and impressed. Mid-vein raised above in the proximal ⅓–½, then impressed, grooved where it is raised; below raised throughout its length but decreasing distally; lateral veins 5–7 per side, wide-spreading, above slightly raised and minutely grooved, beneath very slightly raised; straight but branching and anastomosing before the margin. **Petiole** 2–4 x 2–4mm, sometimes grooved above distally, scaly.

Bracts to 18 x 12mm, the outermost scaly outside, inner ones with scales on the margins, shortly hairy outside and minutely hairy inside. Inflorescence of 5–9 flowers in an open umbel. **Flowers** 60–65 x 35–40mm. Pedicels 30–35 x *c.*1mm, densely scaly. Calyx *c.*4mm in diameter, disc-shaped, densely scaly and fringed on the margin with scales. **Corolla** red; tube 40–62 x 5–6 x 12–27mm, sub-densely scaly outside, densely hairy with irregular or somewhat retrorse hairs inside; lobes 15–23 x 12–21mm, reflexed, overlapping to *c.*halfway, scaly outside except near the margins. **Stamens** exserted to *c.*12mm, clustered on the upper side of the mouth; filaments hairy in the proximal ½–⅔, glabrous distally; anthers *c.*3mm, curved. Disc densely hairy on the upper side, otherwise glabrous. **Ovary** *c.*8 x 3mm, elongate-conical, densely hairy and scaly, tapering gradually distally; style *c.*45 x 1mm, densely hairy and scaly for the proximal 3–5mm, then glabrous distally, purplish-red; stigma *c.*4mm in diameter, rounded, yellow. **Fruit** 28–38 x 6–7mm, fusiform, longitudinally grooved, pale brown.

Papua New Guinea, Western Highlands between Laiagam and Kandep, *c.*4 miles W of Wabag; Southern Highlands, Mt Ambua, Mt Hagen, Mt Kerewa, Mt Giluwe, Ibiwara (Tari Gap), 2500–3300m. Epiphytic in mixed montane forest, secondary forest with climbing bamboo, or terrestrial at forest margins and in fire-induced grassland with *Gleichenia*. *Fl.* July.

Sleumer (1973) records this as being in cultivation at the time of publication of the species both at Michael Black's garden in Grasmere in the UK and in Australia from the seeds from a Vink collection (17041) of 1966. It was distributed by the Australian National Rhododendron Society in 1983. It is a very handsome plant with its distinctive rounded, almost sessile, dark green leaves and beautiful dark red flowers.

298. Rhododendron hirtolepidotum J.J.Sm.
Nova Guinea 1914. 12: 135, *t.*32.
Type: Gjellerup 1133, 28 April 1912. New Guinea (NW), Arfak Mts, Angi Lake, 1900m (L, BO).
Derivation: Latin – *hirti* – hairy; Greek – *lepido* – scaly. With both hairs and scales, possibly alluding to the ovary.

Shrub to 2.5m. Twigs 2–5mm in diameter, rounded, sub-densely covered when young with fragile, sub-stellate, reddish-brown scales, later glabrous and smooth; internodes 2–18cm. **Leaves** 4–8 together in pseudowhorls. **Blade** 40–105 x 20–42mm, elliptic, or obovate-elliptic; apex broadly tapering or shortly sub-acuminate, obtuse to nearly rounded; margin slightly revolute; base broadly tapering, sub-truncate to rounded, rarely sub-cordate; glabrescent above when mature, densely and more persistently scaly beneath. **Scales** small, variously sub-stellate-lobed in the marginal zone; centres dark, slightly impressed, scale pits black and shallow. Mid-vein slightly impressed above, thick and prominent in the proximal part beneath; lateral veins 6–10 per side, spreading, straight below, curved and indistinctly anastomosing before the margin, slightly raised on both sides, or a little impressed above, reticulation obscure. **Petiole** 4–16 x 1.5–2.5mm, semi-rounded, grooved above, scaly and rugulose.

Bracts to 15 x 8mm, ovate to obovate, obtuse, firm-membranous, with some sparse scales at the top outside or quite glabrous. Bracteoles to 22 x 1.5mm, linear below,

sub-spathulate apically, glabrous. Inflorescence 5–9-flowered. Pedicels 30–40 x 0.6–0.8mm, sparsely stellate-scaly proximally, more densely so distally. Calyx *c.*4mm in diameter, oblique, disc-shaped, 5-angular, outside densely scaly. **Corolla** 44–50mm, tubular below, sub-oblique, red, membranous; tube 20–30 x 6–7 x 7–8mm, laxly to sub-densely scaly outside, lobed at the base, shortly hairy in the proximal ½ inside; lobes 9–17 x 10–12mm, obliquely obovate-spathulate. **Stamens** slightly shorter than the corolla; filaments linear, densely hairy proximally, less so distally; anthers 3.5–4 x 1mm, oblong, obtuse at the base. Disc shortly hairy on the upper margin, glabrous below. **Ovary** *c.*8 x 2.5mm, sub-cylindrical, densely stellate-scaly, with some spreading hairs at the top between the scales, gradually tapering distally; style as long as the corolla tube, laxly scaly and sub-densely patently hairy in the proximal 10–15mm, glabrous distally; stigma deeply 5-lobed. **Fruit** 35–40 x 4–5mm, sub-cylindrical, sub-densely covered with red-brown scales.

Indonesia, New Guinea (W), Vogelkop Peninsula, Arfak Mts, Nettoti Range, Mt Watjetoni. Terrestrial or occasionally epiphytic in light mossy forest in poor humus or sandy soil, or in swampy places with *Sphagnum*, 1200–2000m. *Fl.* April, Nov.–Dec.

Never cultivated.

Rhododendron hirtolepidotum.

299. Rhododendron comparabile Sleumer
Reinwardtia 1960. 5: 208.
Type: Brass 27861, 27 Aug. 1956. New Guinea, SE, Milne Bay District, Sudest Isl., Mt Riu, summit, 800m (L, A, K, LAE, PNH, S, US).
Derivation: Latin – *comparandus* – worthy of comparison, alluding to its supposed relationship with *R. lochae* (see below).

Erect shrub to 2m. Twigs 2–4mm in diameter, semi-rounded, laxly and deciduously sub-stellately scaly when young, sometimes whitish; internodes 2–11cm. **Leaves** 4–5 together in pseudowhorls. **Blade** 35–90 x 25–50mm, elliptic to sub-obovate-elliptic; apex broadly tapering or very shortly sub-abruptly acuminate, obtuse, sometimes rounded; margin narrowly but distinctly revolute; base broadly tapering, glabrescent above when mature, laxly, sub-persistently scaly beneath. **Scales** minute, marginal zone irregularly sub-stellately lobed; centre slightly impressed. Mid-vein narrowly impressed above, thick and obtusely prominent beneath; lateral veins 5–9 per side, spreading, sometimes irregular, often divided before the margin, mostly sub-parallel to each other and distinctly curved-anastomosing, slightly impressed above, somewhat raised beneath, reticulation faintly impressed above in old leaves, often inconspicuous. **Petiole** 10–23 x 1–2mm, semi-rounded, grooved above.

Bracts to 20 x 15mm; outer bracts ovate, sub-acuminate, or circular, scaly along the midline distally outside; inner bracts obovate to spathulate, glabrescent or glabrous apart from marginal scales. Bracteoles 15 x 0.5–1.5mm, linear-spathulate, glabrous. Inflorescence an open 8–13-flowered umbel. Pedicels 20–30 x *c*.1mm, densely sub-stellately scaly. Calyx *c*.3mm in diameter, obliquely disc-shaped, shortly and bluntly 5-lobed, scaly outside. **Corolla** 40–48 x 50mm, funnel-shaped, white, scented; tube *c*.25 x 5–6 x 8–12mm, straight, sub-cylindrical, lobed at the base, laxly to sub-densely covered with minute sub-stellate scales outside, shortly hairy inside; lobes 15–20 x 15–20mm, broadly obovate or sub-circular, spreading. **Stamens** sub-equal, exserted; filaments linear and laxly patently hairy in the lower ⅔, more filiform and glabrous distally; anthers 3–3.5 x 0.8mm, narrowly oblong. Disc low, glabrous. **Ovary** 5–6 x *c*.2mm, sub-cylindrical, densely covered with forwardly directed hairs which cover the scales, tapering distally; style slightly shorter than the stamens, densely hairy and scaly for the proximal ¾, scaly at the apex; stigma deeply 5-lobed. **Fruit** 30–35 x 5–6mm, sub-cylindrical. Seeds very narrow, 4–5mm including the long tails.

Papua New Guinea, Milne Bay District, Sudest I., on Mt Riu, 600–800m, scattered in stiff scrub on the summit and on cliffs. *Fl*. Aug.

Sleumer (1966) noted: 'Much related to *R. lochae* F. v. M. from NE Queensland (the only *Rhododendron* in Australia [at that time]), which, however, has red corollas, laxly hairy ovary (the scales thus clearly visible) and 2–5 (rarely up to 7) flowers per umbel'. It would be interesting to know if DNA analysis supported this view. Not known to have been cultivated.

300. Rhododendron luraluense Sleumer
Notizbl. Berl.-Dahl. 1935. 12: 485.
Type: Kajewski 2064. Solomon Islands, Bougainville, Lake Luralu, 1500m (B†, A, BM, BRI, E, fragment, P).
Derivation: Named after the lake around which it was collected.

Ssp. **luraluense**

Shrub or tree to 9m. Twigs rounded, 2–3mm in diameter, laxly scaly at first, later glabrescent; internodes 3.5–8cm. **Leaves** 4–7 together in tight pseudowhorls. **Blade** 35–60 x 20–30mm, obovate-elliptic to elliptic; apex broadly acute to obtuse, or occasionally rounded, sometimes apiculate; margin narrowly recurved; base broadly tapering; glabrescent above, laxly and more persistently scaly beneath. **Scales** small, marginal zone fragile, irregularly lobed; centre dark, slightly impressed. Mid-vein broad and impressed in the proximal ½ above, broadly and obtusely prominent beneath; lateral veins 4–6 per side, irregular, spreading, inconspicuously inarching before the margin, faintly impressed or obscure above, slightly prominent beneath, reticulation lax, slightly raised beneath only. **Petiole** 3–5 x 1–1.5mm, grooved above.

Bracts to 12 x 6mm; outer bracts ovate-acuminate, inner ones obovate to spathulate, glabrous or laxly scaly apically outside. Bracteoles *c*.10mm, filiform, glabrous. Inflorescence of 3–6-flowered open umbels. Pedicels *c*.13 x 1.5mm, laxly sub-stellate-scaly, more densely so towards the apex. Calyx *c*.3mm in diameter, oblique, disc-shaped, very shortly 5-lobed. **Corolla** 35–45 x *c*.50mm, funnel-shaped, white; tube 15–20 x *c*.4 x 7–9mm, sparsely scaly outside, very laxly and shortly hairy inside; lobes 10–15 x 10–14mm, obovate-sub-circular, spreading. **Stamens** exserted to *c*.6mm; filaments linear and densely hairy proximally, filiform and glabrous distally; anthers *c*.2.5mm, oblong. Disc prominent, glabrous. **Ovary** *c*.4 x 1.8mm, sub-cylindrical, densely white-hairy and scaly (the hairs covering the scales), abruptly contracted distally; style slender, slightly shorter than the stamens, sub-densely to laxly hairy and scaly proximally to *c.*¾; stigma rounded.

Papua New Guinea, Bougainville Island, Crown Prince Range. Epiphytic shrub in rain forest, or tree in stunted vegetation, locally common, at 900–1500m. *Fl.* Aug., Oct.

Introduced into cultivation by Lyn Craven in 1964 from the type locality and raised and distributed from Melbourne. It is a very floriferous species which gives a magnificent display at least once a year, covering itself in flowers.

Ssp. **whitmorei** Argent *ssp. nov.*
Type: Whitmore 6360, 27 Aug. 1965. British Solomon Islands Protectorate, New Georgia Is., SW summit peak of Kolombangara, 1680m (K).
Derivation: Named after T.C. Whitmore, famous tropical botanist who collected the type specimen.

A ceteris subspeciebus *R. loranthifloro* stylo per *c.*4mm (styli *c.*⅕ longitudinis) proximaliter tantum piloso lepidotoque (nec per 12–15mm vel styli ¾ longitudinis) differt.

Differing from the type subspecies of *R. luraluense* as the style is hairy and scaly for only *c.*4mm (about ⅕) proximally, not 12–15mm (¾ of the style).

301. Rhododendron wentianum Koord.
Nova Guinea 1909. 8: 188.
Type: Pulle (Versteeg) 1629, 21 Aug. 1907. New Guinea (W), Resi Mts, Noord R., *c.*600m (BO, K, L, U).
Derivation: Named after F.A.F.C. Went who worked for several years in Indonesia, later becoming professor of botany at Utrecht in the Netherlands.

Synonyms:
R. callichilioides Wernham, Trans. Linn. Soc. London, II, Bot. 1916. 9: 95.
R. wollastonii Wernham, Trans. Linn. Soc. London, II, Bot. 1916. 9: 99.

Shrub to 2m. Twigs 2–4mm in diameter, laxly to densely covered with flat scales; internodes 2–20cm. **Leaves** 3–5 large and often with 1 or 2 much smaller in a tight pseudowhorl. **Blade** 60–160 x 30–63mm, ovate, sub-sessile; apex gradually long acuminate to sub-caudate, acute or nearly so; margin entire, narrowly revolute; base rounded to cordate, rarely very broadly tapering, glabrescent above, laxly scaly beneath. **Scales** thin, marginal zone irregularly lobed, impressed. Mid-vein slightly impressed above, prominent beneath; lateral veins 8–11 per side, upper ones spreading and straight at the base, curved towards the edge and inarching, hardly prominent on both sides, reticulation dense, only faintly visible on

Rhododendron wentianum.

313

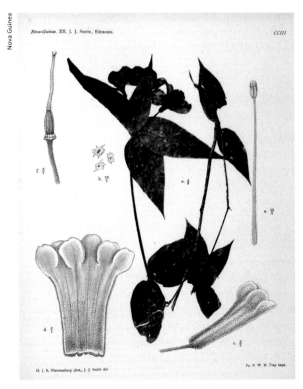

Nova Guinea

Rhododendron wentianum.

both sides, or only above. **Petiole** 2–7 x 2–4mm, weakly or not grooved above, scaly, dark red.

Buds to 30 x 15mm, ovate, acute, green, the bract points standing out away from the surface. Outer bracts ovate acuminate, *c.*18 x 10mm, laxly scaly outside in the distal ½ and along the margins, inner bracts to 30 x 8mm, spathulate, laxly scaly and minutely hairy outside, glabrous inside, with long stalked scales along the margins. Bracteoles subulate, to 20 x *c.*1mm, grooved, with a few scales outside and long stalked scales on the margins. Inflorescence 3–6-flowered in an open or almost complete umbel, the flowers held semi-erect to half-hanging. Pedicels 30–42 x *c.*2.5mm, densely to laxly scaly, not hairy, pink. Calyx irregularly 5-lobed, wavy, densely scaly, *c.*4mm in diameter. **Corolla** shortly funnel-shaped-campanulate, red or orange, with a white or greenish tube and triangular yellow guides inside the base of the upper three lobes; tube 10–14 x 6–7 x 12–15mm, deeply sulcate, sparsely scaly outside, laxly hairy to glabrous inside; lobes *c.*30 x 25mm, broadly obovate, spreading, the three upper overlapping to *c.*½, the two lower not overlapping. **Stamens** clustered in two groups on the lower side of the flower or in a semi-circle on the lower side exserted to *c.*10mm; filaments linear, densely patently hairy in the proximal ½, glabrous distally; anthers 2.5–3mm, oblong. Disc glabrous

below, hairy on the upper ½. **Ovary** 4–6 x 1.5–2mm, conical, obtusely 5-angular, densely scaly and hairy, gradually tapering distally; style lying on the lower side of the flower, pale green, hairy and scaly in the proximal ½–⅓, glabrous distally; stigma thickly globose, green. **Fruit** 65–90 x 4–5mm, slenderly fusiform, laxly scaly and hairy on slender pedicels up to 40mm.

Indonesia, New Guinea (W), Main Range, from Mt Carstensz to the Star Mts. **Papua New Guinea,** Upper Sepik R. region; Southern Highlands Province near Erave. Epiphytic in forest, 600–1500m, locally common. *Fl.* Jan.–Aug., *fr.* July.

Introduced into cultivation by Lou Searle who sent material to Bob Withers in Melbourne in 1974 as a low altitude form of *R. christi* (it had not been collected in flower in the wild). First correctly identified by Lyn Craven (Craven 2002) who said of it 'not only does it have very attractive foliage and a pleasing spreading habit but it has extremely beautiful flowers'. It is now widely distributed and has been growing in Edinburgh since 1995. It flowers irregularly but the flowers are extraordinarily eye-catching, with the bright yellow triangles at the base of the upper three lobes contrasting with the orange red of the remainder of the lobes. It is the most zygomorphic visible colour pattern of any vireya in cultivation. The foliage is very reminiscent of *R. christi* but the flowers are quite different in shape and indumentum, lacking the distinctive white hairs on the outside of the corolla tube that *R. christi* always has; the flower buds also differ in having subulate points to the longest bracts whereas *R. christi* has subulate points only on the shortest bracts, the buds being smooth in outline.

---

302. Rhododendron glabrifilum J.J.Sm.
Nova Guinea 1914. 12: 134, *t.*31.
Type: Janowski 65, June 1912. New Guinea (NW), Legarei R., near Manokwari (BO).
Derivation: Latin – *glaber* – glabrous; *filum* – filament. Alluding to the glabrous filaments.

Synonyms:
R. torricellense Schltr., Bot. Jahr. 1917. 55: 142.
R. mayrii J.J.Sm., Nova Guinea 1936. 18: 97, *t.*20, *f.*2.
R. macgregoriae F.Muell. var. *glabrifilum* Sleumer, Reinwardtia 1960. 5: 206.

Shrub. Twigs slender, sparsely scaly; internodes 3.5–13cm. **Leaves** 3–5 together in tight pseudowhorls. **Blade** 40–160 x 12–50mm, elliptic to narrowly ovate-elliptic; apex acuminate, acute, margin entire, flat, base broadly

Rhododendron glabrifilum.

tapering, sometimes slightly decurrent; glabrescent above, sub-densely and more persistently scaly beneath. **Scales** sub-stellately lobed, margin broad; centre small and slightly impressed. Mid-vein narrowly impressed above, strongly prominent beneath; lateral veins 5–13 per side, spreading at a wide angle, anastomosing before the margin, reticulation lax to obscure. **Petiole** 2–5 x *c*.2mm, grooved above, scaly.

Inflorescence 3–15 flowers in an open to complete umbel, flowers erect to semi-erect. Pedicels 30–50 x *c*.1mm, sparsely scaly. Calyx a low disc, scaly. **Corolla** *c*.27 x 33mm, red or yellow; tube 11–13 x *c*.8.5 x *c*.10mm, scaly outside, glabrous inside, or with a few sparse hairs, 5-angled, lobed at the base; lobes 11–13 x 8–10mm, wide-spreading to reflexed, not or only shortly overlapping, scaly outside. **Stamens** 21–23mm, arranged all round the flower, exserted to *c*.10mm; filaments filiform, glabrous or occasionally very sparsely hairy near the base; anthers *c*.2.5mm, oblong. Disc 10-lobed, glabrous. **Ovary** *c*.5 x 2.5mm, shortly cylindrical, longitudinally grooved, densely covered with distally pointing hairs which hide small scales; style hairy and scaly in the proximal ½, glabrous distally; stigma rounded.

Indonesia, New Guinea (W), Legarei R., near Manokwari, Arfak Mts; Mt Ditschi (as *R. mayrii*), Doormantop; Idenberg R.;

Japen Is. **Papua New Guinea**, Torricelli Mts, Jimmy Valley; 420–1675m. *Fl.* June–Sept. According to Sleumer (1966) it is predominantly or possibly exclusively epiphytic.

This species has been reinstated after having been reduced to a variety of *R. macgregoriae* by Sleumer as it is readily identifiable and appears to have a mostly coherent northerly distribution. The flowers are usually red although the type specimen is recorded with a degree of uncertainty as having yellow flowers. The leaves are generally much larger than those of *R. macgregoriae* and with much shorter petioles relative to the blade length. Not known to be cultivated although pink forms of *R. macgregoriae* are in cultivation which if examined carefully could be this species.

303. Rhododendron schlechteri Lauterb.
In K.Schum. & Lauterb., Nachtr. 1905. 338.
Type: Schlechter 14045. New Guinea (NE), Bismarck Mts, 1700m (B†). Neotype: Schlechter 17845, 22 June 1908. New Guinea (NE), Kani Mts, 1000–1100m (K, E, P).
Derivation: Named after the collector, Friedrich Schlechter, a German botanist most famous for his studies on orchids but who also took a great interest in vireya rhododendrons, publishing many species.

Shrub to 1.5m. Twigs rounded, glabrous; internodes 6–10cm. **Leaves** spiral or in loose pseudowhorls, crowded apically, spreading. **Blade** 130–170 x 60–80mm, elliptic; apex obtuse; margin entire, flat; base broadly tapering to rounded, glabrescent above at maturity, densely scaly beneath. **Scales** small, irregularly stellately lobed in the marginal zone; centre not or very slightly impressed, fragile, leaving blackish points beneath. Mid-vein weakly raised above in the proximal ½, then flat; strongly raised below almost to the apex; lateral veins 8–9 per side, slender, straight or slightly curved, obscurely anastomosing, slightly raised on both sides when dry, reticulation obscure. **Petiole** 15–20 x 2–3mm, semi-rounded, without a groove, scaly.

Inflorescence 7–12-flowered in an open umbel. Pedicels 12–20 x 3–4mm, densely covered with brown scales, which are deeply divided to, or nearly to, the small centre, sometimes laxly hairy distally. Calyx 6–7mm in diameter, disc-shaped, oblique, shallowly 5-lobed and wavy, stellate-scaly outside, glabrous inside. **Corolla** 150–170mm, tubular-funnel-shaped, snow white, very fragrant; tube 90–120 x 10–11 x 22–28mm, cylindrical, 5-lobed at the base, laxly scaly to glabrescent outside, densely hairy and laxly scaly inside; lobes 50–70 x 35–50mm, obliquely and broadly obovate, rounded at the apex, spreading, margin wavy. **Stamens** strongly exserted; filaments 110–135mm, linear, flat, gradually tapering and finally filiform distally, densely hairy, the hairs denser, and retrorse at the margin, glabrescent in the distal ⅓; anthers 16–18 x 1.8mm, with elongate-oblong cells, minutely apiculate at the base. Disc lobed, with tufts of short hairs. **Ovary** *c.*25 x 7–9mm, cylindrical, very densely covered with yellowish, spreading hairs, which cover stellate scales, gradually tapering distally; style *c.*125 x 3.5mm, cylindrical, covered with yellow, sub-patent hairs and stellate scales for the proximal *c.*70mm, becoming almost exclusively scaly distally and ultimately glabrous for 20mm; stigma broadly and shortly obconical, 5-lobed.

Papua New Guinea, New Guinea (E), Bismarck Mts; Kani Mts (Madang Province). **Indonesia**, New Guinea (W), Mt Jaya (Carstensz). Epiphytic in rain forest on tall trees, 1000–1700m. *Fl.* Jan., June.

This species is very similar to *R. leucogigas* but is said to differ in having 5-lobed flowers and leaves spirally arranged or in loose pseudowhorls. The recent collection of a specimen attributed to this species on Mt Carstensz with flowers with 5, 6 and 7 lobes on the same plant questions the real difference between these species, although there does appear to be a difference in leaf shape, petiole and scales. There are also strong similarities to *R. konori*, the biggest difference being that scales are mounted on persistent epidermal tubercles in *R. konori* whereas the scales are from a flat epidermis or even a little impressed in *R. schlechteri*. Seedlings from the Carstensz locality have scales on epidermal tubercles although the wild collected adults do not!

304. **Rhododendron leucogigas** Sleumer
Blumea 1963. 12: 102.
Type: Royen & Sleumer 5981, 24 June 1961. New Guinea (N), Cycloop Mts, S slope of the central part along path Ifar-Ormu, camp site, 1220m (L).
Derivation: Greek – *leuco* – white; *gigas* – a giant. Alluding to the enormous flowers.

Shrub to 3m, erect, few-branched. Twigs 5–12mm in diameter, densely stellate-scaly at the new shoots, early

Rhododendron leucogigas.

Ken Grant

glabrescent; internodes 3–20cm. **Leaves** 3–6 together in pseudowhorls, spreading. **Blade** 180–280 x 60–105mm, elliptic, narrowly elliptic or slightly obovate; apex broadly acute, obtuse or rounded; margin entire, narrowly cartilaginous and revolute; base truncate to cordate; when young, stellately scaly, becoming glabrescent on both sides. **Scales** of two different types: sub-dendroid, stellately lobed, reddish-brown fragile ones, and flat, smaller, paler, less deeply dentate and longer persistent ones, the impressions of these small ones found on the mature leaves beneath. Mid-vein raised above in the proximal ½ and grooved, flat or slightly impressed distally, below strongly raised for most of the length, tapering gradually; lateral veins 9–12 per side, narrowly grooved above, becoming slightly raised when dry, beneath flat or very slightly raised, curved-ascending, joining before the margin, reticulation obscure when fresh, prominent above when dry. **Petiole** 7–20 x 4–5mm, somewhat flattened, not grooved above, scaly when young, upwardly directed, close to the stem to make the leaves appear sub-sessile.

Flower buds to 80 x 40mm, ovoid, dark purple. Bracts to 80 x 40mm, outer bracts ovate, apiculate, inner ones obovate to spathulate, covered with short, appressed hairs and scales outside, and by longer hairs inside. Bracteoles to 85 x 1–2mm, densely hairy at the base, becoming laxly hairy and glabrous distally, also laxly scaly with long-stalked fragile scales, linear, pink. Inflorescence 5–8-flowered, an open umbel, the flowers semi-erect to half-hanging. Pedicels 10–15 x 5–6mm, densely scaly. Calyx 7–9mm in diameter, rim-like, scaly and hairy on the margin, sometimes with irregular linear lobes up to 8 x 2mm. **Corolla** 7-lobed, *c.*140mm, tubular-funnel-shaped, white with pale pink on the tube and at the junctions of the lobes, strongly scented; tube 60–100 x 8–12 x 30–35mm, straight, sub-densely to sparsely stellate-scaly outside, densely hairy inside; lobes 50–60 x 25–40mm, spreading, obovate, apex emarginate or rounded, edge crenulate. **Stamens** 14, exserted to 10mm; filaments hairy; anthers 7–12 x *c.*1.5mm, linear, base obtuse. Disc densely hairy. **Ovary** 15–18 x 6–10mm, cylindrical, dense hairs covering scales; style *c.*70 x 2mm, hairy and scaly in the proximal ½ the hairs becoming laxer distally, densely scaly only in the distal ½, sometimes with a short, glabrous zone below the stigma. **Fruit** 140–160 x 10–18mm, fusiform, densely covered with hairs and scales; stigma large, 7-lobed. Seeds 8–9.5mm, without tails 1.5–2mm, the longest tail 4.5mm.

Indonesia, New Guinea (W), Cycloop Mts. **Papua New Guinea**, Hunstein Range? Epiphytic on tree trunks in riverine

Rhododendron leucogigas.

forest or in sub-mossy *Nothofagus* forest at 1000–1500m, said to be common locally. *Fl.* apparently April–May, *fr.* June.

The original description of the species described the bracteoles as glabrous; the Edinburgh plant which was from Sleumer's original collection has distinctly hairy bracteoles as has the specimen grown at Boskoop. The scales which are described as being of two types are mostly from a completely level epidermis but some are from minutely elevated protuberances similar to, but much smaller than, those generally found in section *Phaeovireya*.

Introduced into cultivation in 1961 by Professor Sleumer, who collected cuttings which were distributed to Boskoop in the Netherlands, Edinburgh and the Strybing Arboretum in the USA. It first flowered in Boskoop in September 1964 and at Strybing in 1968, and seed was widely distributed soon afterwards. It grows very slowly and first flowered in Edinburgh in July 1970. The large fruits also grow slowly, and in Edinburgh took 14 months to mature. Seed is also reported as slow and can take a month or more to germinate (W. Moyles *pers. comm.*). A second collection was made in the Hunstein Mts by

Lyn Craven which was initially known as *R. gardenia aff.* It was later christened *R. leucogigas* 'Hunstein's Secret'. This apparently grows more vigorously and has more flowers in the inflorescence; the scales are also more typical of section *Phaeovireya*, being on much larger epidermal elevations than the type. This 'form' was first flowered by Dr W. Withers in Melbourne, Australia in 1974.

Although the original form is very slow in cultivation, flowering at best every other year in Edinburgh, it is so spectacular when it does flower that it is always the cause of great excitement and comment. It will always be highly sought after for the enormous, powerfully scented flowers. It is the parent of many hybrids which are themselves spectacular horticultural plants; these grow with hybrid vigour and so are easier, quicker and much more floriferous than the parent species.

305. Rhododendron brevipes Sleumer

Reinwardtia 1960. 5: 213.
Type: Womersley & Millar NGF 7605. Papua New Guinea, Western Highlands, Jimmy Valley, near Karap (LAE).
Derivation: Latin – *brevis* – short; *pes* – foot. Alluding to the very short petioles.

Shrub to 3m. Twigs 3–4mm in diameter, rounded or somewhat angled, at first sub-densely covered with flat, sub-stellate scales, later glabrescent; internodes 7–10cm. **Leaves** *c.*5 together in pseudowhorls at the upper 1–2 nodes, sub-sessile. **Blade** *c.*150 x 50–70mm, broadly elliptic to elliptic; apex shortly acuminate, sub-acute; margin flat; base broadly tapering, the extreme base sub-truncate-obtuse; upper surface glabrescent but densely, minutely, pitted; undersurface sub-densely scaly. **Scales** flat, thin, reddish-brown, the marginal area variously lobed; centre small, flat. Mid-vein as wide as the petiole at the base, narrowed upwards and slightly impressed above, prominent beneath; lateral veins 8–10 per side, with additional, less distinct ones between them; straight at the base, curved distally, indistinctly anastomosing along the margin, flat or faintly raised above, more distinct and raised beneath, reticulation visible above, almost obscure beneath. **Petiole** 1–2 x 3–4mm.

Outer bracts to 20 x 10mm, ovate-acuminate, with a distinct, sharp point (3–4mm), very laxly scaly along the outer middle line or glabrous outside, densely scaly at the apex inside; inner bracts elliptic-sub-spathulate, glabrous, except scaly along the margins. Bracteoles *c.*20 x 1mm, filiform, sub-glabrous. Inflorescence a 6–7-flowered umbel. Pedicels 40–60 x *c.*1.5mm, dilated at the apex,

laxly scaly, not hairy. Calyx to 3mm in diameter, oblique, a wavy rim. **Corolla** 75–80mm, funnel-shaped, tube yellow, lobes orange; tube 40 x 4–5 x 15mm, laxly to very laxly sub-stellately scaly outside, shortly hairy in the lower ¾ inside, straight; lobes *c.*40 x 25mm, obovate, spreading. **Stamens** unequal, the longest exserted to *c.*20mm; filaments linear and sub-densely hairy in the proximal ½, filiform and glabrous in the distal ½; anthers *c.*4 x 1.2mm, oblong, the base obtuse. Disc very prominent, white-hairy at the upper margin, glabrous below. **Ovary** 10–12 x 2–2.5mm, cylindrical, tapering distally, very densely scaly and laxly shortly white-hairy; style *c.*55mm, densely scaly and shortly hairy in the lower ⅔, more laxly scaly and without hairs to the apex; stigma thick, rounded, with 5 distinct, almost club-shaped lobes. **Fruit** cylindrical, scaly and hairy, *c.*80 x 3–4mm.

Papua New Guinea, Western Highlands, Jimmy Valley, Karap village. *c.*1725m. One collection only. *Fl. fr.* June.

A poorly known species very reminiscent of *R. aurigeranum* in that the tips of the bracts are scaly on both sides but this species has much shorter petioles. Never cultivated.

306. Rhododendron englerianum Koord.

Nova Guinea 1909. 8: 186.
Type: Versteeg 1632, 3 July 1907. New Guinea (SW), Noord R., Bivak, Alkmaar (BO, K, L, U).
Derivation: Named after Victor G.A. Engler (1885–1917).

Shrub to 1.2m. Twigs 5–7mm in diameter, rounded, scaly at first, quickly becoming glabrescent; internodes 4–10cm. **Leaves** 3–4 together in pseudowhorls, large, sub-sessile. **Blade** 120–250 x 40–90mm, elliptic, or sub-ovate-elliptic; apex short to long-acuminate, acute or sub-acute; margin narrowly but very distinctly revolute; base broadly tapering, the extreme base truncate-rounded or slightly cordate, glabrescent above when mature, laxly scaly beneath. **Scales** small, marginal zone irregularly and shallowly lobed; centre slightly impressed. Mid-vein narrow and markedly impressed above, strongly prominent on the underside proximally; lateral veins 8–14 per side, with additional shorter ones between, irregular and ascending, inarching before the margin, slightly raised above, more distinctly so beneath, reticulation lax, slightly raised on both sides. **Petiole** 4–7 x 3–4mm, grooved above, densely scaly.

Bracts to 55 x 15mm; outer bracts ovate-lanceolate, long acute hairy and scaly outside; inner ones broadly ovate-acuminate and sub-acute to elliptic-spathulate, also hairy and scaly, glabrous inside. Bracteoles to 30 x 1mm, linear-filiform, scaly and hairy. Inflorescence 4–9-flowered, an open umbel. Pedicels 60–110 x *c*.1.5mm, erect, laxly scaly, minutely and sparsely hairy. Calyx *c*.5mm in diameter, rounded or very shortly, obtusely 5-lobed, scaly outside. **Corolla** *c*.80 x 100mm, funnel-shaped, orange or reddish to pink, flushed yellow outside; tube 25–30 x 5–8 x 15–20mm, lobed at the base, laxly stellate-scaly outside, laxly hairy inside, with prominent dark veins running lengthwise to the apices of the lobes in the dry state; lobes 50–60 x 30mm, obovate, spreading. **Stamens** exserted to 25mm; filaments linear and densely hairy in the proximal ½, filiform and glabrous distally; anthers 6–7 x 1mm, linear-oblong, slightly curved. Disc prominent, hairy in the upper ½, glabrous below. **Ovary** 9–10 x *c*.3mm, sub-cylindrical, hairy, with numerous minute brown scales between the hairs, tapering gradually distally; style as long as the stamens and covered with short hairs and clearly visible scales in the proximal ½–⅔; stigma thick, 5-lobed. **Fruit** 60–100 x *c*.5mm, elongate-cylindrical, laxly hairy and scaly.

Indonesia, New Guinea (W), Noord R.; Vogelkop, Dalman, near Nabire. **Papua New Guinea**, Central District, Musgrave Range; Mt Yule. Epiphytic in *Agathis* forest, or terrestrial in rain forest, 400–600m, also reported from rocks near a river, 1220–2745m. *Fl.* March, April, July.

Very similar to *R. baenitzianum* but apparently distinct in the clearly revolute margin to the leaf and longer petioles. Baron von Mueller used the invalid name '*megalostigma*' for this species which has extremely divided stigmatic lobes. Not known to have been cultivated.

307. Rhododendron mollianum Koord.
Nova Guinea 1909. 8(1): 187.
Type: Pulle (Versteeg) 1297, 23 June 1907. New Guinea (SW), Noord R. (BO, K, L, U).
Derivation: Named after Prof. Dr. J.W. Moll, former director of the Groningen botanic gardens.

Terrestrial shrub to 1m. Twigs rounded, 2–5mm in diameter; internodes laxly minutely scaly, lower ones glabrescent and corky, 6–15cm. **Leaves** 4–5 together in pseudowhorls with subulate cataphylls associated with them. **Blade** 110–160 x 15–30mm, narrowly elliptic; apex narrowly acute, caudate-acuminate; margin strongly but narrowly revolute; base narrowly tapering, glabrescent above with age, laxly scaly for some time beneath but eventually glabrescent. **Scales** minute, marginal zone

irregularly sub-stellately lobed and quickly disappearing; centre shallowly impressed. Mid-vein narrow and impressed above except for the broad base; obtusely prominent beneath; lateral veins 10–14 per side, irregular, spreading, obscurely anastomosing near the edge, slightly impressed above and raised beneath, reticulation obscure above, dense and finely prominent beneath. **Petiole** 5–7 x 1–1.5mm, rugose, grooved above.

Inflorescence *c*.3-flowered, an open umbel. Pedicels 25–30 x 0.7mm, laxly scaly, without hairs. Calyx *c*.3mm in diameter, disc-shaped, faintly lobed, oblique. **Corolla** 65–70mm, funnel-shaped, orange, suffused with red; tube *c*.25 x 5 x 10mm, sparsely minutely scaly outside, laxly hairy inside, markedly pouched proximally; lobes 40–45 x *c*.20mm, spreading, obovate-elliptic. **Stamens** sub-equal, exserted to 20mm; filaments linear and sub-densely to laxly hairy in the proximal ⅓, becoming nearly filiform and glabrous distally; anthers 5 x 1mm, elongate-oblong, slightly curved. Disc prominent, shortly greyish hairy. **Ovary** *c*.8 x 2mm, sub-cylindrical, tapering distally, densely minutely scaly and shortly hairy, the scales clearly visible between the hairs; style shortly hairy in the proximal ¼–⅓, hairy and scaly, or scaly only above, slender, equalling the stamens; stigma lobed.

Indonesia, New Guinea (W), Noord R. *Fl.* June.

Known only from the type collection; never cultivated. Very reminiscent of *R. englerianum* with the narrowly revolute margins to the leaves and subulate cataphylls associated with the pseudowhorls.

308. Rhododendron cuspidellum Sleumer
Reinwardtia 1960. 5: 200.
Type: Versteeg BW 3008, 20 March 1959. New Guinea (W), Wissel Lakes, Enarotali, 1900m (L, E).
Derivation: Latin – *cuspis* – a sharp rigid point; *ellum* – diminutive. The leaves being sharply pointed.

Terrestrial shrub to 1.5m. Twigs 3–6mm in diameter, rounded, scaly becoming glabrescent; internodes 8–17cm. **Leaves** 4–7 together in tight pseudowhorls of very variably sized leaves at the same node. **Blade** 70–200 x 20–70mm, narrowly ovate or elliptic; apex acuminate, with long sub-caudate points, acute; margin entire, very narrowly slightly revolute; base broadly tapering, rounded to sub-cordate; glabrescent above, laxly and more persistently scaly beneath. **Scales** small, marginal zone irregularly sub-stellately lobed; centre darker and slightly impressed. Mid-vein narrowly impressed above, strongly raised below, becoming gradually more slender from base to apex; lateral veins 8–10 per side, wide-spreading, straight below, indistinctly curved-anastomosing before the margin, faintly raised on both sides, sometimes inconspicuous especially beneath. **Petiole** 3–6 x 2–3mm, grooved above, scaly.

Flower buds 35 x 25mm, sub-orbicular-ovoid. Bracts to 35 x 23mm; outer bracts ovate, apex very shortly subulate, the inner ones larger, ovate, obtuse, innermost ones spathulate, all laxly sub-stellately scaly and very shortly hairy outside and along the margin. Bracteoles to 30 x 4mm, linear to linear-sub-spathulate, shortly hairy. Inflorescence a 9–12-flowered complete umbel. Pedicels 25–60 x *c.*1mm, laxly scaly, without hairs. Calyx *c.*3mm in diameter, disc-shaped, wavy and obscurely lobed, densely scaly outside. **Corolla** 35–45 x *c.*35mm, tubular-funnel-shaped, orange or orange-yellow; tube 15–20 x 5–6 x 15–17mm, straight, 5-angular, lobed at the base, sub-densely to laxly sub-stellately scaly outside, sparsely or very sparsely hairy proximally inside; lobes 23–27 x 15–22mm, broadly obovate-spathulate or sub-circular. **Stamens** *c.*25mm, sub-equal, slightly exserted; filaments linear and densely patently hairy in the proximal ½, glabrous distally; anthers *c.*4 x 1mm, oblong. Disc hairy. **Ovary** 5–6 x *c.*2.5mm, cylindrical-conical, white-hairy and scaly, abruptly contracted distally; style nearly equalling the stamens, hairy and distinctly scaly in the proximal ⅓–⅔; stigma deeply 5-lobed.

Indonesia, New Guinea (W), Wissel Lakes region; Armina, Sjuga-Wagura area, Babo District. Secondary forest, locally common, 150–1900m. *Fl.* March.

Very similar to *R. baenitzianum* but said to differ by the smaller flowers; more collections are badly needed to evaluate this. Not known to have been cultivated.

309. Rhododendron baenitzianum Lauterb.

In K.Schum. & Lauterb., Nachtr. 1905. 337.
Type: Schlechter 14357, April 1892. New Guinea (E), Torricelli Mts (B†, BO, BRSL, K).
Derivation: Named after Carl G. Baenitz, German botanist and teacher.

Synonym: *R. maboroense* Schltr., Bot. Jahr. 1918. 55: 156.

Shrub to 2m. Twigs 3–6mm in diameter, rounded, densely sub-stellately scaly at first, becoming glabrescent; internodes 3–10cm. **Leaves** 5–10 in tight pseudo-whorls, sub-sessile or shortly petioled. **Blade** 120–250 x 30–85mm, elliptic to ovate-elliptic; apex sub-caudate-acuminate or acute; margin flat; base obtusely or broadly acutely tapering, rarely rounded, often unequal, glabrescent above at maturity; laxly scaly beneath. **Scales** small, flat, marginal zone irregularly lobed; centre small, weakly or not impressed, finally glabrescent beneath and then with dark spots. Mid-vein narrow and impressed above, broader and bluntly prominent beneath; lateral veins 8–12 per side, ascending, curved-anastomosing before the margin, the major veins distinctly grooved above, prominent beneath, reticulation finely raised on both sides. **Petiole** 3–4 x 2–3mm, semi-rounded, grooved above, scaly.

Rhododendron baenitzianum.

Bracts to 25 x 10mm; outer bracts ovate to obovate, cuspidate or shortly acutely acuminate, laxly scaly outside and on the margins, shortly appressed hairy in the middle or towards the apex; inner bracts sub-spathulate, acuminate, laxly scaly outside, but not hairy. Bracteoles to 20mm, filiform to linear-sub-spathulate, sub-glabrous. Inflorescence 4–15-flowered, in a complete umbel. Pedicels 25–55 x *c*.1.5mm, laxly scaly especially at base and apex, without hairs. Calyx *c*.4mm in diameter, sub-oblique, rim-like. **Corolla** 75–100mm, funnel-shaped, yellow with orange or pink lobes; tube 50–60 x 6–8 x 20–25mm, pouched at the base, laxly scaly outside, shortly hairy inside; lobes 30–40 x 25–30mm, spreading, broadly obovate to sub-circular. **Stamens** sub-equal, exserted to *c*.15mm; filaments linear, shortly patently hairy in the proximal ½, glabrous distally; anthers *c*.4 x 1.2mm, oblong. Disc hairy on the upper margin, glabrous below. **Ovary** 10–12 x 2–2.5mm, sub-cylindrical, shortly and densely covered with distally pointing hairs and with scales, tapering gradually distally; style equalling the stamens when receptive, densely covered with sub-patent hairs and with scales to near the top; stigma thick, 5-lobed. **Fruit** 150–200 x 4–5mm, elongate-fusiform, often curved, laxly hairy and scaly.

Papua New Guinea, East Sepik Province, Torricelli Mts; Maboro Range; West Sepik Province, Telefomin; Waria R. region; Bundi to Simbu road; Mendi S District, Kawkawsaw Humu; Southern Highlands Province, Kagua District, Lamame, Vulkara Range; Milne Bay District, Mt Suckling. Terrestrial along rivulets or in rocky places, 215–1600m. *Fl.* April, June, Aug., Nov., *fr.* Aug.

Reported as being visited by a large butterfly by Tom Reeve in 1978. There is a letter in the Sydney Herbarium from T.L. Fenner, of the Department of Primary Industry, with the specimen, confirming the butterfly as *Papilio euchenor*. Living material of this species was collected by Paul Kores from an unknown locality and grown at Wau in Papua New Guinea. This material was rescued by Canon Cruttwell after Kores had returned to America. It was grown on at the Lipizauga Botanical Sanctuary near Goroka from where it was widely distributed in 1989. It caused something of a sensation when its identity was realised and it started to flower in collections. It grows slowly in Edinburgh, probably because it has been kept in our cool house (it has a predominantly lowland distribution), but produces impressively large trusses of flowers. It has sometimes been confused with *R. zoelleri* but the venation on the leaves is different, and *R. baenitzianum* has much shorter petioles which give the leaves a sub-sessile appearance contrasting with the usually long-petiolate leaves of *R. zoelleri*. Sleumer (1973) comments on its close relationship with *R. englerianum*, admitting

that pedicel length would not separate these species but that fruit length would (*R. englerianum* having fruit only up to 100mm). Superficially *R. englerianum* always seems to have much longer, more acuminate leaves than *R. baenitzianum*. Further work is needed to fully understand the variation in these two species.

310. Rhododendron scabridibracteum Sleumer
Reinwardtia 1960. 5: 215.
Type: Womersley NGF 4889, 7 April 1953. New Guinea (E), Western Highlands, Ai River, Nondugl (L, A, BRI, CANB, K, LAE).
Derivation: Latin – *scabri* – rough; *bractea* – a bract. Alluding to the rough or scabrid bracts.

Shrub or tree to 12m. Twigs 4–5mm in diameter, laxly sub-stellately scaly becoming glabrescent; internodes 4–18cm. **Leaves** 3–5 together in tight pseudowhorls. **Blade** 60–120 x 25–60mm, elliptic; apex broadly tapering, obtuse, sometimes rounded or emarginate, occasionally with an inconspicuous apical gland; margin entire, flat or weakly and narrowly revolute; base broadly tapering, the extreme base sometimes truncate or rounded; glabrescent above when mature, laxly scaly beneath. **Scales** brown, rounded, lobed or sub-stellate, with a broad marginal zone and small centre, slightly impressed. Mid-vein narrowly impressed above, grooved in the proximal 1cm; strongly raised throughout its length below; lateral veins 10–12 per side, spreading, at first straight then curved upwards and anastomosing before the margin, with some additional intermediate veins, faintly impressed above, prominent beneath, reticulation dense, hardly impressed above, raised beneath. **Petiole** 8–18 x 3–4mm, grooved above, brown-scaly.

Flower buds to 45 x 22mm, ellipsoid, smooth, imbricate, with all bracts appressed, and rounded apex, pale yellowish-green. Outer bracts to 30 x 18mm, ovate, with appressed silvery or yellowish hairs which are swollen at the base, along the middle line are some small, brown, scales; inside shortly hairy, and on the margins fringed with brown, stellate scales; inner bracts obovate to spathulate, obtuse to rounded or emarginate. Bracteoles *c*.20 x 0.5–1mm, filiform, densely white-hairy. Inflorescence of 6–10 flowers in an open umbel. Pedicels 18–27 x *c*.2mm, densely brown scaly with low, stellate scales. Calyx 4–5mm in diameter, disc-shaped, shortly lobed or rounded with occasionally one lobe up to 4mm, densely scaly outside. **Corolla** 45–60 x 35–40mm, tubular, pale to deep red, distinctly zygomorphic; tube 35–40 x 7–8 x 12–16mm, curved, densely stellate-scaly outside, hairy with retrorse hairs inside; the three upper lobes 16–20 x 16–18mm, the two lower lobes *c.*20 x 12–13mm, wide-spreading forming an oblique mouth, sometimes becoming a little reflexed, the three upper lobes overlapping to *c.*⅓, the two lower not or only slightly overlapping, obovate-spathulate, the apices sometimes slightly retuse. **Stamens** tightly clustered on the upper side of the mouth, exserted to 15mm; filaments linear and densely covered with strong, distally pointing hairs below, more laxly so distally, ultimately glabrous; anthers 4–5 x *c.*1.5mm, brown. Disc thick and prominent, glabrous below, hairy on the upper margin. **Ovary** 8–10 x 3–4mm, narrowly ellipsoid, tapering distally, densely hairy and scaly, (the scales completely hidden by the hairs); style thick, densely hairy and with minute scales below, more laxly so above nearly to the top, lying along the upper side of the corolla tube; stigma *c.*3mm in diameter, obconical, red, positioned just below the mouth at first, becoming exserted to 20mm.

Papua New Guinea, Mt Antares, Western, Southern and Eastern Highlands. In lower montane rain forest or in *Castanopsis*- or *Nothofagus*-forest, terrestrial or often on tree trunks at 1950–2400m. *Fl.* April–Sept.

Cultivated at Edinburgh since 1972 when it was introduced by Lou Searle from the Eastern Highlands of Papua New Guinea; later also distributed by Canon Cruttwell from the Gaihaivisuka Botanical Garden near Goroka where it was cultivated and also grew wild in the forest around the garden. It grows strongly and has handsome bright red flowers. It mostly flowers in cultivation just once a year in late spring but does have occasional out of season flowers.

311. Rhododendron zoelleri Warb.
Bot. Jahr. 1892. 16: 24.
Type: Hellwig 339. Finisterre Mts (B†). Neotype: Schlechter 18017, 16 July 1908. Finisterre Mts, *c.*1000m (P, E, K, L, NY).
Derivation: Named after Hugo Zöller, a German journalist, who led the first expedition to the Finisterre Mountains in New Guinea in 1891.

Synonyms:
R. asparagoides Wernham, Trans. Linn. Soc. London, II, Bot. 1916. 9: 94.
R. moszkowskii Schltr., Bot. Jahr. 1918. 55: 161.
R. oranum J.J.Sm., Fedde Rep. 1932. 30: 167.
R. doctersii J.J.Sm., Nova Guinea 1936. 18: 98, *t.*21, 1.
R. laetum (*non* J.J.Sm. 1914) J.J.Sm., Nova Guinea 1936. 18: 98.

Shrub to 3m or tree to 10m, with a 15cm diameter trunk. Twigs rounded, 3–5mm in diameter, laxly scaly when young, glabrescent below; internodes 3–14cm. **Leaves** 3–6 in tight pseudowhorls. **Blade** 70–160 x 40–80mm, broadly elliptic to elliptic, rarely sub-ovate-elliptic or ovate-oblong; apex broadly acute to acute, often deflexed; margin flat, but the sides often curved upwards; base broadly tapering to rounded, the two sides often slightly unequal; glabrescent above at maturity; laxly brown-scaly beneath, remaining punctate when the scales disappear in old leaves. **Scales** small, marginal zone sub-stellately lobed; centre minute and shallowly impressed. Mid-vein narrowly grooved above in the proximal ½, as wide as the petiole and obtusely prominent for most of its length beneath; lateral veins 6–14 per side, diverging at *c.*45°, irregular, often running down the mid-vein, curved upwards and anastomosing before the margin, slightly raised above, smooth or distinctly prominent beneath, reticulation lax, mostly distinct, but smooth on both sides. **Petiole** 10–16 x *c.*3mm, flattened and shallowly grooved above in the distal ½, scaly initially.

Flower buds to 65 x 26mm, narrowly ovoid, imbricate, smooth, acute. Bracts to 40 x 15mm; outer bracts ovate-triangular, inner ones ovate to obovate or spathulate, all appressed, obtuse and covered by minute appressed hairs, amongst which are pale brown scales; margin fringed with small fragile scales. Bracteoles to 30mm, linear-sub-spathulate, shortly hairy. Inflorescence a complete or slightly open umbel of 4–8 flowers. Pedicels 15–40 x 1–1.5mm, laxly to sub-densely stellate-scaly, and sparsely shortly hairy in the distal part, sometimes throughout. Calyx *c.*5mm in diameter, obliquely disc-shaped, laxly scaly and hairy outside, obtusely 5-lobed. **Corolla** 60 x 90mm, enlarging with age, funnel-shaped, lobed to almost

Rhododendron zoelleri.

halfway, usually with a yellow tube and broad orange margins to the lobes so that the flower appears with a yellow 'star' in the throat; tube 30–45 x 5–8 x 20–27mm, deeply grooved in the proximal ½, and with 5 distinct, translucent veins which run lengthwise to the lobes, sometimes with some hairs at the base within the furrows, otherwise sparsely and indistinctly scaly outside, laxly hairy in the proximal ½ of the tube inside, tube straight or nearly so; lobes 42 x 30mm, the distal ½ reflexed to perpendicular, broadly obovate-spathulate, overlapping to halfway. **Stamens** loosely arranged in the lower ½–⅔ of the mouth, exserted 10–15mm; filaments linear, densely to laxly covered with spreading hairs in the proximal ⅓–½, glabrous and filiform distally; anthers 4–8 x 1.5–2mm, oblong, curved; base obtuse or rarely obscurely apiculate. Disc prominent, densely hairy at least on the upper margin. **Ovary** 9–12 x *c*.3mm, sub-cylindrical, white with stiff distally directed hairs which cover scales, tapering distally; style lying on the lower side of the tube at first, rising to a central position later; equalling the stamens, densely to laxly hairy in the lower ⅔–¾, glabrous distally, with some scattered scales mostly in the proximal ½; stigma *c*.2mm in diameter, green, rounded. **Fruit** 50–90 x 5–8mm, cylindrical, tapering at both ends, slightly curved, densely hairy and scaly. Seeds 8–10mm including the tails at both ends.

Indonesia and **Papua New Guinea**. Throughout the mainland of New Guinea, Maluku, W Seram in the Ora Mts. Epiphytic or terrestrial, often in high forest, terrestrial in lighter mountain forest with *Castanopsis*. Also in secondary forest and common in anthropogenic grassland which is not burnt too frequently, sometimes hanging from precipices. Growing from sea level to 2000m, often abundant, on poor sandy or clayey soil, but also recorded from limestone areas. *Fl. fr.* Jan.–Dec.

Sleumer noted a form with smaller anthers (3–4mm) apparently limited to SE New Guinea in the Central and Milne Bay Districts. A specimen from Seram which keys to this species also has small anthers only 3mm long; it is smaller in most other flower parts and could be a distinct species. Van Leeuwen (1926) observed the flowers of *R. zoelleri* were visited during the daytime by butterflies of the genera *Ornithoptera* and *Papilio*. Flower colour is reported to be variable, usually with yellow at least at the base of the tube but with the upper tube and lobes orange or reddish, and reported (Sleumer 1966) as very rarely white or greenish white and sweet-scented. This he regarded as a hybrid with *R. konori* var. *phaeopeplum*. It also forms hybrid swarms with *R. macgregoriae* in some of the open grassland areas in the Eastern Highlands of Papua New Guinea. Van Royen (1984) reported

Rhododendron zoelleri.

this species 'growing on a slope about 3ft (1m) above sea level, regularly sprayed by seawater', whereas Cruttwell (1971) says that in the Daga country it only grows above 3000ft (900m) and is the second rhododendron to come into the altitudinal zonation after *R. christianae*. It has been confused with *R. baenitzianum* which was unsatisfactorily keyed in Sleumer (1966). It differs in having much larger leaves on shorter petioles than *R. zoelleri*. In our living collections the two species differ on their lateral venation: *R. zoelleri* has the laterals slightly raised on the upper side of the leaf while they are channelled in narrow grooves in *R. baenitzianum*; whether this will separate all living collections remains to be tested.

With its large, flamboyant flowers it has long been one of the most popular New Guinea rhododendrons in cultivation. As might be expected from its relatively low elevation in the wild, it requires more heat than the majority of species. It is one of the main parents of the many heat tolerant hybrids produced in Queensland which are successful garden plants there. It has also been a very successful garden plant in California where it is said to bloom in 3–4 years from seed (Evans 1970). The cultivar 'Golden Gate' is said to be a selection of this species raised from seed sent from Australia to the Strybing Arboretum in the USA. The earliest collection (still growing) in Edinburgh was made by van Steenis from the Wissel Lakes area in 1955. He no doubt distributed material to Boskoop and very probably to Strybing Arboretum. The same material was also grown at Kew from where it was figured for *Curtis's Botanical Magazine* (Hunt 1975). It was also given an Award of Merit by the Royal Horticultural Society on 3 April 1973 as clone 'Decimus'. There have been many subsequent introductions.

312. Rhododendron lochiae F.Muell.

Vict. Nat. 1887. 3: 157.

Type: Sayer 135, 1887? Mt Bellender-Ker, Queensland, Australia (MEL, K).

Derivation: Named after Lady Loch, wife of the governor of Victoria, in recognition of her patronage to Victorian horticulture.

Synonyms:

Azalea lochae (F.Muell.) Kuntze, Rev. Gen. Pl. 1891. 387.
R. notiale Craven, Edinb. J. Bot. 1996. 53(1): 33.

Shrub or small tree to 6.5m. Twigs 2–4mm in diameter, rounded, sub-densely to laxly scaly, quickly glabrescent; internodes 1–10cm. **Leaves** 3–5 together in tight pseudo-whorls. **Blade** 50–90 x 30–50mm, broadly elliptic, occasionally sub-obovate; apex acute to rounded or sometimes minutely emarginate, with a small pale gland which rarely slightly protrudes; margin entire, flat or weakly revolute; base broadly tapering to rounded; laxly scaly and quickly glabrescent above; sub-densely and more persistently brown-scaly below. **Scales** round or weakly lobed with a broad flange and relatively small centre, impressed. Mid-vein impressed above in the proximal ½, smooth distally; below raised proximally, gradually becoming less so and finally smooth in the distal ¼; lateral veins 5–9 per side, minutely impressed above, smooth below, looping and joining before the margin, reticulation loose and weak, more clearly visible beneath. **Petiole** 10–20 x 2–3mm, distinctly grooved above, especially distally, densely brown scaly.

Inflorescence a 2–6-flowered open umbel, the flowers mostly semi-erect. Pedicels 10–40 x *c.*1.5mm, scaly often more densely so distally. Calyx a disc or 5-lobed up to 8 x 3.5mm, pink. **Corolla** 25–55 x 35–45mm, red or pink, without scent; tube 25–40 x 7–11 x 10–20mm, scaly outside, glabrous inside; lobes 15–20 x 15–22mm, spreading horizontally, to slightly reflexed, overlapping ½–⅔. **Stamens** loosely clustered on the upper side of the mouth, not or hardly exserted, slightly dimorphic; filaments 22–31 and 21–30mm, glabrous; anthers *c.*2mm, oblong, pale brown. Disc green, glabrous or hairy. **Ovary** 3.5–5 x 2–3mm, sub-cylindrical, tapering distally, densely scaly and sometimes hairy; style scaly and sometimes hairy as well in the proximal ⅓–½, glabrous distally, held on the upper side of the tube; stigma rounded. **Fruit** 20–25 x 4–5mm, fusiform. Seeds 2.5–3mm, including the tails.

Australia, Bellenden Ker Range, also probably on Bell Peak in the Malbon Thompson Range. Terrestrial in stunted montane forest and shrubberies amongst rocks, 1200–1520m. *Fl.* Oct.–Nov., and Jan. in the wild, reported as flowering Dec.–Feb. in cultivation in Melbourne, Australia. In Edinburgh this species flowers in July–Aug.

Although recorded as being in cultivation on numerous occasions, all early records of this species as live plants are referable to *R. viriosum* and similarly all records of hybrids formed from this species in fact used *R. viriosum* (Hodkins form) as parent, not *R. lochiae*. D.L. Jones collected material in 1975 which was grown and used to describe *R. notiale* (Craven & Withers 1996). This name had to be abandoned when the International Nomenclatural Committee rejected the conservation of *R. lochiae* as the name which had been long misapplied to what is now known as *R. viriosum*. Easy and free flowering in cultivation it is not as vigorous or as attractive as *R. viriosum*.

313. Rhododendron viriosum Craven

Edinb. J. Bot. 2002. 59(3): 448.

Type: Craven 9394, Cultivated Canberra 22 Feb. 1994. Originally from: Jones & Clements 4420, 27 May 1989. Queensland, Mount Windsor Tableland (CANB, A, B, BRI, E, L, MEL, QRS).

Derivation: Latin – *viriosus* – robust or strong, in recognition of its dominant qualities when used in hybridising programmes.

Shrub to 3m. Twigs 2–4mm in diameter, rounded, moderately to laxly scaly, becoming glabrescent; internodes 1–20cm. **Leaves** 2–6 together in tight pseudo-whorls. **Blade** 25–110 x 10–70mm, elliptic to broadly elliptic or obovate; apex shortly acuminate to obtuse; margin entire, narrowly revolute or flat; base broadly tapering to tapering; quickly glabrescent above, more persistently sub-densely scaly below. **Scales** small, flat, marginal zone irregularly lobed or almost entire; centre flat or slightly raised. Mid-vein narrowly impressed above; broadly prominent proximally beneath, gradually tapering distally but remaining prominent to the apex, often coloured red; lateral veins 4–7 per side, wide-spreading, slender, minutely impressed above and minutely raised beneath or obscure, reticulation obscure. **Petiole** 5–20 x 1.5–2mm, grooved above, scaly, usually red.

Inflorescence 2–7-flowered in an open umbel, the flowers half-hanging to hanging. Pedicels 18–35 x *c.*1.5mm, laxly scaly often becoming sub-densely scaly distally and often hairy. Calyx an angular disc *c.*4mm in diameter, sometimes shortly 5-lobed. **Corolla** 50–58 x 50–58mm, red or deep pink, without scent; tube 30–35 x 9–11 x 16–20mm, funnel-shaped, straight, laxly scaly and sparsely hairy outside, hairy inside; lobes 20–27 x 20–27mm, semi-erect to spreading, obovate to sub-circular, usually emarginate, overlapping ½–⅔, scaly on the lower part outside. **Stamens** irregularly spreading all round the

Debbie White

Debbie White

Lynsey Muir

Lynsey Muir

Face and side views of flowers of (A, B) *Rhododendron lochiae* and (C, D) *R. viriosum*.

mouth, or round the lower ⅔ of the mouth, not or only slightly exserted, slightly dimorphic; filaments 23–30 and 21–28mm, hairy; anthers *c.*3mm, oblong, dark red. Disc 10-lobed, hairy. **Ovary** 3–6 x 2–2.5mm, sub-cylindrical, densely scaly and densely hairy, tapering distally; style 14–23mm, central, or appressed to the lower side of the tube, scaly and hairy in the proximal ½–¾, then scaly for 1–2mm and finally glabrous distally; stigma *c.*1.5mm in diameter, rounded. **Fruit** 15–30 x *c.*5mm, ellipsoid.

Australia, Queensland: Mt Finnigan; Thornton Peak; Mount Windsor Tableland; and the Main Coast Range. Terrestrial or epiphytic in rain forest, on open boulder outcrops and mossy shrubberies, reported as epiphytic with a *Vaccinium* in the tops of large *Eugenia* trees on Mt Spurgeon by C.A. White, but it is normally found above the tree line (this however may reflect the difficulty of seeing epiphytes in the tops of trees). 910–1330m, said to be common above 1050m. *Fl.* Aug.–March. The main flowering season appears to be Feb. and March in the southern hemisphere and July in the north. It has been recorded as producing occasional out of season flowers at any month of the year in Australia but in Edinburgh it is more strictly seasonal than the majority of vireyas, perhaps because of its extreme southerly distribution.

The earliest formal report of *R. viriosum* growing in cultivation was from Kew (as *R. lochiae*) where it was recorded flowering in the temperate house on 26 September 1939 (Hutchinson 1943). This was grown from seed sent by Herbert Solomon of Sydney in 1936. It is reported verbally as growing in Essendon in Australia at the family home of Bob Hodkins in the 1930s. This is likely to be reliable, as a fully documented record remains as a cultivated specimen in the Melbourne herbarium. By this time it must have been in a number of collections in SE Australia. The species was given an Australian Award of Merit in 1952, and a selected form 'Down Under' exhibited by the Crown Estate, Windsor, received an Award of Merit from the Royal Horticultural Society in 1957. This is justifiably one of the most famous vireyas in cultivation. Although recorded in the wild as growing several metres high (up to 6m in the original description) it will flower very freely when very small and does not rapidly grow into a large plant, especially when confined in a pot. The largest plant recorded in cultivation (Withers 1992) was said to be 1.5m high and 1m across. It is the parent of many hybrids and imparts the red coloration of its flowers

Rhododendron viriosum.

to its progeny in a dominant manner. The tough texture of the flowers is also a very useful character when transmitted to the hybrid offspring, making the flowers resilient and long lasting. Dr Withers (1992) lists 48 registered hybrids using this species in the parentage and there are certainly many more unregistered hybrids in collections, especially in Australia. This species also has the distinction of being one of the only species of *Vireya* to have been

reliably recorded as successfully being crossed with a rhododendron outside *Vireya*. The hybrid 'Little Pioneer', admittedly a very weakly growing plant, was the result of a cross made between *R. viriosum* and *R. virgatum*, first by Os Blumhart in New Zealand and later by John Rouse in Australia. Several other crosses between *R. viriosum* and non-*Vireya* rhododendrons are recorded (Withers 1992) but none have grown beyond the seedling stage.

VIREYA RHODODENDRON BUDS SHOWING VARIATION IN MORPHOLOGY

R. lamrialianum

R. suaveolens

R. konori

R. sessilifolium

R. kochii

R. niveoflorum

R. himantodes

R. meijeri

R. exuberans

R. madulidii

R. buxifolium

R. lanceolatum

327

6 COLLECTING AND CONSERVATION

Introduction

Vireyas, with their often flamboyant flowers, are often actively collected by botanists and horticulturists. Because they can easily be grown from seed and cuttings and can be rapidly increased by these methods of propagation it is not usually necessary to remove whole plants, and the threat from actual collecting is much less than the general threat to the vegetation which often provides an essential niche habitat. For instance, the probable disappearance of *R. retrorsipilum* from New Guinea is unlikely to have been influenced by the repeated collections made from the very restricted known range of this species but more likely because the site was very close to the conurbation of Lae in Papua New Guinea. The forest vegetation was destroyed for firewood and the mountain slopes used for vegetable gardening, leaving the site where *R. retrorsipilum* was known to occur totally exposed and unsuitable for the continued existence of the rhododendron. It is still to be hoped that this species may turn up elsewhere but the very restricted distributions of so many vireya species means this is not particularly likely. Unfortunately *R. retrorsipilum* was never introduced into cultivation, so that we do not even have cultivated specimens for modern DNA studies or for gaining a more complete knowledge of its morphology. Of course, it is sensible not to completely denude a lone plant of all its leafy stems when taking cuttings, and it should be understood that it is pointless to harvest immature seed as this fails to germinate. The techniques used for growing immature embryos of orchids have not so far been successful in vireyas.

Collecting vireyas is undoubtedly becoming more difficult for two main reasons. The first is that the bureaucracy of collecting is becoming more complicated. Governments are becoming very protective of their biodiversity as possible loss of control over potentially lucrative drug discoveries has become a major issue – not that vireyas offer any great hope on this front, and it is usually far from the mind of most collectors who are just keen to collect a potentially attractive horticultural plant or just to advance biological knowledge in some small degree. It is nevertheless imperative that one is informed about laws and restrictions governing the collection of plants and that local regulations are respected.

The second reason is that because of vegetation loss it is becoming more and more difficult to get to unspoilt places where new finds can be made. The richest and most accessible sites have all been well collected and are usually protected with National Park or biological reserve status. There are undoubtedly many exciting discoveries still to be made but they will mostly involve a considerable amount of trekking in rough mountainous country where the weather is unpredictable (it can be very cold on tropical mountains), water can be in too great or too little supply for convenience, and leeches and ticks can be a nuisance. On the plus side, however, the advent of cheap and fast air transport makes the transmission of live material from the wild to a garden location in a sufficiently strong living state to be grown successfully more likely than ever.

Collecting expedition on the east ridge of Kinabalu.

What should be collected

Cuttings

The most reliable means of getting a species discovered in the wild into cultivation is to take cuttings off the plant itself using sharp secateurs. This is most reliable in that what you see is what you get, the material being clonal. Barring mishaps of muddled labels, plants grown from cuttings will be exactly the same as the plant they were collected from. These cuttings should be slightly longer than those taken for garden propagation as they will often need to be shortened on arrival at the garden site. Any dead or unhealthy looking tissue will have to be cut off and burned when being prepared for the propagation bed. The actual size of the cuttings will depend on the species being collected but 3–4 nodes are usually sufficient. A sensible balance has to be struck between what is convenient for transport and what is ideal for the time likely to be taken between collection and its arrival at the propagation bed. The leaves can be shortened for convenience and the lower leaves stripped from the stems at the time of collection.

Ideally cuttings should be from one parent plant only and they should be clearly labelled with a unique number which links to full collecting details: location, date, altitude, habitat, and collector. Locations and altitudes are often easy to provide using GPS systems but these often do not work under forest cover. The name of any mountain or significant geographical feature,

the nearest village and the administrative province should all be recorded. A description of the plant as it is in the wild is also very useful, sometimes allowing collections to be identified when labels become detached.

A small handful of moss should be wetted and squeezed out so that it is damp but not soaking wet. This is placed around the base of the cuttings which are then wrapped in polythene and bound sufficiently tightly that the cuttings do not move relative to each other but not so tightly as to bruise or otherwise damage the tissues. The top leafy part of the cuttings is left free and uncovered by this polythene. While trekking the cuttings are best boxed, packed firmly so that they do not get bruised. It is important to keep the cuttings as cool as possible and they should be kept out of any direct sun, particularly at rest stops. A polystyrene box is ideal in keeping the temperature of the cuttings even but is not always practicable. When camping for the evening, especially when carrying cuttings for several days, they should be unpacked. The leafy parts can be exposed to any remaining daylight (but not direct sun), and they can be misted over with a fine spray. When doing this the bundles of cuttings should be placed horizontally or even upside down so that excess water does not run to the cutting bases under the polythene and cause rotting.

If cuttings are kept out of direct sun and suitably 'aired' allowing some photosynthesis without them drying out they can be kept in good condition for at

Processing plants in camp.

least 10 days before final transportation, although in hot lowland conditions this time should perhaps be halved. In hotels with air conditioning the cuttings can be similarly 'aired' but they should be covered loosely with polythene to prevent drying out and misted over whenever possible. The salad compartment of a fridge can also usefully be employed for a few days but care should be taken that the specimens do not get frozen. Final packing for postage or air freight should be in a strong box. The cuttings should be packed tightly so that they do not move in transit and should be wrapped in dry absorbent newspaper which will help to insulate them from extremes of temperature as well as absorbing excess transpired water. Far more cuttings are lost in transit from being too wet than from being too dry. Being completely sealed in polythene often results in total leaf drop and death. Some people use 'stayfresh' polythene bags which are designed to 'breathe' and have been treated with a natural stone powder which is said to absorb harmful ageing chemicals. If cuttings are placed in these they should not be opened except at their final destination. Cuttings packed in boxes and committed to the post or freight should arrive in seven days when a high percentage usually arrives in good enough condition for them to be rooted and grown on. Every day after this the viability drops significantly, and there is usually little chance of growing cuttings that are sealed and in transport beyond two weeks. On arrival at their final destination the cuttings should be inspected for pests and diseases, ideally quarantined, shortened to healthy stem and treated as normal.

Seedlings

Seedlings are often abundantly available, frequently in places where they will never grow to maturity, and it is easy to collect specimens with the root systems complete and surrounded with natural moss. Larger specimens can be treated like cuttings, with the roots bound in polythene but the upper leafy stem left exposed. This leafy part can often be shortened with advantage; it makes the plant more manageable and will compensate for root damage. Small seedlings can be completely immersed in polythene bags which are best inflated so that leaves are not in direct contact with the polythene. Loose strands of moss added will prevent the plants moving too much. Seedlings collected in this way and carried as for cuttings will often

survive better than cutting material and will grow away faster. The drawback is that you cannot be sure of what you have collected. Roadside banks where seedlings are often abundant can produce a high percentage of hybrids or species which may not have been apparent at the collecting site. The other consideration is that importation of soil into most countries is not permitted, and seedlings with anything like soil attached may receive harsh treatment and be reduced to cuttings or destroyed by inspecting authorities at the point of importation.

Seed

Seed is in many ways the easiest way to collect wild vireyas. It is light, very easy to transport and has least impact on the wild population. It will survive travel conditions that cuttings and seedlings will not. It should ideally be collected just as the capsules are beginning to split, although searching old capsules for a few lingering seeds can be profitable – this was the way *Rhododendron flavoviride* was brought into cultivation. It should be dried quickly but not harshly, packeted with full collecting details and kept dry and cool. Most wild collected seed will germinate readily if sown within a month of collection without particularly elaborate preparation, although damp seed loses its viability very quickly. If seed is to be kept longer than a month it should be dried more carefully, ideally with some desiccating agent, and sealed and kept very dry, in a refrigerator. Seed carefully dried and stored at low temperatures will keep its viability for many months. Seed does however suffer from the same drawback as the collection of seedlings: a remarkably high proportion of wild collected seeds can be hybrid. It is very important when growing wild collected seed not to grow on just the most vigorous seedlings. These are more likely to be hybrids, the pure species growing much more slowly in a mixed batch.

Local people

It cannot be stressed too strongly that a good relationship with local people is of overriding importance for the success of collecting in the wild. On arrival in a village there is often a protocol of meeting the local leader to explain what you are trying to do and who you are. It is important to allow plenty of time to hire guides and porters. Arrival in the middle of a rice

Zak, a local guide, decorated with rhododendrons in his hair.

harvest or a local wedding will mean people will not be rushing to help. At the best of times people need some time to make domestic arrangements before commit-

ting themselves to being away for an extended period and they may need an 'advance' to buy the family tinned food during their absence. It is rarely profitable to show irritation or annoyance. Most village people are very family orientated and a few pictures of one's own family often 'breaks the ice'. A few small gifts are often appreciated by people who frequently go out of their way to be hospitable, often cooking and providing hot water or even moving out of a house so that one can sleep without having to make a camp.

Expect to be a spectacle! A few pictures of the sort of plant that one is looking for often sparks intense debate and can be useful, but expect the unexpected when asking people to look for a particular plant. Negotiate firmly and clearly what rates will be paid to guides and carriers and make sure this is understood and accepted. It is useful to have asked around beforehand what the going rates of pay are but don't expect to stick to them too rigidly; it does not pay to be mean. It is sometimes worthwhile offering a bonus if one reaches the summit of a particular peak. This can concentrate the minds of guides wonderfully. All too often one can be led to a different, easier destination and then not have the time or resources to accomplish what one has set out to do. Treat the local people with respect and they almost invariably will prove to be wonderfully knowledgeable companions who help all they can.

7 CULTIVATION AND PROPAGATION

David Mitchell and Louise Galloway

Royal Botanic Garden Edinburgh

Introduction

The secret of growing vireyas successfully is to have an understanding of their natural environment. Vireyas range in the wild from sea level in the tropics to over 4000m but are most commonly found on mountains at altitudes between 1000m and 3000m, in moist cloud forest growing as epiphytes on trees. Some species grow above 4000m and can be subject to night frosts but this does not make them 'hardy' in temperate cultivation, all but a few of the extreme lowland species preferring cool frost free conditions.

General requirements

Vireya rhododendrons, like all members of the Ericaceae, require acidic conditions to grow in. As they experience daily downpours whether clinging onto trees as epiphytes or growing terrestrially in shallow forest soils, their root systems require good air circulation and available water but will not tolerate water logging, therefore an acidic, very free-draining mix is essential. Whether growing in a lofty position in the rain forest canopy or on open ground above the tree line, vireyas are accustomed to high light levels and regular exposure to cloud and mist. An ideal situation for growing vireyas therefore would be exposure to the sun in the morning, with more dappled shade as the day goes on and humidity levels drop.

For cultivation purposes vireyas can be divided into three groups: tropical (0–1000m), temperate (1000–3000m), and alpine (3000–4000m).

In temperate climates vireyas require to be grown in a glasshouse or conservatory, which will provide heated protection from the cold in winter, and good air circulation during the summer. The structure can be either glass or twin wall polycarbonate sheeting; the choice seems to have very little effect on growth. Vireyas can also be grown in a polythene tunnel providing there is adequate ventilation.

Compost

In 1982 Royal Botanic Garden Edinburgh (RBGE) horticulturist Ian Sinclair had the opportunity to spend six weeks plant collecting in Sarawak and Sabah, where he observed 'the way the roots forced their way through and over the moss and humus that covered the trees of the moss forest'. It was very open and free draining and therefore would have a high oxygen level with no water logging or stagnation (Sinclair 1984). On his return to Edinburgh, Sinclair was able to begin to identify the needs of the vireyas more thoroughly, using his experience to create a much more open, loam free mix. Three expeditions were mounted between 1991 and 1995 to Brunei, Irian Jaya and Mt Kinabalu (Sabah) which built on Sinclair's observations. Soil structure and nutrient availability from different topographical and climatic regions were analysed and compared with the growing conditions provided within the vireya collection in Edinburgh. The data provided valuable information on how we could develop optimum compost and liquid feeding programmes. These are now completely peat free as is environmentally desirable (Mitchell 2003).

The current compost used in Edinburgh is approximately pH 5.5. It is completely bark based with additional fritted trace elements and magnesium limestone. Rouse (1979) demonstrated that despite vireyas requiring acid conditions they in fact have a high requirement for calcium. Magnesium limestone provides this necessary nutrient without raising the pH. After some years in use, it has been found to be ideal for a wide range of species, from all altitudinal zones (Mitchell 2003).

Edinburgh compost

- 60 litres medium grade potting bark (2.5–3cm)
- 40 litres fine grade propagation bark (0.5–1cm)
- 80g magnesium limestone
- 40g fritted trace elements

This provides an ideal acid, moisture-retentive yet free-draining, open medium for vireyas. If these materials are not available, many similar products can be obtained from orchid growers as orchids often require similar conditions. Other substrates which may be available include coir (coco-fibre), redwood bark, and ground pumice, the aim always being to create an open, well-drained, acid medium.

Supplementary lighting

Tropical light levels are fairly uniform, with 12 hours of light and darkness every day of the year. Although often found growing in dappled shade, vireyas are generally highly light demanding in the wild, experiencing a period of direct sunlight at some point over the course of the day. This can pose problems for vireya growers living anywhere with seasonal variation. If the vireyas are to benefit from the optimum light levels during the winter months the simplest way to ensure good light availability is to carry out a yearly internal and external glass-cleaning programme before the onset of winter. In addition to improving the light quality this practice avoids the build up of algae and moss on the inside of the roof which can cause a wick-like drip effect during wet weather. Any rainwater dripping into pots can be lethal, causing roots to rot, especially during the winter months.

Artificial lighting is not essential but it can be beneficial, especially for those species from higher altitudes. Additional lighting can also help young plants or those which are slow growing or shy to flower. For larger collections 400W high-pressure sodium lamps provide the optimum spectrum of light for photosynthesis. For smaller scale collections a fluorescent tube lighting bank can be constructed consisting of two twin waterproof fluorescent tube fittings, suspended 600–800mm above the bench. These should be fitted with a combination of warm white and day light tubes, paired; this combination gives the best available spectrum of light for plant growth.

Although expensive to install and run, lighting is definitely something which the serious grower of high altitude species such as *R. ericoides*, *R. ultimum* and many of the densely scaly malayovireyas should consider, as the benefits can be substantial, if not critical to their survival. A sensor can be installed to deactivate the lights once adequate radiation levels have been reached. The RBGE currently has two benches of lighting banks, which provide supplementary lighting to our high altitude species through the long, dark winter months. They are set to come on from 06.30 in the morning and go off at 18.30, which imitates the 12-hour day they would experience in the wild.

Shading

Good light improves flowering and can enhance flower colour (although sudden changes in direct sunlight can scorch the leaves). In northern latitudes the

Plants on the light bench at RBGE.

Vireya house with shading.

rapid increase in the length and intensity of spring sunlight, especially after so many months in poor light, can be a shock to the system for many vireya species which can result in leaf damage. To prevent this plants can be shaded from May through to mid August, using either an internal shade screen, which blocks out 30% of the sunlight, or a liquid shade paint applied outside. It is essential that the shade can be easily removed at the latest before the end of September when the sun's strength is diminishing rapidly.

In temperate frost free regions with hot dry periods in the summer vireyas are best grown in a shade house which provides good air circulation, clad in a material which will reduce strong sunlight by about approximately 30–50%.

Heating, cooling and humidity

The mid-montane species are the easiest and least demanding of the vireyas and in Edinburgh we have found a minimum night temperature of 8–10°C (46–50°F) and a day temperature of 13°C (55°F) with venting at 15°C (59°F) ideal. Thus they are well suited to a cool greenhouse or conservatory. Lowland species are not inherently difficult but do require more heat, with minimum night temperatures of 15–18°C (59–64°F). Plants whose foliage turns bright red in winter are being chilled and are showing signs of stress. They can recover from this but it indicates that they are close to their tolerance limits and spring growth may be delayed. It is best to avoid hot air fan systems as these

can drastically reduce the humidity levels and will be detrimental to the health of the plants.

Humidity is essential for healthy growth and development for all species; ideally it should be maintained around 70%, as an atmosphere that is too dry can lead to distorted foliage and flowers, as bud scales fail to open properly and persist on the plant. Maintaining this level of humidity can be especially difficult during the hottest part of the year, and an overhead misting system, or low-level sprinkler system, will help to sustain humidity. The use of overhead mist systems can increase the risk of damage to leaves and flowers through scorch and should be avoided on very sunny days. Overhead misting can also increase maintenance by encouraging the build up of algae, liverworts and weeds. Time is wisely invested damping down paths and gravel benches at least twice a day by hand during hot periods, although this will rarely be needed in the winter.

Rhododendron macgregoriae and *R. laetum*
showing red coloration due to cold.

Debbie White

Good ventilation is vital in the cultivation of vireyas, especially in warmer climates. Most species become stressed above 28°C (85°F) and they will not tolerate prolonged high temperatures. A good glasshouse should have at least 33% of its floor area available as ventilator space, with the vents being fitted to both the sides and the ridge ensuring good air movement. In very hot climates, a paddle and/or extractor fan and misting system may also be required to regulate the temperature.

Containers and bark sections for epiphytes

Although some species can be either epiphytic or terrestrial in nature many species grow in both situations, which makes them well suited to being grown in containers as their root systems are small and not adversely affected by confinement. Many growers believe that vireyas perform better in clay pots than plastic, as the roots remain cooler; however, they can perform equally well in plastic. Within the RBGE the main species collection is cultivated in clay pots, with plenty of crocks in the bottom. Plastic pots are used only for propagation and very young plants. Clay pots dry out faster than plastic ones which means that the watering has to be monitored carefully; however, this is an advantage for two reasons – clay pots keep the delicate roots cool during the summer, and they also prevent water logging which will kill plants outright very quickly. For taller plants the clay pots also act as a heavy anchor preventing often top-heavy plants from falling over.

Due to the fine nature of the roots and natural surface rooting it is vital to provide aeration to the roots. Growers in Australia have experimented with plastic pots with 'vents' cut into the sides and used these to insert cuttings, with positive results, concluding that 'a greater number of holes at close to one and a half inch centres' proved excellent for these epiphytes which 'thrive with good aeration to the roots' (Clancy 1974). Vireyas are also being grown successfully in aquatic plant baskets with open mesh sides in Bremen, Germany, as these similarly provide the abundant aeration which is so beneficial.

When growing vireyas in containers, to ensure that pots drain as efficiently as possible and to avoid pests entering the container, plants should be raised off the ground. Greenhouse benches are ideal and should be of a strong construction, with either a slatted base or a solid base, which is covered in coarse 'pea' gravel (4–5mm, ¼in.) which will help to increase humidity around the plants. Sand can be used but it generally becomes too wet and is best avoided. A vertical rack with a simple overhead misting system of the sort often used in orchid cultivation for epiphytic specimens can be very successful and economical with space. Young plants can be gently tied on cork bark slabs or sections of tree-fern using nylon monofilament (fishing line) and a small quantity of moss. Once established these plants rarely need to be replanted.

Re-potting

Re-potting is best carried out annually on young plants, but this can be reduced to every two or three years for mature specimens to avoid stressing the older roots which can get more vulnerable to disturbance with age. The aim should be to give room for new root growth and to keep the growing medium open. Old compost can degenerate into a compact mass which excludes the vital air. Re-potting can begin as soon as the 'growing' season commences. It is important not to pot up too late in the season as the roots must have time to move into new compost or they can be susceptible to rot in the winter. When handling plants during re-potting great care must be taken to avoid damaging the fine roots – do not tease out too vigorously. It is also good practice to ensure that the roots are moist before being handled; watering the previous day is ideal. Pot on gradually each year simply moving up through the pot sizes. Over-potting should also be avoided as the plants will take longer to establish themselves effectively in the container, making them very susceptible to over-watering and drought, both of which can result in death. Plants should never be re-potted any deeper than they were in the previous container as the fine surface roots can suffocate, the problem often not showing up until sudden death occurs some months later for no apparent reason. Potting should be firm using fingertips, not thumbs as they can exert too much pressure! Leave at least 15mm (just over ½in.) between the top of the compost and the rim of the pot to stop the compost being washed over the side when watering, and water immediately after potting to settle the roots in the compost.

Watering and misting

For collections that contain both juvenile and mature plants in a range of container sizes with a mixture of clay and plastics, hand watering is the best method to avoid over-watering, although in warmer climates drip watering systems can be used to good effect if monitored closely.

It is best to check the watering every day, especially small pots during warm weather. In the wild these plants would experience tropical downpours, thus vireyas prefer a good soaking as long as the water is draining freely through the pot, and should then be allowed to almost dry out between waterings to avoid root rot. More vireyas are killed through too much water than not enough! Water evenly using a 'soft rain' lance over the surface of the pot to ensure that the entire root-ball is covered and the compost is not displaced. During the winter months water more sparingly, keeping plants slightly on the dry side; however, they must not be allowed to dry out completely.

Water quality is important: it should be as soft as possible, with few dissolved salts. Ideally rainwater should be used, especially if the local supply is hard with large quantities of dissolved salts. In areas of hard water containing high volumes of solids and water with high salt levels a reverse osmosis system can be used to remove solids and salinity (Anon. 1996). During cold spells it is advantageous to store the water in a water butt at close hand to your plants and to warm the water to the ambient temperature of the growing area; this is especially useful when growing on seedlings and young plants.

Plants cultivated on frames on sections of cork bark or tree-fern should be misted over twice daily in the summer in the morning and evening, and as and when they feel dry in the winter.

Feeding

Vireyas are not voracious feeders but species do require some extra nutrition in pot culture, especially when growing in such an open mix. Regular light applications are best, especially when used in conjunction with a foliar feed containing trace elements. Fast acting, high dosage feeds should be avoided as they can burn the fine surface roots.

Tod (1969) working in Scotland showed that rhododendrons develop best when the nitrogen supply is from ammonium salts and that the plants are 'detrimentally affected if the nitrogen supply is in the form of nitrate' (Sinclair 1984).

A water-soluble fertiliser is simple, effective and easy to use and can be applied in different strengths depending on the overall health of the plant. Feeding at a quarter or half the recommended strength every two weeks throughout the growing season is successful. This allows the containers to be flushed through in between feeding to avoid a build up of salts which would raise the pH and be harmful to the roots. A foliar feed can also be applied once a month. It is important not to over-feed as although this can make the plants wonderfully lush and green, flowering is reduced.

Higher amounts of nitrogen can be added early in the growing season to green the plants up, as after the winter the plants can look a little 'off colour' and chlorotic. During the summer a balanced approach works well, using N.P.K. 1:1:1; this will keep the vireyas in steady growth with improved colour. Towards the end of the growing season a feed with higher potassium levels can be applied to strengthen stems which will lessen the chance of attack from pests and disease through the winter. Various different feeds can be successful. Fish fertiliser at half strength has been used successfully in America (White Smith 1994).

Pinching and pruning

Pinching refers to the practice of removing the growing tip or bud of a stem to encourage branching. If carried out regularly, particularly when a plant is young, it can lead to a better shaped bush and potentially more flowers, although it may delay the first flowering. Feeding at the same time often helps but with some species there is no guarantee that more than one new shoot will appear, and it is sometimes difficult to counteract the very 'leggy' upright nature of some species. It is possible to begin pinching once a cutting has established roots, unless a 'standard' is required, in which case this procedure is not carried out until the plant has reached the desired height. Pinching is best done when the plants are beginning to grow in spring (Fairweather 2003). Pruning is not always necessary – although some vireyas are rather 'leggy', most plants will eventually fill out from lower down a bare stem given time and space to develop.

Pruning should be undertaken with some caution and if it needs to be severe should be carried out over a period, allowing the plant time to recover. Feeding beforehand is often worthwhile to ensure the bush is growing strongly, and afterwards the compost should be kept slightly drier than usual until new growth emerges.

Deadheading

Regular deadheading is strongly recommended: it stops the plant diverting energy into seed production and reduces the time between flowerings. By removing dead flowers many species can be induced to flower several times a year. *Rhododendron burttii* with its bright starry red flowers will flower 6–8 times a year when deadheaded regularly.

Hanging baskets

Although hanging baskets require more frequent watering they are a very effective way of cultivating vireyas and there are some wonderful hybrids suitable for this purpose (Fairweather 2003). Species vireyas tend not to make elegant specimens in hanging baskets, although a few can be very successful; *R. rubineiflorum*, *R. leptanthum* and *R. gracilentum* are of a suitable size and habit. Additionally, strongly epiphytic species such as *R. christi* with its beautiful red and yellow bicoloured flowers would do well in baskets, and some species actually perform better: Cavendar (1993) records his 5–6-year-old *R. pauciflorum* (which he states is misnamed as it actually means shy to flower) had been in bloom continuously for 18 months in a hanging basket.

Wire baskets are the most universally used containers, although slatted aquatic pots are growing in popularity. The benefit of aquatic pots is that they do not require a liner. If a liner is required there are several materials on the market but coir is the most widely used.

Landscape cultivation techniques, inside and out

In northern latitudes, vireyas can be grown to wonderful effect within a glasshouse landscape, especially when planted with species that would naturally grow alongside them in the wild. This is rarely practical as a large area is required. In favourable parts of Australia, New Zealand, Hawaii or North America, vireyas can be grown outdoors with considerable success, and can reach their true potential.

In preparation of planting beds, as with all forms of vireya cultivation, good drainage is essential, as plants will not tolerate their 'feet in water'. First lay a central drain with angled spurs as required and position it to take water away from the centre of the bed before finally connecting it to the main glasshouse drainage system. Above this lay a gravel 'raft' over the entire cultivation area using a 250mm (10in.) layer of 10–20mm (½in.) washed gravel. Although elaborate, this system allows large amounts of water to drain away rapidly. Once the drainage is installed raised edges can be constructed from a combination of artificial peat blocks, large ornamental stones, logs and tree stumps. Anything can be used which looks attractive, as long as it does not raise the pH and it facilitates the creation of planting niches. Finally a layer of compost is laid over the whole area or it can be added to with terracing to give additional height.

A raised bed with a central plastic drain contained in a gravel raft.

Display of vireya rhododendrons.

The planting mix for beds is slightly different from the container compost as when planted out the vireyas can be more vigorous, requiring more nutrients, and the compost has to stay in place for a longer period.

Planting mix for beds

- 70% potting and ornamental pine bark
- 20% sterilised loam
- 10% charcoal
- Slow release granular fertiliser (optional)

The bark keeps the compost open, only decaying slowly. The loam provides a reservoir of nutrients and the charcoal keeps the compost sweet and fresh. Stepping stones with a firm underlying base should be placed on the surface of the beds to aid access for

planting and maintenance so that the growing area does not get unnecessarily compacted. It is important to water the bed for a day or two before planting commences to ensure that the compost is fully wetted.

In some parts of America where outdoor cultivation is necessary due to long hot summers which are detrimental to plants through excess heat but where winter protection is required it is possible to remove the skin of the greenhouse during warm weather and replace it through the cold spell (Halligan 1985). It is always advantageous to create a raised bed planting to maximise drainage for healthy root systems. Planting straight into the ground will not work if the soil is heavy, as water will accumulate and root problems will follow (Deul 1981). Areas can be built up using sections of tree-fern, railway sleepers (railroad ties), brick or rockwork. Tree-fern trunks are an ideal medium for creating raised beds in countries where they are available as 'they provide ideal anchorage for the plant and good aeration for the roots', it is difficult to over-water sections of tree-fern as they are naturally free draining, and each log will last 15–20 years (Clancy 1973b).

The rules described for pot culture still apply. Planting depth is critical: vireyas will not tolerate being planted too deeply and they also dislike root disturbance. Outdoors it is advisable to establish an annual mulching programme, as this helps to maintain moisture as well as suppressing weeds which compete with the fine roots. Suitable materials include bark, pine needles, tree-fern fibre and leaf mould.

In some areas frost protection may be required. Where this is only occasional and not too severe, it can be achieved with temporary removable structures covered in shade netting. Sometimes planting on banks or under natural tree cover will be enough to protect the plants.

Feeding will vary; a slow release granular fertiliser may be advantageous where rainfall and leaching are not too severe. In wetter areas more frequent applications of a faster acting granular fertiliser can be used. The aim should be to keep the N.P.K. ration either 1:1:1 (early in the growing season) or 1:1:3 (before any period of slower growth or dormancy).

Propagation

The two main methods of propagating vireyas are by cuttings and seed. Grafting, layering and tissue culture have all been used in special circumstances.

Cuttings

These are a rapid way of increasing plants and retaining the true identity of the parent plant, essential for the propagation of select hybrids (Kenyon & Walker 1997). Vireya cuttings are very easy to root using semi-ripe nodal cuttings, when the stem is beginning to firm yet still remains flexible. Cuttings will vary in size depending on the species: 8–10cm (3–4in.) lengths of stems with two nodes will suffice. On some of the larger species, or where woodier material has to be

A, Shortening a cutting to just below the node. B, Wounding a cutting to expose cambium. C, Dipping a cutting in hormone solution. D, A rooted cutting.

used, wounding is beneficial. This is done by slicing away either one or two very thin slivers, approximately 1–2cm (½–¾in.) in length, from the base of the cutting. It provides a larger surface area for root initiation by exposing more cambium (Argent & Galloway 2003). Another technique which has been found to be beneficial in rooting very scaly species is to remove the scales from the base of the cuttings with a stiff brush such as a tooth brush.

Remove all the leaves in the basal half of the cuttings and cut the top half off the upper leaves. This will reduce water loss, make the cuttings less top-heavy and allow more to be packed into the propagation area. A fungicide may be applied to reduce the risk of rotting but this is not normally necessary. A proprietary rooting hormone is advantageous and the instructions should be followed for semi-ripe, woody plants. A very light open acid compost is again required and a mix of 50:50 propagation bark and vermiculite or perlite has proved very successful. Bark separates readily when potting on which keeps damage to the delicate roots to a minimum. After insertion cuttings are watered in thoroughly with tepid water and ideally placed into a closed case or a mist bench with a basal temperature of approximately 21–25°C together with supplementary lighting. In this situation rooting should occur within 8–12 weeks; larger species with thicker stems and those which are densely scaly often take longer. A less sophisticated technique is to place the cuttings in a pot, completely enclose the pot and cuttings in a polythene bag and place this somewhere where it will not be disturbed and will receive good light but not direct sunlight. Cuttings will root in this way but can take a long time.

Once rooted, the cuttings should be removed from the closed case or mist bench and hardened off for at least two weeks in an open case, with reduced basal heat which still gently encourages root formation with supplementary lighting. The cuttings can then be potted on into the regular vireya mix, taking great care not to damage the fine, delicate root systems which are easily broken. After potting the young plants should be returned to an open case where they should remain on basal heat and supplementary lighting until they are showing signs of new growth.

Amateur seed-raising box.

Seed

Growing vireyas from seed, although not difficult, demands dedication as plants can take more than six years from sowing to flowering. It is however rewarding, especially for those who wish to experiment with hybridising. Seed should be harvested from mature capsules which have just started to split naturally. Moyles (2001) stressed the importance of fully mature seed. If it is to be stored it should be quickly and thoroughly dried and kept dry stored in a fridge or freezer. In these days of import permits, plant passports, and quarantine restrictions, growing from seed can be a simple way to add to a collection.

The techniques described by Rouse (1985) have proved very successful. His growing case (see next page) is in outward appearance almost identical to a standard closed case, but internally it is quite different with the basal heat being provided from a reservoir of warm water rather than a sand bed. A fan ventilator is placed at one end towards the bottom just above the surface of the water; this pulls steady streams of air from an opposing vent over the warm water and up through the pots. The fan, which runs continuously, allows a humid atmosphere to be maintained within the case whilst preventing the build up of condensation, lowering the risk of pathological problems to which young seedlings can be prone.

The water is heated to 25°C (77°F) using standard aquatic, 150W fish tank heaters and the seed trays are suspended above the water and the fan on a metal grill. Supplementary lighting is provided by a combination of warm white and day light fluorescent tubes suspended just above the perspex lid of the case; this is essential as light is necessary for germination of

A, Outside of Rouse box. B, Inside of Rouse box with seedlings and *Pinguicula* (pink flower) to trap flies.

vireya seed and low levels of light will result in a poor percentage germination (Rouse 1985).

The duration of supplementary lighting for seed germination varies. The seedlings grow happily in 24-hour light and this may be advisable in northern latitudes, but Rouse (1985) found little advantage above 16 hours' light in a day and Moyles (2001) also reports success with 16 hours. Pots of insectivorous *Pinguicula cordata* (butterwort) are useful to control sciarid flies which stick to the leaves like fly-paper. Sciarids can

be a problem as the larvae will eat the fine seedling roots.

Clean seed and sow directly onto the surface of compost (use boiling water to sterilise but allow to cool!). This should eliminate infestations of sciarid fly larvae. Plastic pots must be heat tolerant for sterilising with boiling water. There are various composts: finely riddled bark works well in Edinburgh. Other growers use milled sphagnum moss mixed with perlite: this it is claimed 'is easy to use, doesn't cake, or become soggy',

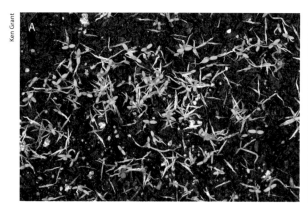

A, Germinating seeds. B, One-year-old seedlings. C, Three-year-old seedlings.

and 'seedlings rarely damp off' (Moyles, unpublished ARS report).

Sow the seed evenly and settle them on the surface by spraying with a fine mist (hand held spray). Place a glass lid on top: this creates a moist microclimate in which the seeds will not dry out. The lids must be turned daily to avoid the build up of condensation. If you cannot check daily you could use fine polythene film, as 'Poly film breathes, yet retains moisture' (Moyles, unpublished ARS report). Fresh seed should germinate in two weeks, older seed may take longer. Once the first leaves have developed remove the glass lids to avoid damping off. Once seedlings begin to grow together prick them out into seed trays or individual pots containing riddled/sieved vireya mix (the general mix can be too coarse at this stage), and place back under the lights to avoid long, etiolated seedlings. Seedlings often take a check at this stage and it is sometimes advantageous to prick out small clumps of seedlings rather than individuals. Once the seedlings have reached approximately 2–3cm (1in.), they can be potted on into individual pots. Vireya seedlings can be quite slow to develop initially and can benefit from regular weak feeds.

Other methods

Grafting has not been found necessary in Edinburgh but in Australia John Rouse used simple whip and tongue grafts to propagate species which were prone to root rots in the high temperature of summer using vigorous hybrid stocks.

Layering – Some species such as *R. bagobonum* will naturally send roots out from their nodes if surrounded by moss.

Micro/tissue propagation – This technique is used for producing large numbers of identical plants, for which there is rarely sufficient demand. It is often unsuccessful as most vireya material is contaminated with bacteria within the tissues.

8 PESTS, DISEASES AND DISORDERS

Stephan Helfer

Royal Botanic Garden Edinburgh

Introduction

Considering the sheer number of harmful arthropods and micro-organisms (according to *Encyclopaedia Britannica* 10,000 species of insects alone) which afflict plants worldwide, it is always encouraging to find how healthy, hardy and vigorous rhododendrons are in general. This also applies to a large extent to vireyas. Fortunately few pests and diseases are known in this group, and this does not appear to be because they have been overlooked. Vireyas are true rhododendrons with respect to most of their pathogens and pests. However, as their growing requirements are different from those of other rhododendrons, mainly the temperature regimes, the occurrence of their troubles may be quite different.

As with all other plants, disease and pest development in vireyas are dependent on three variables: host plant, pathogen (or pest organism) and environment. Within each variable, a number of factors are important: host plant susceptibility, physiological condition, age and, in some cases, previous exposure to pathogens; pathogen virulence and fitness; soil, water and air conditions, weather and climate. Only when all three variables are conducive will pests and diseases occur. Serious epidemics can happen, when these variables are relatively uniform over a wide area (monoculture) or a longer period of time. Apart from short-lived outbreaks of powdery mildew and rust (Helfer 2003; G. Smith *pers. comm.*), this has not seriously affected vireyas so far, and diversity in cultivation is the best method to avert severe outbreaks of epidemics.

Good plant husbandry and hygiene are important for keeping problems away and essential for control, should a problem have penetrated the defences (Watling 2003). Where appropriate, new plants should be quarantined for a period of three months or more (unpublished data); the Royal Botanic Garden Edinburgh (RBGE), for instance, currently quarantines all incoming rhododendrons, irrespective of origin. The choice of plant and environmental conditions is equally important, in order to establish vigorous plants, which will be more likely to resist or tolerate parasites.

The pest problems of vireyas

There are at least 12 groups of pests troubling vireyas. Below, they are ordered into three categories: chewing pests, stationary sap-sucking pests and mobile sap-sucking pests. It is difficult to state which ones are the most troublesome, as each can cause great concern when appearing in high numbers. Additionally, it should be remembered that many pests carry virus particles or open protecting plant tissue, thus making the plants vulnerable to fungal or bacterial attack.

Chewing pests

• Weevils (Cucurlionidae): Vine weevils and other species appear to be a problem only in greenhouses in otherwise cooler climates. Apparently the pest cannot survive in tropical conditions (Nielsen 1986). Treatment with pathogenic nematodes, which infect the root-feeding weevil grubs with a fatal bacterial disease, has been successful and there are proprietary chemical treatments on the market.

• Sciarid fly (*Bradysia paupera* Tuomikoski): Sciarid fly larvae gnaw roots and may cause damage on seedlings (see Cultivation, chapter 7).

• Caterpillars (Lepidoptera): Leaves of vireyas in the wild are often severely damaged by herbivorous insects (presumably mainly caterpillars and adult weevils). In cultivation these pests can cause losses occasionally, but if problems are discovered early and the culprits removed, successful control is straightforward.

• Cockroaches (Dictyoptera): Occasionally cockroaches cause damage to vireyas, especially when the plants are grown under glass. This is usually mainly cosmetic damage; flowers and flower buds can be chewed and sometimes young leaves but it is rarely life threatening to the plants. Good housekeeping by eliminating

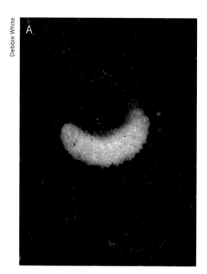

Vine weevil. A, Larva. B, Adult beetle. C, Damage on *Rhododendron crassifolium* (ringbarked base of cutting).

places where they can hide and avoiding litter build up discourages these pests.

• Slugs and snails (Pulmonata): Some growers record problems caused by these pests. They are particularly harmful on small seedlings, whereas larger plants are generally left alone. Good pest awareness and physical removal of the animals is normally all that is needed to protect the plants. Moist traps are very effective, especially when laced with beer dregs and kept in a dark spot. Commercial slug baits or soil drenches with a pathogenic nematode are also available.

• Parrots: For those fortunate enough to live in a climate that supports these birds, parrots may become a problem, as they selectively go for the bright *Vireya* flowers (Anon. 2004b).

Stationary sap-sucking pests

• Soft scale (*Coccus hesperidum* L.): This is a relatively new pest of vireyas, normally preferring hosts in cooler environments. The adult insect is stationary, sucking leaf juices from the stems and lower leaf surface. As it does so a sticky honeydew will be excreted onto foliage below the insect, and may become contaminated by sooty moulds. The adult is up to 5mm long and produces hundreds of crawler nymphs (soft scale lays its eggs underneath its own body). The crawlers can spread very rapidly across the whole plant. If discovered early, soft scale can be controlled by removing the scales or affected leaves and stems before the crawlers spread out. There is also a parasitic wasp available as a biological control against this pest.

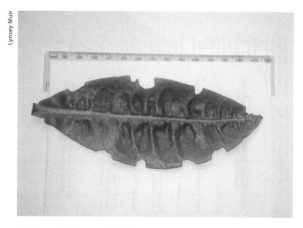

Cockroach damage to leaf.

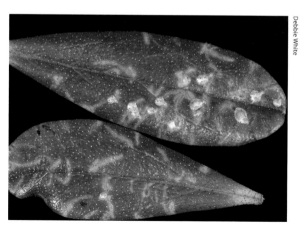

Scale insect damage to leaves.

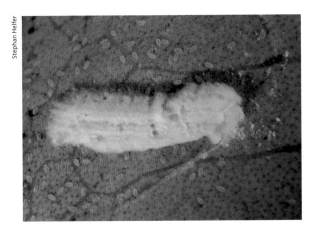

Cottony cushion or fluted scale egg case surrounded by crawlers.

• Cottony cushion or fluted scale (*Icerya purchasi* Maskell): This is a potentially serious pest of many woody plants, known better from citrus plantations, where it causes extensive damage. It has only very occasionally been found on vireyas (L. Galloway *pers. comm.*).

• Mealybugs (*Pseudococcus* sp.): This is another piercing, sucking insect common to many plants, especially in warmer areas (or under glass). Adults are pinkish brown and up to 4mm long. They frequently infest leaf axils and other hidden places, and are often noticed only when their host becomes sticky with honeydew in their vicinity. They produce a fluffy white wax from their bodies which also serves to conceal their eggs. They can be a really persistent problem which may cause severe disfigurement. A ladybird predator can be used in biological control (Anon. 2004a) and there are various proprietary chemical sprays which give

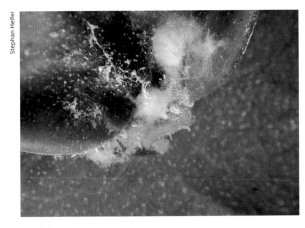

Mealybug.

Sooty mould on leaves of *Rhododendron apoanum*.

control, although this often needs to be repeated as the eggs are well hidden and the waxy coatings have considerable resistance to wetting. Every opportunity should be taken to hand pick both adults and egg masses.

Mobile sap-sucking pests

• Thrips (Thysanoptera): Together with mealybugs, thrips are the most troublesome pests for vireyas in outdoor cultivation. The tiny insects (up to 2mm long) feed on the sap of individual cells, causing a characteristic mottling effect on the leaves. There is a predatory mite (*Neoseiulus = Amblyseius* sp.) that can be used against these pests (Loomans & van Lenteren 1995; Anon. 2005a). Where legally authorised, sprays are also recommended (Anon. 2005b).

• Lace bug (*Stephanitis* spp.): There are a few species of lace bug that attack rhododendrons including vireyas. They are insects up to 4mm in length (excluding the antennae) with dark wing markings, reminiscent of lace. The nymphs and adult insects feed on plant juices through piercing into the leaves. This causes yellow

Lace bug damage.

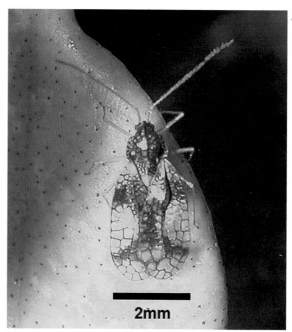

Roger Van Loon

Lace bug.

mottling on the upper sides of leaves whereas the lower sides are speckled with the brown droppings of the pests. They prefer warm sunny situations, just like vireyas. On young and small plants they may cause enough defoliation to threaten the survival of the host. General purpose pesticides are recommended for their control.

• Aphids (Aphididae), whitefly (Aleyrodidae) and leafhoppers (Cicadellidae): These pests are of relatively minor importance for vireyas. Leafhoppers in other rhododendrons are particularly important as they act as vectors of the bud blast fungus, which has not been reported on vireyas.

• Mites (Arachnida: Acari: Tetranychidae): Greenhouse mites such as spider mite can cause problems on vireyas. The characteristic fine web across the leaf surface confirms their presence. Note that there are also beneficial mites, such as the predatory mite *Phytoseiulus persimilis* Athias-Henriot (Phytoseiidae), which feeds on spider mites and can be used as a control agent (Anon. 2005a, 2005c).

Diseases

• *Armillaria*, honey fungus: Members of this genus can kill mature rhododendrons through root infection. They are a more general problem in many areas where woody plants are grown. *Armillaria luteobubalina* Watling & Kile has been found to infect cultivated vireyas in Australia (B. Summerell *pers. comm.*) but other species may affect vireyas elsewhere. This fungus survives in the soil by means of 'boot lace' rhizomorphs on rotting timber. Infected plants characteristically show white sheets of mycelium under the bark at soil level. The fact that some people like eating the mushroom fruiting bodies is little consolation to growers losing their valued woody plants.

• *Asterina*: This is a tropical micro-fungus, producing colonies of about 5mm diameter on the leaves of its host plants; there is only one record of this genus on vireyas: *Rhododendron loranthiflorum* in Papua New Guinea (Shaw 1984). The genus is also known to parasitise *R. arboreum* Sm. in Sri Lanka (Hosagoudar & Abraham 2000).

• *Chrysomyxa rhododendri* (DC.) de Bary (Uredinales): Rust, caused by this pathogen, can be one of the most serious problems of vireyas. It has a complicated life cycle, which requires species of spruce (*Picea*) for its completion. Most rusts have narrow host ranges, restricted to one genus or even one species in some cases. In nature *Picea* spp. and vireya rhododendrons do not share common distributions (Earle 2002; Schmidt 2003) making it very unlikely that the rust ever occurred naturally on vireyas, and all collections of the fungus on vireyas to date are from cultivated specimens. Nevertheless, some vireya rhododendrons are very susceptible to this pathogen, a fact which can be interpreted as indicating their similarity with the other members of the genus. Currently there is insufficient information about the host range of *C. rhododendri* on vireyas or about any genetic resistance to the rust. Artificial inoculations from other rhododendrons have led to successful infections on vireyas at RBGE (A. Bennell *pers. comm.*).

The rust typically attacks young growth. After an incubation period of 7–10 days in which the pathogen invades the leaf tissues, it produces yellow-orange uredinial pustules, mostly on the underside of the leaves. Airborne spores (urediniospores) from these pustules can in turn infect healthy leaves, resulting in rapid spread of the disease. As infections mature, leaves often become necrotic, and in many situations premature defoliation follows. To date no teliospores formation has been observed on vireyas, although this is quite common on many temperate rhododendrons. Whereas spores are normally airborne in nature, spread by humans on hands, clothing, vehicles and tools is probably the most significant mode of dissemination of this pathogen on cultivated plants. There are chemicals marketed to control this fungus but this must be combined with strict hygiene, washing of hands, clothing and tools known to have been in contact with infections, and regular inspection and burning of all infected leaves.

• *Coccomyces*: Whilst this scab-causing genus is known from a number of other Ericaceae, the only record for vireya rhododendrons comes from Java (Sherwood 1980), *C. javanicus* Sacc. & P.Syd. on *R. javanicum*.

• *Colletotrichum*: Species of this genus cause leaf spots on many plants including many rhododendrons. Currently *R. zoelleri* from New Guinea is the only vireya recorded to be affected (Farr *et al.* 2004).

• *Dimerium*: *Rhododendron loranthiflorum* in Papua New Guinea has been found infected by this genus of dark, superficial ascomycetes (Shaw 1984).

• Powdery mildews (Erysiphales): Several species of powdery mildew have been found on vireyas in cultivation. Unfortunately none has reproduced sexually so far, and molecular methods have not been employed to assign the anamorphic stages (oidium) to their respective teleomorphs. Currently the following species have been implicated: *Erysiphe cruciferarum* on *R. aurigeranum*, *R. christianae*, *R. stenophyllum* and *R. zoelleri*; *E. polygoni* on *R. javanicum*, and *Sphaerotheca pannosa* on all the above and more (Gardner *et al.* 1970; Amano 1986; Munro 1986; Basden & Helfer 1995; Helfer 2003).

Rhododendron powdery mildews affect all herbaceous parts of their hosts, producing surface mycelia which send extensive feeder cells (haustoria) into the

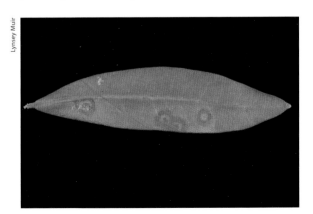

Rust on rhododendron leaf.

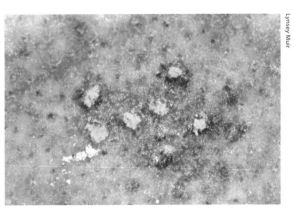

Close-up of rust on leaf.

A, Powdery mildew on rhododendron.
B, Powdery mildew on fruit.
C, Mildew on *Rhododendron christi*.

epidermal layer. The primary effect of this on infected plants is water loss, often leading to drought stress and early defoliation. Asexual spores (conidia) are produced after seven days in optimal conditions (Kenyon 1995). Typically chains of conidia develop on infected hosts, and infection is spread by the deposition of these spores onto healthy leaves.

Both chemical control using fungicides and rigorous hygiene have been employed to combat powdery mildews. In temperate cultivation mildews are a summer problem exacerbated by high temperatures and rarely give cause for concern in the winter months.

• *Exobasidium*: Two species of this genus, well known for producing leaf galls on azaleas, have been recognised on vireyas – *E. papuanum* Otani on *R. womersleyi* in Papua New Guinea and *E. vulcanicum* Racib. on *R. javanicum* in Indonesia (Farr *et al.* 2004).

• *Echidnodella crustacea* (Cooke) Arx: Similar to *Asterina* and *Dimerium* (see above) this fungus produces dark external mycelium on leaves of rhododendrons and other Ericaceae (Goos 1999). It has been reported from *R. retusum* in India and Indonesia and *R. vidalii* in the Philippines (Farr *et al.* 2004).

• *Leptosphaeria*: This genus of ascomycetes produces leaf spots containing dark pycnidia (raised fungal structures) on the leaves of many host plants. The only report on vireyas is on *R. womersleyi* in Papua New Guinea (Shaw 1984).

• *Lophodermium*: This fungus is known as Lophodermium leaf spot on many rhododendrons. It produces

raised corky structures in leaf spots and is most often found on decaying leaf litter. There are a number of species known on rhododendrons, with *L. schweinitzii*, *L. intricatum* and *L. lanceolatum* known in particular on vireyas in the wild (Shaw 1984; Spooner 1991).

• *Mycophaga*: This ascomycete has been reported on *R. loranthiflorum* in Papua New Guinea (Shaw 1984).

Fungal galls on *Rhododendron malayanum*.

• *Phyllosticta* and *Pestalotia*: These genera are well known to cause leaf spotting and grey blight on temperate rhododendrons (Coyier 1986). On vireyas they have so far been reported only on *R. macgregoriae* in Papua New Guinea (Shaw 1984; Farr *et al.* 2004).

• *Phytophthora*: *Phytophthora cinnamomi* Rands is probably one of the most dreaded diseases of rhododendrons, as it is both non-specific and widespread. There are reports of this disease affecting vireyas from many vireya-growing areas (see the *Vireya Vine*, for instance). Other hosts are a wide range of shrubs and trees. The pathogen is soil- and water-borne and affects the roots, causing root death and rot. Whilst not yet reported on vireyas, the dreaded *P. ramorum* Werres, de Cock & Man in't Veld could well become a problem, as it has been found on numerous species of *Rhododendron* and all phytophthoras seem to thrive in higher temperatures. Control of *Phytophthora* is difficult, but adequate drainage is essential to keep these pathogens at bay.

• Virus diseases have not been reported on vireya rhododendrons. However, as non-vireya rhododendrons are attacked by these particles, and viruses are generally widespread, it is to be expected that vireyas also harbour these diseases. Necrotic ringspot, mosaic and leaf spot viruses are all candidates (Corbett 1986). Most virus diseases are spread by insect pests, but in the case of rhododendron man has also been implicated, especially through the use of infected tools when pruning and grafting plants. If viruses occur, it is recommended to destroy affected plants and sterilise any tools used in order to remove the inoculum.

Disorders

Being of tropical origin and frost tender, the biggest threat to the cultivation of vireyas is adverse (i.e. too cold) weather conditions. There are very few disorders affecting vireyas, providing suitable growing conditions are met (see Cultivation chapter). Kenyon & Walker (1997) include in this category leggy growth, bud dieback, sickly foliage, flower wilt and split flowers. Most of these disorders are due to sub-optimal growing conditions: leggy growth is largely a matter of lack of sufficient quality light, and can be a problem under

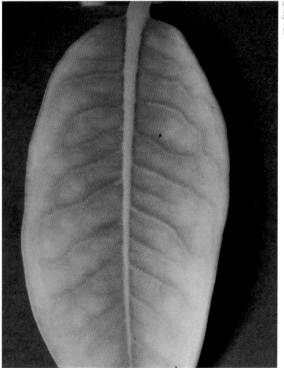

Nutrient deficiency in *Rhododendron loboense*.

glass; bud dieback may happen in mineral-deficient soils, and sickly foliage may be caused by a number of climatic conditions. Flower wilt can be attributed to pollinating bees, and split flowers are a phenomenon linked to the sudden onset of bright warm weather after a period of cool, overcast conditions (Kenyon & Walker 1997). Clearly, the only way to control these problems is to address the root causes.

Other problems

Nematodes, dodders (parasitic higher plants) and algae all can cause trouble on rhododendrons (Benson 1986; Benson & Barker 1986; Holcomb 1986). There are currently no reports of these specifically on vireyas. Good cultural practice, problem awareness and an integrated approach are control strategies of choice against these problems, should they occur on vireya rhododendrons.

GLOSSARY

acid	Of soil being below pH 7 (neutral).
acuminate	With a long gradually tapering point, the sides inwardly curving (fig. III).
acute	With a narrow point less than 45° (fig. III).
alpine	Of plants growing above the tree line on mountains.
anther(s)	The pollen-containing organs (fig. VIII).
pores	The holes through which the pollen is shed (fig. VIII).
apex	The parts furthest from the main part of the plant, usually the growing point or the extremity of an organ such as a leaf tip.
apical	At or near the apex of an organ.
apiculate	With a short, narrow point (fig. III).
appressed	Pressed close to another organ but not united with it.
aromatic	Pleasantly scented.
ascending	Curving upwards, particularly of veins in the leaf (fig. V).
asymmetric	An unequal shape not divisible into two mirror images (fig. II).
attenuate	Gradually tapering (fig. III).
auricles	Small ear-like projections at the base of a leaf (fig. III).
auriculate	With projecting ear-like lobes, usually at the base of a leaf (fig. III).
axil	The internal angle or corner of a branching structure, usually that between leaf and stem (fig. I).
axillary	Arising laterally in the axil of a leaf or bract.
blade	The broad expanse (lamina) of the leaf excluding the petiole (fig. V).
bract	A modified leaf subtending the flower or associated with the inflorescence. This includes the protective leaves surrounding the flower buds (the perulae of Sleumer 1966) (fig. VII).
bracteole	The slender often filamentous structures associated in pairs at the base of each pedicel.
branch	A lateral stem after the leaves have fallen from it (cf. *twig*).
bulbous	With a rounded swelling like a bulb.
calyx	The outer whorl of floral parts, the sepals as a whole. Mostly reduced to a minute ring (fig. VIII).
campanulate	Bell-shaped (fig. IX).
capsule	A dry dehiscent fruit derived from an ovary of several fused carpels. The fruit typical of all rhododendrons (fig. XII).
cartilaginous	Like cartilage – translucent, firm and smooth.
cataphyll	Early leaf form of a shoot, with a much reduced leaf blade (fig. I).
caudate	With a tail, usually describing a leaf apex (fig. III).
cells	Used here for small chambers or cavities, e.g. anther cells (fig. VIII).

channelled	With an elongate groove.
ciliate	Fringed with simple hairs along an edge or margin (fig. VII).
circular	A round shape (fig. II).
conical	Cone-shaped, from a circular base, tapering to a point (three-dimensional).
cordate	Heart-shaped, with two rounded lobes at the base (fig. III).
corolla	The petaloid, most colourful whorl of floral parts (fig. VIII).
tube	The fused portion of the corolla at the base (fig. VIII).
lobe	The free portions of the corolla (fig. VIII).
crenulate	Of a margin with very small rounded teeth (fig. III).
crimped	Of seed tails gathered into folds (fig. XII).
cuspidate	With a short abrupt point (fig. III).
cylindrical	In the form of a cylinder (fig. XII).
decurrent	Having the base prolonged, as in leaves where the blade is continued downwards as a wing on the petiole (fig. III).
dehiscent	Of an organ which opens to shed its contents, usually pollen or seed.
dendroid	Tree-like; of scales, with a long thin stalk and branched flange (fig. VI).
dense	Usually describing a covering of scales which are not touching or overlapping but mostly 1–2 diameters apart (fig. VI).
denticulate	With small teeth along the margin (fig. III).
dimorphic	Of two kinds (e.g. of stamens alternately long and short).
disc	A fleshy circular or lobed outgrowth at the base of the ovary which secretes nectar (fig. VIII).
disc-shaped	A flat circular plate-like shape.
ellipsoid(al)	In the form of an ellipse (three-dimensional).
elliptic	In the form of an ellipse (two-dimensional) (fig. II).
elongate	Considerably longer than broad (more than 3x).
emarginate	Of a leaf or corolla lobe – as if with a notch cut out at the top (fig. III).
endemic	Native to only one country or area.
entire	With a smooth edge, not toothed or cut (fig. III).
epidermis	The surface layer of cells, usually referring to the leaf.
epiphyte	Living perched on a tree or shrub but not deriving any nourishment directly from it.
epiphytic	Living as an epiphyte.
ericoid	Having the form of an *Erica*, with very small xeromorphic leaves.
exocarp	The outer layer of the fruit (fig. XII).
exserted	Protruding; standing out (of stamens or style sticking out beyond the mouth of the corolla) (fig. X).
extrorse	Of the anther when the pollen is shed towards the perimeter of the flower (cf. *introrse* and *apical*) (fig. VIII).

fertile	Producing seed capable of germinating, or of anthers producing viable pollen.
filaments	The long sterile stalks of the anthers (fig. VIII).
filiform	Thread-like, very slender long thin structures (see *bracteole*).
flange	The outer peripheral thin portion of the scale (fig. VI).
floral	Of the flower or flowers.
flower	The fertile branch of an angiosperm including: calyx, corolla, stamens and pistil (fig. VIII).
fluted	With longitudinal channels or grooves (fig. XII).
forma	A minor variant of a species.
free	Of any parts which are separate and not fused together or to another organ.
fruit	The mature state of the ovary; the seed-containing structure (fig. XII).
fusiform	Spindle-shaped, narrowly ellipsoid and tapering at both ends (fig. XII).
glabrescent	Becoming glabrous, i.e. the hairs or scales falling off.
glabrous	Without hairs or scales of any kind.
gunung/gunong	Indonesian/Malaysian for mountain.
hairs	Simple unbranched filamentous structures constructed from a single cell (see *scales*) (fig. IV).
hairy	Of an organ covered in hairs.
half-hanging	Of flowers which hang at *c.*45° to the vertical (fig. XI).
herbarium (pl. herbaria)	Collection of dead, usually dried plants for scientific use, or the building containing them.
holotype	The specimen chosen by the author of the species at the time of publication.
hybrid	The offspring of two different parents (usually of two different species).
swarm	A population of hybrids showing great variability through secondary crossing with each other and/or back crossing to one or both parents.
imbricate	Of organs with their edges overlapping; when in bud, like tiles on a roof (figs VII and XI).
imbrication	The particular pattern of overlapping (fig. XI).
impressed	Sunk into a channel or pit below the general level of the organ (of veins or scales) (fig. IV).
included	Of stamens whose anthers lie in the tube below the mouth of the corolla (fig. X).
indumentum	The hairy covering as a whole.
inflexed	Bent inwards.
inflorescence	The terminal unit of flowers with associated stem, bracts and bracteoles.
internode	Used here to mean the more or less bare length of stem between the pseudowhorls of leaves (often with cataphylls or cataphyll scars). This is not the conventional meaning (fig. I).
introgress(ion)	The introduction of characters of one species into another by hybridisation which may obscure the morphological boundaries between them.

introrse	Facing inwards (of stamens shedding pollen towards the centre of the flower).
inverted-funnel-shaped	Having the floral tube narrowing regularly from base to apex (fig. IX).
involute	With the margins rolled upwards.
isotype	Duplicate of the holotype.
keeled	With a ridge like the keel of a boat.
kerangas	Heath-forest. A vegetation of small canopied trees with mostly small, pole-sized trunks, occurring on poor, acid, sandy soil overlain by peat. Often with conspicuous members of the Ericaceae and insectivorous and ant plants.
lacerate	With the appearance of being cut into sharply pointed segments.
lamina	The blade of a leaf or petal; a thin flat piece of tissue.
lanceolate	Spear-shaped; a shape roughly 3x as long as wide and broadest in the lower ½ (fig. II).
lateral	On or at the side.
leaf	A lateral appendage of the stem, usually with a bud in its axil (fig. I).
lectotype	A specimen subsequently designated to serve as the type from syntypes or from isotypes if the holotype has been lost or destroyed.
lenticels	Small spots of spongy tissue on the bark of the stem which allow gas exchange.
linear	Narrow shapes with parallel sides (of leaves) (fig. II).
Malesia	The area covered in *Flora Malesiana* from Sumatra and Peninsular Malaysia to New Guinea (as distinct from the country Malaysia) (see map, p.2).
margin	The edge of a flat structure such as a leaf or corolla lobe.
marginal	Situated at or close to the margin (cf. *flange*).
membranous	Thin and semi-transparent.
mid-vein	The central and usually the largest vein of the leaf.
montane	Of mountains, usually referring to the cool upper zones often covered in cloud.
morphological	Relating to the form or general structure of the plant.
moss forest	Forest developed on tropical mountains usually in the zone where cloud persists and where stems, branches and often leaves of trees become conspicuously covered in bryophytes.
mouth (of the flower)	The top of the floral tube where the corolla lobes are attached (fig. X).
mycorrhiza	The association of the roots with a fungus which is usually considered mutually beneficial.
nectary	Structures which secrete nectar – see *disc* (fig. VIII).
neotype	A specimen chosen to serve as a standard reference when all the type material has been destroyed.
node	Used here for the area in which the foliage leaves arise when these are compressed into pseudowhorls. Not the conventional meaning (fig. I).
obovate	The shape of the outline of an inverted egg (fig. II).
obtuse	Broadly pointed, with the apex more than 90° wide (fig. III).

open (umbel)	Of the inflorescence when it has a circle of flowers not a complete hemisphere (fig. IX).
ovary	The swollen area at the base of the style containing the ovules (fig. VIII).
ovate	Egg-shaped (two-dimensional) (fig. II).
overlapping	Of scales which form a continuous layer with little or no epidermis visible (fig. VI).
ovoid	Egg-shaped (three-dimensional) (fig. VII).
ovule	A structure within the ovary containing the egg and developing into the seed after fertilisation.
papilla (pl. papillae)	A small rounded projection from a surface (fig. VI).
papillose	Having papillae.
patent	Usually of hairs standing out at right angles from the surface of origin (fig. IV).
pedicel	The individual flower stalk (fig. VIII).
peduncle	The main stalk of an inflorescence. The floral (or fruiting) stem to which the pedicels are attached.
petal	The unit of the corolla, in rhododendrons always brightly coloured.
petaloid	Brightly coloured and resembling petals.
petiole	The leaf stalk (fig. V).
placenta	The ridge in the ovary or fruit to which the ovules or seeds are attached (fig. XII).
pollen	Microspores; granules containing the male element for fertilising flowers. These occur as tetrads of four together and are further stuck together with sticky (viscin) threads.
pores	Small rounded openings; of anthers, the terminal holes through which the pollen is shed (fig. VIII).
pro parte	In part.
procumbent	Lying along the surface of the ground.
prominent	Raised above the surrounding surface.
prostrate	Lying closely along the surface of the ground.
pseudowhorl	A false whorl or ring; looking like a whorl but not strictly so; of the leaves often being in ring-like clusters (fig. I).
raised mid-vein	With the main vein of the leaf prominent above the surrounding leaf surface (fig. IV).
reflexed	Abruptly bent backwards or downwards (fig. VII).
reticulate(-ion)	Like a net (of the veins of the leaf) (fig. V).
retuse	With a central depression in a round end (fig. III).
revolute	With the edges rolled downwards; of leaves (fig. IV).
rounded	Of the leaf base; of the leaf tip (fig. III).
rugose	Thrown into broad folds or wrinkles (fig. V).
saucer-shaped	Of short, very broadly expanded flowers (fig. IX).
scale(s)	Small multicellular protuberances (strictly multicellular hairs) on the leaves and other parts (fig. VI).
leaf	A small leaf with a very much reduced blade; see also *cataphyll* (fig. I).
seed	The fertilised and matured ovule, the dormant unit of dispersal (fig. XII).

semi-erect	Of the flowers standing at *c*.45° to the vertical (fig. XI).
sepal	The unit of the calyx, a member of the outermost whorl of the flower.
septicidal	Of a capsule which splits along the lines where the walls of the carpels join the outer wall of the ovary.
sessile	Without a stalk or apparently so, the stalk being very short and inconspicuous.
shrub	A woody plant branching abundantly from the base and usually without a well-defined trunk.
simple	Of hairs which consist of a single long unbranched cell (fig. IV).
sinuate	Having a wavy outline (fig. III).
sparse	Describing the scales when they are more than 4 diameters apart (fig. VI).
spathulate	Spatula-shaped (fig. II).
species	In this case a population or populations of plants with a degree of uniformity produced by genetic relationship, usually maintained by interbreeding and separated from all other species by definite morphological differences.
spherical	A three-dimensional round shape (fig. VII).
spindle-shaped	A cylindrical shape, tapering regularly at both ends (fig. XII).
stamens	The male organs consisting of filaments and anthers (fig. VIII).
stellate	Like a star, star-shaped (fig. VI).
stem	The organ to which the leaves are, or have been, attached (cf. *twig*).
sterile	Not producing seed capable of germinating, or (of stamens) viable pollen.
stigma	The cushion-like or lobed end to the style which becomes sticky when mature and traps the pollen (fig. VIII).
striate	Marked with long narrow depressions or ridges.
style	The slender neck connecting the stigma with the ovary (fig. VIII).
sub-	Below or almost.
-montane (forests)	The often very mossy forests of medium altitudes.
-sessile	Nearly sessile, only very shortly stalked.
-species	A group of plants which are insufficiently distinct to be a species but whose distinctive characters are genetically based and ecologically or geographically correlated.
subulate	Awl-shaped; with a long straight sharp point (fig. II).
superior	Of the ovary – with the calyx, corolla and stamens inserted around the base, the ovary being free (the condition in all rhododendrons).
syntype	Specimens cited by the author of a species without designating a holotype.
terminal	At the top of an organ (terminal bud, fig. I).
gland	A gland protruding at the apex of a leaf, often appearing as an extension of the mid-vein (fig. III).
terrestrial	Growing on the ground.
transverse	Of the secondary veins spreading at approximately right angles to the mid-vein (fig. V).
tree	A woody plant with normally a single main stem or trunk.
trumpet-shaped	With a long narrow tube and short lobes set more or less at right angles (fig. IX).

truncate	As though cut off at the end (fig. III).
tubercles	Raised warty protuberances usually from leaves or stems.
tubular	In the shape of a tube, a cylinder without ends.
twig	In this account, the youngest stems which still have leaves attached.
type	A specimen usually held in a scientific institution to which a published name is permanently attached. Often the first collection of a species and not necessarily typical of the species.
ultrabasic	Of rocks which are relatively low in silica and calcium and rich in magnesium, iron and certain heavy metals. They often support peculiar communities of plants.
umbel	A racemose inflorescence in which the pedicels all arise from the top of the main stem; an umbrella-shaped inflorescence without a main stalk (fig. IX).
full	With a solid hemisphere of flowers (fig. IX).
open	With the flowers arranged in a circle, without any pointing vertically upwards (fig. IX).
valves	Mesocarp and endocarp – the outermost units into which the fruit breaks, excluding the thin skin (exocarp) which often peels away (fig. XII).
variety	A minor variant of a species or subspecies with usually only one character to distinguish it from the normal form.
vegetative	Leaf and stem characters excluding flower and fruit organs. Of buds – enclosing only leaf primordia, without flowers inside.
vein	The main transport channels of the leaves, usually showing up as lines on one or both surfaces (fig. V).
venation	The pattern of veins on the leaf (fig. V).
viscin	The sticky threads to which the pollen is attached.
whorl	Of organs of the same type arising in a ring at the same height on the stem (cf. *pseudowhorl*).
zygomorphic	Bilaterally symmetrical; of the flower, being equally divisible only in one (vertical) plane.

FIGURES (drawn by Eve Bennett):

Fig. I. Twigs – leaf arrangements.
Fig. II. Leaf shapes.
Fig. III. Leaf: apices, bases, margins.
Fig. IV. Transverse section through leaves, and simple hairs.
Fig. V. Venation.
Fig. VI. Scale types and density.
Fig. VII. Buds and bracts.
Fig. VIII. Parts of the flower.
Fig. IX. Flower shapes.
Fig. X. Anther arrangements.
Fig. XI. Flowers.
Fig. XII. Fruits.

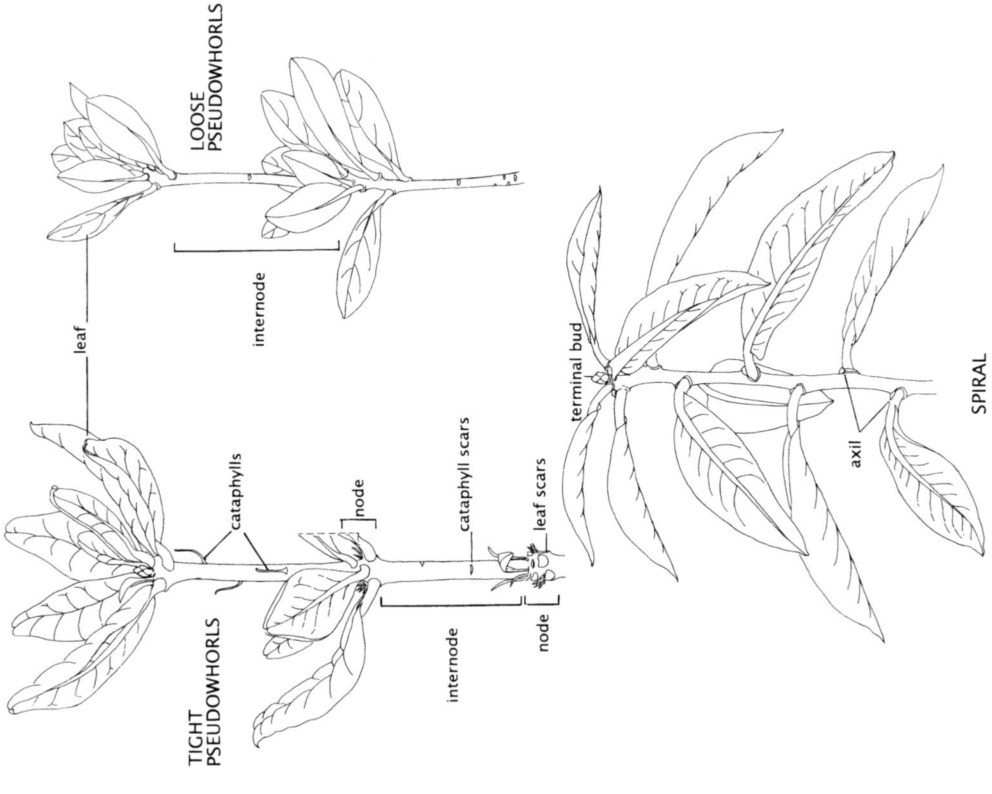

Fig. II. Leaf shapes.

broadly elliptic

narrowly lanceolate

circular

obovate

broadly lanceolate

linear   subulate

spathulate

ovate

asymmetric

narrowly elliptic

oblanceolate

Fig. I. Twigs – leaf arrangements.

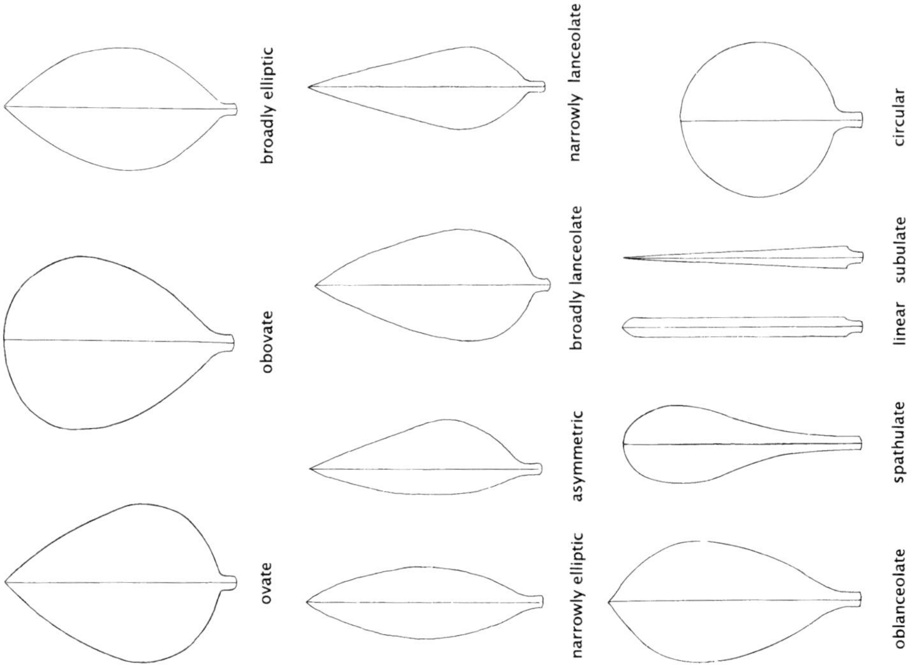

LOOSE PSEUDOWHORLS

internode

leaf

TIGHT PSEUDOWHORLS

cataphylls

node

cataphyll scars

leaf scars

internode

node

terminal bud

axil

SPIRAL

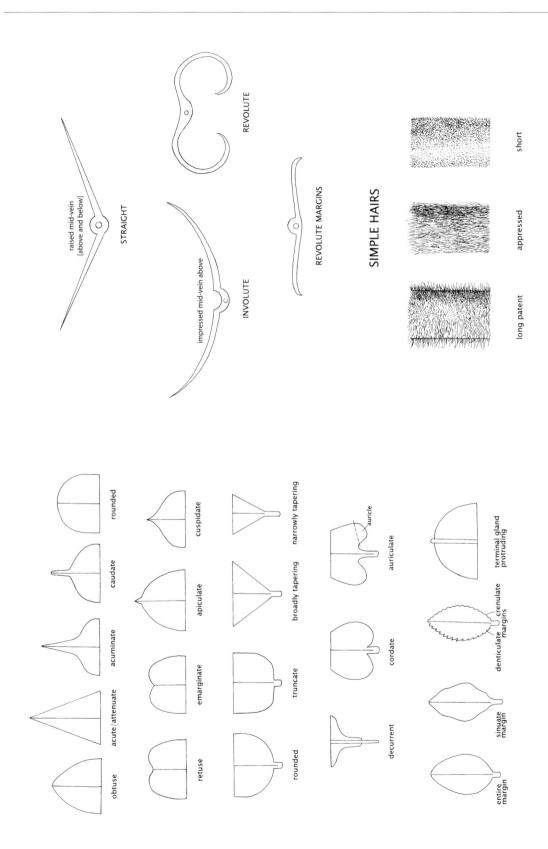

Fig. IV. Transverse section through leaves, and simple hairs.

Fig. III. Leaf: apices, bases, margins.

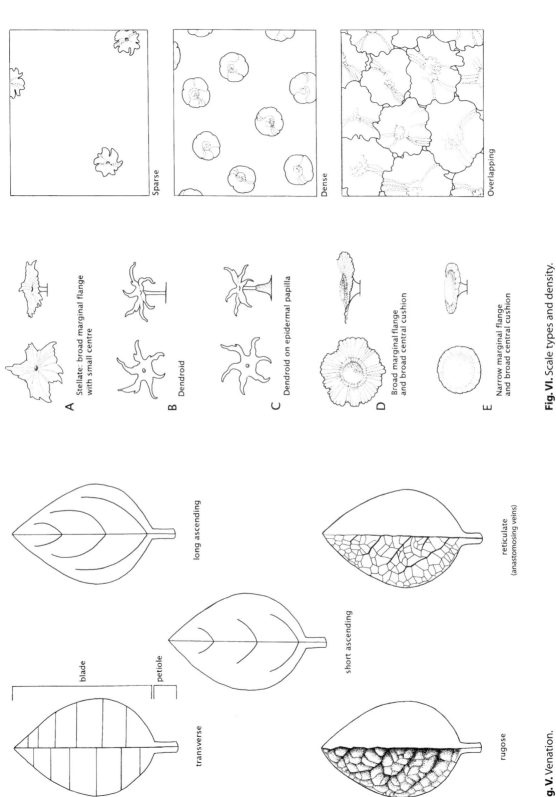

Sparse

Dense

Overlapping

A Stellate: broad marginal flange with small centre

B Dendroid

C Dendroid on epidermal papilla

D Broad marginal flange and broad central cushion

E Narrow marginal flange and broad central cushion

Fig. VI. Scale types and density.

blade

petiole

long ascending

short ascending

transverse

reticulate (anastomosing veins)

rugose

Fig. V. Venation.

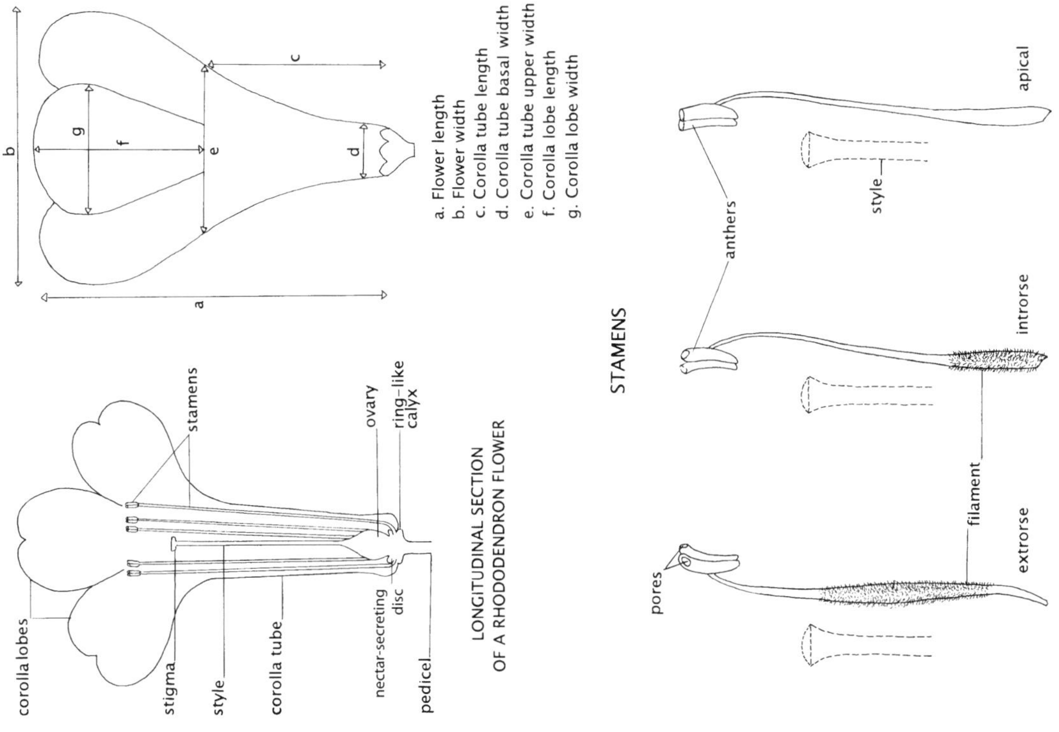

a. Flower length
b. Flower width
c. Corolla tube length
d. Corolla tube basal width
e. Corolla tube upper width
f. Corolla lobe length
g. Corolla lobe width

corolla lobes

stigma
style
corolla tube

nectar-secreting disc
pedicel

stamens

ovary
ring-like
calyx

LONGITUDINAL SECTION
OF A RHODODENDRON FLOWER

STAMENS

anthers
style
apical

introrse
filament

pores
extrorse

Fig. VIII. Parts of the flower.

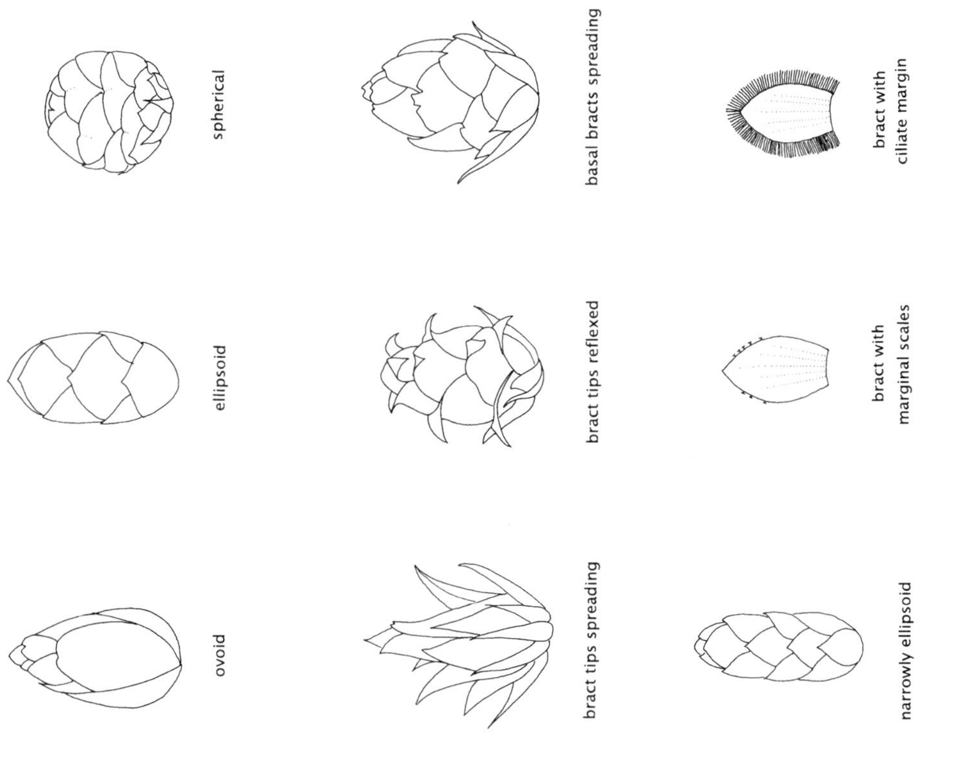

spherical

ellipsoid

ovoid

basal bracts spreading

bract tips reflexed

bract tips spreading

bract with
ciliate margin

bract with
marginal scales

narrowly ellipsoid

Fig. VII. Buds and bracts.

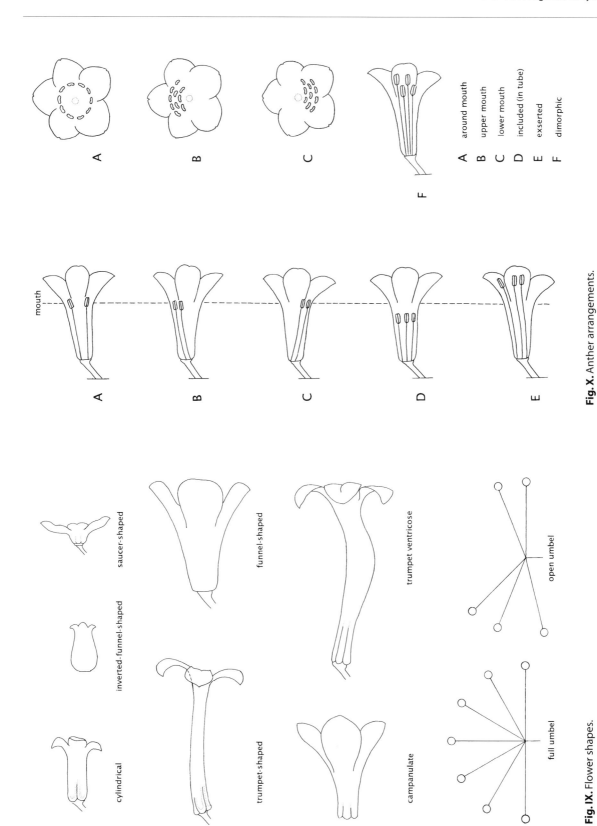

Fig. X. Anther arrangements.

A around mouth
B upper mouth
C lower mouth
D included (in tube)
E exserted
F dimorphic

mouth

A B C D E F

saucer-shaped

inverted-funnel-shaped

cylindrical

funnel-shaped

trumpet-shaped

trumpet ventricose

campanulate

open umbel

full umbel

Fig. IX. Flower shapes.

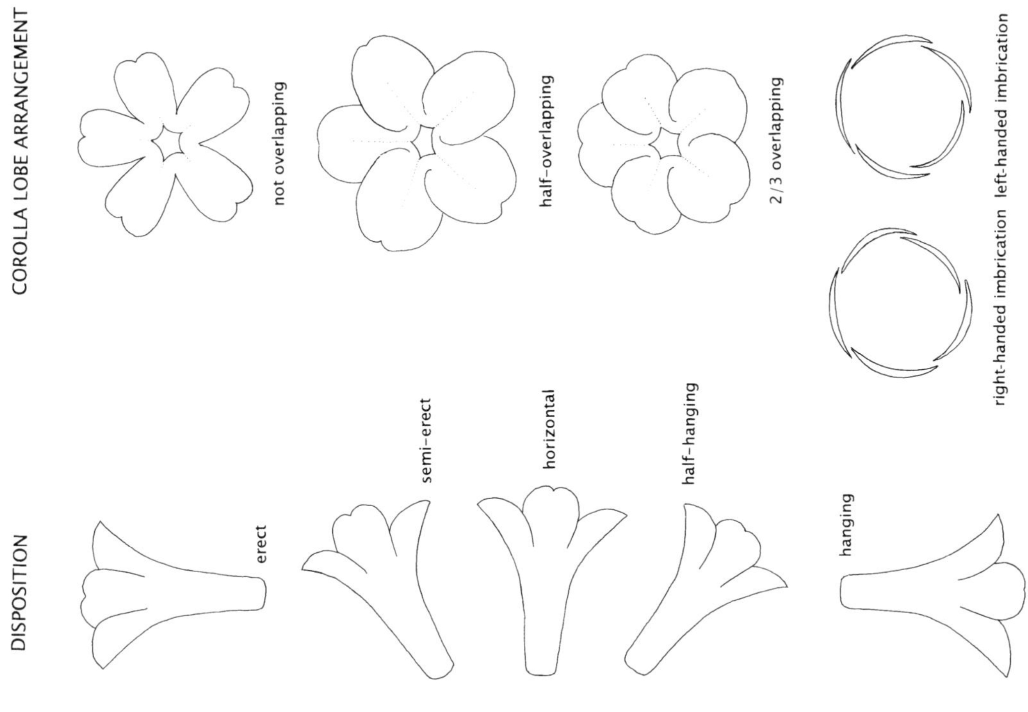

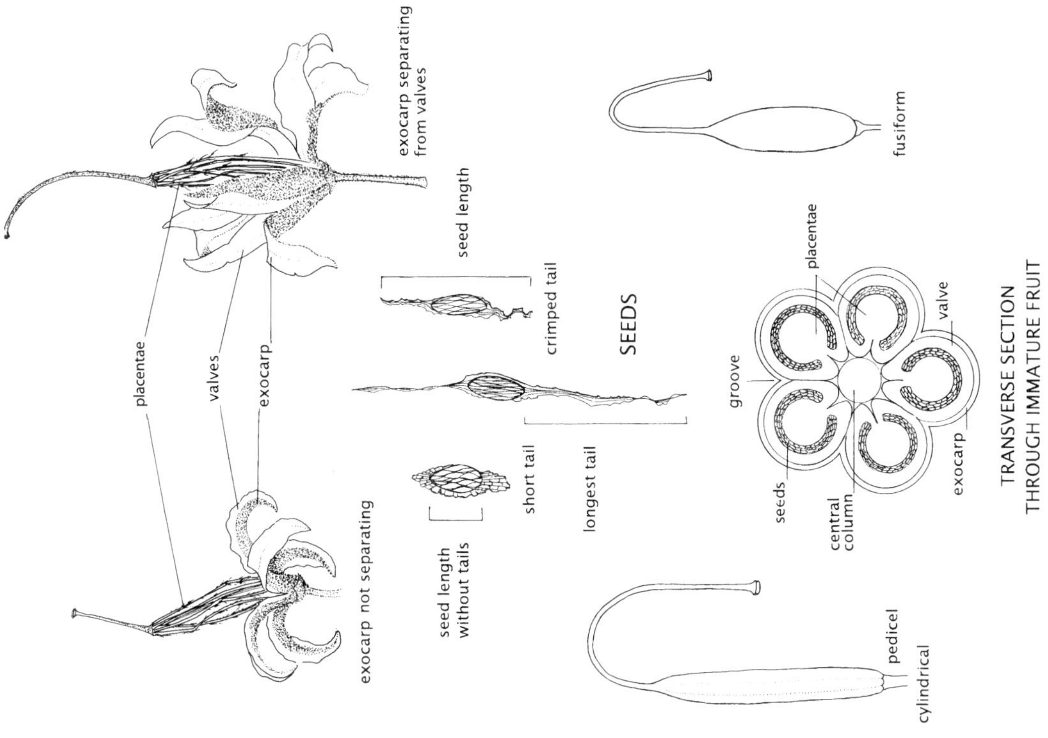

Fig. XII. Fruits.

Fig. XI. Flowers.

REFERENCES

Amano, K. (1986). *Host Range and Geographical Distribution of the Powdery Mildew Fungi*. Japan Scientific Society Press, Tokyo, 741pp.

Anon. II (1962). Terminology of simple symmetrical plane shapes. *Taxon* 11(5): 145–156, Chart I.

Anon. (1996). Vireya Culture Roundtable Southern California Chapter. *Journal of the American Rhododendron Society* 50(1): 8.

Anon. (2004a). RHS advice profiles 901. http://www.rhs.org.uk/advice/profiles0901/mealybug.asp

Anon. (2004b). The joys of gardening. *Australian Rhododendron Society Newsletter*, July 2004: 3–4.

Anon. (2005a). Commercially used biological control agents: Arachnida, Acarina. http://www.eppo.org/STANDARDS/biocontrol/acarina.htm

Anon. (2005b). RHS advice profiles 801. http://www.rhs.org.uk/advice/profiles0801/thrips.asp

Anon. (2005c). RHS advice profiles 601. http://www.rhs.org.uk/advice/profiles0601/red_spider_mite.asp

Argent, G. (1988). Some attractive vireya rhododendrons. *Kew Magazine* 5(3): 99–119.

Argent, G. (2003). Species patterns in *Rhododendron* section *Vireya* from sea level to the snowline in New Guinea. In: Argent, G. & McFarlane, M. (eds) *Rhododendrons in Horticulture and Science*, pp.160–170. Royal Botanic Garden Edinburgh.

Argent, G. (2004). New species and comments on *Rhododendron* (Ericaceae) from the island of Palawan, Philippines. *Gardens Bulletin Singapore* 56: 79–94.

Argent, G. & Galloway, L. (2003). Rhododendrons for the shortest day. *The Garden* 128(12): 910–913.

Argent, G., Lamb, A., Phillipps, A. & Collenette, S. (1988). *Rhododendrons of Sabah*. Sabah National Parks Publication No. 8. Kota Kinabalu, Sabah, Malaysia, 1–146.

Argent, G. & Madulid, D. (1995). Rediscovery of *Rhododendron acrophilum*. *Rhododendrons with Camellias and Magnolias* 47: 39–40, f.14.

Argent, G. & Madulid, D. (1998). *Rhododendron rousei* (Ericaceae): a beautiful new species from the Philippines. *The New Plantsman* 5(1): 25–31.

Argent, G., Mendum, M. & Smith, P. (1999). The smallest *Rhododendron* in the world, *R. caespitosum*. *The New Plantsman* 6(3): 152–157.

Atkinson, R., Jong, K. & Argent, G. (2000). Chromosome numbers of some tropical rhododendrons (section *Vireya*). *Edinburgh Journal of Botany* 57: 1–7.

Basden, N. & Helfer, S. (1995). World survey of *Rhododendron* powdery mildews. *Journal of the American Rhododendron Society* 49: 147–156.

Benson, D.M. (1986). Diseases caused by higher plants. In: Coyier, D.L. & Roane, M.K. (eds) *Compendium of Rhododendron and Azalea Diseases*, p.34. APS Press.

Benson, D.M. & Barker, K.R. (1986). Diseases caused by nematodes. In: Coyier, D.L. & Roane, M.K. (eds) *Compendium of Rhododendron and Azalea Diseases*, pp.34–35. APS Press.

Binney, D. (2003). Rhododendron collecting in Sulawesi, Indonesia. In: Argent, G. & McFarlane, M. (eds) *Rhododendrons in Horticulture and Science*, pp.111–114. Royal Botanic Garden Edinburgh.

Black, M. (1966). Collecting rhododendrons in New Guinea. *Rhododendron and Camellia Yearbook* 20: 78–88, f.38–40, pl.9.

Black, M. (1969). Historical survey of rhododendron collecting, with emphasis on its close associations with horticulture. *Journal of the American Rhododendron Society* 23(4): 194–208.

Brown, G.K., Craven, L.A., Udovicic, F. & Ladiges, P.Y. (2006). Phylogeny of *Rhododendron* section *Vireya* (Ericaceae) based on two non-coding regions of cpDNA. *Plant Systematics and Evolution* 257(1–2): 57–93.

Burbidge, F.W. (1880). *The Gardens of the Sun*. John Murray, London, 1–364.

Cavendar, R. (1993). Hanging basket rhododendrons. *Journal of the American Rhododendron Society* 47(2): 93–94.

Chamberlain, D.F. (1982). A revision of *Rhododendron*. II. Subgenus *Hymenanthes*. *Notes from the Royal Botanic Garden Edinburgh* 39: 209–486.

Clancy, B. (1973a). *Journal of the American Rhododendron Society* 27: 4.

Clancy, B. (1973b). Rhododendrons in fern logs. *The Rhododendron* 12(4): 11–12.

Clancy, B. (1974). Three new ideas. *The Rhododendron* 13(3): 8–10.

Clancy, B. (2005). *Vireya Vine* 76, Aug. 2.

Clyde Smith, J. (1984). Rhododendron rat poison. *The Rhododendron* 23(1): 3.

Copeland, H.F. (1929). Philippine Ericaceae I: The species of *Rhododendron*. *Philippine Journal of Science* 40(2): 133–176, pls.1–16.

Copeland, H.F. (1943). A study, anatomical and taxonomic, of the genera of Rhododendroideae. *American Midland Naturalist* 30(3): 533–625.

Corbett, M.K. (1986). Diseases caused by viruses. In: Coyier, D.L. & Roane, M.K. (eds) *Compendium of Rhododendron and Azalea Diseases*, pp.30–34. APS Press.

Cox, P.A. (1985). *The Smaller Rhododendrons*. Batsford, London, 1–271.

Cox, P. (1989). First flowering of *Rhododendron lowii*. *Vireya Vine*, 201.

Coyier, D.L. (1986). Leaf spots. In: Coyier, D.L. & Roane, M.K. (eds) *Compendium of Rhododendron and Azalea Diseases*, pp.25–26. APS Press.

Craven, L.A. (1973). Vireya rhododendrons, a history of their introduction and cultivation. *The Rhododendron* 12(3): 9–15.

Craven, L. (1980). A new *Rhododendron* (Ericaceae) from New Guinea. *Notes from the Royal Botanic Garden Edinburgh* 38(1): 141–144.

Craven, L. (1993). Bringing a conclusion to confusion: *Rhododendron* 'Gardenia Odyssey'. *The Rhododendron* 33: 11–12.

Craven, L.A. (1996). Proposal to conserve the name *Rhododendron lochiae* F. Muell. (Ericaceae) with a conserved type. *Taxon* 45: 135–136.

Craven, L. (2002). *Rhododendron wentianum* – from low altitude to high flyer. *The Rhododendron* 42: 64–65.

Craven, L.A. & Brown, G.K. (2005). Collection of *Rhododendron* section *Vireya* in Sulawesi, Indonesia for studies into their evolutionary relationships and biogeography. *Journal of the American Rhododendron Society* 59(4): 195–201.

Craven, L.A. & Withers, R.M. (1996). A second species of *Rhododendron* (Ericaceae) from Australia. *Edinburgh Journal of Botany* 53: 27–37.

Cruttwell, N.E.G. (1971). Rhododendrons of the Daga Country (part I). *The Rhododendron* 10(3): 9–16.

Cruttwell, N.E.G. (1972). The ascent of South Suckling. *The Rhododendron* 11(4): 7–13.

Cullen, J. (1980). A revision of *Rhododendron*. I. Subgenus *Rhododendron* sections *Rhododendron*

and *Pogonanthum*. *Notes from the Royal Botanic Garden Edinburgh* 39(1): 1–207.

Cullen, J. (1988). The accurate identification of garden plants. *The Plantsman* 10(3): 141–147.

Danet, F. (2005). Trois nouvelles espèces et un nouvel hybride naturel de *Rhododendron* (Ericaceae) de Nouvelle-Guinée. *Adansonia* 27(2): 267–280.

Deul, C.A. (1981). A fifteen year report on vireya rhododendrons in Southern California – A comprehensive study of their cultural requirements. *Quarterly Bulletin of the American Rhododendron Society* 35(1): 2–10.

Earle, C.J. (2002). Gymnosperm Database. http://www.botanik.uni-bonn.de/conifers/pi/pic/

Elmer, A.D.E. (1911). The Ericaceae of Mount Apo. *Leaflets in Philippine Botany* 3: 1089–1107.

Evans, J.P. (1970). *Rhododendron zoelleri*. *Quarterly Bulletin of the American Rhododendron Society* 24: 4.

Eversole, S. (1985). *Rhododendron goodenoughii*. *Journal of the American Rhododendron Society* 39(4): 193.

Fairweather, C. (2003). Commercial production of *Vireya* rhododendrons. In: Argent, G. & McFarlane, M. (eds) *Rhododendrons in Horticulture and Science*, pp.154–159. Royal Botanic Garden Edinburgh.

Farr, D.F., Rossman, A.Y., Palm, M.E. & McCray, E.B. (n.d.). Fungal Databases, Systematic Botany and Mycology Laboratory, ARS, USDA. Retrieved September 2004 from http://nt.ars-grin.gov/fungaldatabases/

Feng Kuomei (1983). New species and varieties of *Rhododendron* from Yunnan. *Acta Botanica Yunnanica* 5(3): 265–270.

Feng Guomei (1992). *Rhododendrons of China* Vol. II. Science Press, New York, Beijing, 1–237.

Gardner, M.W., Yarwood, C.E. & Raabe, R.D. (1970). Unreported powdery mildews. IV. *Plant Disease Reporter* 54: 399–402.

Gibbs, L.S. (1914). A contribution to the flora and plant formations of Mt Kinabalu and the highlands of British North Borneo. *Journal of the Linnean Society, Botany* 42: 1–24, pls.1–8.

Goetsch, L.A., Eckert, A.J. & Hall, B.D. (2005). The molecular systematics of *Rhododendron* (Ericaceae): A phylogeny based upon RPB2 gene sequences. *Systematic Botany* 30(3): 616–626.

Goos, R.D. (1999). Notes on the genus *Echidnodella* (Asterinaceae). *Mycotaxon* 73: 455–464.

Greuter, W. *et al.* (2000). *International Code of Botanical Nomenclature (St Louis Code)*. Regnum Vegetabile 138. Koeltz, Königstein, Germany, 1–474.

Hall, B.D., Craven, L.A. & Goetsch, L.A. (2006). Two distinctly different taxa within subsection *Pseudovireya* and their relation to the rooting of section *Vireya* within subgenus *Rhododendron* (in press).

Halliday, P. (1985). *Rhododendron christi*. *Kew Magazine* 2(1): 208–210.

Halliday, P. (1987). *Rhododendron pleianthum*. *Curtis's Botanical Magazine* pl.88, 165–168.

Halligan, P. (1985). Experiences with growing tropical rhododendrons. *Journal of the American Rhododendron Society* 39(2): 74–75.

Hein, B. (1988). Liste der Arten und infraspezifischen Taxa von P. Hennings. *Englera* 10: 1–374.

Helfer, S. (2003). *Rhododendron* powdery mildew – a continuing challenge to growers and pathologists. In: Argent, G. & McFarlane, M. (eds) *Rhododendrons in Horticulture and Science*, pp.66–72. Royal Botanic Garden Edinburgh.

Henslow, G. (1891). Hybrid rhododendrons. *Journal of the Royal Horticultural Society* 13: 240–283.

Holcomb, G.E. (1986). Diseases caused by algae. In: Coyier, D.L. & Roane, M.K. (eds) *Compendium of Rhododendron and Azalea Diseases*, pp.35–36. APS Press.

Holmgren, P.K. & Holmgren, N.H. (1998 onwards) (continuously updated). *Index Herbariorum*. New York Botanical Garden. http://sciweb.nybg.org/science2/IndexHerbariorum.asp

Hooker, J.D. (1884). *Rhododendron multicolor*. *Curtis's Botanical Magazine* t.6769.

Hosagoudar, V.B. & Abraham, T.K. (2000). A list of *Asterina* Lev. species based on the literature. *Journal of Economic and Taxonomic Botany* 24: 557–587.

Hunt, D.R. (1970). *Rhododendron orbiculatum*. *Curtis's Botanical Magazine* 178(I): pl.575.

Hunt, D.R. (1971). *Rhododendron rarum* (Ericaceae). *Curtis's Botanical Magazine* N.S., t.610.

Hunt, D.R. (1972). *Rhododendron suaveolens* (Ericaceae). *Curtis's Botanical Magazine* N.S., 178: t.600.

Hunt, D.R. (1974). *Rhododendron aequabile* (Ericaceae). *Curtis's Botanical Magazine* t.673, 61–63.

Hunt, D.R. (1975). *Rhododendron zoelleri*. *Curtis's Botanical Magazine* t.682, 105–107.

Hunt, D.R. (1978). *Rhododendron phaeochitum* (Ericaceae). *Curtis's Botanical Magazine* t.766, 73–75.

Hunt, D.R. (1979). *Rhododendron aurigeranum* (Ericaceae). *Curtis's Botanical Magazine* 182: t.787, 153–155.

Hunt, D.R. (1981a). *Rhododendron rugosum* (Ericaceae). *Curtis's Botanical Magazine* 183(II): t.808, 69–71.

Hunt, D.R. (1981b). *Rhododendron impositum* (Ericaceae). *Curtis's Botanical Magazine* N.S., t.816, 97–98.

Hunt, D.R. (1982). *Rhododendron goodenoughii* (Ericaceae). *Curtis's Botanical Magazine* 183(IV): t.826, 129–131.

Hutchinson, J. (1943). *Rhododendron lochae*. *Curtis's Botanical Magazine* t.9651.

Jermy, A.C. & Sayers, C.D. (1967). An expedition to the Finisterre Mountains of Eastern New Guinea. *Journal of the Royal Horticultural Society*, March: 117–128.

Kenyon, D.M. (1995). *The biology and pathogenic variation of* Erysiphe species *on rhododendron*. PhD thesis, Strathclyde University.

Kenyon, J. & Walker, J. (1997). *Vireyas, A Practical Gardening Guide*. Timber Press, Portland, Oregon, 1–95.

Kores, P. (1978). A new species of *Rhododendron* from New Guinea (Ericaceae). *Blumea* 24: 181–183.

Kores, P. (1984). Notes on the genus *Rhododendron* (Ericaceae) in Papua New Guinea. *Blumea* 30: 45–49.

Kurashige, Y., Etoh, J.L., Handa, T., Takayanagi, K. & Yukawa, T. (2001). Sectional relationships in the genus *Rhododendron* (Ericaceae): evidence from matK and trnK intron sequences. *Plant Systematics and Evolution* 228: 1–14.

Leach, D.G. (1978). The ancient curse of the rhododendron. *Garden (U.S.A.)* 2(4): 4–9.

Leeuwen, W.M. Docters van (1926). Schets van de flora en fauna van het van Rees-gebergte rondom Albatros-bivak Nieuw-Guinee. *De Tropische Natuur* 15: 177–186, f.10.

Liu, T. & Chuang, T. (1960). New additions to the flora of Taiwan (1). *Quarterly Journal of the Taiwan Museum* 13: 63–66, pls.1–3.

Loomans, A.J.M. & van Lenteren, J.C. (1995). Biological control of thrips pests: a review on thrips parasitoids. *Wageningen Agricultural University Papers* 95: 89–200.

Mitchell, D. (2003). Ecologically based cultivation techniques for *Vireya* rhododendron species. In: Argent, G. & McFarlane, M. (eds) *Rhododendrons in Horticulture and Science*, pp.53–60. Royal Botanic Garden Edinburgh.

Moyles, B. (2001). A vireya seed odyssey: some observations. *Journal of the American Rhododendron Society* 55(2): 70–72.

Moyles, B. (n.d.). *On growing rhododendron from seed with special consideration given to* Vireya *section seed: some personal observations*. Unpublished report, American Rhododendron Society.

Munro, J.M. (1986). Infection studies with powdery mildew from *Rhododendron* and *Erysiphe cruciferarum*. *Transactions of the British Mycological Society* 86: 686–687.

Nielsen, D.G. (1986). Black vine weevil and other weevils. In: Coyier, D.L. & Roane, M.K. (eds) *Compendium of Rhododendron and Azalea Diseases*, pp.37–39. APS Press.

Nilsen, E.T. (2003). Unique anatomical traits in leaves of *Rhododendron* section *Vireya*: a discussion of functional significance. In: Argent, G. & McFarlane, M. (eds) *Rhododendrons in Horticulture and Science*, pp.20–35. Royal Botanic Garden Edinburgh.

Nilsen, E.T. & Scheckler, S.E. (2003). A unique 'giant cell' type in leaves of vireyas. *Journal of the American Rhododendron Society* 57(1): 6–11.

Palser, B.F., Philipson, W.R. & Philipson, M.N. (1991). Characteristics of ovary, ovule and mature megagametophyte in *Rhododendron* L. (Ericaceae) and their taxonomic significance. *Botanical Journal of the Linnean Society* 105(4): 289–390.

Rouse, J.L. (1979). Notes on the growing media for *Rhododendron*. *The Rhododendron* 18(1): 8–11.

Rouse, J.L. (1985). The propagation of *Rhododendron* section *Vireya* from seed. *Notes from the Royal Botanic Garden Edinburgh* 43(1): 99–115.

Rouse, J.L. (1987). Floral features related to pollination ecology in *Rhododendron*. *The Rhododendron* 27(1): 4–6.

Rouse, J.L., Knox, R.B. & Williams, E.G. (1993). Inter- and intraspecific pollinations involving *Rhododendron* species. *Journal of the American Rhododendron Society* 47(1): 23–28, 40–45.

Rouse, J.L. & Williams, E.G. (1994a). Barriers to grafting section *Vireya* scions on elepidote *Rhododendron* stock. *The Rhododendron* 34: 14–23, 42a–d.

Rouse, J.L. & Williams, E.G. (1994b). Sexual and graft compatibilities within section *Vireya* and between this section and other lepidote rhododendrons. In: Jordan, N. (ed.) *Proceedings of the 1994 Pacific Region International Rhododendron Conference*, pp.27–34. Australian Rhododendron Society.

Rouse, J.L., Williams, E.G. & Knox, R.B. (1986). Floral features related to pollination ecology in *Rhododendron*. In: Williams, E.G. *et al.* (eds) *Pollination 86: Proceedings of a Symposium held at the Plant Cell Biology Research Centre, School of Botany, The University of Melbourne*, pp.65–69. (Reprinted in *The Rhododendron* 27(1): 4–6.)

Royen, P. van (1984). Field observations on rhododendrons in New Guinea. *Journal of the American Rhododendron Society* 38(2): 49–53.

Royen, P. van & Kores, P. (1982). *The Ericaceae of the High Mountains of New Guinea* (1485–1900, pls.120–147, f.467–585 of the third volume of 'The Alpine Flora of New Guinea', P.J. van Royen). Cramer, Germany.

Rushforth, K. (1993). Rhododendron hunting in Vietnam. *Rhododendrons with Camellias and Magnolias* 45: 38–46.

Schmidt, P.A. (2003). The diversity, phytogeography and ecology of spruces (Picea: Pinaceae) in Eurasia. In: Mill, R.R. (ed.) Proceedings of the Fourth International Conifer Conference. *Acta Horticulturae* 615: 189–201.

Shaw, D.E. (1984). Microorganisms in Papua New Guinea. *Department of Primary Industries, Research Bulletin* 33: 1–344.

Shen-you Lu & Yuen-po Yang (1989). A revision of *Rhododendron* (Ericaceae) of Taiwan. *Bulletin of the Taiwan Forest Research Institute* N.S., 4(4): 155–166.

Sherwood, M.A. (1980). Taxonomic studies in the Phacidiales: The genus *Coccomyces* (Rhytismataceae). *Occasional Papers of the Farlow Herbarium of Cryptogamic Botany* 15: 1–120.

Sinclair, I. (1984). A new compost for *Vireya* rhododendrons. *The Plantsman* 6(2): 101–104.

Sleumer, H. (1949). Ein System der Gattung *Rhododendron* L. *Botanische Jahrbuch Systematik* 74: 511–553.

Sleumer, H. (1958). The genus *Rhododendron* L. in Indochina and Siam. *Blumea*, Suppl. IV(2): 39–59. Dr H. Lam Jubilee Volume.

Sleumer, H. (1960). Rhododendron in Malaysia. *Reinwardtia* 5: 1–230.

Sleumer, H. (1961). Florae Malesianae Precursores XXIX. Supplementary notes towards the knowledge of the genus *Rhododendron* in Malesia. *Blumea* 11(1): 113–131.

Sleumer, H. (1963). Florae Malesianae Precursores XXXIX. Suppl. II. Towards the knowledge of the Ericaceae in Malesia. *Blumea* 12: 339–347.

Sleumer, H. (1966). Rhododendron. *Flora Malesiana* 6: 474–667.

Sleumer, H. (1973). New species and noteworthy records of *Rhododendron* in Malesia (Ericaceae). *Blumea* 21(2): 357–376.

Sleumer, H. (1980). A system of the genus *Rhododendron*. In: Luteyn, J.L. & O'Brien, M.E. (eds) *Contributions Toward a Classification of Rhododendron*, pp.1–18. New York Botanical Garden, Bronx, New York.

Smid, T.C. (1990). *Rhododendron Species Names* (Private publication by Theo C. Smid, 1150 W. Winton Ave. #466, Hayward, CA 94545, USA), 1–58.

Spethmann, W. (1980). Flavonoids and carotenoids of *Rhododendron* flowers and their significance for the classification of the genus *Rhododendron*. In: Luteyn, J.L. & O'Brien, M.E. (eds) *Contributions Toward a Classification of Rhododendron*, pp.247–276. New York Botanical Garden, Bronx, New York.

Spethmann, W. (1987). A new infrageneric classification and phylogenetic trends in the genus *Rhododendron* (Ericaceae). *Plant Systematics and Evolution* 157: 9–31.

Spooner, B.M. (1991). *Lophodermium* and *Hypoderma* (Rhytismatales) from Mt. Kinabalu, Sabah. *Kew Bulletin* 46: 73–100.

Stapf, O. (1894). *On the Flora of Mount Kinabalu*. Linnean Society of London, 1–195.

Steenis-Kruseman, M.J. van (1950). Malaysian plant collectors and collections. *Flora Malesiana* Series 1, 1: 1–639.

Stein, B. (1885). I Originalabhandlungen. *Gartenflora* 34: 193–195, *t.*1195 & 1196.

Stevens, P.F. (1985). Malesian vireya rhododendrons – towards an understanding of their evolution. *Notes from the Royal Botanic Garden Edinburgh* 43: 63–80.

Stonor, C.R. (1952). Rhododendrons in New Guinea. *Royal Horticultural Society Rhododendron Yearbook* 1951–52: 48–51.

Tod, H. (1969). Nitrogen sources for rhododendron. *Gardeners' Chronicle* 165(11): 26.

Veitch, J.H. (1906). *Hortus Veitchii*. London, 1–542.

Watling, R. (2003). Rhododendron husbandry and hygiene: essential steps towards survival. In: Argent, G. & McFarlane, M. (eds) *Rhododendrons in Horticulture and Science*, pp.218–232. Royal Botanic Garden Edinburgh.

White Smith, E. (1994). Culture notes on vireya rhododendron. *Journal of the American Rhododendron Society* 48(3): 162.

Withers, R.M. (1974). The quest for *Rhododendron hellwigii*. *The Rhododendron* 13(4): 19.

Withers, R.M. (1991). A history of the introduction of *Vireya* rhododendron species into cultivation in Australia. *The Rhododendron* 31: 3–15.

Withers, R.M. (1992). *Rhododendron lochae*, Australia's only known rhododendron, cultivation and hybridisation. *The Rhododendron* 32: 2–23.

Withers, R.M. & Rouse, J.L. (1988). *Rhododendron hellwigii* in flower. *The Rhododendron* 28(1): 23–25, *f.*1 & 2.

Withers, R.M. & Womersley, J. (1986). The non-Malesian rhododendrons, Section *Vireya*. *The Rhododendron* 26(2): 26–36.

INDEX

Page numbers in **bold** indicate main references; page numbers in *italics* refer to illustrations.

Index prepared by Dorothy Frame